IRRIGATION ENGINEERING

Volume I

Agricultural and Hydrological Phases

IRRIGATION ENGINEERING

Volume I
Agricultural and Hydrological Phases

IVAN E. HOUK

Consulting Engineer
Denver, Colorado

NEW YORK · JOHN WILEY & SONS, INC.
LONDON · CHAPMAN & HALL, LIMITED

PREFACE

Irrigation engineering is the application of engineering principles to the development and maintenance of irrigation enterprises. It includes considerations of contemplated irrigation projects, planning of water-supply systems, construction of necessary works for distributing water, maintenance of project structures, and efficient operation of all features, so that farmers can be supplied with the water needed to produce profitable crops. It also includes such investigational activities as may be necessary to obtain data for planning, building, and operating irrigation projects.

The practice of irrigation engineering includes applications of material from nearly all branches of science. Some sciences are drawn upon more heavily than others. Determinations of project feasibility depend largely on considerations of soils, crop growth, water requirements, weather, and hydrology. Planning and construction of project features depend largely on applications of design principles as developed for earth, rock, concrete, and steel structures.

In compiling material on irrigation engineering, two major divisions seem logical: (1) agricultural and hydrological phases; and (2) project planning and structures. This volume is confined to the first division.

Several books on irrigation subjects were published during the early years of the present century, prior to about 1935. Very few have appeared recently. Many important developments in irrigation work have been made since the early books were written. Results of many comprehensive irrigation investigations have also become available. This volume is an attempt to bring the subject up to date from the viewpoint of agricultural and hydrological phases.

In preparing this volume, two general criteria have been kept in mind: (1) to include the basic information engineering students need to acquire if they are planning to follow irrigation careers; and (2) to include digests of such investigational data as practicing engineers may find useful. Inasmuch as space limitations preclude detailed discussions of irrigation investigations, many references to original reports are listed at the ends of the chapters. Some are referred to in the text.   Others are listed simply as sources of supplemental information.

Large irrigation enterprises in the United States are located almost entirely in Arkansas, Louisiana, and the 17 western states, as tabulated in the census reports.   Therefore most discussions pertain to conditions in the West.   A few references are made to irrigation in western Canada, also to supplemental irrigation in the humid states.   Irrigation in other countries is not discussed, except for brief statements in the historical sections of Chapter 1.

During the preparation of the manuscript, data were requested and received from many sources.   Appropriate acknowledgments are made at locations of use.   If any omissions have been made, they have been unintentional and apologies are hereby offered.

Special acknowledgments for material should be made to several state agricultural experiment stations, the United States Department of Agriculture, Weather Bureau, Geological Survey, Bureau of the Census, and the Bureau of Reclamation with which the author was associated for many years.   Senators Edwin C. Johnson and Eugene D. Millikin of Colorado and Congressman John A. Carroll of Denver courteously supplied many federal documents.

In conclusion, I wish to express my appreciation to Dr. Arthur E. Holch, E. B. Gittings, G. J. Turre, Robert Follansbee, and I. B. Hosig, for their reviews of various chapters; to Dr. S. M. Woodward for his review of the entire manuscript; to Mrs. Houk for her assistance in checking, revising, and editing the manuscript; and to Mrs. Ula Lillibridge for her patience and care in typing the entire copy.

Ivan E. Houk

Denver, Colorado
August 1951

CONTENTS

Contents

Preparing Field Surfaces. Irrigation Methods. Wild Flooding. Flooding from Field Ditches. Flooding in Border Strips. Flooding in Level Checks. Flooding with Portable Pipes. Furrow Irrigation. Use of Porous Hose. Irrigation by Sprinkling. Sprinkling Installations. Subirrigation. Time and Depth of Irrigation. Determining Moisture Conditions. Improper Applications of Water.

Chapter 1

INTRODUCTION

Irrigation is the controlled application of water to arable lands to supply crop requirements not satisfied by rainfall. The growth of crops under irrigation is an important part of agriculture in countries where arid and semiarid lands comprise large proportions of the total areas. In arid countries, adequate food supplies, which are essential for national prosperity, cannot be produced without irrigation.

In western United States, irrigation developments have transformed large tracts of unused lands into valuable agricultural regions. Similar statements can be made for many foreign countries. Millions of acres of arable lands are irrigated in Mexico, Argentina, France, Egypt, China, India, and other countries.

In general, irrigation is required in regions where the mean annual precipitation is less than 15 inches, necessary to some extent in regions where the annual precipitation varies from 15 to 30 inches, and not commonly required where the annual precipitation exceeds 30 inches. Seasonal distributions of rainfall and summer temperatures affect the need for irrigation. In cool regions, where growing seasons are relatively short, some crops can be grown with 15 inches of summer rainfall. In warm regions, where growing seasons are longer, 20 to 25 inches are needed.

Because of yearly variations in summer rainfall, irrigation in semiarid regions may be required in some years and not in others. For the same reason, irrigation in humid regions may be desirable as insurance against crop losses, even though summer rainfalls ordinarily are sufficient for crop growth. More profitable crop yields usually can be produced when water can be supplied as needed, without waiting for rainfall. This is especially true when valuable fruit and truck crops are grown.

In western United States, about 1 million square miles receive an average annual rainfall of less than 20 inches. Throughout these areas, successful agriculture is dependent primarily on irrigation. Wheat is grown by dry farming in some regions, where soil and weather

1

conditions are favorable, but profitable yields cannot be secured every year.   One good crop in three or four is about as much as can be expected.   Most agricultural communities in the West owe their existence to irrigation.   Many large cities owe their development largely to irrigation.   Boise, Salt Lake City, Phoenix, Los Angeles, and others can be cited as examples.

History of Irrigation.   The history of irrigation began with the history of man.   Primitive methods of irrigating fields for crop production were used before the dawn of civilization.   In fact, some authorities claim that irrigation constituted the basis for civilization.   The British Society of Anthropology accepts as a fundamental premise that the development of irrigation preceded the development of civilization.   Our earliest records of man show that civilizations grew and prospered on lands along the banks of irrigation canals.

References to irrigation have been found on prehistoric tablets unearthed during archaeological explorations.   References to the conveyance of water in ditches are made in the Bible (II Kings, 3:16–17).   Irrigation and irrigation practices often are mentioned in historical literature from the birth of Christ to the present century.   Throughout the ages, irrigation has constituted an essential element in the life and welfare of people living in desert countries.

Ancient Irrigation.   Egypt usually is considered the birthplace of irrigation.   Irrigation was practiced in Egypt long before the beginning of the Christian Era.   Nile River water was conveyed to adjoining arable lands as early as 5000 B.C.   King Menes built a large masonry dam across the Nile near Memphis, to divert water for irrigation, more than 4,000 years before the time of Christ.

Queen Semiramis, who ruled Egypt about 4,000 years ago, is said to have directed her government to divert Nile River water for irrigation.   Since her reign, irrigation and main canals in Egypt have been built and maintained by the national government.   Some canals constructed during her time are still in operation.

Irrigation was practiced in Arabia, Persia, and other parts of the Near East more than 3,000 years ago.   Irrigation was well developed in Babylon prior to 2000 B.C.   Hammurabi, King of Babylon about 2200 B.C., established regulations governing the maintenance and operation of irrigation ditches and provided severe penalties for farmers who did not use water in accordance with the rules.   His regulations were included in the Code of Hammurabi which was recorded on a stone pillar unearthed in 1902.

Although irrigation practices during ancient eras were mostly of a primitive nature, records and explorations show that considerable skill and ingenuity were exercised in constructing irrigation works. The masonry dam built by King Menes was one example. A much larger masonry dam, to impound water for irrigation, was built across the Wadi Shibwan near Saba, Arabia, about 1700 B.C. Long systems of kanats, underground conduits to convey water for irrigation, were constructed in Persia, Egypt, and other countries during periods prior to the Christian Era. Many additional examples of ancient irrigation could be mentioned.

Early Irrigation in America. Arid lands were irrigated by the natives of Argentina, Peru, and other South American countries more than 1,000 years ago. In southwestern United States, irrigation was practiced by the Indians long before Columbus discovered America, probably before the end of the seventh century. Remains of early irrigation ditches many miles long may be seen in Arizona and New Mexico. Some canals were located on approximately uniform grades and excavated to widths of 20 feet or more.

In Mexico, where the natives had long practiced irrigation, Spanish settlers of the sixteenth century built large irrigation systems, including storage dams, long canals and aqueducts, and extensive distribution works. During the latter part of the same century, some of the Spaniards moved northward, settled in the Rio Grande Valley, New Mexico, and began the development of similar irrigation systems. Remains of some of their canals still may be seen along the edges of the valley.

About the end of the eighteenth century, Spanish padres from Mexico began the establishment of missions in southern Arizona and California. The padres built small diversion dams, ditches, and conduits, to bring water to the missions and irrigate their gardens and fields. The Old Mission Dam on the San Diego River near San Diego, California, was built by the San Francis padres about the beginning of the nineteenth century, using baked brick faced with rubble masonry. This probably was the first masonry dam built for irrigation in the United States. It was described by Professor Griffith of Corvalis, Oregon, in 1930, and at that time still was standing.

Modern Irrigation in United States. Modern irrigation in the United States began when the Mormons settled in the Salt Lake Valley, Utah, in 1847. Following the California gold rush of 1849, pioneers began irrigating arid lands in other parts of the West. By 1860, the national census showed a total of 752 irrigation enterprises, with a total irrigated area of more than 400 thousand acres.

The extension of transcontinental railroads through the western mountains was a boon to the settlement of the western states. By 1890, irrigation developments had grown until more than 54 thousand farms were being irrigated. At that time, the total irrigated area in the West included 3.7 million acres. At the time of the last census, 1940, about 21 million acres were under irrigation.[30] *

Table 1 shows the expansion of irrigated acreages and growth of capital investments in irrigation in western United States, by 10-year

TABLE 1

GROWTH OF IRRIGATION IN WESTERN UNITED STATES DURING 1890 TO 1940 [30] *

Census year (1)	Area irrigated, million acres (2)	Capital invested, million dollars (3)	Area works could supply, million acres (4)	Investment per acre based on column 4 (5)
1940	21.00	1,052.0	28.06	37.50
1930	19.55	892.8	26.10	34.20
1920	19.19	697.7	26.02	26.81
1910	14.43	321.5	20.29	15.85
1900	7.74	70.0	.....	9.04 †
1890	3.72	29.5	.....	7.95 †

* See reference 30 at end of chapter.
† Based on area irrigated, column 2.

periods from 1890 to 1940, as given by census reports. The data are totals for nineteen states. Arkansas and Louisiana, where rice is grown under irrigation, are included with the seventeen western states. Areas irrigated are given in column 2, capital investments in column 3, and areas the irrigation works could supply with water in column 4. Capital investments per acre are given in column 5.

The data in Table 1 show that capital investments in irrigation increased from about 30 million dollars in 1890 to a little more than a billion dollars in 1940. Investments per acre increased from about 8 dollars in 1890 to 37.50 dollars in 1940.

About the beginning of the present century, the federal government began developing large irrigation projects with funds obtained from the sale of public lands. Since that time, the Bureau of Reclamation,

* See reference 30 at end of chapter.

United States Department of the Interior, has built many extensive irrigation projects in the western states, involving the construction of costly storage, diversion, conveyance, and distribution works, together with numerous appurtenant and incidental structures of lesser magnitudes.

The Office of Indian Affairs, another branch of the Department of the Interior, has developed some irrigation projects in connection with its administration of Indian reservations.

Toward the end of the nineteenth century, the production of rice under irrigation, a crop that requires continuous flooding during the growing season, was begun in southern Louisiana, southeastern Texas, and parts of Arkansas. Some rice crops were irrigated in southeastern United States prior to 1899. Irrigation of orchard fruits and truck crops in humid states, in order to insure the application of sufficient water when needed, also was begun about the end of the nineteenth century.

Irrigation operations in some eastern states were considerably expanded following the drought years of the early 1930's. Cranberries are now extensively irrigated in Atlantic seaboard states, potatoes in Michigan, and fruit and truck crops in Ohio, Pennsylvania, and other humid states. During recent years, small areas of pasture lands have been irrigated in some eastern states.

Although irrigation is not financially feasible for general farming in humid regions, irrigation of special crops often is profitable, not only in preventing crop failures during dry years but also in producing higher yields during normal years. On some farms, increased yields in one season more than paid for the installation of irrigation facilities.

Status of Irrigation. Table 2 shows the status of irrigation in the western states at the time of the 1940 census. Irrigated areas are given in units of 1,000 acres, also in percentages of the total. Capital investments are given in units of 1,000 dollars, also in percentages. Areas the irrigation works could supply with water are given in column 6, and capital investments per acre in column 7. Irrigated acreages are for the year 1939.

The total investment of 1.052 billion dollars shown at the bottom of Table 2 includes 26.4 million dollars for water rights. The remainder represents the cost of irrigation works and equipment. Capital investments per acre varied from about 15 dollars in Kansas, where semiarid conditions prevail, to approximately 99 dollars in Arizona, where the climate is arid and costly storage reservoirs are necessary in order to insure ample supplies of water.

TABLE 2

STATUS OF IRRIGATION IN THE WESTERN STATES, 1940 CENSUS [30]

State (1)	Irrigated areas		Capital invested in irrigation		Area works could supply,	Investment per acre, based on column 6
	1,000 acres (2)	Per cent (3)	1,000 dollars (4)	Per cent (5)	1,000 acres (6)	(7)
Arizona	653	3.1	83,526	7.9	844	98.94
Arkansas	162	0.8	5,767	0.5	288	20.04
California	5,070	24.3	318,889	30.3	7,399	43.10
Colorado	3,221	15.3	106,849	10.2	3,914	27.30
Idaho	2,278	10.8	102,586	9.8	2,594	39.55
Kansas	100	0.5	2,154	0.2	142	15.12
Louisiana	447	2.1	11,566	1.1	760	15.22
Montana	1,711	8.1	67,353	6.4	2,344	28.73
Nebraska	610	2.9	39,056	3.7	993	39.33
Nevada	740	3.5	16,907	1.6	841	20.10
New Mexico	554	2.6	32,736	3.1	732	44.72
North Dakota	22	0.1	1,755	0.2	37	48.07
Oklahoma	4	....	272	....	9	31.56
Oregon	1,049	5.0	50,961	4.8	1,261	40.41
South Dakota	60	0.3	5,396	0.5	122	44.28
Texas	1,045	5.0	66,441	6.3	1,774	37.46
Utah	1,176	5.6	41,897	4.0	1,358	30.86
Washington	615	2.9	56,415	5.4	732	77.12
Wyoming	1,486	7.1	41,523	3.9	1,914	21.70
Total	21,004	100.0	1,052,049	100.0	28,055	37.50*

* Average for states listed.

California, Colorado, and Idaho, in the order named, are the three leading irrigation states. Irrigated areas and capital investments in these states comprised a little more than half the 1940 totals. Oklahoma had only 4 thousand acres under irrigation. The Dakotas, where irrigation is required only in the western sections, had relatively small irrigated areas.

For eastern states, the 1940 census showed a total irrigated area of 166 thousand acres. This was greater than the total area irrigated in Oklahoma, Kansas, or the Dakotas. It was about the same as the area irrigated in Arkansas. Areas irrigated in Florida totaled 126 thousand acres, about 76 per cent of the total for the humid states. Irrigation operations in humid states differ from those in the West in that they are confined to relatively small areas and are conducted by the farmers individually. The average area irrigated per farm in the eastern states in 1940 was about 21 acres.

Federal Irrigation Projects. Figure 1 shows acreages irrigated during 1945 on projects built entirely by the Federal Bureau of Reclama-

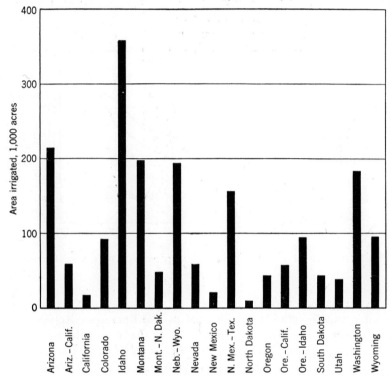

FIGURE 1. Areas irrigated during 1945 on projects built by the Bureau of Reclamation.

tion. Data for plotting were taken from the Annual Report of the Secretary of the Interior for the year 1946. The data are shown by states, or by two states where large projects cross state lines. The total area irrigated on all Bureau of Reclamation projects during 1945 was approximately 2.0 million acres.

Figure 2 shows cumulative crop values and annual irrigated areas on Bureau of Reclamation projects from 1906 to 1945, also plotted from data in the Annual Report of the Secretary of the Interior for 1946. Plotted data include projects where supplemental water was

furnished from government storage works, but not Warren Act lands
and special contracts.

During 1945, the total value of crops grown on about 2.5 million
acres was more than 232 million dollars, about 94 dollars per acre.
On some projects where fruit crops are raised, crop returns during 1945
were more than 600 dollars per acre. On the Tieton Division of the
Yakima Project, an apple-growing district in Washington, 1945 crop
returns averaged 854 dollars per acre.

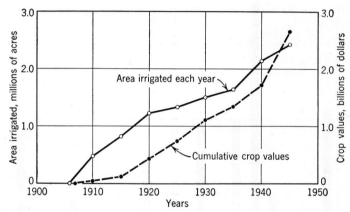

FIGURE 2.   Growth of irrigated areas and crop values.   Bureau of Reclamation
projects.

Most irrigation projects operated by the Indian Service are considerably smaller than those operated by the Bureau of Reclamation.
Some projects, such as the Flathead, the Wapato, and the San Carlos
projects, are designed for irrigable areas of more than 100 thousand
acres. In 1945, more than 250 projects, including about 535 thousand
acres, produced crops valued at over 32 million dollars. This was
about one-half the total cost of building the projects.

Future Irrigation Developments. Irrigation projects contemplated
for future development in western United States are principally those
requiring storage supplies, pumping facilities, or importation of water
from other drainage basins. Some relatively small areas may be developed by spreading flood flows over porous surface formations, to increase underground storage. Natural streamflows that can be diverted
during the irrigation season have been fully appropriated in most
regions. Excess water supplies are still available in the Columbia
River and some smaller streams of the Northwest.

Most large irrigation projects where water supplies can be secured at reasonable costs have already been constructed. Future developments will be expensive. They probably will be feasible only as federal undertakings. Some future developments probably will be made in connection with the construction of special multiple-purpose projects, where considerable proportions of the costs can be charged to other uses of water or repaid by sales of hydroelectric power.

In 1934, the Water Planning Committee, National Resources Board, estimated that ultimately about 50 million acres might be irrigated in the West. This would be about 2.4 times the area under irrigation in 1940. The Committee further estimated that with ultimate developments the total required storage would be about 175 million acre-feet, or about twice the capacity already constructed or under construction. When needs for further irrigation developments become sufficiently urgent, additional storage capacities probably will be made available to such extents as they can be utilized in storing unused runoff.

Limitations on irrigation developments are imposed primarily by quantities of water that can be secured at reasonable costs. Current researches regarding the practicability of purifying salt water and conveying the purified water to irrigable lands, if successful, will prove a boon to many arid areas not too far inland. Unlimited supplies of water are available in the Pacific Ocean. If these supplies can be tapped, purified, and conveyed inland at reasonable costs, further irrigation developments in coastal regions will be possible.

Irrigation Enterprises. The first irrigation enterprises included small areas of arable land along stream banks, where sufficient water was available during the growing season. Water was diverted by temporary dams and brought to the fields through small ditches excavated by hand. The projects were operated by individual farmers, adjacent landowners, or small community associations.

As irrigable acreages along the streams became fully utilized, conveyance of water to more distant areas became desirable. This required more permanent, complicated, and expensive irrigation works. In order to finance, construct, and operate such expanded irrigation systems, it was necessary to form larger projects and adopt more comprehensive methods of administration.

In 1865, the Territory of Utah passed a law providing for the formation of irrigation districts. The act permitted taxation to defray expenses of supplying water but did not authorize the issuance of bonds to provide funds for constructing irrigation works. Although many districts were organized under the law, the act was not generally successful in promoting the development of irrigation. It was therefore repealed and subsequently replaced by more satisfactory legislation, enacted in 1909.

The first adequate irrigation district law was the Wright Act, passed by the California Legislature in 1887. This act authorized the issuance of bonds as well as taxation of district lands. Since 1887, all the principal irrigation states have enacted irrigation laws modeled after the Wright Act. Many irrigation districts now operate under such laws.

Other types of irrigation enterprises organized under state laws during the development of the West include commercial companies, promoted for profit, and mutual companies, nonprofit organizations that supply water to their stockholders at cost.

Commercial companies often were organized during the earlier periods of irrigation. Some were successful and still are operating. Some were not successful and have passed out of existence or have been absorbed by other enterprises. Large financial losses frequently were suffered by investors in irrigation company securities. Irrigated acreages controlled by commercial companies have decreased since about the beginning of the present century.

Many mutual irrigation companies were organized in Utah during the latter part of the nineteenth century, beginning about 1870. Such companies constitute the principal type of irrigation enterprise in Utah and are common in parts of Colorado, California, Montana, Wyoming, and other western states. They are more numerous than irrigation districts but usually much smaller. They may or may not be incorporated. Incorporation generally is an advantage.

Irrigation Engineering. Early irrigation projects were planned and built by the water users, without engineering assistance. Relatively small projects located along stream channels and including only one or a few adjacent farms could be constructed by hand labor and horse-drawn equipment, without detailed surveys or technical planning.

The development of modern engineering practices as applied in reclaiming arid lands throughout the West began during the latter part of the nineteenth century, when the building of large projects became desirable. The design and construction of large projects, involving the building of complicated hydraulic structures as well as the excavation of main canals using power equipment, required competent engineering planning and supervision. After the projects were built, efficient operation and adequate maintenance activities required continued engineering advice.

Later, as special problems developed and natural streamflows became fully utilized, engineering considerations of all agricultural and hydrological factors pertaining to irrigation became necessary. On some lands, drainage systems had to be constructed to prevent or relieve waterlogged conditions. On other lands, special practices had to be adopted to control accumulations of undesirable salts in the surface soils. On projects where water supplies were limited, special efforts had to be exerted to conserve water.

Today, irrigation engineering includes all technical activities required in securing necessary data, planning projects, designing structures, building irrigation systems, pumping water supplies, maintaining project works, operating projects, applying irrigation water, and relieving such objectionable agricultural and hydrological conditions as may develop.

Agricultural and Hydrological Phases. Agricultural and hydrological phases of irrigation engineering include all land and water problems involved in developing and maintaining profitable crop production in irrigated regions. They also include such items of information as may be required in designing project structures.

In general, agricultural and hydrological items include problems of land preparation, division of fields into irrigating units, development and maintenance of soil fertility, saline and alkali soil conditions, suitable irrigation methods, and desirable cultural procedures. They include determinations of available streamflow, necessary water supplies, proper qualities of irrigation water, water requirements of crops, irrigation requirements, adequate irrigation deliveries, and losses and waste of irrigation water. They include considerations of climatic factors, effects of weather conditions on crop growth, possible flood flows, necessary storage capacities in project reservoirs, quantities of water available in underground storage, artesian water supplies, and various additional items.

Agricultural and hydrological factors always were important in developing irrigation enterprises. They became more and more important as choice areas of land became fully developed and natural streamflows became fully utilized. Thus, they received more and more attention as irrigation developments progressed.

Many experimental tests, laboratory studies, and field investigations of agricultural and hydrological questions involved in irrigation have been conducted in the western states. The more comprehensive researches usually have been carried on by state agricultural experiment stations in cooperation with interested federal agencies. They have included most items enumerated above. Soil-moisture problems and water requirements of crops have received particular attention. The more important investigations are discussed briefly in the following chapters on agricultural and hydrological phases of irrigation engineering.

REFERENCES

The following list of references includes a few of the many technical books that contain valuable information regarding the agricultural and hydrological phases of irrigation engineering. Some were helpful in preparing this chapter. Others were helpful in preparing one or more subsequent chapters. Many were consulted frequently during the preparation of this volume. Grateful acknowledgments for their assistance are hereby made. They are not relisted in subsequent references pertaining to particular chapter material.

1. American Society of Civil Engineers, *Glossary: Water and Sewage Control Engineering,* New York, 1949 (prepared in cooperation with other societies).
2. —— *Hydrology Handbook,* New York, 1949.
3. Baker, Donald M., and Harold Conkling, *Water Supply and Utilization,* John Wiley & Sons, Inc., New York, 1930.
4. Barrows, H. K., *Floods, Their Hydrology and Control,* McGraw-Hill Book Company, Inc., New York, 1948.
5. Baver, L. D., *Soil Physics,* John Wiley & Sons, Inc., New York, 2nd ed., 1948.
6. Bear, Firman E., *Soils and Fertilizers,* John Wiley & Sons, Inc., New York, 3rd ed., 1942.
7. Buckley, Robert Burton, *Irrigation Pocket Book,* E. & F. N. Spon, Ltd., London, 4th ed., 1928.
8. Davis, Calvin V., and others, *Handbook of Applied Hydraulics,* McGraw-Hill Book Company, Inc., New York, 1942.
9. Etcheverry, B. A., and S. T. Harding, *Irrigation Practice and Engineering,* Volume I, *Use of Irrigation Water and Irrigation Practice,* McGraw-Hill Book Company, Inc., New York, 2nd ed., 1933.
10. Fortier, Samuel, *Use of Water in Irrigation,* McGraw-Hill Book Company, Inc., New York, 3rd ed., 1926.
11. Foster, Edgar E., *Rainfall and Runoff,* The Macmillan Company, New York, 1948.
12. Graf, Dorothy W., "Irrigation—A Selected Bibliography," *Bur. Agr. Eng.. U.S. Dept. Agr.,* Washington, 1938 (mimeographed).
13. Grover, N. C., and A. W. Harrington, *Stream Flow—Measurements, Records and Their Uses,* John Wiley & Sons, Inc., New York, 1943.
14. Harris, F. S., *Soil Alkali—Its Origin, Nature, and Treatment,* John Wiley & Sons, Inc., New York, 1920.
15. Haurwitz, Bernard, and James M. Austin, *Climatology,* McGraw-Hill Book Company, Inc., New York, 1944.
16. Hazen, Allen, *Flood Flows—A Study of Frequencies and Magnitudes,* John Wiley & Sons, Inc., New York, 1930.
17. Hewson, E. Wendell, and Richmond W. Longley, *Meteorology, Theoretical and Applied,* John Wiley & Sons, Inc., New York, 1944.

18. Hilgard, E. W., *Soils—Their Formation, Properties, Composition, and Relations to Climate and Plant Growth in the Humid and Arid Regions,* The Macmillan Company, New York, 1918.

19. Israelsen, Orson W., *Irrigation Principles and Practices,* John Wiley & Sons, Inc., New York, 2nd ed., 1950.

20. Kellogg, Charles E., *The Soils That Support Us,* The Macmillan Company, New York, 1947.

21. Kittredge, Joseph, *Forest Influences,* McGraw-Hill Book Company, Inc., New York, 1948.

22. Linsley, Ray K., Jr., Max A. Kohler, and Joseph L. H. Paulhus, *Applied Hydrology,* McGraw-Hill Book Company, Inc., New York, 1949.

23. Meinzer, Oscar E., and others, *Physics of the Earth—IX—Hydrology,* Dover Publications, Inc., New York, 1949.

24. Meyer, Adolph F., *The Elements of Hydrology,* John Wiley & Sons, Inc., New York, 2nd ed., 1928.

25. Pickels, George W., *Drainage and Flood Control Engineering,* McGraw-Hill Book Company, Inc., New York, 2nd ed., 1941.

26. Robinson, G. W., *Soils—Their Origin, Constitution, and Classification,* Thomas Murby and Company, London, 1936.

27. Tolman, C. F., *Ground Water,* McGraw-Hill Book Company, Inc., New York, 1937.

28. United States Department of Agriculture, *Soils and Men, Yearbook of Agriculture,* Washington, 1938.

29. ——— *Climate and Man, Yearbook of Agriculture,* Washington, 1941.

30. United States Department of Commerce, *Sixteenth Census of the United States, 1940, Irrigation of Agricultural Lands,* Bur. Census, Washington, 1942.

31. Weaver, John E., *Root Development of Field Crops,* McGraw-Hill Book Company, Inc., New York, 1926.

32. Weaver, John E., and William E. Bruner, *Root Development of Vegetable Crops,* McGraw-Hill Book Company, Inc., New York, 1927.

33. Weaver, John E., and F. E. Clements, *Plant Ecology,* McGraw-Hill Book Company, Inc., New York, 1938.

34. Wisler, C. O., and E. F. Brater, *Hydrology,* John Wiley & Sons, Inc., New York, 1949.

35. Yocum, L. Edwin, *Plant Growth,* The Ronald Press Company, New York, 1915.

Chapter 2

IRRIGATION SOILS

Soils on irrigated lands are originally of arid or semiarid types. Like soils in humid regions, they may have been formed by sedimentation on old lake beds, by deposition of flood-borne materials along streams, by disintegration of surface-rock formations, by gradual accumulations of wind-blown particles, or by decay and consolidation of organic materials in swamp areas as on peat and muck lands.

Because of dearth of rainfall, desert soils usually differ from soils of humid regions in certain important characteristics. They are generally deficient in organic matter, but well supplied with mineral nutrients needed for crop growth, since supplies of such elements have not been depleted by vegetation or leached out of the root zones by rainfall. Arid soils, when first placed under irrigation, are commonly more productive than soils that have been cultivated for some time in humid sections of the country. Desert soils are likely to be saline or alkaline, inasmuch as the soluble salts have not been leached away.

For general irrigation agriculture, the most satisfactory soils probably are the deep, well-drained alluvial deposits of medium or medium to fine texture that are readily tilled and highly productive. Such soils permit easy development of root systems, proper circulation of air and water through the root zones, and relatively large storage of moisture for plant use between irrigations. Comparatively fine loess deposits of wind-blown origin also constitute good irrigation soils.

Open sandy soils are usually less productive and less satisfactory than soils of medium to fine texture. They permit too rapid percolation of water to depths below the root zones and do not hold sufficient quantities of moisture within reach of the plant roots. Therefore, they require frequent irrigations. Heavy clay soils are hard to cultivate, are likely to be inadequately aerated, and do not permit ready penetration of water to the root systems. In irrigating heavy clay soils, water must be held on the field surfaces for considerable intervals of time, often resulting in large losses of water by evaporation and surface waste. Clay soils are suitable for rice crops, where continuous

14

flooding is necessary during the growing season. Some peat and muck soils are highly productive.

Relatively deep soils are more satisfactory for irrigation than shallow soils. Deep soils store more moisture for plant use between irrigations, provide more space for the development of root systems, and contain greater supplies of plant nutrients. Shallow soils require frequent irrigations. When they are permeable and underlaid by porous sand or gravel formations, excessive percolation losses may be unavoidable.

No irrigation project can prove successful if the soil is not suitable, or cannot be made suitable, for continuous profitable crop production. Many failures of early irrigation developments resulted from improper or insufficient considerations of soil problems. Soil conditions have important influences on the selection of crops, choice of farm practices, planning of farm distribution systems, and methods of applying water. Consequently, irrigation soils require thorough investigation and attention, not only in working out plans for new projects but also in maintaining profitable crop yields on existing projects.

Brief discussions of general soil conditions, soil properties, and soil surveys, such as are important in irrigation work, are given in the following sections of this chapter. Soil fertility, moisture in irrigation soils, soil-moisture movements, and problems involved in the irrigation of alkali areas are taken up in subsequent chapters.

General Terminology. Soils may be defined as natural masses of materials on the surface of the earth, where plants can grow when temperature and moisture conditions are favorable. They are made up of mineral and organic materials. When composed largely of mineral matter, they are referred to as mineral soils. When composed largely of organic matter, they are referred to as organic soils.

Soils are sometimes designated residual or transported, depending on whether they were formed from materials in their natural positions or from materials transported by wind or water. Residual soils are largely results of chemical and physical disintegration. Developments of both types of soils are aided materially by successions of plant life and effects of root growth during the xerosere.

Soils formed from accumulations of fine wind-blown particles, sometimes called aeolian deposits, are often referred to as loess. Fine sands deposited by winds are often called blow sands. Soils formed from depositions of water-borne materials along stream channels are referred to as alluvial soils. Soils formed from materials deposited during the melting of ice sheets, sometimes called moraines, are usually referred to as glacial tills.

In discussing soils, the vertical section through the soil formation is termed the soil profile. The upper part of the soil profile, that is, the 5 to 7 inches that may be disturbed by plowing, cultivating, or other tillage operations, is known as the topsoil or surface soil. Portions of the soil profile below the topsoil are commonly referred to as the subsoil. Layers or strata of soil having particular characteristics are known as horizons. Horizons are usually designated by capital letters beginning with the A horizon as the upper soil layer.

Dense layers of impermeable clay that sometimes underlie the upper portion of the soil profile are known as claypans. Indurated or hardened layers of soil that cannot be penetrated by plant roots are known as hardpans. Hardpans are soil layers that have been compacted or cemented by calcium carbonate, iron oxide, silica, or other binding materials, usually deposited from percolating solutions.

Additional terms used in discussing soils are explained later. A lengthy glossary of soil nomenclature may be consulted in the United States Department of Agriculture *Yearbook* for 1938.

Soil Conditions. Soil conditions vary greatly on different irrigation projects, not only at the field surfaces but also at depths below the surfaces. For some widely separated projects, differences in soils may be due largely to differences in the original geological strata from which the soils were formed, or to different processes involved in the development of the soils. However, soils formed from similar geological strata, or by similar processes of development, may vary greatly, not only on different projects but also on different areas of the same project. They may even vary in different parts of the same field.

The soil conditions that are essential for the growth of crop plants were briefly summarized by Morgan and his associates in 1938.[28] Except for slight changes in arrangement, they are listed verbatim as follows:

1. Suitability for the cultural implements required for most efficient production.

2. Effective resistance to destructive soil erosion or soil depletion under the cropping system involved in profitable management.

3. Adequate moisture storage to meet the water requirements of the crop, under normal rainfall or irrigation.

4. Adequate aeration to a suitable depth to permit the development of a favorable root system for the mature plant.

5. Available plant nutrients sufficient for profitable yields.

6. Freedom from adverse chemical conditions such as harmful concentrations of soluble constituents, and from other special soil conditions that favor the development of organisms parasitic to the crop.

Soils on most irrigation projects in western United States are mineral soils. Organic soils occur in some parts of the West, but their total areas, although seemingly large when expressed as acreages, are relatively small in comparison with the much larger areas where mineral soils prevail. Except where otherwise stated, the following discussions are written from the viewpoint of mineral soils. A special section on organic soils is included later in the chapter.

Composition of Soils. Most irrigation soils are composed of inorganic or mineral materials, with only relatively small proportions of organic matter and humus. The air and moisture that fill the pore spaces between the soil grains might be considered as parts of the soil. However, since air and water contents are always more or less variable and transitory, it seems better to think of soil constituents as including only the solid particles.

Mineral soil particles are classified as sand, silt, and clay, depending on the size of the grains. Sand grains and most silt particles are essentially products of the physical disintegration of surface rocks, whereas clay particles are mostly products of chemical weathering. Unusually fine clay and organic particles, generally too small to be visible with an ordinary microscope, constitute the soil colloids. Colloidal materials have beneficial effects on the storage of soil moisture and plant nutrients but may have detrimental effects on soil permeability when present in excessive amounts.

Appreciable proportions of well-graded sand and silt grains are desirable in irrigation soils, in that they facilitate tilth as well as air and water circulation. Some proportions of clay particles are needed, since they supply the most of the chemical foods essential for plant growth. Large proportions of clay particles are a disadvantage, because of objectionable physical conditions. Clay particles have plastic properties and cause stickiness of the soil when wet. They also cause cracking as the soil dries, impede root penetration, and make cultivation more difficult. Heavy clay soils are usually more impermeable than is desirable for ordinary farm crops.

Chemical compositions of soils, particularly as regards the various elements needed for plant growth and the elements that may be toxic to food plants, are discussed in the next chapter.

Organic Matter and Humus. Some proportions of organic matter and humus are needed in irrigation soils but usually are not present in appreciable amounts when arid lands are first irrigated. The presence of organic materials is desirable from the viewpoint of tilth as well as fertility. Organic materials supply plant nutrients, improve soil structures, and modify other physical properties of the soil. They probably have some beneficial effects on the moisture properties of the soil, especially when the soils are composed mainly of sand particles.

Virgin soils in desert regions seldom contain more than small fractions of 1 per cent of organic materials. Even in well-developed agricultural regions, quantities present in the upper foot of mineral soils rarely amount to more than 10 per cent. Analysis of 68 soils in various parts of the country, reported by Free, Browning, and Musgrave, showed contents of organic matter varying from 0.7 to 6.8 per cent in the surface soils and from 0.3 to 3.2 per cent in the subsoils.[12]

Organic matter in soils is supplied principally by vegetation. Total organic contents include living organisms as well as the remains and residues of plants, animals, worms, insects, fungi, bacteria, and other forms of soil life. Proportions of total organic matter made up by the remains of animal life usually are small in comparison with the proportions made up by the remains of vegetable growth.

The organic remains and residues in soils are continuously undergoing decomposition and mineralization. When they reach a well-decomposed, more or less stable condition, they are commonly referred to as humus. Fresh or only partially decomposed organic materials are sometimes referred to as raw humus. During the processes of decomposition, some of the residues of decay become organic colloids.

Texture of Soils. The texture of a soil is determined by the proportions and gradations of the three size groups of soil grains, namely, sand, silt, and clay. These groups are sometimes called soil separates. Sand separates include grains from 2.0 to 0.05 millimeter in diameter, silt separates include particles from 0.05 to 0.002 millimeter in diameter, and clay separates include particles of less than 0.002 millimeter in diameter. Prior to 1938, the division between silt and clay particles was placed at 0.005 millimeter in diameter, instead of 0.002 millimeter, and particles smaller than 0.002 millimeter in diameter were called colloidal clay.

In mechanical analysis of soils, sand separates are divided into five intermediate size groups, namely, fine gravel, coarse sand, medium sand, fine sand, and very fine sand. The size limits are shown in the second column of Table 1. Coarse gravel constituents, that is, par-

TABLE 1

MECHANICAL ANALYSES OF SOME SURFACE SOILS IN KINGS COUNTY, CALIFORNIA [31]

(Percentages by weight)

Soil particles	Size, mm. or μ	Grangeville fine sandy loam	Lethent silty clay loam	Merced clay loam	Kettle-man loam
Fine gravel (size in millimeters)	2.0 –1.0	0.6	....	Trace	1.3
Coarse sand	1.0 –0.5	3.3	Trace	0.1	4.7
Medium sand	0.5 –0.25	1.6	0.1	0.3	11.2
Fine sand	0.25–0.10	29.0	1.0	1.8	25.9
Very fine sand	0.10–0.05	25.1	5.5	4.9	15.9
Silt (size in μ)	50–5	31.7	58.3	50.9	26.3
Coarse clay	5–2	3.2	6.0	15.8	5.1
Fine clay *	2–0	5.8	29.3	27.1	10.3
Colloidal clay	....	2.9	16.3	15.2	5.8

* Percentages include colloidal clay.

ticles larger than 2.0 millimeters in diameter, are screened from the samples before the analyses are made. Proportions of the different separates are given as percentages of the total weight of the organic-free, oven-dried sample.

Table 1 shows mechanical analyses of some surface soils in Kings County, California, abstracted from a tabulation in a soil survey report.[31] The analyses were made by the modified International method. Particles from 50 to 5 microns in size are designated silt, particles from 5 to 2 microns are designated coarse clay, and particles smaller than 2 microns are designated fine clay. Particles smaller than 1 micron are designated colloidal clay.

Classification of Soils. The classification of soils now in common use in connection with soil surveys includes three categories, namely, series, types, and phases. This method of classification has been developed primarily from considerations of the suitability of surface soils for use in crop production.

A soil series includes soils of similar characteristics and profile arrangements, formed from similar parent materials. A particular series may include one or several soil types. Likewise, a particular soil type may include one or several soil phases. Soil types are determined according to their principal mineral sizes and gradations, that is, on the basis of texture. Different phases of soil types are determined according to special characteristics or topographic conditions that affect the agricultural use of the land, such as depths, stoniness, gravel contents, ground slopes, and conditions of drainage or erosion.

Soil series are usually named after the localities where they were first identified. A Fort Collins clay loam means a clay loam type of soil in the Fort Collins soil series. Shallow phases of the Fort Collins clay loam mean the same surface soils in places where the subsoil is comparatively shallow or nonexistent.

Soil types constitute the classification groups of primary importance in irrigation considerations. They also constitute the groups commonly used in conducting soil researches from the agricultural viewpoint.

Other methods of classifying soils have been developed, particularly in connection with the designing of engineering projects where soils are involved in the building of roads, airfields, levees, earth dams, and other works, as well as in furnishing foundations for various structures. For such uses, certain soil properties and gradations of grain size assume more significance and importance than in considerations of crop growth. A recent review of the various methods of classification, including methods based on texture, has been published.[9] A new permeability classification of soils that may be useful in irrigation studies is discussed later.

Soil Types. Soil types are classified according to textural gradations. The principal textural designations used by the Bureau of Plant Industry, Soils, and Agricultural Engineering, United States Department of Agriculture, in 1947, together with limiting proportions of sand, silt, and clay separates, are shown in Table 2. Some minor modifications in the Bureau's standards were pending before Dr. Alexander's committee at the time the table was prepared.

Variations of the types listed in Table 2 may be designated fine sand, very fine sand, loamy fine sand, fine sandy loam, very fine sandy loam, or coarse sandy loam, depending on the particular size of the coarser particles. When particles larger than 2.0 millimeters in diameter are present in appreciable proportions, the soils may be called gravelly sand loam, gravelly loam, cobbly loam, stony loam, stony clay, stony clay loam, or other appropriate names, depending on the soil types and the nature of the oversize constituents.

Soils of relatively coarse texture such as sand or sandy types are sometimes referred to as light or open soils. Soils of relatively fine texture such as clay or clay types are sometimes referred to as heavy or tight soils. Adobe and gumbo soils are unusually heavy clay soils

TABLE 2

TEXTURAL DESIGNATIONS USED IN IDENTIFYING SOIL TYPES *

Soil separates, per cent by weight

Soil types	Sand	Silt	Clay	Silt and clay
Sand	90–100	......	......	0–10
Loamy sand	80–90	......	......	10–20
Sandy loam	55–80	......	0–27	.....
Sandy loam	Less than 55	Less than 50	0–10	.....
Loam	Less than 55	Less than 50	10–27	.....
Silt loam	......	50 or more	0–27	.....
Sandy clay loam	More than 45	......	27–40	.....
Clay loam	20–45	......	27–40	.....
Silty clay loam	20 or less	......	27–40	.....
Sandy clay	40–60	......	40–60	.....
Silty clay	......	40 or more	40 or more	.....
Clay	40 or less	40 or less	40 or more	.....

* Compiled from data supplied by Bureau of Plant Industry, Soils, and Agricultural Engineering, U.S. Department of Agriculture, March 1947.

that swell and become practically impervious when wet, then shrink and crack as they dry.

Soil Structure. Soil structure, that is, the arrangement and coherence of the soil grains, is an important factor in successful irrigation agriculture. Soils in which the different particles cling together in groups or aggregates of various sizes are desirable, inasmuch as such structures facilitate air and water circulation through the soil as well as the development of adequate root systems. They also increase the resistance of the soil to erosion.

Types of soil structures include crumby, granular, cloddy, nutlike, platy, columnar, prismatic, fragmental, and others. Soils without definite structures may be single-grain types such as sands, or massive types such as heavy clay soils. Crumby or granular structures are desirable for proper crop growth. These types are likely to develop in soils seeded to grass or other close-growing crops. Consequently, well-planned crop rotations tend to maintain satisfactory soil structures.

Soil structures may be affected by freezing and thawing during the winter and spring months. They may be impaired by excessive irrigation, untimely cultivations, or vibrations of heavy farm machinery. The application of too much water during irrigations may break down the aggregates and result in puddling of the soil. Plowing too soon after irrigation may damage soil granulation. Plowing clay soils when too wet may cause the formation of undesirable clods in the surface layers. Trampling by livestock on wet soils may break down the soil structures and cause puddled conditions at the soil surfaces.

Soils deficient in organic matter can be improved structurally by adding organic materials. In sandy soils, structures sometimes can be improved by irrigating with silt-laden water. Structures of puddled soils can be improved or rebuilt by applying dust mulches to the wet soils or by the use of a dry fallow.[26] Methods of improving soil structures, determining soil structures, measuring soil aggregates, and effects of cultivation on soil structures have been investigated at several agricultural experiment stations, particularly in Arizona and South Dakota.[30]

Consistence of Soils. The consistence, or consistency, of a soil describes the relative cohesion and plasticity of the soil particles; that is, their resistance to separation, to the crushing of the structural aggregates, and to the deformation of the whole soil mass. Consistence includes the different degrees of soil compactness.

Self-explanatory terms are commonly used in describing consistence. For instance, sandy soils may have loose, open, or incoherent consistencies. Silty types may be coherent, mellow, friable, or crumbly. Clay soils may be stiff, tight, tenacious, or of varying degrees of compactness. Other terms used in describing consistence include brittle, soft, firm, hard, dense, tough, plastic, sticky, or cemented, as for hardpans. The consistency of a soil varies with changes in moisture content. A soil may be mellow, crumbly, or friable when moist; and coherent, hard, or tenacious when dry.

Soil consistency may be altered by untimely tillage or traffic operations. Sometimes compacted zones, called plow soles, develop at relatively shallow depths below the ground surfaces, owing to continued cultivation and passage of heavy equipment before the soil becomes sufficiently dried following an irrigation. Huberty described such conditions in some California orchards in 1944.[15] The compaction seemed to be greater in soils having wide ranges in particle sizes.

Color of Soils. The color of a soil may indicate fertility, presence of organic matter, presence of saline or alkali salts, adequate drainage, inadequate drainage, or other pertinent conditions pertaining to the suitability of the soil for agricultural use. However, the same soil color may be due to different causes in different sections of the country, so that the causes must be understood before making predictions of soil values on the basis of color.

Soils containing appreciable proportions of humus are dark colored or black and usually are productive. Soils turned black or white by alkali salts are unproductive until the excess salts are removed. In general, white or light-colored soils in humid regions are poorly drained, deficient in organic matter, and unsatisfactory for farm crops. In arid regions, light-colored soils usually owe their color to the presence of calcium carbonate or other salts and often prove satisfactory when properly drained, leached, and irrigated.

Soils colored red or reddish brown by unhydrated iron oxide are generally well drained and aerated. Soils colored yellow by hydrated iron oxide, also soils colored gray or grayish blue by reduced iron, often lack adequate drainage. In India, some soils are colored black by the presence of magnetite grains.

Porosity of Soils. The porosity of a soil is the amount of volume occupied by pores between the solid particles, spaces between soil aggregates, and any cavities that may be present. It is the portion of the soil that may be occupied by air and water. It is expressed as a percentage by volume.

The total porosity of a soil is usually determined from the real specific gravity of the solid particles and the volume weight or apparent specific gravity of the soil mass. When the volume weight is known, the porosity of the soil can be calculated, using an assumed mean specific gravity of the solid particles in the formula

$$P = \frac{100(S - V)}{S}$$

where P is the porosity in per cent, V is the volume weight, and S is the assumed specific gravity of the soil grains.

Porosities of soils vary with the size, shape, gradation, and arrangement of the soil grains, the structure of the soil, and the presence of plant roots or other organic matter. The porosity of a surface soil may be relatively high when covered with grass or other close-growing vegetation, or immediately after cultivation. The porosity of the subsoil at a particular site is less variable than the porosity of the surface soil, inasmuch as the physical conditions of the subsoil are less likely to be altered by agricultural procedures.

In a theoretical soil made up entirely of spherical particles of uniform size, the porosity might vary from about 26 to 48 per cent, depending on the arrangement of the particles, but would be independent of the particle size. In a soil made up of well-graded particles, where the smaller grains are just sufficient to fill the spaces between the larger grains, the porosity may be comparatively low. In general, sandy soils have relatively low porosities, and clay soils relatively high porosities. Loamy soils usually have porosities of intermediate magnitudes. However, soils are so variable that some fine-textured soils may have porosities practically as low as some coarse-textured soils.[38]

Most irrigation soils have porosities varying from about 30 to 55 per cent but may have porosities as low as 25 per cent or as high as 65 per cent. Table 3 shows minimum and maximum surface-soil

TABLE 3

POROSITIES OF SOME SURFACE SOILS AND SUBSOILS
OF DIFFERENT TEXTURE [12]

(Percentages by volume)

Soil types	Number of sites	Surface-soil porosity		Subsoil porosity *	
		Minimum	Maximum	Minimum	Maximum
Sandy loams	13	36.4	52.3	40.4	43.1
Loams	5	45.7	54.9	40.2	49.4
Silt loams	22	44.3	61.1	40.7	52.9
Gravelly silt loams	11	45.8	60.9	43.9	48.9
Clay and clay loams	17	41.4	64.1	49.3	52.8

* At sites where minimum and maximum porosities of the surface soil were observed.

porosities for some soils of different texture as reported by Free and his associates, also porosities of the subsoils at the same sites.[12]

The total porosity of a soil is sometimes considered as being made up of two groups of pore spaces: (1) the relatively large noncapillary pores through which water percolates downward, owing to gravity, and (2) the smaller capillary pores wherein moisture is retained by capillarity and moved by capillary tensions. The most desirable soils for irrigation agriculture probably are those in which the volume of noncapillary pores is about the same as the volume of capillary pores.

Specific Gravities and Weights. In most irrigation soils, the individual soil grains consist principally of quartz, feldspar, and clay particles. The specific gravities of such minerals vary from about 2.4 to 2.8. A value of 2.65, the average for quartz, is commonly assumed to represent the mean specific gravity of the solid grains. Soils containing appreciable quantities of iron oxides or other heavy minerals may have somewhat higher mean specific gravities of the solid particles.

The apparent specific gravity of a soil mass, also called bulk specific gravity or volume weight, is the ratio of the dry weight of a unit volume of the soil to the weight of an equal volume of water. In considerations of irrigation soils, the apparent specific gravity or volume weight of the soil is more useful than the mean specific gravity of the solid particles. Apparent specific gravities of soils vary through a wider range than real specific gravities of the soil grains. When the apparent specific gravity or volume weight of a soil is determined, the porosity can be computed as explained in the preceding section.

Table 4 shows volume weights and corresponding unit dry weights for the different surface soils listed in Table 3. Minimum volume

TABLE 4

VOLUME WEIGHTS AND UNIT WEIGHTS OF SURFACE
SOILS LISTED IN TABLE 3

Soil types	Number of sites	Volume weight		Unit weights, lb. per cu. ft.	
		Minimum *	Maximum	Minimum *	Maximum
Sandy loams	13	1.26	1.66	79	104
Loams	5	1.16	1.44	73	90
Silt loams	22	1.05	1.46	66	91
Gravelly silt loams	11	1.02	1.42	64	89
Clay and clay loams	17	0.94	1.54	59	96

* Minimum volume weights and unit weights are for soils having maximum porosities, and vice versa.

weights and unit dry weights are for the soils having maximum total porosities and vice versa.

In general, mineral soils utilized in irrigation agriculture have volume weights varying from about 1.0 to 1.8, and unit dry weights varying from about 60 to 115 pounds per cubic foot.

Soil Permeability. The permeability of a soil is the property that allows moisture to move through the soil mass. It is largely dependent on soil texture and structure but may be influenced by the presence of plow soles, plant roots, earthworm excavations, or the activities of other forms of soil life. It may also be influenced by reactions of base exchange, depending on the chemical composition of the colloidal material and the soil solution. Maintenance of adequate soil permeability is essential for continued profitable production of crops on irrigated lands.

When the pore spaces in a soil are relatively large, as in sandy soils of coarse texture, the passage of moisture is facilitated and the soil has a high degree of permeability. When the pore spaces are relatively small, as in clay soils of fine texture, the passage of moisture is retarded and the soil has a low degree of permeability. Some heavy clay soils of unusually fine texture, also some puddled soils, are too tight to permit appreciable movements of moisture and are said to be impermeable.

Most soils of medium texture are sufficiently permeable for satisfactory irrigation farming, especially as long as crumby or granular structures can be maintained. Continued cultivation, particularly if the tillage operations are conducted too soon after irrigation, may compact the soil just below the depth of cultivation and reduce the permeability.[15]

The permeability of a soil may be altered by base exchange when large proportions of sodium or calcium salts are present. Sodium constituents may be transformed into gelatinous products that tend to fill the pore spaces and reduce permeability. Such transformations are often called puddling, dispersion, or deflocculation. Calcium constituents may be changed into granular products that increase permeability. Therefore, calcium compounds such as gypsum are sometimes added to irrigation soils to increase their permeabilities. Other elements in the soil composition or the soil solution may cause reactions of base exchange, but their effects on permeability probably are not so pronounced as when sodium or calcium are present in excess proportions.[34]

Inasmuch as sodium salts cause detrimental effects on soil permeability, the possible presence of excess sodium should receive special consideration in soil studies. This problem is discussed in more detail in later chapters on quality of irrigation water and irrigation of alkali areas.

Permeability Classifications. A method of classifying soil permeabilities on the basis of permeability rates and amounts of pore space drained was proposed by Bendixen and his associates in 1948.[3] The method was developed during a laboratory investigation of 310 soil cores taken from different depths in seven Coastal Plains soils. The soils varied in texture from loamy sands to heavy clays. Percolation rates through saturated cores, also volumes of pore space drained in 1 hour following saturation, were measured during water tensions of 60 centimeters. The percolation rates as observed were not much greater than gravitational flow.

Table 5 shows the seven permeability classes proposed on the basis of the tests, their designations, and the permeability rates tentatively assigned as limits for the different classes. The permeability rates vary from less than 0.05 inch per hour for the lowest permeability class,

TABLE 5

PERMEABILITY CLASSIFICATION OF SOILS BASED
ON RATES OF PERCOLATION [3]

Class number	Permeability designation	Permeability rate, in. per hr.
1	Very slow	Less than 0.05
2	Slow	0.05– 0.2
3	Moderately slow	0.2 – 0.8
4	Moderate	0.8 – 2.5
5	Moderately rapid	2.5 – 5.0
6	Rapid	5.0 –10.0
7	Very rapid	10.0 or more

designated very slow, to more than 10.0 inches per hour for the highest permeability class, designated very rapid.

The suitability of the proposed method of classification was tested by application to various soils in Ohio and Missouri. The method was found to be in practical agreement with field classifications of the Missouri soils. For the Ohio soils, the relation between percolation rates and amounts of pore space drained had to be shifted somewhat to allow for definite differences in soil structure.

Soil Reactions. Soil reactions, in other words degrees of acidity or alkalinity, are commonly discussed on the basis of pH values. The pH value is the logarithm of the reciprocal of the hydrogen ion concentration. Inasmuch as the concentration of hydrogen ions in pure water is 1 in 10 million, the logarithm of the reciprocal is 7. Soils with pH values of 7 are said to be neutral. Values less than 7 indicate acidity, and values greater than 7 indicate alkalinity. Since the scale is logarithmic, a soil with a pH value of 5 is 10 times as acid as a soil with a pH value of 6. Similarly, a soil with a pH value of 9 is 10 times as alkaline as a soil with a pH value of 8.

In general, soil productivity increases as the pH value approaches neutrality. For most farm crops, soils with pH values between 6.5 and 7.5 are preferable. Certain special crops grow best on soils that are slightly acid. Others grow best on soils that are slightly alkaline.

Most soils utilized for crop production in irrigated regions have pH values varying from about 6.0 to 8.5. In arid and semiarid climates, soils are more often alkaline than acid. When the pH values are higher than 8.5, the presence of black alkali is indicated. Such soils require special treatments and cultural procedures, as discussed in a subsequent chapter. In humid climates, where alkali salts are leached beyond the root zones by rainfall, soils are more often acid than alkaline. When the pH values are lower than about 6.0, applications of lime are usually desirable.

Soils with different pH values may be designated as shown in Figure 1. Alkaline soils are sometimes called saline soils when the pH values are lower than 8.5, and alkali soils when the pH values are

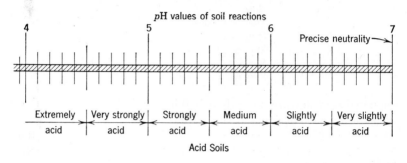

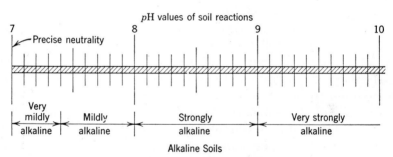

FIGURE 1. Soil designations based on pH values of reactions.

higher than 8.5. Soils with pH values between 6.6 and 7.3 are so nearly neutral that they are often called neutral soils.

Organic Soils. Organic soils, sometimes referred to as bog soils, are formed by gradual accumulations of dead and decaying vegetable matter in bogs, marshes, swamps, and other undrained areas where water tables stand at about ground-surface elevations. Such soils are usually considered in two groups: (1) peat soils, where the organic materials are only partially decomposed, mineralized, and consolidated; and (2) muck soils, where the organic materials are more fully decomposed, mineralized, and consolidated. Thus, muck soils are essentially decomposition products of peaty materials. They are usually darker in color than peat soils.

The dividing line between peat and muck soils has sometimes been stated in terms of the mineral or ash content. For instance, soils that show more than 35 per cent of ash have been designated muck soils, and those that show less than 35 per cent of ash have been designated peat soils.

Peat materials are commonly designated according to the types of vegetation from which they originated. The principal descriptive terms used in designating particular peats are sedimentary, fibrous, woody, moss, reed, and sedge. Woody peats develop in forest-covered swamps and may be designated coniferous or deciduous, depending on the type of forest. A type of moss peat that forms in the cooler moist climates is often called sphagnum moss peat.

Organic soils have greater porosities than mineral soils, lower specific gravities of the soil particles, and much lower volume weights. Some moss peats weigh less than 10 pounds per cubic foot when dry. Therefore, moisture contents of organic soils, expressed as percentages by weight, may be several times as great as in mineral soils. Peat and muck soils usually show acid reactions, but some fibrous peats may be slightly alkaline.

In western United States, peat and muck lands occur in the Sacramento-San Joaquin delta east of San Francisco, the Klamath region of northern California and southern Oregon, the Willamette Valley of western Oregon, parts of northwestern Washington, Sanpete County, Utah, and certain other local areas.

Soil Surveys. Detailed surveys of soil conditions on areas to be supplied with water are needed in planning new irrigation projects, also in planning extensions of existing projects. When soil surveys have been made for the areas under consideration, all survey reports should be carefully analyzed before proceeding with project developments. If soil reports are not available, arrangements for conducting soil surveys should be made as a part of the project investigations.

Cooperative arrangements for soil surveys usually can be made with state agricultural experiment stations and agencies of the national government. The Bureau of Plant Industry, Soils, and Agricultural Engineering, United States Department of Agriculture, is the principal federal agency now conducting soil survey work.

The investigation, surveying, and mapping of soils in the United States was begun by the Department of Agriculture and the state agriculture experiment stations about the end of the nineteenth century. This cooperative work has progressed more or less continuously since that time, so that soil reports on at least some areas are now available in practically all parts of the country. The investigations have been conducted primarily from the viewpoint of possible agricultural uses of the soil areas.

Soil Survey Methods. Soil surveys are made by examining and recording all pertinent soil conditions in the field, taking representative samples throughout the areas included in the surveys, and analyzing selected samples in the laboratory. Valuable information regarding soil profiles usually can be obtained from exposures along highway or railroad cuts, or at other places where excavations have been made. Test pits are dug at appropriate locations, and borings are made as needed to determine characteristics of the principal soil horizons. All soil conditions are carefully observed and accurately recorded, including surface drainage, subsoil drainage, presence of alkali salts, types of existing natural vegetation, stoniness, gravel constituents, organic matter, texture, structure, consistence, color, and estimated field classifications of soil types.[18]

Samples for chemical analyses are commonly taken from the upper 6 to 12 inches of the soil profile. Samples for mechanical analyses and for general data on specific soil horizons are taken at different depths, down as far as may be necessary to determine all major surface and subsoil characteristics. Soil reactions are determined from the samples. Results of the surveys are plotted on maps, and detailed reports on the investigations are prepared and published. The more recent soil survey reports often include estimated soil ratings.

Some reconnaissance surveys of soil conditions over large areas have been made by photographing land tracts from the air.[10] The principal land-surface features, such as topography, farm crops, natural vegetation, drainage, erosion, and color, show on the aerial photographs and indicate the more important characteristics of the soil formations. Such surveys furnish general data that may be useful in preliminary studies of contemplated irrigation projects. However, they do not affect the necessity for detailed ground-surface surveys as discussed above.

Soil Ratings. Ratings for different areas included in a soil survey are sometimes estimated to indicate relative values of the lands for agricultural uses. Such ratings are based on the physical and chemical properties of the surface soils, the general characteristics of the subsoils, drainage conditions, land slopes, and other features that may affect crop production. The Storie soil index, developed by Storie in 1933, has been used in rating many soils in California.[37] A somewhat similar method of rating agricultural lands was proposed by Kellogg and Ableiter in 1935.[20]

In surveying soils where lands are under cultivation or can be compared with nearby lands that are under cultivation, crop yields obtained on typical soils are sometimes used as a basis for soil ratings. Ratings prepared by such methods are logically called productivity ratings. Productivity ratings have been used in a number of soil surveys. One method of classifying soils on the basis of productivity was proposed by Anderson and his associates in 1938.[1]

Because of the nature of soil surveys, soil ratings are necessarily approximate. Probably in any particular survey, the accuracy of the ratings depends largely on the experience and skill of the surveyor. Inasmuch as different methods of rating are used in different locations, ratings for similar soils in different soil surveys may not be comparable. Brief descriptions of rating methods are commonly given in reports on soil surveys which included soil ratings. Soil ratings are valuable in considering different land units in a contemplated irrigation project, particularly if the project lands are all located in one soil survey area, so that the ratings can be accepted as comparable.

Soils and Natural Vegetation. Reconnaissance surveys of soil conditions may be based on inspections of existing types of natural vegetation. Some types of vegetation indicate the presence of soils that are suitable for crop production when amply supplied with irrigation water. Other types indicate the presence of soils of shallow depth, poor drainage, improper texture, objectionable contents of alkali salts, or other undesirable physical or chemical properties, so that the lands may not prove satisfactory when irrigated.

Whenever sudden changes in prevailing types of natural vegetation are apparent, definite changes in soil conditions may be anticipated. Different types of natural vegetation may indicate different soil characteristics in different climates. However, when areas bearing certain types of plant growth have been reclaimed and found satisfactory, extensions of the irrigable acreages to adjoining lands bearing the same types of plant growth usually can be made with confidence.

In general, soil conditions suitable for irrigation are indicated by the presence of sagebrush, galleta, giant wild rice, creosote bush, desert saltbrush, mesquite, and sacaton. Alkaline or saline soils that may not be suitable for irrigation without leaching are indicated by shadscale, salt sage, white sage, narrowleaf saltbrush, greasewood, seepweed, pickleweed, samphire, salt grass, and alkali sacaton.[35]

Areas of undesirable seleniferous soils that should be developed with caution may be indicated by certain species of *Aplopappus, Astralagus, Stanleya,* and *Xylorhiza,*[39] including some plants more commonly known as desert-plume, two-grooved milk vetch, Hayden's poison vetch, and Patterson's loco.[14]

REFERENCES

1. Anderson, Arthur, and others, "A Proposed Method for Classifying and Evaluating Soils on the Basis of Productivity and Use Suitabilities," *Nebr. Agr. Exp. Sta. Res. Bull.* 98, 1938.

2. Baldwin, Mark, Charles E. Kellogg, and James Thorp, "Soil Classification," *U.S. Dept. Agr. Yearbook,* 1938, pp. 979–1001.

3. Bendixen, T. W., M. F. Hershberger, and C. S. Slater, "A Basis for Classifying Soil Permeabilities," *Jour. Agr. Res.,* Sept. 1, 1948, pp. 157–168.

4. Bendixen, T. W., and C. S. Slater, "Effect of Time of Drainage on the Measurement of Soil Pore Space and Its Relation to Permeability," *Procs. Soil Sci. Soc. Am.,* Vol. 11, 1946, pp. 35–42.

5. Botkin, C. W., and L. B. Shires, "The Effect of Irrigation and Cropping on Desert Soils," *N. Mex. Agr. Exp. Sta. Bull.* 263, 1939.

6. Bouyoucos, G. J., "Simple and Rapid Methods for Ascertaining the Existing Structural Stability of Soil Aggregates," *Jour. Am. Soc. Agron.,* Vol. 27, 1935, pp. 222–227.

7. Brown, L. A., and others, "Land Types in Eastern Colorado," *Colo. Agr. Exp. Sta. Bull.* 486, 1944.

8. Buehrer, T. F., "The Movement of Gases through the Soil as a Criterion of Soil Structure," *Ariz. Agr. Exp. Sta. Tech. Bull.* 39, 1932.

9. Casagrande, Arthur, "Classification and Identification of Soils," *Trans. Am. Soc. C. E.,* Vol. 113, 1948, pp. 901–991.

10. Civil Aeronautics Administration, "The Origin, Distribution, and Airphoto Identification of United States Soils," *U.S. Dept. Com. Tech. Devel. Rep.* 52, 1946.

11. Dachnowski-Stokes, A. P., "Grades of Peat and Muck for Soil Improvement," *U.S. Dept. Agr. Cir.* 290, 1933.

12. Free, G. R., G. M. Browning, and G. W. Musgrave, "Relative Infiltration and Related Physical Characteristics of Certain Soils," *U.S. Dept. Agr. Tech. Bull.* 729, 1940.

13. Gardner, William, "Permeability of Soil," *Procs. Soil Sci. Soc. Am.,* Vol. 6, 1941, pp. 126–128.

14. Hershey, A. L., "Some Poisonous Plant Problems of New Mexico," *N. Mex. Agr. Exp. Sta. Bull.* 322, 1945.

15. Huberty, M. R., "Compaction in Cultivated Soils," *Trans. Am. Geop. Union,* 1944, Part VI, pp. 896–899.

16. Johnson, W. M., and C. F. Bortfield, "The Effect of Soil Texture and Slope of Land on Productivity in Two North Dakota Counties," *N. Dak. Agr. Exp. Sta. Bull.* 315, 1942.

17. Kellogg, Charles E., "Development and Significance of the Great Soil Groups of the United States," *U.S. Dept. Agr. Misc. Pub.* 229, 1936.
18. ——— "Soil Survey Manual," *U.S. Dept. Agr. Misc. Pub.* 274, 1937.
19. ——— "Conflicting Doctrines about Soils," *Sci. Monthly,* June 1948, pp. 475–487.
20. Kellogg, Charles E., and J. K. Ableiter, "A Method of Rural Land Classification," *U.S. Dept. Agr. Tech. Bull.* 469, 1935.
21. Leamer, R. W., and B. Shaw, "A Simple Apparatus for Measuring Noncapillary Porosity on an Extensive Scale," *Jour. Am. Soc. Agron.,* Vol. 33, 1941, pp. 1003–1008.
22. Marbut, C. F., "The Contribution of Soil Surveys to Soil Science," *Procs. Soc. Prom. Agr. Sci.,* Vol. 41, 1920, pp. 116–142.
23. ——— "Soils of the United States," *U.S. Dept. Agr. Atlas of Am. Agr.,* Part III, 1935.
24. Marbut, C. F., and others, "Soils of the United States," *U.S. Bur. Soils Bull.* 96, 1913.
25. McGeorge, W. T., "Studies on Soil Structure: Some Physical Characteristics of Puddled Soils," *Ariz. Agr. Exp. Sta. Tech. Bull.* 67, 1937.
26. McGeorge, W. T., and J. F. Breazeale, "Studies on Soil Structure: Effect of Puddled Soils on Plant Growth," *Ariz. Agr. Exp. Sta. Tech. Bull.* 72, 1938.
27. Middleton, H. E., C. S. Slater, and H. G. Byers, "The Physical and Chemical Characteristics of the Soils from the Erosion Experiment Stations—Second Report," *U.S. Dept. Agr. Tech. Bull.* 430, 1934.
28. Morgan, M. F., J. H. Gourley, and J. K. Ableiter, "The Soil Requirements of Economic Plants," *U.S. Dept. Agr. Yearbook,* 1938, pp. 753–776.
29. Nikiforoff, Constantin C., "Soil Organic Matter and Soil Humus," *U.S. Dept. Agr. Yearbook,* 1938, pp. 929–939.
30. Puhr, Leo F., and Oscar Olson, "A Preliminary Study of the Effect of Cultivation on Certain Chemical and Physical Properties of Some South Dakota Soils," *S. Dak. Agr. Exp. Sta. Bull.* 314, 1937.
31. Retzer, John L., and others, *Soil Survey of Kings County, California,* U.S. Dept. Agr. and Calif. Agr. Exp. Sta., 1946.
32. Rice, T. D., and L. T. Alexander, "The Physical Nature of Soil," *U.S. Dept. Agr. Yearbook,* 1938, pp. 887–896.
33. Russell, M. B., "Pore-Size Distribution as a Measure of Soil Structure," *Procs. Soil Sci. Soc. Am.,* Vol. 6, 1941, pp. 108–112.
34. Scofield, C. S., "Soil, Water Supply, and Soil Solution in Irrigation Agriculture," *U.S. Dept. Agr. Yearbook,* 1938, pp. 704–716.
35. Shantz, H. L., "Plants as Soil Indicators," *U.S. Dept. Agr. Yearbook,* 1938, pp. 835–860.
36. Shantz, H. L., and R. L. Piemeisel, "Types of Vegetation in Escalante Valley, Utah, as Indicators of Soil Conditions," *U.S. Dept. Agr. Tech. Bull.* 713, 1940.
37. Storie, R. Earl, "An Index for Rating the Agricultural Value of Soils," *Calif. Agr. Exp. Sta. Bull.* 556, 1933.
38. Veihmeyer, F. J., and others, "Report of the Committee on Physics of Soil-Moisture, 1934–35," *Trans. Am. Geop. Union,* 1935, Part II, pp. 426–432.
39. Williams, K. T., H. W. Lakin, and H. G. Byers, "Selenium Occurrence in Certain Soils in the United States, with a Discussion of Related Topics; Fourth Report," *U.S. Dept. Agr. Tech. Bull.* 702, 1940.

40. Wilson, LeMoyne, "Muck-Soil Management and Crop-Production Studies, Sanpete County Experimental Farm—1927 to 1933, Inclusive," *Utah Agr. Exp. Sta. Bull.* 267, 1936.

41. Yoder, R. E., "A Direct Method of Aggregate Analysis of Soils and a Study of the Physical Nature of Erosion Losses," *Jour. Am. Soc. Agron.*, Vol. 28, 1936, pp. 337–351.

Chapter 3

SOIL FERTILITY

Adequate soil fertility is essential for the production of profitable agricultural crops. On any irrigation project, the maintenance of satisfactory soil fertility is necessary for continued financial success. For continued production of maximum crop yields, with minimum quantities of irrigation water, the highest possible soil fertility is desirable.

In general, soils are fertile when they contain ample supplies of organic material, the source of nitrogen, and sufficient soluble compounds of the mineral elements needed for the growth of food plants. When soils meeting these requirements have satisfactory surface topography, physical properties, and subsoil drainage, the application of adequate amounts of irrigation water at proper intervals during the growing season usually results in profitable crop production.

When arid lands are first supplied with irrigation water, the soils may be deficient in organic matter and nitrogen. Therefore, steps to correct such deficiencies may be needed during the early life of an irrigation project. Newly irrigated soils generally contain ample proportions of the mineral elements required for crop growth, since supplies of such elements have not been leached out by rainfall or depleted by the previously existing types of desert vegetation. Later, as crop production continues, supplies of some mineral nutrients may be gradually decreased by plant growth until they need replenishment by the application of suitable fertilizers.

The following pages present brief discussions of the mineral constituents of soils, elements needed by food plants, certain undesirable soil compositions, some cultural practices, and various other matters involved in developing and maintaining soil fertility. A final section takes up the depths of root zones that are desirable for different crops. Inasmuch as space limitations preclude adequate treatments of these subjects, a rather lengthy list of references is given at the end of the chapter.

Mineral Constituents of Soils. Mineral constituents of soils are derived initially from rocks that make up the surface of the earth. This is true whether the minerals remain in their original locations or are transported by wind or water agencies and redeposited many miles away. The mineral constituents include various products resulting from the physical and chemical weathering of quartz, feldspar, hornblende, pyroxene, mica, limonite, and other minerals contained in surface rocks. Sand particles in soils usually come from the physical disintegration of quartz materials. Clay particles usually come from the chemical decay of feldspars.

Table 1 shows approximate percentages of mineral matter in rocks, soils, food plants, and man, as compiled by Browne.[11] The major

TABLE 1

APPROXIMATE AMOUNTS OF MINERAL MATTER IN
ROCKS, SOILS, FOOD PLANTS, AND MAN [11]

(Percentages by weight)

Element	Rocks *	Soils	Food plants	Man
Silicon	51.96	71.63	2.05	....
Aluminum	15.14	13.74	Trace	....
Iron	9.48	6.86	1.58	0.13
Calcium	6.85	1.02	8.44	42.24
Potassium	4.84	3.02	52.85	8.34
Sodium	5.16	1.08	5.56	6.03
Magnesium	3.90	0.68	6.06	1.32
Titanium	1.16	1.06	Trace	....
Phosphorus	0.25	0.12	16.77	23.85
Manganese	0.17	0.12	Trace	Trace
Sulphur	0.10	0.10	3.03	13.14
Barium	0.09	0.17	Trace	....
Chlorine	0.08	0.07	3.50	4.84
Chromium	0.07	0.01	Trace	....
Fluorine	0.05	0.06	Trace	0.06
Other elements †	0.71	0.26	0.16	0.05

* Igneous and sedimentary.
† Including zinc, copper, iodine, cobalt, boron, and others.

mineral constituents in rocks and soils, in the order of decreasing percentages, are silicon, aluminum, and iron. In food plants, the major constituents are potassium, phosphorus, and calcium. In man, the major constituents are calcium, phosphorus, and sulphur.

Table 2 shows chemical analyses of some alluvial surface soils in Montana, South Dakota, Nebraska, and Kansas, as reported by Holmes

TABLE 2

CHEMICAL ANALYSES OF SOME ALLUVIAL SURFACE SOILS [29]

(Percentages by weight)

Constituent	Symbol	Havre clay, Valley Co., Mont.	Havre silty clay loam, Richland Co., Mont.	Laurel loam, Walworth Co., S. Dak.	Lamoure fine sandy loam, Lincoln Co., Neb.	Lincoln loam, Ford Co., Kans.
Silica	SiO_2	67.32	68.04	70.35	79.67	70.00
Titanium oxide	TiO_2	0.69	0.57	0.47	0.33	0.49
Alumina	Al_2O_3	15.05	12.73	11.46	9.06	10.93
Ferric oxide	Fe_2O_3	5.42	4.68	3.70	2.95	3.88
Manganese oxide	MnO	0.05	0.26	0.04	0.04	0.05
Lime	CaO	1.42	2.42	3.28	1.55	4.32
Magnesia	MgO	1.81	2.89	2.17	0.99	1.12
Potash	K_2O	2.82	2.38	2.07	2.57	2.41
Soda	Na_2O	0.80	0.34	1.57	1.58	1.22
Phosphoric acid	P_2O_5	0.20	0.15	0.20	0.14	0.18
Sulphur trioxide	SO_3	0.23	0.18	0.17	0.11	0.28
Carbon dioxide	CO_2	0.42	2.68	3.75	0.00	3.32
Combined water	.....	3.53	3.04	1.20	0.91	1.33
Total		99.76	100.34	100.43	99.90	99.58
Ignition loss	.....	6.57	7.97	6.86	4.58	6.30
Organic matter	.....	2.72	2.40	2.00	3.70	1.72
Nitrogen	N	0.16	0.10	0.13	0.19	0.11
Soil reaction	pH	7.7	8.0	8.8	6.6	7.9

and Hearn.[29]   The principal mineral constituents are shown as oxides, in accordance with usual analytical procedures. The analyses also included determinations of combined water, ignition loss, organic matter, nitrogen, and soil reactions. All quantities are expressed as percentages, except soil reactions, which are given in pH values.

Dissolved amounts of soluble mineral compounds present in the soil are commonly contained in the soil water, generally referred to as the soil solution. In irrigation soils, soil solutions usually contain chlorides, carbonates, nitrates, and sulphates, as acid ions; and calcium, magnesium, potassium, and sodium, as basic ions. Some additional constituents may be present in relatively small concentrations. Soil solutions are discussed in greater detail in subsequent chapters.

Elements Needed by Food Plants. The ten principal elements needed for normal growth of food plants are oxygen, carbon, hydrogen, nitrogen, potassium, phosphorus, calcium, magnesium, sulphur, and iron. Oxygen, carbon, and hydrogen are obtained from air and water. Nitrogen is obtained from the air, indirectly, through organic matter in the soil, or through the activities of soil bacteria, as when leguminous crops are grown. The other elements are dissolved from soil minerals, by soil moisture, and taken up by plant roots through the soil solution.

Recent investigations indicate that under certain conditions mineral nutrients may be absorbed directly from soil colloids, without going through solution; but quantities of plant food obtained in such a manner probably are not of appreciable proportions.[34] Exact methods by which different mineral elements are absorbed by plant roots are not fully understood. Current researches using radioisotopes should throw light on some unsolved problems.

Phosphorus, potassium, calcium, and magnesium are the four major mineral elements required by food plants. Silicon and aluminum, the two major mineral constituents of soils, are not included in the principal elements needed for plant growth. However, plants may derive some benefits from their presence in the soil. Some forms of vegetation, such as certain grasses, may contain relatively large proportions of silica. In fact, some grasses may develop fungus diseases if sufficient supplies of silica are not available.[42]

In addition to the ten elements enumerated above, some types of plant life may require small or minute amounts of manganese, zinc, copper, boron, cobalt, and possibly molybdenum. Small percentages or traces of these secondary elements are usually present in irrigation soils. Small proportions of boron are sometimes contained in irrigation waters.

Table 3 gives approximate percentages of the principal mineral constituents of some field and vegetable crops, as reported by Browne.[11] The data were determined by ash analyses and reported as resulting oxides. The original compilation shows ranges in percentages for the different minerals in the ashes of the various crops, as well as average values; but only average values are given in Table 3. Percentages of any particular element in any particular crop usually vary widely, owing to differences in soil characteristics, water supply, climate, use of fertilizers, cultural procedures, and other growth conditions. For the analyses used in compiling Table 3, maximum percentages of minor constituents were often several times as great as minimum percentages.

The data in Table 3 show relatively high potash contents for all crops except spinach, high soda contents for spinach and young asparagus

TABLE 3

MINERAL CONSTITUENTS OF SOME FIELD AND VEGETABLE CROPS[11]

(Approximate average percentages)

Crop	Pure ash in dry crop	Potash	Soda	Lime	Magnesia	Iron oxide	Phosphoric acid	Sulphuric acid	Silica	Chlorine
Meadow hay	6.98	26.71	3.70	15.95	6.89	1.54	**7.11**	5.21	28.73	6.16
Timothy grass	6.82	34.69	1.83	8.05	3.24	0.83	11.80	2.85	32.17	5.19
Red clover in bloom	6.86	32.29	1.97	34.91	10.90	1.08	9.64	3.23	2.69	3.78
Alfalfa, beginning of bloom	7.38	23.55	1.76	40.67	4.92	1.86	8.50	5.74	9.54	3.01
Winter wheat, grain	1.96	31.16	2.07	3.25	12.06	1.28	47.22	0.39	1.96	0.32
Maize, grain	1.45	29.78	1.10	2.17	15.52	0.76	45.61	0.78	2.09	0.91
Peas	2.73	43.10	0.98	4.81	7.99	0.83	35.90	3.42	0.91	1.59
Garden beans	3.22	44.01	1.49	6.38	7.62	0.32	35.52	4.05	0.57	0.86
Potatoes, tubers	3.79	60.06	2.96	2.64	4.93	1.10	16.86	6.52	2.04	3.46
Potatoes, vines	8.58	21.78	2.31	32.65	16.51	2.86	7.89	6.32	4.32	5.78
Sugar beets, roots	3.83	53.13	8.92	6.08	7.86	1.14	12.18	4.20	2.28	4.81
Sugar beets, leaves	14.88	26.26	13.75	20.20	11.33	0.54	4.75	5.30	10.17	8.47
Grapes, entire fruit	5.19	56.20	1.42	10.77	4.21	0.37	15.58	5.62	2.75	1.52
Asparagus, young stalks	7.26	24.04	17.08	10.85	4.32	3.38	18.57	6.18	10.09	5.93
Cabbage, hearts	9.62	44.69	8.14	12.14	3.62	0.45	11.89	13.69	0.48	5.64
Cauliflower, hearts	8.35	44.36	5.89	5.58	3.66	1.02	20.22	13.01	3.76	3.44
Spinach	16.48	16.56	35.29	11.88	6.38	3.35	10.25	6.87	4.52	6.20

stalks, high lime contents for red clover, alfalfa, potato vines, and sugar beet leaves, high magnesia contents for clover, grain, potato vines, and sugar beet leaves, and high phosphoric acid contents for several crops, particularly grains, peas, and beans. Young asparagus stalks and spinach show relatively high percentages of iron. Meadow hay and timothy show high percentages of silica. Cabbage and cauliflower hearts show relatively high percentages of sulphuric acid.

Although Table 3 shows appreciable percentages of soda, silica, and chlorine in the ashes of most crops, these elements are not generally considered as essential for normal plant growth.

Toxic Elements. Some elements contained in irrigation soils may be toxic to plants if present in excessive amounts. Certain salts of some of the primary elements required for plant growth, such as calcium, magnesium, and potassium, also certain salts of sodium, an element not required for plant growth, may be harmful to plants if present in excess proportions. Some of the salts may also be harmful to the irrigation soils. Toxic percentages of sodium, calcium, magnesium, and potassium, also their harmful effects on plants and soils, are discussed in a later chapter on irrigation of alkali areas.

Secondary elements required for plant growth, such as manganese, zinc, copper, boron, cobalt, and possibly molybdenum, may be toxic if present in amounts only slightly larger than those needed. This is especially true of boron, which probably has been more troublesome than most secondary elements. A cattle disease experienced in parts of California has been traced to excessive amounts of molybdenum in some pasture legumes.

Irrigation soils probably should contain about 10 to 15 parts per million of soluble boron compounds, in order to produce satisfactory crop growth. However, if they contain much larger proportions, or if undesirable percentages of boron are present in the irrigation water, crops may be injured. Some difficulties in maintaining proper amounts of available boron have been experienced in a few irrigated sections of western United States, particularly southern California. Some studies indicate that plants may withstand high boron concentrations better in cool humid climates than in regions where relatively high rates of transpiration are experienced.

Other elements that may be toxic if present in more than minute or trace proportions include aluminum, arsenic, barium, chromium, fluorine, lead, nickel, selenium, strontium, and thallium.

Toxic proportions of selenium occur in some semiarid regions, where the soils have been derived from Cretaceous shales. The alkali disease of animals experienced on some western range lands in Montana, Wyoming, South Dakota, and other states is generally attributed to the presence of selenium in the root zones. Plants growing on soils where proportions of selenium are as low as 1 part per million may absorb enough selenium to become poisonous. Where ample supplies of irrigation water are used, the selenium content usually is reduced to nontoxic values by leaching.

In some localities, arsenic contents of surface soils may be increased to undesirable proportions by the continued spraying of fruit trees or by the use of arsenates in controlling insects. Arsenic is often present in soils in relatively small proportions. Analyses of a number of soils that had not been affected by spraying showed arsenic contents varying from less than 1 to about 40 parts per million. Analyses of some soils that had been contaminated by spraying showed arsenic contents as high as 550 parts per million.[68]

The presence of more than normal proportions of arsenic in soils may cause considerable reductions in the yield and quality of certain crops. Some crops may not grow at all on soils that are high in arsenic compounds. Others may show slight increases in the arsenic contents of the crop products. However, plants do not generally absorb soil arsenic in toxic amounts as they do selenium.

Soil Deficiencies. In irrigated regions, low contents of organic matter, nitrogen, phosphorus, and potassium constitute the principal soil deficiencies that may be experienced and may affect profitable crop production. Some soils may be low in available supplies of iron, sulphur, zinc, and boron. Other primary and secondary elements needed for normal plant growth may be deficient in certain local areas but usually are present in ample proportions.

Deficiencies in organic matter affect the structure, tilth, and moisture-holding capacity of the soil, also the solvent properties of the soil solution, as well as the supply of nitrogen in forms available for plant use. Deficiencies in nitrogen, phosphorus, and potassium injure plant growth, cause poor color and appearance of the plants, affect the quality of the crop products, and result in decreased crop returns.

Lack of sufficient nitrogen affects the reproductive elements of the plants and the ability of the plants to utilize other nutrients. Phosphorus deficiencies cause poor plant growth, delayed maturity, and reduced phosphorus contents of the plants. Potassium deficiencies decrease plant vigor, affect the assimilation of carbon dioxide, impair the quality of the products, and increase the susceptibility of the plants to disease. On soils low in potassium, potatoes may be watery and have low starch contents, cereal kernels may be poorly filled, tobacco leaves may have poor flavor, and other crops may have certain undesirable qualities.

When crop plants are grown on soils low in available compounds of iron, magnesium, and manganese, the leaves may turn yellow, a condition called chlorosis. Lack of sufficient sulphur may cause effects somewhat similar to those caused by inadequate supplies of nitrogen. Copper deficiencies, which sometimes occur in peat soils, reduce plant turgidity, cause citrus dieback, and may result in other abnormal conditions of growth.

Many plant diseases, often called deficiency diseases, may be caused by inadequate supplies of certain elements in the root zones. Manganese deficiencies may cause gray speck of oats, sulphur deficiencies may cause the yellow disease of the tea bush, and magnesium deficiencies may cause sand drown of tobacco. Zinc deficiencies may cause pecan rosette, spotting of tobacco leaves, white bud of corn, and a yellow mottling of fruit-tree leaves known as little leaf. Boron deficiencies may cause dry rot of sugar beets, top rot of tobacco, internal browning of cauliflower, cracked stem of celery, brown heart of turnips, and internal cork of apples. Inadequate supplies of boron may also cause a yellowing of alfalfa foliage known as alfalfa yellows.[4]

Deficiencies in available zinc compounds have been reported for some lands in Utah where fruit crops are grown on granitic soils.[52] Deficiencies in zinc, manganese, and copper have been reported for some local areas in California where walnut crops are grown.[3] Deficiencies in phosphorus have been experienced in some of the older irrigated regions, and deficiencies in potassium in some peat soils.

Different crops need different amounts of the various plant nutrients. Consequently, as far as a particular element is concerned, a soil may be deficient for some crops and adequately supplied for others. Although plant and soil relations have been studied exhaustively for many years, effects of some elements on plant growth, particularly the trace elements, are still more or less uncertain.

Maintaining Soil Fertility. Assuming soils of suitable texture and structure and adequately drained, satisfactory fertility for the growth of most farm crops usually can be maintained on irrigated lands by the adoption of proper cultural procedures. Such procedures should include the spreading of all barnyard manures over the cropped areas and the planting of different crops in rotation on the different areas. They may include, if needed, the plowing under or disking in of green manures and the application of carefully selected commercial fertilizers. In general, applications of lime to correct soil acidity, so often needed in humid regions, are not required on irrigated lands, inasmuch as the soils are generally alkaline or only slightly acid. The use of silty water in irrigating, when available, also improves soil fertility.

The careful conservation and efficient spreading of barnyard manures is one of the best methods of maintaining soil fertility. Farm manures supply the soil with organic materials as well as fertilizing elements. Consequently, they tend to improve the physical conditions of the soil as well as to maintain adequate supplies of plant nutrients. On many irrigated areas, applications of barnyard manures, together with carefully planned crop rotations, are sufficient to maintain satisfactory soil fertility through long periods of years.

Three types of crops are commonly used in rotation on irrigated farms, namely, legumes and grasses, small grains, and cultivated or row crops. Legumes are particularly beneficial, since the plants derive nitrogen from the air. Alfalfa is a deep-rooted legume that can abstract mineral nutrients from greater depths than most crops. Proper crop rotations tend to maintain desirable soil structure, improve tilth, decrease erosion, increase the moisture-holding capacity of the soil, maintain adequate supplies of organic matter and nitrogen, prevent depletion of other plant nutrients, and improve the quality of the crop products. Crop rotations may also be beneficial in controlling insect pests, weed growths, and some plant diseases.

Effects of crop rotations on soil fertility and crop yields have been investigated at several agricultural experiment stations and special field stations maintained cooperatively by state agencies and the United States Department of Agriculture. Investigations were begun at the Scotts Bluff Field Station, western Nebraska, in 1910,[46] and at the Huntley Branch Station, Huntley, Montana, in 1912.[25]

The plowing under or disking in of crop plants or native vegetation as green manures adds organic matter and fertilizing elements to the soil. Faulkner, who tested cultural procedures on a farm in Ohio, concluded that disking green manures into the surface soil is more desirable than turning them under with a moldboard plow.[20] In fact, he concluded that deep plowing is not only unnecessary but also actually undesirable.

Stubble-Mulch Farming. Stubble-mulch farming is a recently developed method of crop tillage that leaves the stubble and other residues of the preceding crop on or close to the soil surface to provide a surface mulch. The mulch tends to conserve moisture and maintain soil fertility. It reduces compaction of the surface soil by rainfall, decreases surface runoff, and largely prevents soil erosion by wind as well as water.

The stubble-mulch method of farming, like Faulkner's, avoids deep plowing and the turning over of the surface soil. For some crops, it may involve light disking in the spring, to cut up the stubble and straw left by the preceding crop and to keep down early weed growths. Surface soils are loosened to depths of 2 to 6 inches by specially constructed subsurface tillers that cut through the soil without turning it over and without burying the surface mulch. Subsurface tillers, like most cultural implements, operate best on light or medium soils. They may be difficult to operate, or even impracticable, on some heavy clay soils.

Investigations of stubble-mulch farming were made at the Nebraska Agricultural Experiment Station, Lincoln, Nebraska, in cooperation with the United States Soil Conservation Service. The investigations were carried on from about 1939 to 1945, and the results were described in a government bulletin by Duley and Russel.[17]

In general, the investigations at Lincoln showed that, during wet years, yields of corn, wheat, and oats obtained under stubble-mulch procedures were about the same as those obtained under usual farming methods. During dry years, yields of corn were about twice as great. During wet years, the principal advantage of the stubble-mulch method was the greater protection against soil erosion.

Stubble-mulch methods of farming may be desirable in some semi-arid regions where depths of rainfall sufficient for crop production are uncertain and where supplies of irrigation water cannot be obtained. Whether or not they may be generally desirable in irrigation agriculture remains to be established. Although stubble-mulch methods tend to maintain fertility, because of the greater protection against runoff and erosion, they do not eliminate the need for proper crop rotations.

Green-Manure and Cover Crops. Green-manure crops are crops that are plowed under or disked into the soil to provide organic materials and fertilizing elements. Cover crops are crops that are grown to shade the ground, improve soil structures, reduce erosion, and otherwise protect the surface soils. However, green-manure crops also improve soil structures and protect surface soils, and cover crops are commonly worked into the soil to maintain fertility. Consequently, the two types of crops fulfill essentially the same purposes. In many discussions, the two terms are used synonymously.

Probably crops grown to be turned under and maintain fertility on farm tracts are more often referred to as green-manure crops, and crops grown for similar purposes in orchards are more often referred to as cover crops.

On areas devoted to the production of orchard fruits, soil fertility usually can be maintained by the use of fertilizers and the growth of cover crops. In southern California, where citrus and other subtropical fruits are produced, cover crops are often planted between the trees in the fall, grown during the winter months when moisture is available from rainfall, and disked in or plowed under as green manure in the early spring, before soil moisture becomes appreciably depleted and before the fruit trees begin consuming large quantities of water. In some orchard regions, natural growths of native vegetation during the winter months constitute cover crops that can be turned under as green manures. Where water supplies are limited, clean cultivation is commonly practiced during the summer months.

In regions where ample water supplies are obtainable and climatic conditions are favorable, cover crops may be grown during the summer as well as during the winter. Sometimes cover crops can be harvested, thus increasing cash returns. In the more northerly sections of the country, where low winter temperatures are experienced, winter cover crops are seldom possible. Sometimes perennial grasses are grown as cover crops in orchards, so that sod surfaces can be maintained throughout the year. When summer growths become too luxuriant, orchard operations can be facilitated by grazing, rolling, or dragging the areas between the trees, to keep down the cover vegetation. In regions where water supplies are limited, cover crops for orchards should be shallow-rooted types of vegetation that do not consume appreciable amounts of soil moisture needed for tree growth.

Leguminous plants such as vetch, beans, peas, and sweetclover, non-leguminous plants such as mustard, barley, oats, and rye, or various combinations of legumes and nonlegumes may be used as cover crops in orchards. Perennial grasses that may be used include fescue, blue-grass, Bermuda grass, redtop, timothy, and other grasses.[8] In some cases, the growth of cover crops may tend to facilitate the development of insect pests.

Crops that may be grown on farm lands for green manure and soil improvement include alfalfa, red clover, soybeans, cowpeas, velvet-beans, sweetclover, and such nonleguminous plants as millet, buckwheat, Sudan grass, and others.[41]

Commercial Fertilizers. If necessary, commercial fertilizers can be applied to the fields to correct soil deficiencies and maintain fertility. Elements that may become depleted from irrigation soils during early periods of agricultural use are usually nitrogen, phosphorus, and potassium. Table 4 shows the quantities of these elements, also the quantities of calcium and magnesium, that may be removed from the soil annually during the production of specified crop yields, as compiled by the American Agricultural Chemical Company.[1]

Many brands of commercial products containing nitrogen, phosphorus, and potassium in forms suitable for fertilizers are on the market. Mixed fertilizers containing two or more of these elements, also mixed fertilizers containing additional mineral elements needed for plant growth, can be obtained if desirable. However, mixed fertilizers may not be economical unless tests demonstrate actual needs for all the elements included in the mixtures.

Special fertilizer materials may be necessary when the soils are deficient in some of the secondary elements required for normal plant growth, such as manganese, zinc, copper, and boron. In some parts of the West, soils utilized in the production of both citrus and deciduous fruits have been found deficient in adequate supplies of certain

TABLE 4

PLANT NUTRIENTS REMOVED FROM SOILS BY DIFFERENT CROPS *

(Pounds per acre per year)

Crop	Yield per acre	Nitrogen (N)	Phosphoric acid (P_2O_5)	Potash (K_2O)	Calcium (CaO)	Magnesium (MgO)
Corn, grain and stover	50 bu.	78.4	27.6	55.2	22.3	17.0
Oats, grain and straw	50 bu.	48.0	18.0	40.8	10.7	9.7
Wheat, grain and straw	35 bu.	59.5	23.3	29.4	11.8	10.3
Onions, bulbs	300 bu.	39.3	15.4	37.6	23.1	5.8
Potatoes, white	300 bu.	63.0	27.0	90.0	5.0	12.0
Potatoes, sweet	300 bu.	41.2	16.5	82.5	5.5	17.1
Tobacco	1,000 lb.	59.0	7.7	78.0	64.0	11.3
Beans, field	25 bu. †	88.0	24.0	57.5	45.2	11.9
Spinach, stems and leaves	5 tons	50.0	15.0	25.0	?	13.2
Tomatoes, fruit	10 tons	48.0	16.8	84.0	?	6.0
Celery, tops	5 tons	25.0	20.0	75.0	?	?
Cabbage, heads	10 tons	60.0	20.0	80.0	81.2	4.2
Beets, tops	3 tons	21.0	6.0	33.0	19.9	9.7
Beets, roots	12½ tons	62.5	25.0	125.0	4.6	6.3
Turnips, tops	2½ tons	20.0	6.0	27.5	21.2	2.6
Turnips, roots	10 tons	50.0	20.0	90.0	14.3	5.0
Peaches, N. Y.	120 trees	74.5	18.0	72.0	114.0	35.0
Apples, N. Y.	35 trees	51.5	14.0	55.0	57.0	23.0
Alfalfa	4 tons	190.4	43.2	178.4	126.6	53.4
Clover	2 tons	82.0	15.6	65.2	69.2	19.5
Pasture, mixed grasses	1½ tons	45.0	12.0	40.5	?	?
Timothy	1½ tons	37.5	16.5	30.0	8.1	5.6

* Copyrighted by the American Agricultural Chemical Company.[1]
† Plus vines.

secondary elements, particularly zinc. Secondary elements such as zinc, manganese, and copper are sometimes supplied to citrus trees by spraying.

Fertilizer requirements of particular soils should be carefully determined by trial, either on small field plots or by potted-plant tests in a laboratory, before purchasing and applying large amounts of any commercial product. Methods of determining fertilizer requirements by chemical analyses of soils have been investigated but have not been developed to a wholly satisfactory basis, especially for irrigation soils.

Valuable information regarding fertilizers that may be beneficial for particular soils usually can be secured from state agricultural experiment stations. General information on the selection and use of different fertilizers can be obtained from a government publication.[43] Comprehensive articles on all phases of fertilizing materials and practices, prepared by recognized authorities, may be consulted in the 1938 *Yearbook of Agriculture.*

Since about 1933, the Tennessee Valley Authority has been conducting laboratory researches and field tests of fertilizers, particularly phosphorus compounds. New forms of phosphate fertilizers have been developed at the Authority plants and have been tested by actual use on agricultural lands. Detailed tests have been carried on in cooperation with state experiment stations and several thousand practical farmers. Although most field tests have been carried on in the central and eastern sections of the United States, where soil minerals have been seriously depleted by long periods of continuous crop production, some tests have been conducted in western states where irrigation agriculture is practiced.[60]

The investigational and development program conducted by the Tennessee Valley Authority will become increasingly valuable to western agriculture as irrigation farming gradually reduces the present available supplies of mineral nutrients needed by crop plants.

Soil Erosion. In some irrigated regions where topographic and climatic conditions are conducive to high rates of soil erosion, suitable procedures for reducing or controlling erosion may constitute important roles in maintaining soil fertility. In such regions, failure to practice proper control measures may result in the gradual removal of valuable topsoils by erosive agencies.

Soil erosion is generally caused by surface runoff during intense rainfalls or by continued winds of high velocity at times when the ground surfaces are devoid of vegetation and the surface soils too dry to hold together. In irrigated fields, soil erosion may also occur during applications of irrigation water. High winds occur at times in most sections of the country. Intense rainfalls of short duration may occur in semiarid and arid regions, even though total depths of annual precipitation are relatively small. In fact, rainfalls of short duration are often more intense in arid regions than in humid regions.

Soil erosion is commonly considered in two classes, namely, water erosion and wind erosion. Wind erosion may occur on either level or sloping land. Water erosion occurs mostly on sloping land. Rates of water erosion increase with increasing land slopes and increasing rainfall intensities. Rates of wind erosion increase with increasing wind velocities. Both types of erosion are affected by the texture of the surface soil, the magnitude of the moisture content, the amount of organic matter in the soil, and the presence of vegetation or vegetal litter on the ground surfaces. A dense cover of close-growing plants, such as alfalfa or other forage crops, is many times more effective in holding topsoil in place than cultivated row crops such as corn.

Wind erosion may be serious at times on irrigation projects where surface soils are relatively light and sometimes devoid of plant growth. Water erosion on irrigated fields may be serious, locally, when intense rainfalls occur. However, water erosion resulting from rainfall on cropped areas usually is less severe in irrigated regions than in humid regions, because the fields are graded to comparatively flat slopes when the lands are prepared for irrigation agriculture.

Water erosion is generally considered in three classes: (1) sheet erosion, the slow and gradual removal of topsoil from field tracts; (2), rill erosion, the washing out of small, shallow, closely spaced, drainage courses running approximately parallel down the field slopes; and (3) gully erosion, the cutting out of large deep channels running down the field slopes along the principal drainage courses. Some of the rill erosion courses, if not prevented by prompt remedial measures, may develop into gully erosion channels.

Reduction of soil erosion by crop rotations, stubble-mulch methods of farming, and growth of cover crops is briefly mentioned on the preceding pages. On many irrigation projects, proper crop rotations and the growth of carefully selected cover crops are sufficient to prevent serious soil erosion. In orchards, suitable cover crops usually provide adequate protection. On some farm lands, additional control measures may be needed.

Additional methods of reducing and controlling water erosion on farm tracts may include the following:

1. Plowing and planting row crops along contours instead of up and down the field slopes.

2. Strip cropping, the production of close-growing and clean-cultivated crops in alternate strips, located either along the contours or at about right angles to the general field slopes.

3. Constructing terraces approximately along contour lines at intervals down the steeper field slopes, with intercepting ditches to collect and remove the drainage water.

4. Maintenance of permanent close-growing types of vegetation on areas that are particularly susceptible to erosion.

Wind erosion may be reduced by strip cropping, by listing the soil into ridges after harvesting the crops, or by providing hedges or other obstructions to act as windbreaks. In all such measures, the strips, ridges, or hedges should be located at about right angles to prevailing wind directions.

Several additional methods of controlling soil erosion have been developed and tested on farm lands during recent years. The subject has received a great deal of careful investigation by various state and federal agencies, particularly the state agricultural experiment stations and the Soil Conservation Service, United States Department of Agriculture.

Erosion during Irrigation. Losses of soil by erosion during deliveries of irrigation water usually result from poorly planned land preparations, inadequate distribution systems, or improper procedures in applying water. Some items that may result in topsoil erosion are the following:

1. Improper subdivision of fields.
2. Irrigation runs of excessive length.
3. Excessive slopes along the runs.
4. Inadequate control of flows in ditches, furrows, and corrugations.
5. Deliveries of water at too rapid rates.
6. Application of water by inexperienced irrigators.
7. Careless supervision during irrigation.
8. Insufficient organic matter in the soil.

Complete prevention of erosion during the irrigation of loose sandy loam soils is difficult to attain. However, experienced irrigation farmers generally can divide their fields into irrigating units, prepare the field surfaces, build their distribution systems, plan their irrigation procedures, and deliver water to the cropped areas in such a manner as to minimize losses of valuable topsoils. On some farms where valuable crops are produced, the expensive installation of underground pipe distribution systems or the construction of lined surface conduits may be justified as an aid in controlling erosion during irrigation.

Detailed investigations of soil erosion in small irrigation furrows were made near Logan, Utah, and reported by Israelsen, Clyde, and Lauritzen in 1946.[33] Their principal conclusions were as follows:

1. Irrigation furrow slopes of 2 percent and higher are *excessive* and cause harmful erosion during the irrigation of loose silty loam and sandy loam soils when streams of 10 gallons per minute, or more, are run into each furrow.

2. Doubling the furrow slope more than doubles the erosion of loose silty loam and sandy loam soils.

3. The erosion on a given furrow slope is dependent on the size of irrigation stream and length of furrow, and doubling the stream more than doubles the erosion.

4. In furrow slopes of 3.0 percent, or smaller, the erosion is less from flat furrows than from V-shaped furrows, and on slopes of 3.0 percent, or higher, the erosion is greater from flat furrows.

5. The erosion of loose soil from V-shaped furrows is a maximum at the time when the water first reaches the lower end of the furrow, and it decreases as time advances.

6. Under the conditions of the studies here reported, collecting samples of the water and eroded soil at furrow outlets as a means of measuring amount of erosion is superior to [the] cross-section method, with which results obtained were unsatisfactory.

Root-Zone Depths. Root-zone depths in irrigated fields are usually dependent on soil types, subsoil formations, depths to water table, kind of crops grown, and amounts of water supplied during irrigations. Clay soils may be so tight that roots cannot penetrate to considerable depths.   Soils of satisfactory texture may be underlaid at shallow depths by claypan or hardpan strata that prevent further downward movements of plant roots.   High water tables may limit the depths to which root systems can develop.   Where these limitations do not exist, root-zone depths may be determined by plant characteristics or by the extent of the zones supplied with adequate moisture during irrigations.

Some plants, such as certain grasses and vegetables, do not normally utilize deep root zones.   Other crop plants, such as fruit trees and some perennial field crops, especially those with taproot systems, may extend their roots to considerable depths when moisture is available in the subsoil.   Apple trees in mature orchards may have roots more than 30 feet deep.   Alfalfa plants, several years old, may have taproots reaching even farther into the subsoil.

In general, crop plants develop most of their roots and derive most of their moisture supplies in the upper portions of the root zones. The principal depths of soil utilized are sometimes called working depths.   For most crops, working depths probably are less than one-half, or possibly two-thirds, of the maximum depths of root development.   Common field crops in irrigated regions, such as corn, small grains, and sugar beets, usually obtain the greater portions of their moisture supplies from the upper 3 or 4 feet of soil.   Citrus trees probably derive most of their moisture from the upper 4 or 5 feet of soil. Mature date palms, walnut trees, and the more common deciduous fruits derive moisture from somewhat greater depths.

Figure 1 shows the seasonal use of moisture from different depths of soil at the United States Scotts Bluff Field Station, western Nebraska,

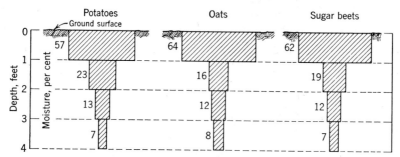

FIGURE 1. Seasonal crop use of moisture from different soil depths at Scotts Bluff Field Station, western Nebraska. (*Bur. Recl. Conservation Bull.* 2.)

as measured during the production of potatoes, oats, and sugar beets. These crops secured 80 per cent of their moisture from the upper 2 feet of soil, and a little more than 90 per cent from the upper 3 feet. Alfalfa, not shown in the figure, secured 62 per cent of its moisture

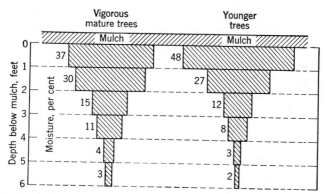

FIGURE 2. Seasonal use of moisture from different soil depths. Citrus trees, Orange County, California. (After Pillsbury.)

from the upper 2 feet of soil, 77 per cent from the upper 3 feet, and 89 per cent from the upper 4 feet. The crops were grown on deep sandy loams, where the water table was too deep to supply moisture.

Figure 2 shows the seasonal use of moisture from different depths in citrus orchards, southern California, as reported by Pillsbury and others.[51]   Mature trees used 37 per cent from the upper foot, 67 per cent from the upper 2 feet, and 93 per cent from the upper 4 feet. Younger trees used 48 per cent from the upper foot, 75 per cent from the upper 2 feet, and 95 per cent from the upper 4 feet.

Table 5 shows normal root-zone depths of vegetable plants for favorable soil conditions in Arizona, as given by Tate.[63]   The plants are

TABLE 5

NORMAL ROOT-ZONE DEPTHS OF VEGETABLE PLANTS [63]

Shallow-rooted, 0–2 ft.	Moderately deep-rooted, 0–4 ft.	Deep-rooted, 0–6 ft.
Broccoli, sprouting	Beans, bush	Artichoke
Brussels sprouts	Beans, pole	Asparagus
Cabbage	Beets	Beans, lima
Cauliflower	Carrots	Cantaloupes
Celery	Chard	Parsnips
Corn, sweet	Cucumbers	Pumpkins
Lettuce	Eggplant	Squash, winter
Onions	Mustard	Sweet potatoes
Potatoes, Irish	Peas	Tomatoes
Radishes	Peppers	Watermelons
Spinach	Squash, summer	
	Turnips	

classified as shallow-rooted, moderately deep-rooted, and deep-rooted, depending on whether the roots penetrate to depths of 2, 4, or 6 feet, respectively.

Most plants send their roots to more than normal depths when moisture cannot be obtained at higher levels and is still available at the greater depths.   Similarly, most plants derive their moisture from shallow depths when moisture is available at the higher levels but cannot be obtained at normal depths.   Alfalfa plants, growing on sandy soil where the depth to the water table was only 3 feet, developed about 98 per cent of their root systems in the upper 2 feet of soil.

When the water table is so deep that moisture cannot be raised to the root zone by capillarity, the depth of the root zone may be limited by the distance irrigation water can percolate into the soil.   If water is applied in small amounts, so that only shallow depths of soil are wetted, plant roots tend to congregate near the ground surface where moisture is available.   Under such conditions, crop plants obtain their mineral nutrients from the upper soil layers.   Consequently, they may soon reduce available supplies of plant food to degrees where applications of fertilizers are required in order to maintain soil fertility.

In general, deep root zones are desirable whenever soil conditions and water supplies permit deep penetration of irrigation water. If the soil can be wetted to appreciable depths, greater supplies of mineral nutrients may be drawn upon for plant growth, greater supplies of moisture can be stored for use between irrigations, and less frequent irrigations are required.

REFERENCES

1. American Agricultural Chemical Company, *Getting the Most Out of Your Soil,* Carteret, New Jersey, 1937.
2. Anderson, M. S., Mary G. Keyes, and G. W. Cromer, "Soluble Material of Soils in Relation to Their Classification and General Fertility," *U.S. Dept. Agr. Tech. Bull.* 813, 1942.
3. Batchelor, L. D., O. L. Braucher, and E. F. Serr, "Walnut Production in California," *Calif. Agr. Exp. Sta. Cir.* 364, 1945.
4. Baur, Karl, G. A. Huber, and L. C. Wheeting, "Boron Deficiency of Alfalfa in Western Washington," *Wash. Agr. Exp. Sta. Bull.* 396, 1941.
5. Beeson, Kenneth C., "The Mineral Composition of Crops with Particular Reference to the Soils in Which They Were Grown," *U.S. Dept. Agr. Misc. Pub.* 369, 1941.
6. Botkin, C. W., and E. C. Smith, "Effect of Irrigation Waters and Cropping on the Nutrients and Exchangeable Bases of Desert Soils," *N. Mex. Agr. Exp. Sta. Bull.* 292, 1942.
7. Breazeale, J. F., and W. T. McGeorge, "Studies on Soil Structure: Some Nitrogen Transformations in Puddled Soils," *Ariz. Agr. Exp. Sta. Tech. Bull.* 69, 1937.
8. Bregger, John T., and Grover F. Brown, "Conserving Soil and Moisture in Orchards and Vineyards," *U.S. Dept. Agr. Farmers' Bull.* 1970, 1945.
9. Brown, Irvin C., and Horace G. Byers, "The Chemical and Physical Properties of Dry-Land Soils and of Their Colloids," *U.S. Dept. Agr. Tech. Bull.* 502, 1935.
10. Brown, I. C., and M. Drosdoff, "Chemical and Physical Properties of Soils and of Their Colloids Developed from Granitic Materials in the Mojave Desert," *Jour. Agr. Res.,* Sept. 1, 1940, pp. 335–352.
11. Browne, C. A., "Some Relationships of Soil to Plant and Animal Nutrition— The Major Elements," *U.S. Dept. Agr. Yearbook,* 1938, pp. 777–806.
12. Byers, Horace G., "Selenium Occurrence in Certain Soils in the United States, with a Discussion of Related Topics," *U.S. Dept. Agr. Tech. Bull.* 482, 1935.
13. ——— "Selenium Occurrence in Certain Soils in the United States, with a Discussion of Related Topics, Second Report," *U.S. Dept. Agr. Tech. Bull.* 530, 1936.
14. Byers, Horace G., and others, "Selenium Occurrence in Certain Soils in the United States with a Discussion of Related Topics, Third Report," *U.S. Dept. Agr. Tech. Bull.* 601, 1938.
15. Cooper, H. P., Oswald Schreiner, and B. E. Brown, "Soil Potassium in Relation to Soil Fertility," *U.S. Dept. Agr. Yearbook,* 1938, pp. 397–405.

16. Crafts, A. S., "The Relation of Nutrients to Toxicity of Arsenic, Borax, and Chlorate in Soils," *Jour. Agr. Res.*, May 1, 1939, pp. 637–671.

17. Duley, F. L., and J. C. Russel, "Stubble-Mulch Farming to Hold Soil and Water," *U.S. Dept. Agr. Farmers' Bull.* 1997, 1948.

18. Eaton, Frank M., "Deficiency, Toxicity, and Accumulation of Boron in Plants," *Jour. Agr. Res.*, Sept. 15, 1944, pp. 237–277.

19. Eaton, Frank M., and L. V. Wilcox, "The Behavior of Boron in Soils," *U.S. Dept. Agr. Tech. Bull.* 696, 1939.

20. Faulkner, Edward H., *Plowman's Folly*, Grosset and Dunlap, New York, 1943.

21. Gilbert, Frank A., *Mineral Nutrition of Plants and Animals*, Univ. of Okla. Press, Norman, Okla., 1949.

22. Goss, R. W., and M. M. Afanasiev, "Influence of Rotations Under Irrigation on Potato Scab, Rhizoctonia, and Fusarium Wilt," *Nebr. Agr. Exp. Sta. Bull.* 317, 1938.

23. Greaves, J. E., and C. T. Hirst, "The Influence of Cropping on the Nitrogen, Phosphorus, and Organic Matter of the Soil under Irrigation Farming," *Utah Agr. Exp. Sta. Bull.* 310, 1943.

24. ——— "Influence of Rotation and Manure on the Nitrogen, Phosphorus, and Carbon of the Soil," *Utah Agr. Exp. Sta. Bull.* 274, 1936.

25. Hansen, Dan, and A. H. Post, "Irrigated Crop Rotations, Huntley Branch Station, Huntley, Montana," *Mont. Agr. Exp. Sta. Bull.* 414, 1943.

26. Hastings, Stephen H., "Irrigated Crop Rotations in Western Nebraska, 1912–34," *U.S. Dept. Agr. Tech. Bull.* 512, 1936.

27. Hastings, Stephen H., and Dan Hansen, "Irrigated Crop Rotations at the Huntley (Mont.) Field Station, 1912–35," *U.S. Dept. Agr. Tech. Bull.* 571, 1937.

28. Hinkle, D. A., and Glen Staten, "Fertilizer Experiments with Acala Cotton on Irrigated Soils," *N. Mex. Agr. Exp. Sta. Bull.* 280, 1941.

29. Holmes, R. S., and W. E. Hearn, "Chemical and Physical Properties of Some of the Important Alluvial Soils of the Mississippi Drainage Basin," *U.S. Dept. Agr. Tech. Bull.* 833, 1942.

30. Hopper, T. H., L. L. Nesbitt, and A. J. Pinckney, "The Chemical Composition of Some Chernozem-Like Soils of North Dakota," *N. Dak. Agr. Exp. Sta. Tech. Bull.* 246, 1931.

31. Hopper, T. H., and H. L. Walster, "Chemical Composition of the Soils of McHenry County," *N. Dak. Agr. Exp. Sta. Bull.* 240, 1930.

32. Hutton, Joseph Gladden, "Thirty Years of Soil Fertility Investigations in South Dakota," *S. Dak. Agr. Exp. Sta. Bull.* 325, 1938.

33. Israelsen, Orson W., George D. Clyde, and Cyril W. Lauritzen, "Soil Erosion in Small Irrigation Furrows," *Utah Agr. Exp. Sta. Bull.* 320, 1946.

34. Jenny, H., and R. Overstreet, "Contact Effects between Plant Roots and Soil Colloids," *Procs. Natl. Acad. Sci.*, Vol. 24, 1938, pp. 384–392.

35. King, C. J., R. E. Beckett, and Orlan Parker, "Agricultural Investigations at the United States Field Station, Sacaton, Ariz., 1931–35," *U.S. Dept. Agr. Cir.* 479, 1938.

36. Knight, S. H., and O. A. Beath, "The Occurrence of Selenium and Seleniferous Vegetation in Wyoming," *Wyo. Agr. Exp. Sta. Bull.* 221, 1937.

37. Lakin, H. W., and H. G. Byers, "Selenium Occurrence in Certain Soils in the United States, with a Discussion of Related Topics, Sixth Report," *U.S. Dept. Agr. Tech. Bull.* 783, 1941.

References 55

38. Lakin, H. W., and H. G. Byers, "Selenium Occurrence in Certain Soils in the United States, with a Discussion of Related Topics, Seventh Report," *U.S. Dept. Agr. Tech. Bull.* 950, 1948.
39. McGeorge, W. T., and J. F. Breazeale, "Studies of Soil Structure: Effect of Puddled Soils on Plant Growth," *Ariz. Agr. Exp. Sta. Tech. Bull.* 72, 1938.
40. ——— "Fertilization of Alfalfa on Alkaline Calcareous Soils," *Ariz. Agr. Exp. Sta. Bull.* 154, 1936.
41. McKee, Roland, "Summer Crops for Green Manure and Soil Improvement," *U.S. Dept. Agr. Farmers' Bull.* 1750, 1947.
42. McMurtrey, J. E., Jr., and W. O. Robinson, "Neglected Soil Constituents That Affect Plant and Animal Development," *U.S. Dept. Agr. Yearbook,* 1938, pp. 807–829.
43. Merz, Albert R., "Selecting Fertilizers," *U.S. Dept. Agr. Cir.* 487, 1940.
44. Miller, John T., and H. G. Byers, "Selenium in Plants in Relation to Its Occurrence in Soils," *Jour. Agr. Res.,* July 1, 1937, pp. 59–68.
45. Moxom, Alvin L., "Alkali Disease or Selenium Poisoning," *S. Dak. Agr. Exp. Sta. Bull.* 311, 1937.
46. Nuckols, S. B., and Lionel Harris, "Effect of Crop Rotation and Manure on the Yield and Quality of Sugar Beets, United States Scotts Bluff (Nebr.) Field Station, 1930–41," *U.S. Dept. Agr. Cir.* 779, 1948.
47. Parker, E. R., and L. D. Batchelor, "Effect of Fertilizers on Orange Yields," *Calif. Agr. Exp. Sta. Bull.* 673, 1942.
48. Peech, Michael, and others, "Methods of Soil Analysis for Soil-Fertility Investigations," *U.S. Dept. Agr. Cir.* 757, 1947.
49. Pendleton, Ray A., and W. W. Robbins, "Fertilizers for Sugar Beets on Some California Soils," *Calif. Agr. Exp. Sta. Bull.* 694, 1945.
50. Pierre, W. H., "Phosphorus Deficiency and Soil Fertility," *U.S. Dept. Agr. Yearbook,* 1938, pp. 377–396.
51. Pillsbury, Arthur F., O. C. Compton, and W. E. Picker, "Irrigation-Water Requirements of Citrus in the South Coastal Basin of California," *Calif. Agr. Exp. Sta. Bull.* 686, 1944.
52. Pittman, D. W., and D. W. Thorne, "Fertilizers for Utah Soils," *Utah Agr. Exp. Sta. Cir.* 116, 1941.
53. Proebsting, E. L., "Fertilizers and Cover Crops for California Deciduous Orchards," *Calif. Agr. Exp. Sta. Cir.* 354, 1943.
54. Robinson, W. O., "Method and Procedure of Soil Analysis Used in the Division of Soil Chemistry and Physics," *U.S. Dept. Agr. Cir.* 139, 1939.
55. Schreiner, Oswald, and B. E. Brown, "Soil Nitrogen," *U.S. Dept. Agr. Yearbook,* 1938, pp. 361–376.
56. Singleton, H. P., C. E. Nelson, and C. O. Stanberry, "Fertilizers for Irrigated Alfalfa," *Wash. Agr. Exp. Sta. Bull.* 465, 1945.
57. Slater, C. S., and H. G. Byers, "Base Exchange and Related Properties of the Colloids of Soils from the Erosion Experiment Stations," *U.S. Dept. Agr. Tech. Bull.* 461, 1934.
58. Slater, C. S., R. S. Holmes, and H. G. Byers, "Trace Elements in the Soils from the Erosion Experiment Stations, with Supplementary Data on Other Soils," *U.S. Dept. Agr. Tech. Bull.* 552, 1937.
59. Spurway, C. H., "Soil Testing—A Practical System of Soil Fertility Diagnosis," *Mich. Agr. Exp. Sta. Tech. Bull.* 132, 1944.

60. Tennessee Valley Authority, *Food at the Grass Roots—The Nation's Stake in Soil Minerals*, Knoxville, Tenn., 1947.

61. Thorne, D. W., W. Derby Laws, and Arthur Wallace, "Zinc Relationships of Some Utah Soils," *Soil Sci.*, December 1942, pp. 463–468.

62. Tower, Harold E., and Harry H. Gardner, "Strip Cropping for Conservation and Production," *U.S. Dept. Agr. Farmers' Bull.* 1981, 1946.

63. Turville, E. S., Donald L. Hitch, and others, "Irrigating in Arizona," *Univ. Ariz. Agr. Ext. Service Cir.* 123, 1944.

64. Whetstone, R. R., W. O. Robinson, and H. G. Byers, "Boron Distribution in Soils and Related Data," *U.S. Dept. Agr. Tech. Bull.* 797, 1942.

65. Williams, K. T., "Selenium in Soils," *U.S. Dept. Agr. Yearbook*, 1938, pp. 830–834.

66. Williams, K. T., H. W. Lakin, and H. G. Byers, "Selenium Occurrence in Certain Soils in the United States, with a Discussion of Related Topics, Fourth Report," *U.S. Dept. Agr. Tech. Bull.* 702, 1940.

67. ——— "Selenium Occurrence in Certain Soils in the United States, with a Discussion of Related Topics, Fifth Report," *U.S. Dept. Agr. Tech. Bull.* 758, 1941.

68. Williams, K. T., and R. R. Whetstone, "Arsenic Distribution in Soils and Its Presence in Certain Plants," *U.S. Dept. Agr. Tech. Bull.* 732, 1940.

69. Zook, L. L., and H. E. Weakly, "Crop Rotation and Tillage Experiments at the North Platte (Nebr.) Substation, 1907–34," *U.S. Dept. Agr. Tech. Bull.* 1007, 1950.

Chapter 4

MOISTURE IN IRRIGATION SOILS

The maintenance of proper moisture conditions in irrigation soils during the growing season is one of the most important factors in successful irrigation agriculture. Crop plants require relatively large quantities of water in order to grow and mature properly. These requirements must be satisfied by the absorption of moisture from the soil within reach of the plant roots. Therefore, root zones throughout the fields, down to the principal depths utilized in crop growth, should be kept supplied with adequate amounts of moisture, from the time of seeding until satisfactory maturity is assured.

Although soils in irrigated fields should be kept moist, they should not be supplied with excessive amounts of water. Most crop plants, with the exception of aquatic types such as rice, need appreciable quantities of air as well as water throughout the root zones. If too much irrigation water is applied to some fine-textured soils, the plants may suffer from lack of oxygen rather than from lack of water. If too much cold water is applied during spring irrigations, soil temperatures may be held at low levels and plant development retarded or even prevented.

On lands where adequate subsoil drainage is not available, applications of excessive amounts of irrigation water cause rising ground-water levels. If excessive applications are continued for a few years, water tables may rise into the root zones, causing rotting of submerged roots, gradual accumulations of undesirable salts at the ground surfaces, and even complete waterlogging of the soils.

The efficient application of irrigation water, in proper amounts and at proper times, involves a thorough practical knowledge of soil-moisture phenomena. The following sections of this chapter present short treatments of soil-moisture conditions from the viewpoint of irrigation agriculture, also brief discussions of certain soil-moisture constants that are valuable in considering different irrigation soils. Space limitations do not permit adequate treatments of the physics of soil moisture. However, some statements regarding the more pertinent aspects of the subject are included, and some references to published material are given. Movements of soil moisture are discussed in the next chapter. Depths of irrigation water required for crop growth and losses of water that may be experienced in irrigation procedures are discussed in later chapters.

Soil-Moisture Conditions. Soil-moisture conditions that are pertinent in irrigation work and that should be considered in planning irrigation procedures are those relating to the quantities of water that can be taken up by plant roots and used in maintaining crop growth. These quantities are contained in the pore spaces between soil particles and are free to move in response to gravity and capillary forces. Their amounts are limited on the one hand by the extent of the pore spaces, and on the other hand by the soil-moisture contents below which soil particles hold the moisture too firmly to permit absorption by the roots.

When all pore spaces in a soil are filled with water, the soil is said to be saturated. Saturated conditions exist in soil strata below the water table, in the region known as the zone of saturation. They do not occur in the zone of aeration, that is, in the zone above the water table, except temporarily, near field surfaces, during and immediately following irrigations. When the subsoil is adequately drained, saturated conditions near field surfaces usually become dissipated by percolation before crop plants are injured.

The subsequent discussions apply primarily to soil-moisture conditions in well-drained root zones within the zone of aeration, when the water table is maintained at considerable depths below the ground surfaces. Some references are made to soil-moisture conditions within the capillary fringe, that is, in the comparatively shallow zone just above the water table. Soil-moisture conditions in the capillary fringe are important on projects where crops are produced by natural sub-irrigation methods.

In general irrigation work, the two more important soil-moisture properties are the field capacity and the permanent wilting point. Moisture contents at times of field capacity and permanent wilting determine the quantities of water that can be stored in the root zones for the maintenance of crop growth during periods between irrigations.

Quantities of moisture in the soil are commonly expressed as percentages of the oven-dry weight of the soil. However, when the dry weight of the soil per unit volume is known, that is, the volume weight or apparent specific gravity, the moisture contents may be given as equivalent depths of water on the field surfaces per foot of soil depth. Porosities are usually given in percentages by volume, as stated in Chapter 2.

Forms of Soil Moisture. Forms of soil moisture are generally classified as (1) gravity water, (2) capillary water, and (3) hygroscopic water. Gravity water, sometimes called hydrostatic water or free water, is moisture that percolates downward, owing to the force of gravity, largely through noncapillary pore spaces. Gravity water can be absorbed by plant roots and used in maintaining plant growth, but it is available for plant use only during relatively short periods following irrigations, while it is percolating downward through the root zones.

Capillary water is moisture held in the soil by capillarity, the molecular tension that raises kerosene oil into a lamp wick. It is free to move in any direction, in accordance with capillary tensions, but its movements are influenced to some extent by gravity. Capillary water occurs as thin films of moisture on the soil grains, as tiny particles of water in the capillary pore spaces, and as continuous threads of moisture within the smaller pore passages, sometimes referred to as capillary tubes. Capillary water constitutes the principal source of moisture utilized in plant growth. It is gradually absorbed by plant roots during periods between irrigations.

Hygroscopic water is moisture held by the soil so firmly that it cannot move in accordance with gravity or capillary forces. It is moisture held in equilibrium with atmospheric water vapor. This form of soil moisture occurs as exceedingly thin films of water on the soil grains, or as minute particles of water wedged between the smallest soil particles. Hygroscopic water is closely associated with soil colloids. Quantities of hygroscopic water in irrigation soils may vary from less than 1 per cent in light sandy soils to as much as 15 per cent in heavy clay soils. Hygroscopic water is not available for the growth of crop plants but may be utilized to some extent by certain types of trees and desert vegetation during periods of extreme drought.

A fourth form of soil water sometimes included in discussions of soil moisture is water held by chemical rather than physical forces, usually known as combined water. Combined water does not freeze or evaporate at ordinary temperatures. It can be removed from soil samples by heating to the ignition point. The percentage of combined water in most irrigation soils is relatively small but may be as high as 10 per cent in some clays. The amount of combined water is a rough indication of the quantity of clay or colloidal material in the soil. Except for this indication it probably has but little significance in considerations of irrigation soils. Combined-water contents of some alluvial soils are given in Table 2, Chapter 3.

In soils containing large proportions of colloidal material and fine clay particles, water so tightly held by physical and chemical forces that it cannot move or be absorbed by plant roots is sometimes re-

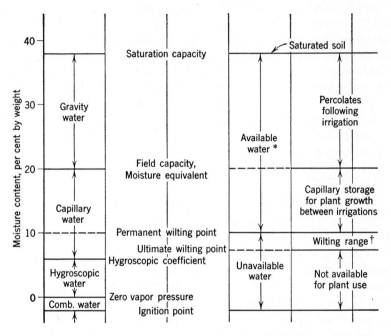

*Part above field capacity available only temporarily.
†Sustains plant life but not available for plant growth.

FIGURE 1. Soil-moisture forms and properties for an assumed fine sandy loam soil.

ferred to as bound water. In puddled soils, more than half the total moisture content may be bound water.[4] Proportions of bound water in puddled soils may be reduced by treatments that improve soil structure.

Considerations of gravity water and capillary water are of primary importance in irrigation work. If excess quantities of gravity water are absorbed during applications of irrigation water, losses by percolation to groundwater levels or to subsoil drains are incurred. If insufficient quantities of capillary water are furnished, soil-moisture storage in the root zones may not be great enough to maintain satisfactory plant growth until further irrigations are possible.

There are no definite or permanent boundaries between gravity water and capillary water. Some gravity water near field surfaces during and immediately following irrigation becomes capillary water as it percolates downward and reaches depths where capillary water has been depleted by plant growth. Capillary water in soil pores just above the zone of saturation may become gravity water and percolate to lower levels if the water table is lowered. With a stationary or rising water table, gravity water in the zone of saturation may be lifted above the water table and become capillary water as moisture in the capillary fringe is absorbed by plant roots. This condition occurs in natural subirrigation, where the water table is relatively close to the lower limits of the root zone.

Approximate percentages of the different forms of moisture that may be present in an assumed fine sandy loam are shown diagrammatically in Figure 1.

Soil-Moisture Constants. Moisture contents of a soil during certain conditions of equilibrium are often referred to as soil-moisture constants. The principal soil-moisture constants involved in considerations of irrigation soils are shown on Figure 1. Beginning at the top of the diagram and reading downward, they include the following:

1. Saturation capacity.
2. Field capacity.
3. Moisture equivalent.
4. Permanent wilting point.
5. Ultimate wilting point.
6. Hygroscopic coefficient.

The above soil-moisture constants, also quantities of water that may be present in the soil between these points of equilibrium, are taken up in the following sections. Some additional soil-moisture constants that have been proposed on the basis of laboratory investigations, but which have not come into general use among irrigation engineers, are discussed later in the chapter.

The designation soil-moisture constant is misleading in a way. None of the so-called soil-moisture constants is really constant, except for certain definite physical conditions of a soil of unvarying texture and composition. It probably would be better to think of these equilibrium points as soil properties instead of soil constants. In this chapter the designation soil-moisture property is frequently used in lieu of soil-moisture constant.

Hygroscopic Coefficient. The hygroscopic coefficient of a soil, shown in the lower part of Figure 1, represents the maximum amount of hygroscopic moisture a soil can contain. It is the amount of moisture a soil can hold in equilibrium with saturated atmospheric water vapor.

The hygroscopic coefficient of a soil is usually determined by weighing the moisture a thin layer of dry soil absorbs when kept in an atmosphere containing saturated water vapor, at constant temperature, for 24 hours. It is sometimes determined by weighing the moisture a dry sample absorbs when kept 5 days in an atmosphere containing water vapor at 99 per cent of saturation. Neither method is entirely satisfactory, inasmuch as the samples, if held under the same conditions through longer periods, generally continue to absorb small additional quantities of moisture.

Methods of measuring the hygroscopic coefficient were developed by Hilgard about the middle of the nineteenth century. Probably, this particular soil-moisture percentage is the oldest of the so-called soil-moisture constants. The hygroscopic coefficient is an approximate indication of the amount of colloidal material in a soil. Except for this indication, the coefficient probably has but little significance in considerations of irrigation soils.

In general, the hygroscopic coefficient is about two-thirds of the permanent wilting point. Hygroscopic coefficients for irrigation soils may vary from less than 1 per cent for sandy soils to about 15 per cent for heavy adobe soils.

Saturation Capacity. The saturation capacity of a soil, shown at the top of Figure 1, is the amount of water required to fill all the pore spaces between the soil particles. In other words, it is the upper limit of the possible moisture content. In order for a soil to become saturated, all air held in the pore spaces must be replaced by water. The saturation capacity is sometimes referred to as the maximum moisture-holding capacity.

Surface soils are said to become saturated during applications of irrigation water or during continued rainfalls that produce surface runoff. However, conditions of complete saturation seldom are reached at such times. Because of trapped or entrained air, proportions of water in the soils, even after long-continued irrigation or rainfall, seldom amount to more than about 85 to 95 per cent of the total volume of the pore spaces. The amount of soil air that can be replaced by infiltrating water varies with the physical and chemical properties of the soil.

Although conditions approaching saturation occur in well-drained soils only temporarily, during and immediately following irrigation, it may be useful to point out how much moisture might be present in the upper soil layers if complete saturation were attained at such times.

When the porosity of a soil is known, the saturation capacity can be expressed as equivalent inches of water per foot of soil depth. For instance, if the porosity is 50 per cent by volume, the moisture in each foot of saturated soil is equivalent to a depth of 6 inches on the field surface. If the dry weight of the soil per unit volume, that is, the volume weight, is known, the porosity can be calculated as explained in Chapter 2, and the saturation capacity can be expressed either as a percentage of the dry weight or as equivalent inches of water per foot of soil depth. When the porosity P and the volume weight V are known, the saturation capacity C, in percentage by weight, is simply P divided by V.

Table 1 shows saturation capacities in percentages by weight and equivalent inches of water per foot of soil depth for some different

TABLE 1

SATURATION CAPACITIES OF SOME DIFFERENT
TYPES OF SURFACE SOIL [7]

Soil types	Dry weight, lb. per cu. ft.	Volume weight	Total porosity, per cent by volume	Saturation capacity Per cent by weight	Saturation capacity In. per ft. of soil
Maximum total porosities					
Sandy loams	79	1.26	52.3	41.5	6.28
Loams	73	1.16	54.9	47.3	6.59
Silt loams	66	1.05	61.1	58.1	7.34
Gravelly silt loams	64	1.02	60.9	59.6	7.31
Clay and clay loams	59	0.94	64.1	68.1	7.70
Minimum total porosities					
Sandy loams	104	1.66	36.4	21.9	4.37
Loams	90	1.44	45.7	31.7	5.48
Silt loams	91	1.46	44.3	30.3	5.32
Gravelly silt loams	89	1.42	45.8	32.2	5.50
Clay and clay loams	96	1.54	41.4	26.9	4.97

types of surface soil, computed from data reported by Free, Browning, and Musgrave.[7] The original publication presented data for a large number of samples of each soil type. Only data for samples that showed maximum and minimum porosities for each type are included in Table 1.

Figure 2 shows calculated saturation capacities for soils of different unit weights, based on an average value of 2.65 for the specific gravity of the soil particles. For a soil weighing 80 pounds per cubic foot when dry, curve *A* shows a saturation capacity of 40.4 per cent by weight, curve *B* shows a total porosity of 51.7 per cent by volume, and curve *C* shows a total moisture content equivalent to 6.21 inches of

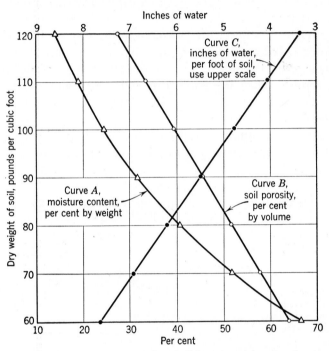

FIGURE 2. Saturation capacities for soils of different weights based on a specific gravity of 2.65 for the soil particles.

water, the scale for inches of water being placed at the top of the diagram and reversed in direction as indicated.

In irrigation soils, saturation capacities may vary from about 15 per cent for light sandy soils to about 60 per cent for heavy clay soils. Equivalent depths of water per foot of soil vary from about 3.5 to 7.5 inches.

Field Capacity. Field capacity is one of the two more important soil-moisture properties involved in irrigation work. It is the maximum amount of capillary water that can be held in a freely drained root zone, where the water table is so deep that moisture cannot be raised to the plant roots from the zone of saturation. It is the percentage of moisture retained in the soil when percolation practically ceases following an irrigation that produced approximately saturated conditions in the upper soil layers.

In coarse-textured sandy soils, field capacity is the moisture content reached within 1 to 3 days following irrigation. In medium-textured sandy silt and clay soils, it is the moisture content reached within 4 to 8 days following irrigation. In fine-textured soils containing large proportions of clay, somewhat longer periods are required for the moisture content to reach field capacity. Although relatively small rates of percolation may continue for some time following such intervals, field capacity is practically the amount of moisture that can be held against gravity; in other words, the amount of moisture that can be retained owing to the excess of capillary tensions over gravity forces.

Field capacity is sometimes referred to as capillary capacity, maximum field-carrying capacity, field capillary moisture capacity, or effective water-holding capacity. It is essentially the same as specific retention, a more general term used in studies of groundwater, except that specific retention is usually given as a percentage by volume whereas field capacity is usually given as a percentage by weight. When field capacity is expressed as a percentage by volume, it is practically the same as capillary porosity. For most irrigation soils of desirable texture, the field capacity is about the same as the moisture equivalent, a soil constant determined in the laboratory as discussed later.

As a general rule, soils with high field capacities are desirable for irrigation agriculture. However, field capacities should be appreciably lower than saturation capacities, so that air contents of the soil will be great enough for satisfactory crop growth. In general, the volume of soil air when the moisture content is at field capacity should be about the same as the volume of soil moisture. For most crops, the field capacity, on a volume basis, probably should not be less than about one-third, or more than about two-thirds, of the saturation capacity.

In well-drained soils, field capacities depend primarily on texture, structure, surface area of the soil grains, and shape, size, and proportion of the pore spaces. Contents of organic matter and soil temperatures probably have small effects on field capacity. Inasmuch as the surface tension of water decreases slightly with increasing temperature, field capacities in late summer may be slightly lower than in the winter or early spring months.

Irrigation soils of different types may have field capacities varying from about 7 per cent for light sandy soils to about 40 per cent or

more for heavy clay soils. The third column of Table 2 shows average field capacities at different depths for heavy clay soils in two
Oregon pear orchards, compiled from data reported by Lewis, Work,
and Aldrich.[12]

TABLE 2

MOISTURE CONDITIONS AT DIFFERENT DEPTHS IN
TWO HEAVY IRRIGATION SOILS [12]

(Percentages by weight)

Descriptive data	Depth, ft.	Field capacity, per cent	Permanent wilting point, per cent	Available moisture capacity, per cent
Fitch orchard, Meyer	0–1	24.7	13.3	11.4
silty clay loam	1–2	27.4	15.6	11.8
(averages for 4 plots)	2–3	28.5	17.4	11.1
	0–3	26.8	15.4	11.4
Klamath orchard,	0–1	28.7	15.8	12.9
Meyer clay adobe	1–2	28.0	17.2	10.8
(averages for 4 plots)	2–3	27.3	16.7	10.6
	0–3	28.0	16.5	11.5

Moisture Equivalent. The moisture equivalent is a soil-moisture
constant that can be quickly determined in a laboratory and used as
an approximate measure of field capacity. Briefly, it is the percentage
of moisture a small sample of wet soil, $3/8$ inch deep, can retain when
subjected to a centrifugal force 1,000 times as great as gravity, usually
for a period of 30 minutes.

Briggs and McLane originally proposed the moisture equivalent as
a basis for comparing different soils, under similar conditions of capillary moisture, in 1907.[1] Since that time, it has received further investigation by several soil specialists, has been widely used in studies
of soils for crop production, and has become one of the most useful
of the various soil-moisture constants.

For most irrigation soils of desirable texture, the moisture equivalent
is a fairly satisfactory measure of field capacity. For some light sandy
soils, the moisture equivalent may be appreciably lower than the field
capacity. For heavy clay soils, the moisture equivalent may be appreciably higher than field capacity. Moisture equivalents for irrigation
soils may vary from about 5 per cent for coarse sandy soils to more than
50 per cent for heavy fine-textured clay soils. For some clean sands,
the moisture equivalent may be as low as 2 per cent.

Although moisture equivalents increase gradually with increasing fineness of soil texture, they often differ widely for different soils of the same textural type. Considerations of data reported by Richards and Weaver show moisture equivalents ranging from 6.9 to 16.0 per cent for sandy loam soils, 7.7 to 26.1 for fine sandy loams, 5.2 to 32.0 for loams, 10.9 to 31.0 for clay loams, 20.9 to 43.2 for silty clay loams, and 15.6 to 45.9 for clays. Values as low as 1.3 per cent were reported for washed and screened sands.[19]

During the early use of the moisture equivalent, it was believed to bear approximately constant relations to other soil-moisture constants. For instance, it was believed to be about 1.84 times the wilting coefficient and about 2.71 times the hygroscopic coefficient, as concluded by Briggs and Shantz.[2] However, subsequent investigations, particularly those by Veihmeyer and Hendrickson, showed that actual ratios of moisture equivalents to other soil-moisture constants, especially the permanent wilting point, vary widely for soils of similar texture as well as for soils of different texture.[29] Consequently, the moisture equivalent, although constituting a fair index of field capacity for most irrigation soils, cannot be depended upon as a reliable measure of other soil properties.

Permanent Wilting Point. The permanent wilting point of a soil is the amount of moisture present when plants first become permanently wilted; that is, when they wilt and do not regain turgidity unless water is added to the soil. In other words, it is the moisture content below which water cannot be taken up by plant roots fast enough to satisfy transpiration requirements.

The permanent wilting point is the second of the two more important soil-moisture properties involved in irrigation work, inasmuch as it represents the level of moisture content below which crop growth can no longer be maintained. Additional water should always be applied to the fields before the average moisture content of the root zone is reduced to the permanent wilting point. Since plant roots can absorb moisture from different depths in the root zone, soil samples taken at some depths may show moisture contents below the permanent wilting point while moisture sufficient for plant growth is still available at other depths.

Briggs and Shantz originally used the term wilting coefficient to designate the moisture content of the soil at the time permanent wilting begins.[2] In subsequent treatments of the subject, other writers have used such terms as the permanent wilting coefficient, permanent wilting percentage, permanent wilting point, or more briefly the wilting percentage.

Permanent wilting points differ widely for different soils but have approximately the same values for different plants grown on the same soil. They may vary from values as low as 2 per cent for light sandy soils to values as high as 30 per cent for heavy clay soils. Permanent wilting points for the fine-textured soils in the two Oregon pear orchards are given in the fourth column of Table 2. They vary from about 54 to 61 per cent of the field capacity.

Whenever feasible, permanent wilting points for irrigation soils should be determined in a laboratory, where plants can be grown on representative soil samples, in pots or tanks, subject to careful observation and control. Sunflower plants are commonly used as indicators in laboratory determinations of permanent wilting points.

Wilting Range. Plant roots may absorb small quantities of water from the soil after the moisture content has been reduced to the permanent wilting point. Such quantities, although not sufficient to maintain plant growth, are valuable in that they tend to maintain plant life until further supplies of water become available. Although this condition had long been recognized, it was first discussed in detail in a contribution by Taylor, Blaney, and McLaughlin in 1934.[23]

Taylor and his associates used the term wilting range to designate the range in soil-moisture contents, below the permanent wilting point, in which small amounts of moisture may be drawn upon to maintain plant life. They used the term ultimate wilting point to designate the lower limit of the wilting range. They described the wilting range as "the range in moisture content of the soil while the plant is undergoing the progressive stage of wilt from the wilting of the lower leaves to the complete wilting of the entire plant."

In 1945, Furr and Reeve discussed studies of soil moisture in the wilting range, based on laboratory tests of about 80 soil samples taken on different areas in southern California.[8] The samples included about 50 soil types of widely varying texture. Most of them were taken from the top foot of cultivated soil in orchards or fields, but a few were obtained from desert areas or brush lands.

Considerations of the Furr and Reeve report show (1) that the moisture content at the ultimate wilting point may vary from about 1 to 25 per cent of the dry weight of the soil; (2) that the amount of moisture available to sustain plant life during the wilting stage may vary from less than 1 to about 5 per cent of the dry weight; and (3) that the moisture in the wilting range may vary from about 10 to 30

per cent of the total moisture available for plant use above the ultimate wilting point. In general, the moisture content at the ultimate
wilting point and the amount of moisture available within the wilting
range increase gradually with the textural fineness of the soil.

Soil moisture in the wilting range probably is important on irrigation projects where water supplies are limited, especially in the production of fruit crops where plant life must be maintained during
comparatively long periods between successive irrigation seasons.

Available Soil Moisture. The amount of soil moisture available
for plant growth at any time is the difference between the moisture
content of the soil and the permanent wilting point. The amount of
capillary moisture that may be available in the wetted zone following
an irrigation is the difference between the field capacity and the permanent wilting point. This quantity may be designated the available
moisture capacity of the soil. Since some soil moisture at moisture
contents below the permanent wilting point may be available for plant
use, although not for plant growth, capillary moisture in excess of the
permanent wilting point is sometimes referred to as readily available
moisture.

In irrigation work, soils capable of holding large quantities of available moisture are desirable because they require less frequent applications of irrigation water. Inasmuch as the available moisture capacity
is the difference between two moisture contents, some soils of medium
texture, with high field capacities and nominal wilting points, may
provide greater available moisture capacities than some fine-textured
soils with relatively high field capacities and high wilting points.

Available moisture capacities in irrigation soils may vary from about
5 to 20 per cent. Somewhat higher percentages of capillary moisture
available for the growth of natural vegetation have been observed in
parts of northern California.[33] Available moisture capacities of the
fine-textured soils in the two Oregon pear orchards are given in the
last column of Table 2. They vary from 10.6 to 12.9 per cent.

Quantities of readily available moisture that may be held in some
soils of southern California, plotted from data reported by Richards
and Weaver, are shown in Figure 3.[19] These were the soil samples
collected by Furr and Reeve for use in studying the wilting range.
In Figure 3 the vertical bars show moisture equivalents, permanent
wilting points, and ultimate wilting points, plotted as percentages by
weight. Quantities of readily available moisture, moisture in the
wilting range, and unavailable moisture are represented by the dif-

ferences in percentages as indicated. Field capacities probably were
about the same as the moisture equivalents for the most of the soils
represented on the figure, probably for all except two or three near
each end of the horizontal scale.

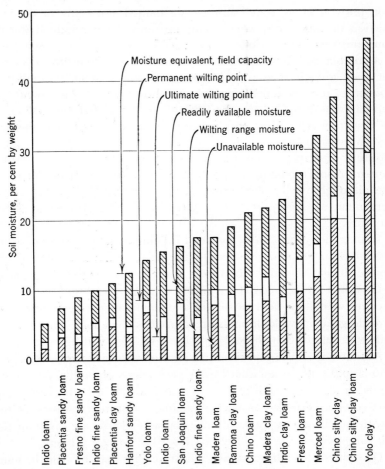

FIGURE 3.   Soil-moisture properties of some soils in southern California.   (Plotted
from data in reference 19.)

Investigations show that the ease with which plant roots can absorb
readily available moisture is not greatly affected by decreasing moisture contents, until the percentages are reduced almost to the permanent wilting points; that is, until the supplies of readily available
moisture are almost exhausted.

Storage of Soil Moisture. The root zone in an irrigated field is essentially a reservoir in which capillary moisture can be stored for plant use during periods between successive irrigations. The moisture in excess of the permanent wilting point can be drawn upon for plant growth and consequently may be considered as available soil-moisture storage. The moisture below the wilting point cannot be drawn upon for plant growth and consequently may be considered as unavailable soil-moisture storage. It is similar to dead storage in a surface reservoir.

When some of the moisture stored in the wilting range is utilized in maintaining plant life during periods between irrigations, such depletions must be replenished and the soil-moisture contents increased to percentages higher than the permanent wilting point before stored moisture again becomes available for plant growth.

The amount of capillary moisture that can be stored in the root zone depends on the depth of the root zone as well as on the percentage of moisture the soil can retain. Therefore, in considerations of soil-moisture storage, the moisture contents are preferably expressed as equivalent inches of water per foot of soil depth, instead of percentages by weight. If M is the moisture content in percentage by weight, D the equivalent depth of water in inches per foot of soil depth, and V the volume weight of the soil, the soil-moisture storage in inches of water per foot of depth may be calculated by the equation,

$$D = \frac{12MV}{100}$$

The total soil-moisture storage in the root zone is then D multiplied by the depth of the root zone in feet.

The maximum amount of moisture that can be stored in the root zone is determined by the field capacity and the depth of the root zone. The maximum amount of available moisture that can be stored in the root zone is determined by the field capacity, the permanent wilting point, and the depth of the root zone; or, in other words, by the available moisture capacity and the depth of the root zone.

In irrigation soils, the maximum available soil-moisture storage usually varies from about 1 to 3.0 inches per foot of soil depth.

Gravity Water. The amount of gravity water in an irrigation soil at any time is approximately the excess of the moisture content over the field capacity. The maximum amount of gravity water that can be present during saturation is approximately the difference between the saturation capacity and the field capacity. It is essentially the same as the total volume of the noncapillary pore spaces.

Table 3 shows quantities of gravity water in some different types of soils at times of saturation, expressed as percentages by weight, also as

Table 3

GRAVITY WATER IN SOME SATURATED SURFACE SOILS [7]

Soil types	Dry weight, lb. per cu. ft.	Volume weight	Non-capillary porosity, per cent by volume	Gravity water	
				Per cent by weight	In. per ft. of soil
Maximum total porosities					
Sandy loams	79	1.26	32.4	25.7	3.89
Loams	73	1.16	30.4	26.2	3.65
Silt loams	66	1.05	36.3	34.6	4.36
Gravelly silt loams	64	1.02	35.0	34.3	4.20
Clay and clay loams	59	0.94	36.7	39.0	4.40
Minimum total porosities					
Sandy loams	104	1.66	17.7	10.7	2.12
Loams	90	1.44	17.2	11.9	2.07
Silt loams	91	1.46	13.3	9.1	1.60
Gravelly silt loams	89	1.42	15.2	10.7	1.82
Clay and clay loams	96	1.54	14.0	9.1	1.68

equivalent depths of water in inches per foot of soil depth. The data were calculated from values of noncapillary porosity reported by Free, Browning, and Musgrave.[7] Data are included for samples that showed maximum and minimum total porosities, that is, for the same samples used in compiling Table 1. Depths of gravity water in inches per foot of soil depth vary from 2.12 to 3.89 for sandy loams, from 2.07 to 3.65 for loams, from 1.60 to 4.36 for silt loams, from 1.82 to 4.20 for gravelly silt loams, and from 1.68 to 4.40 for clay and clay loams.

Some puddled soils or heavy clay adobe soils, not represented in Table 3, may be so tight that only very small percentages of their moisture contents, even when saturated, could logically by considered as gravity water. Although such soils have relatively high total porosities, the pore spaces are so small that the soils are practically impermeable.

Most soils of textural properties desirable for irrigation may hold appreciable quantities of gravity water when saturated. In general, quantities of gravity water present near field surfaces during and immediately following copious irrigations probably vary between about 8 and 40 per cent for different soil types.

In groundwater studies, the amount of gravity water that will drain out of a saturated material, expressed as a percentage by volume, is designated specific yield. Specific yield represents the total volume of the noncapillary pores, specific retention represents the total volume of the capillary pores, and specific yield plus specific retention represents total porosity.

Summary of Moisture Conditions. Approximate limits of moisture conditions that may be experienced in most irrigation soils are shown in Table 4. The lower limits of the various soil-moisture contents

TABLE 4

APPROXIMATE LIMITS OF MOISTURE CONDITIONS IN
MOST IRRIGATION SOILS

Item	Soil-moisture condition	Approximate limits, per cent by weight	
		Lower	Upper
1	Hygroscopic moisture content	1—	15
2	Hygroscopic coefficient	1—	15
3	Saturation capacity	15	60
4	Field capacity	7	40
5	Moisture equivalent	5	50
6	Permanent wilting point	2	30
7	Ultimate wilting point	1	25
8	Moisture in wilting range	1—	5
9	Available moisture capacity	5	20
10	Maximum available storage	1 *	3.0 *
11	Gravity water in saturated soils	8	40

* Inches per foot of soil depth.

probably apply to sands or light sandy soils in all cases. The upper limits probably apply to heavy clay soils in the case of items 1 to 8, inclusive, but may apply to soils of medium texture in the case of items 9, 10, and 11.

The ranges in soil-moisture contents given in Table 4 probably cover all general types of irrigation soils with increasing fineness of texture from coarse sandy types to heavy but tillable clay types. Moisture properties of different soils vary so widely, even for soils of the same textural type, that approximate limits can hardly be given for soils of particular textural classifications. The tabulated limits do not apply to special types of irrigation soils such as peat and muck.

Moisture in Peat Soils. Moisture properties of peat soils, which are composed largely of vegetable matter in varying stages of decomposition, are materially different from those of the mineral soils commonly utilized in irrigation agriculture. Peat soils have considerably higher wilting points, moisture equivalents, and saturation capacities. They may absorb three or more times as much water as mineral soils. Because of their organic nature, peat soils sometimes have been used as soil amendments, to improve physical conditions and moisture properties of light sandy and heavy clay soils.

Moisture properties of peat soils, when given as percentages of dry weights, are seemingly exaggerated because of the unusually low volume weights. Peat soils weigh only a few pounds per cubic foot when dry. Therefore, the volume of water required to saturate a cubic foot of dry peat soil may weigh several times as much as the dry soil itself. In considering moisture contents of peat soils, it would be better to give the data as percentages by volume rather than percentages by weight.

Table 5 shows permanent wilting points, moisture equivalents, saturation capacities, and available moisture capacities for some peats,

TABLE 5

MOISTURE PROPERTIES OF SOME PEATS, MINERAL SOILS, AND
PEAT-SOIL MIXTURES [6]

		Moisture properties, per cent by weight			
Material	Mixtures by volume	Wilting point	Moisture equivalent	Saturation capacity	Available capacity
Clay loam soil	...	7.1	20.2	44.3	13.1
Moss peat	...	82.3	166	1057	83.7
Clay loam and moss peat	1:1	14.5	31	114	16.5
Clay loam and moss peat	4:1 *	8.5	21.6	57.3	13.1
Reed peat	...	70.7	110	289	39.3
Clay loam and reed peat	1:1	21.2	39.1	94.1	17.9
Clay loam and reed peat	4:1	10.8	26.5	56.8	15.7
Loamy fine sand	...	2.1	6.5	30.9	4.4
Loamy fine sand and moss peat	1:1	6.6	16.9	101	10.3
Loamy fine sand and moss peat	4:1	3.1	9.1	48.1	6.0
Loamy fine sand and reed peat	1:1	16.2	26.4	79.3	10.2
Loamy fine sand and reed peat	4:1	5.6	12.4	47.4	6.8

* Four parts of clay loam to 1 part of moss peat.

mineral soils, and peat-soil mixtures, abstracted or computed from comprehensive test data reported by Feustel and Byers.[6] Moisture contents are expressed as percentages by weight. Mix proportions by volume are given in the second column. The moss peat weighed 7 pounds per cubic foot, and the reed peat 24 pounds. The clay loam soil contained 23.6 per cent of clay. The loamy fine sand contained 44.1 per cent of fine sand and 26 per cent of medium sand. Percentages of available moisture capacity, obtained by subtracting wilting points from moisture equivalents, are shown in the last column.

The data in Table 5 show that permanent wilting points, moisture equivalents, and saturation capacities of both clay loam and loamy fine sand soils may be increased by additions of peat. The increases were appreciable for the 4:1 mixtures and pronounced for the 1:1 mixtures. Available moisture capacities were increased somewhat for both soils but were more important for the loamy sand. The available moisture capacity of the loamy sand was increased about 50 per cent by adding 20 per cent of peat, and more than doubled by adding equal parts of peat. Changes in the physical properties of the soils caused by the additions of peat were not reported. They probably were beneficial.

Effects of Manure. Applications of barnyard manures to field surfaces are often said to improve the moisture properties of the soil as well as the physical and chemical properties. Beneficial effects of manure on soil structures, aeration, temperatures, available plant nutrients, tillage, and crop returns are well established. However, there seems to be some question as to the beneficial effects on moisture properties.

Table 6 shows effects of well-rotted barnyard manures on permanent wilting points, moisture equivalents, and available moisture capacities for some different types of soil in California, abstracted from data reported by Veihmeyer.[27] The values tabulated are for applications of 75 tons of manure per acre, mixed into the top foot of soil. Such applications are several times as great as those normally made on farm areas. Moisture contents are shown for both treated and untreated soils. Available moisture contents are differences between moisture equivalents and permanent wilting percentages.

The data in Table 6 show that, although the permanent wilting point and moisture equivalent for the fine sand were increased somewhat by the manure treatment, the increases produced no change in the available moisture capacity. Moisture properties of the other soils were not altered materially. In some cases, the manure treatments

TABLE 6

EFFECTS OF MANURE ON MOISTURE PROPERTIES OF SOILS [27]

(Moisture contents in percentages)

Soil type	Wilting point		Moisture equivalent		Available moisture	
	Untreated	Treated *	Untreated	Treated	Untreated	Treated
Fine sand	1.0	1.5	3.2	3.7	2.2	2.2
Sandy loam	2.9	3.0	9.5	9.7	6.6	6.7
Silt loam	7.5	7.6	16.1	15.9	8.6	8.3
Loam	10.3	9.8	21.7	20.9	11.4	11.1
Clay	13.4	14.2	28.4	29.3	15.0	15.1

* 75 tons per acre mixed with top foot of soil.

caused decreases in moisture percentages rather than increases. Data for different applications of manure varying from 10 to 200 tons per acre, not included in Table 6, showed essentially the same effects.

The investigations reported by Veihmeyer indicate that applications of barnyard manures, although desirable from other viewpoints, cannot be depended upon to improve moisture properties of irrigation soils.

Soil-Moisture Samples. Soil samples, to determine moisture contents at different depths following irrigations, may be taken near field surfaces and at about 1-foot intervals of depth down to the lower limits of the root zones. Locations for sampling should be carefully selected, so as to represent typical soil conditions in the irrigated areas. Inasmuch as soil conditions may vary considerably from place to place, approximately the same locations should be used in taking samples at different times during the irrigation season. In large fields, soil samples may be needed at several locations.

When great accuracy is not essential, soil samples can be removed with a post-hole digger of small diameter, or with a large carpenter's auger welded to a long steel rod. When more precise data are needed, the samples should be taken with a well-designed type of soil-sampling tube, which will permit the removal and disposition of the samples with minimum disturbance and exposure.

A tube for removing soil samples used by King in early soil investigations, also used by others in many subsequent investigations, is often referred to as the King soil tube. An improved design of soil tube, more recently used on many irrigation projects, was described by Veihmeyer in 1929.[26] An efficient jack for raising soil tubes after they have been driven several feet into the soil was described by Taylor and Blaney in 1929.[22]

Moisture contents of soil samples are determined by weighing. Samples are weighed at the time of removal, dried in an oven at about 100 or 110 degrees C. for about 48 hours or until loss of moisture ceases, then reweighed to determine the total amount of moisture evaporated. The weight of moisture evaporated multiplied by 100 and divided by the dry weight of the sample gives the moisture content at the time of sampling, expressed as a percentage by weight. The oven-dry weight is considered as the zero point for moisture contents, as shown on Figure 1.

Continuous Measurements of Soil Moisture. Continuous measurements of soil moisture at different depths in the root zone are desirable during scientific investigations of relations between plant growth and soil moisture, particularly as the moisture contents are reduced from field capacities to permanent wilting points. Such measurements, besides supplying continuous data on soil-moisture changes, are advantageous for other reasons. For instance, they eliminate the necessity for disturbing the plants and soil during the growth period, the need for taking soil samples periodically at different locations and depths, and the need for analyzing the moisture contents of the samples.

Two methods of making continuous measurements of soil moisture under field conditions have been developed: (1) an electrometric method, based on differences in electrical resistance caused by differences in soil-moisture contents; and (2) a tensiometric method, based on differences in tension between soil particles and soil moisture caused by differences in soil-moisture contents. Both methods show increases or decreases in moisture contents directly but require calibration in order to determine actual quantities of moisture in the soil. When actual moisture contents of the soil are to be evaluated for different seasons of the year, observations by both methods need some adjustments for differences in soil temperature.

Tensiometric methods may be used to determine moisture contents of soils from about saturation values, when the tension is zero, down to points where the greater parts of the available moisture have been depleted. As moisture contents approach permanent wilting points, tensions become too high for accurate measurement. A tension of about 0.85 atmosphere is approximately the maximum that can be measured, whereas the tension at the permanent wilting point may be from 5 to 15 atmospheres.

Electrometric methods may be used to measure moisture contents of soils from about field capacities down to permanent wilting points; that is, through the entire range of available capillary moisture. Although they may be used to measure moisture contents a little higher than field capacity, they cannot be used throughout the range from field capacity to saturation. They are particularly useful in measuring moisture contents as the capillary moisture becomes exhausted by plant growth.

Electrometric Measurements. Installation and equipment for electrometric measurements of soil moisture were described by Bouyoucos and Mick in 1940.[3] Briefly, the installations in the soil consist of small blocks of plaster of Paris, each block containing two embedded electrodes with insulated leads running to the ground surface. Measurements of electrical resistance between the two electrodes are made with a portable, modified type of Wheatstone bridge. Observations can be made in 30 to 40 seconds, so no great amount of time is required at a particular location, even when several blocks are installed in the soil.

The plaster blocks are sufficiently porous, and the pores of proper size, to permit rapid movements of capillary moisture. Consequently no appreciable lag occurs between changes in moisture contents in the surrounding soil and in the blocks. The growth of plant roots apparently is not affected by the presence of the blocks. The blocks are durable and probably can be expected to supply reliable data as long as the insulation on the leads remains effective. Insulated lamp-cords are used as leads. Electrodes are made by stripping the insulation and soldering the strands before casting the blocks.

The electrical resistance between the electrodes is about 400 to 600 ohms when the moisture content is at field capacity. The resistance increases as the moisture content decreases and reaches 60,000 to 75,000 ohms when the moisture content reaches the permanent wilting point. In most soils, changes in salt contents of the soil solution caused by changes in moisture contents probably do not materially affect the electrometric measurements.

In 1946, Colman described a somewhat similar electrical soil-moisture meter developed by the United States Forest Service for use in soil investigations at the San Dimas Experimental Forest, southern California.[5] He described the soil unit as follows:

The soil unit of this instrument is a disk-shaped, methacrylate-type plastic base, upon which are mounted two monel screen electrodes separated by several layers of Fiberglas fabric. The Fiberglas serves as the porous dielectric. Imbedded in the rim of the disk is a coil of 50 ft. of fine copper wire which serves as a resistance thermometer. The temperature measurement is necessary in order to obtain the most precise measurement of soil-moisture content.

Inasmuch as the resistance between the electrodes of an electric soil-moisture meter changes as the moisture passes from the liquid to the solid phase, it is possible that such meters may be adapted to investigations of freezing and thawing of soil moisture as well as to measurements of moisture contents.

Tensiometric Measurements. Tensiometric measurements of moisture conditions in soils on several irrigation projects were described by Scofield in 1945.[21] Details of construction of the tensiometer were described by Richards in 1942.[18] Briefly, the method involves the measurement of the tension between the soil particles and the soil moisture, by means of a mercury manometer attached to a porous cup installed in the soil. A flexible copper tube of small diameter connects the soil cup with the manometer.

When an installation is made, the tensiometer system is filled with freshly boiled, air-free water, and connection with the soil moisture is promptly made through the porous cup. The soil-moisture tension is then shown by the height of the mercury column in the manometer. Conversions from soil-moisture tensions to actual soil-moisture contents are made with calibration curves determined for each particular installation.

Inasmuch as the soil-moisture tension for a particular soil-moisture content varies with the apparent density of the soil, special care must be exercised in developing the calibration curves. Scofield used three methods: (1) comparison of tensiometer readings with actual moisture contents of soil samples taken at the location of the porous cup; (2) observations of tension values on cores in closed containers, where actual quantities of water added to the cores could be determined by weighing; and (3) observations of tension values on soils in open containers, with growing plants, where evapo-transpiration losses of moisture could be determined by weighing. He concluded that the third method is the most satisfactory.

Tensiometric measurements of soil moisture are most reliable when the tensions vary from about 0 to a little less than 1 atmosphere; that is, from about saturation down to moisture contents somewhat higher than the permanent wilting point. Richards and Weaver found that the portions of the available soil moisture that could be measured with tensiometers varied from less than 0.5 in fine soils to about 0.8 in coarse soils.[19]

Soil-Moisture Tension. In some reports on laboratory investigations, tensions between soil particles and soil water have been used as a basis for discussing soil-moisture relations. Soil-moisture tensions for different soil-moisture contents may be measured in the laboratory with centrifuge, pressure-membrane, pressure-plate, suction-plate, or tensiometer types of equipment. Tension values may be expressed as equivalent atmospheres or equivalent heights of water or mercury columns. In converting soil-moisture tensions to equivalent atmospheres, 1 atmosphere is usually assumed to equal a pressure of 14.7 pounds per square inch.

Richards and Weaver used atmospheres in discussing the moisture relations of 71 southern California soils, varying in texture from washed and screened sands to heavy clays.[19] The results of their investigations indicate (1) that the moisture equivalent is closely represented by the moisture retained under a tension of $\frac{1}{3}$ atmosphere; (2) that the field capacity may be represented by the moisture retained under a tension a little lower than $\frac{1}{3}$ atmosphere, possibly as low as 0.1 atmosphere; and (3) that the permanent wilting point may be approximately represented by the moisture retained under tensions of from 7 to 9 atmospheres. For most soils investigated, the 15-atmosphere tension was within the wilting range and the 30-atmosphere tension was below the ultimate wilting point.

Investigations of 12 of the 71 soils showed that increases in soil temperature from 32 to about 100 degrees F. caused decreases varying from less than 1 to about 3 per cent in the moisture retained for a tension of $\frac{1}{2}$ atmosphere; and decreases varying from less than 1 to about 8 per cent in the moisture retained for a tension of 15 atmospheres. In general, the effects of temperature changes increased with increasing fineness of soil texture.

The pF Designation. In 1935, Schofield suggested using the logarithm of the capillary soil-moisture tension, measured in centimeters of water, as a free-energy scale in studies of soil-moisture relations.[20] He proposed the term pF as a designation of the capillary tension logarithm, a designation somewhat analogous to the pH scale for alkali-acidity reactions. Since that time, the pF concept of soil moisture has been discussed in many technical contributions and has received some unfavorable as well as favorable comments. A symposium of opinions, assembled by Veihmeyer as a committee activity, was published in 1944.[35]

Investigations of some soils of medium to fine texture have shown pF values of about 7.0 for oven-dry conditions, 4.3 for the permanent wilting point, 3.2 for field capacity, and about 3.0 for the moisture equivalent.

In irrigation soils where soil solutions may contain appreciable salt concentrations, pF values may be misleading unless corrected for osmotic effects. The pF method of consideration may have some merits in theoretical studies of soil-moisture science. However, in practical irrigation work, actual soil-moisture contents and their relations to permanent wilting points, expressed as percentages of the dry weight of the soil or as equivalent inches of water, constitute the information needed in planning irrigation procedures.

Additional Soil-Moisture Constants. Some additional soil-moisture constants that can be determined in a laboratory were proposed by Olmstead in 1937. They include centrifugal moisture, normal moisture capacity, and minimum water of saturation. These constants are not shown on Figure 1, inasmuch as they are not commonly used by irrigation engineers.

Olmstead's investigations were made mostly on soil samples from the erosion experiment stations of the Department of Agriculture. They were described in a government bulletin which has been freely utilized in preparing the following paragraphs.[15]

Centrifugal moisture is defined as the moisture held by a soil when subjected to a centrifugal force of 300,000 times gravity. It is slightly higher than the amount of moisture absorbed by an oven-dry sample when placed in an atmosphere of 99 per cent relative humidity, but probably lower than the moisture content at the time of permanent wilting. In other words, it is somewhere between the hygroscopic coefficient and the permanent wilting point.

The normal moisture capacity, a term proposed by Shaw in 1927, is the maximum moisture content a wet sample of soil can retain when placed in contact with a dry layer of soil. In other words, it is the moisture content of the wet sample after capillary movements of moisture from the wet soil to the dry soil become very slow. It was developed in an attempt to obtain a more reliable laboratory test of field capacity. Olmstead concluded that the normal moisture capacity is a better measure of field capacity than the moisture equivalent, especially for sandy soils.

The minimum water of saturation is the smallest percentage of moisture that will saturate a sample of soil after it has been kneaded into a condition in which the soil particles have the closest packing. It is somewhat lower than the saturation capacity. Inasmuch as it is determined for an artificial arrangement of the soil grains, it is not representative of saturated soils under field conditions.

Plasticity Terms. In plastic soils, that is, soils containing appreciable proportions of clay particles or colloidal materials, certain special terms are used to designate the limits of the plastic conditions. The principal plasticity designations are the upper plastic limit, the shrinkage limit, the sticky point, and the lower plastic limit. Plasticity conditions are produced wholly by the clay and colloidal contents of the soil. Silt and sand particles are not plastic.

Plastic properties of soils were discussed by Olmstead and Smith in the Department of Agriculture *Yearbook* for 1938.[16] The following statements and quotations, abstracted and rearranged from their discussions, explain the different plasticity terms:

> The upper plastic limit is "the moisture content below which soil pastes no longer behave like liquids."
>
> "The shrinkage limit is the moisture content of a molded cake of drying soil at which shrinkage ceases."
>
> The sticky point is the "lowest moisture content at which stickiness first appears. . . . This is also approximately the moisture condition of a soil at which a plow or tillage instrument just fails to scour."
>
> "The lower plastic limit is the lowest moisture content at which the soil can be molded with the fingers into a single-grain mass. At all higher moisture contents the soil is plastic."
>
> "It has been found that the greater the moisture range between the upper and lower plastic limit the more plastic the soil will be. The sticky point always lies in this range. As plasticity decreases the lower plastic limit rises to the sticky point, and then both disappear. When this occurs, the soil is not plastic."

REFERENCES

1. Briggs, Lyman J., and John W. McLane, "The Moisture Equivalent of Soils," *U.S. Dept. Agr. Bull.* 45, 1907.
2. Briggs, Lyman J., and H. L. Shantz, "The Wilting Coefficient for Different Plants and Its Indirect Determination," *U.S. Dept. Agr. Bull.* 230, 1912.
3. Bouyoucos, G. J., and A. H. Mick, "An Electrical Resistance Method for the Continuous Measurement of Soil Moisture under Field Conditions," *Mich. Agr. Exp. Sta. Tech. Bull.* 172, 1940.
4. Buehrer, T. F., and M. S. Rose, "Studies in Soil Structure, V, Bound Water in Normal and Puddled Soils," *Ariz. Agr. Exp. Sta. Tech. Bull.* 100, 1943.

5. Colman, E. A., "The Place of Electrical Soil-Moisture Meters in Hydrologic Research," *Trans. Am. Geop. Union,* December 1946, pp. 847–853.

6. Feustel, I. C., and H. G. Byers, "The Comparative Moisture-Absorbing and Moisture-Retaining Capacities of Peat and Soil Mixtures," *U.S. Dept. Agr. Tech. Bull.* 532, 1936.

7. Free, G. R., G. M. Browning, and G. W. Musgrave, "Relative Infiltration and Related Physical Characteristics of Certain Soils," *U.S. Dept. Agr. Tech. Bull.* 729, 1940.

8. Furr, J. R., and J. O. Reeve, "Range of Soil-Moisture Percentages through Which Plants Undergo Permanent Wilting in Some Soils from Semiarid Irrigated Areas," *Jour. Agr. Res.,* Aug. 15, 1945, pp. 149–170.

9. Houk, Ivan E., "Rainfall and Runoff in the Miami Valley," *Miami Conservancy Dist. Tech. Rep.,* Part VIII, Dayton, Ohio, 1921.

10. Israelsen, Orson W., and Frank L. West, "Water-Holding Capacity of Irrigated Soils," *Utah Agr. Exp. Sta. Bull.* 183, 1922.

11. Lee, Charles H., "Report of the Committee on Absorption and Transpiration, 1934–35," *Trans. Am. Geop. Union,* 1935, Part II, pp. 392–404.

12. Lewis, M. R., R. A. Work, and W. W. Aldrich, "Studies of the Irrigation of Pear Orchards on Heavy Soil near Medford, Oreg.," *U.S. Dept. Agr. Tech. Bull.* 432, 1934.

13. Meinzer, Oscar E., "The Occurrence of Ground Water in the United States with a Discussion of Principles," *U.S. Geol. Sur. Water-Supply Paper* 489, 1923.

14. —— "Outline of Ground-Water Hydrology with Definitions," *U.S. Geol. Sur. Water-Supply Paper* 494, 1923.

15. Olmstead, L. B., "Some Moisture Relations of the Soils from the Erosion Experiment Stations," *U.S. Dept. Agr. Tech. Bull.* 562, 1937.

16. Olmstead, L. B., and W. O. Smith, "Water Relations of Soils," *U.S. Dept. Agr. Yearbook,* 1938, pp. 897–910.

17. Piper, Arthur M., "Notes on the Relation between the Moisture-Equivalent and the Specific Retention of Water-Bearing Materials," *Trans. Am. Geop. Union,* 1933, pp. 481–487.

18. Richards, L. A., "Soil Moisture Tensiometer Materials and Construction," *Soil Sci.,* Vol. 53, 1942, pp. 241–248.

19. Richards, L. A., and L. R. Weaver, "Moisture Retention by Some Irrigated Soils as Related to Soil-Moisture Tension," *Jour. Agr. Res.,* Sept. 15, 1944, pp. 215–235.

20. Schofield, R. K., "The *pF* of the Water in Soil," *Trans. Third Intern. Cong. Soil Sci.,* Vol. 2, 1935, pp. 37–48.

21. Scofield, Carl S., "The Measurement of Soil Water," *Jour. Agr. Res.,* Nov. 1, 1945, pp. 375–402.

22. Taylor, C. A., and H. F. Blaney, "An Efficient Soil Tube Jack," *Soil Sci.,* Vol. 27, 1929, pp. 351–353.

23. Taylor, C. A., H. F. Blaney, and W. W. McLaughlin, "The Wilting-Range in Certain Soils and the Ultimate Wilting-Point," *Trans. Am. Geop. Union,* 1934, Part II, pp. 436–444.

24. Taylor, C. A., and J. R. Furr, "Use of Soil-Moisture and Fruit-Growth Records for Checking Irrigation Practices in Citrus Orchards," *U.S. Dept. Agr. Cir.* 426, 1937.

25. Thysell, J. C., "Conservation and Use of Soil Moisture at Mandan, N. Dak.," *U.S. Dept. Agr. Tech. Bull.* 617, 1938.

26. Veihmeyer, F. J., "An Improved Soil-Sampling Tube," *Soil Sci.*, Vol. 27, 1929, pp. 147–152.

27. ——— "Evaporation from Soils and Transpiration," *Trans. Am. Geop. Union,* 1938, Part II, pp. 612–619.

28. Veihmeyer, F. J., and N. E. Edlefsen, "Interpretation of Soil-Moisture Problems by Means of Energy-Changes," *Trans. Am. Geop. Union,* 1937, Part II, pp. 302–318.

29. Veihmeyer, F. J., and A. H. Hendrickson, "Soil Moisture at Permanent Wilting of Plants," *Plant Physiology,* July 1928, pp. 355–357.

30. ——— "The Moisture Equivalent as a Measure of the Field Capacity of Soils," *Soil Sci.*, Vol. 32, 1931, pp. 181–193.

31. ——— "Essentials of Irrigation and Cultivation of Orchards," *Calif. Agr. Ext. Service Cir.* 50, revised, 1950.

32. ——— "The Permanent Wilting Percentage as a Reference for the Measurement of Soil Moisture," *Trans. Am. Geop. Union,* December 1948, pp. 887–896.

33. Veihmeyer, F. J., and C. N. Johnston, "Soil-Moisture Records from Burned and Unburned Plots in Certain Grazing Areas of California," *Trans. Am. Geop. Union,* 1944, Part I, pp. 72–84.

34. Veihmeyer, F. J., and others, "Report of the Committee on Physics of Soil-Moisture, 1933–34," *Trans. Am. Geop. Union,* 1934, Part II, pp. 302–312.

35. ——— "Report of the Committee on Physics of Soil Moisture, 1943–44," *Trans. Am. Geop. Union,* 1944, Part V, pp. 699–712.

36. Work, R. A., and M. R. Lewis, "Moisture Equivalent, Field Capacity, and Permanent Wilting Percentage and Their Ratios in Heavy Soils," *Agr. Eng.,* October 1934, pp. 355–362.

Chapter 5

SOIL-MOISTURE MOVEMENTS

When irrigation water is applied to a field surface or when rainfall occurs, moisture enters the soil by infiltration, sometimes referred to as absorption. In some studies of rainfall and runoff, the portion of the precipitation that enters the soil has been called retention. After moisture enters the soil, it moves through the soil formations in accordance with gravity forces and capillary tensions, aided by hydrostatic pressures at the ground surface as long as water remains on the ground.

After the field surface becomes drained, following the discontinuance of irrigation or the cessation of rainfall, moisture continues to move through the soil formations in accordance with gravity forces and capillary tensions. When gravity movements have reduced the moisture content of the wetted zone to field capacity, moisture continues to move slowly in accordance with capillary tensions. Later, as capillary water becomes depleted by plant growth and surface evaporation, small amounts of moisture may be transferred from place to place through the soil as water vapor, in accordance with differences in vapor pressure.

Downward movements of soil moisture caused by gravity and hydrostatic pressures during irrigation or rainfall, also downward movements caused by gravity after the field surface becomes drained, are commonly referred to as percolation. Movements of soil moisture caused by capillary tensions, which may take place in any direction, are commonly referred to as capillary movements. Movements of moisture in the vapor stage are referred to as vapor movements.

Infiltration, percolation, and capillary movements of soil moisture are of great importance in irrigation work. Rates of infiltration affect the quantities of water that can enter the soil during irrigations. Rates of percolation affect the distribution of the soil moisture and the portions of the infiltrated water that may move to depths below the root zones. They also affect the losses of water that may take place by seepage through the bed and banks of irrigation canals. Rates of capillary movements affect the distribution of soil moisture and the amounts of moisture that may be absorbed by plant roots during crop growth.

Rates of infiltration and percolation resulting from precipitation in upstream drainage basins affect the quantities of water that may reach stream channels and subsequently become available for irrigation on downstream lands. Small changes in infiltration rates on upstream areas may have pronounced effects on the proportions of surface and groundwater runoff. In general, increased rates of infiltration mean increased storage in the groundwater reservoir and increased streamflow during the summer months when water is needed for irrigation.

Vapor movements of soil moisture are of academic interest but probably are not of appreciable significance in irrigation considerations. They seldom, if ever, produce material effects on the quantities of water available for crop plants.

Movements of soil moisture should be carefully considered in planning irrigation procedures. Rates at which water can enter the soil and percolate to desirable depths below the surface may affect the design of farm distribution systems, quantities of irrigation flow required, and periods water must be held on the fields in order to insure adequate penetration. Rates of moisture movements depend principally on the size and arrangement of the soil particles and the size of the pore spaces but may be influenced by temperature and other conditions within the root zones or at the field surfaces. In general, moisture moves at comparatively rapid rates through coarse-textured sandy soils and at relatively slow rates through fine-textured silt and clay soils.

Many field and laboratory investigations of soil-moisture movements following irrigation, rainfall, or sprinkling to simulate rainfall have been made. Measurements of capillary movements, also investigations of the transference of moisture in the vapor stage, can best be made in the laboratory. Measurements of infiltration and percolation supply more valuable information when made in the field, inasmuch as some field conditions that affect such movements are difficult to reproduce in laboratory specimens.

Results of some investigations of soil-moisture movements that are important from the viewpoint of irrigation are taken up on the following pages. Reports on a few additional investigations that contain valuable data are listed in the references at the end of the chapter. Discussions in this chapter pertain primarily to movements of moisture into and within the root zones, but some discussions of percolation in zones of saturation, below the water table, are included. Losses of irrigation water by deep percolation and by seepage from canals are taken up in a later chapter.

Infiltration. Infiltration of water into a soil during an irrigation takes place most rapidly when water is first applied to the field surface. As irrigation continues and the topsoil gradually becomes saturated, the rate of infiltration, sometimes called infiltration capacity, gradually decreases and soon reaches a nearly constant value. This nearly constant rate of infiltration then continues until the supply of irrigation water is discontinued. When the water supply is shut off, the rate of infiltration decreases rapidly and reaches zero as soon as the field surface becomes drained.

Infiltration during rainfall takes place in about the same way as during irrigation, except that rates of infiltration vary with rates of rainfall, also with differences in ground slopes which often are more pronounced under natural conditions than in fields that have been leveled and graded for irrigation. Maximum rates of infiltration occur when the rainfall begins, then gradually decrease as the surface storage becomes filled and the surface soil becomes saturated. After the topsoil becomes saturated, rates of infiltration on particular areas increase or decrease with increases or decreases in rates of rainfall. On some soils, water falling during the beginning of a rainstorm washes fine soil particles into the surface pores, forming a thin impervious coating that rapidly reduces infiltration rates.

When water is applied to a field devoid of vegetation, either by rainfall or irrigation, the initial rate of infiltration depends principally on the looseness of the topsoil. Fields that have just been cultivated can absorb all, or nearly all, of the water during the first few minutes of application. Fields covered with mulches or close-growing vegetation such as grasses can also absorb large proportions of the water applied.

When water is applied to a compact field surface, either by rainfall or irrigation, the initial rate of infiltration depends on the soil structure, texture, porosity, size of pore spaces, presence of vegetation, and moisture content of the topsoil. It is also affected to some extent by soil and water temperatures, amount of organic matter in the soil, presence of trapped air, plow soles, earthworm excavations, cracking, or other conditions that influence soil permeability and water movements. Water enters the soil rapidly through noncapillary pore spaces and through openings between soil structures. Water is also drawn into the capillary pore spaces by capillary tensions.

After the surface soil becomes saturated, the rate of infiltration usually depends on the rate at which water can move downward through the most impermeable layer of the subsoil. However, if the subsoil portions of the soil profile are more permeable than the surface soil, the continued rate of infiltration depends on the rate at which water can move through the topsoil. The latter condition occurs when open gravel or coarse sand formations are present at relatively shallow depths below the field surfaces.

Rates of infiltration are materially affected by depths of water on the fields during rainfall or irrigation. Increased intensities of rainfall and increased depths of flooding during irrigation cause increased rates of infiltration, due to increased hydrostatic heads on the ground surfaces. Grass covers and surface mulches tend to hold water on the fields and thus to provide hydrostatic heads that increase infiltration.

Effects of hydrostatic heads on infiltration are pronounced during leaching operations, when depths of 12 or 15 inches may be maintained on the fields. This is an advantage, since the purpose of leaching is to produce rates of infiltration and percolation that will wash excess quantities of undesirable alkali salts down to subsoil drainage outlets or to depths beyond reach of the plant roots.

Miami Sprinkling Tests. Many of the above-stated conditions of infiltration during rainfall were demonstrated by the Miami Conservancy District's sprinkling tests, conducted on experimental plots near Dayton, Ohio, in connection with the development of designs for flood-control works. The tests were reported by the author in 1921.[22] Although they were made primarily as an investigation of rainfall and runoff relations, determinations of infiltration rates and total amounts of infiltration were included in the observations. In the report on the tests, portions of the rainfall absorbed by the soil were designated retention.

The Miami tests showed that on level sandy clay loam, devoid of vegetation, initial rates of infiltration might be as high as 3.65 inches per hour when the topsoil was dry and compacted, and as high as 4.25 inches per hour when the topsoil was dry and loose. Dry and loose sandy clay soil on a sloping hillside, also devoid of vegetation, absorbed as much as 3.00 inches per hour. Dry silty clay loam, without plant growth, absorbed as much as 3.69 inches per hour when compacted, and as much as 3.90 inches per hour when loosened.

The above-noted rates of absorption were rates of applying water during intervals before runoff began, when all water applied was being retained by the soil. If the water had been applied at higher rates, or if the plots had been suddenly flooded, as in irrigation, the initial rates of absorption would have been higher, especially when the top-soils were in a loosened or cultivated condition.

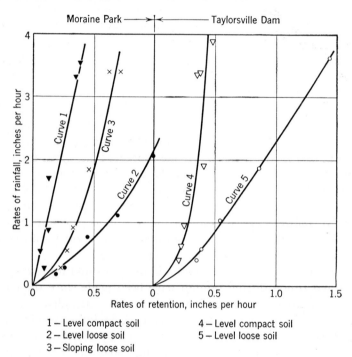

1 – Level compact soil   4 – Level compact soil
2 – Level loose soil   5 – Level loose soil
3 – Sloping loose soil

FIGURE 1. Rates of retention during different rates of rainfall, saturated soils near Dayton, Ohio. (Plotted from data in reference 22.)

After runoff began, rates of infiltration gradually decreased for a short time, then continued at about constant rates as long as sprinkling was continued at uniform rates. When rates of applying water were increased or decreased, rates of infiltration also increased or decreased. For saturated topsoils, rates of infiltration were almost directly proportional to rates of rainfall. Formations of thin impermeable coatings during early periods of sprinkling did not occur to a noticeable degree on the Miami test plots.

Figure 1 shows rates of retention plotted against rates of rainfall for saturated soil conditions during five of the Miami tests. Curves 1 and 2 were determined on sandy clay loam, curve 3 on sandy clay,

and curves 4 and 5 on silty clay loam. Differences between curves
1 and 2, also between curves 4 and 5, show effects of cultivation on
rates of retention. Although the Moraine Park soil was a little more
impermeable at the hillside plot than at the level plot, the differences
in rates of retention shown by curves 2 and 3 were mostly due to
differences in field slopes. The Miami investigations showed that
at the level plots saturated loosened soils could absorb rainfall as
fast as it fell up to rates of about 0.20 to 0.30 inch an hour. When
rainfall intensities increased to higher values, rates of retention also
increased, but not so rapidly as rates of rainfall, so that surface runoff
took place.

Values of retention determined during the Miami experiments included soil absorption, percolation, and evaporation. Inasmuch as
the tests were usually conducted on warm summer days, often when
some wind was blowing, rates of evaporation at times may have been
as high as 0.05 inch per hour. At the Moraine Park plots, the surface
soils were underlaid by porous sand and gravel formations at relatively
shallow depths. Consequently, as soon as the surface soils became
saturated, rates of retention represented rates of percolation as well
as rates of infiltration. At the Taylorsville plots, the soils extended
to considerable depths, so that continued infiltration produced continued downward extensions of the wetted zones.

Other Sprinkling Tests. Several additional sprinkling tests of infiltration and runoff during rainfall have been made since the completion of the Miami investigations. Some have included tests on a
greater number of soil types. Others have included special studies
of effects on runoff and infiltration produced by different surface conditions at the time of rainfall. Although some of the experiments
were planned and conducted from the viewpoint of erosion rather
than infiltration, most of the tests supply valuable data on the proportions of the precipitation that can be absorbed by the soil.

Sprinkling tests on eight soils at ten different locations in southeastern Nebraska were conducted by the Nebraska Agricultural Experiment Station and the Soil Conservation Service, United States
Department of Agriculture, during April to October 1938. The soils
included sandy loam, silt loam, clay loam, and silty clay loam types.
Tests were made for different conditions of surface soil and surface
cover, on plots 6.6 feet by 33 feet in size, with wood or metal borders
set 6 inches into the ground. Results of the tests were reported by
Duley and Kelley in a state bulletin in 1939,[12] also in a federal bulletin
in 1941.[13]

Table 1 shows data for a few of the Nebraska tests on moist cultivated soils with different surface conditions, selected from detailed
tabulations published in the federal bulletin. The tests included in

TABLE 1

SELECTED DATA FOR SPRINKLING TESTS ON MOIST
SOILS IN NEBRASKA [13]

Soil type	Surface condition	Date of test	Length of test, hr.	Total ap-plied, in.	Rate ap-plied, in. per hr.	Final rate of in-take, in. per hr.
Pawnee clay loam	Cultivated, bare	9/24	1.00	1.49	1.49	0.29
Pawnee clay loam	Cultivated, straw cover	9/26	1.00	3.56	3.56	1.28
Pawnee clay loam	Cultivated, straw cover	9/27	0.83	2.98	3.58	0.48
Butler silty clay loam	Cultivated, straw cover	9/28	1.00	3.27	3.27	0.89
Butler silty clay loam	Cultivated, bare	10/21	1.00	1.74	1.74	0.17
Knox silt loam	Cultivated, bare	6/18	1.50	4.69	3.13	0.22
Knox silt loam	Cultivated, bare	6/18	1.50	2.25	1.50	0.12
Knox silt loam	Respaded, straw cover	7/22	0.76	3.24	2.46	1.15
Marshall silt loam *	Cultivated, bare	4/22	1.50	5.10	3.40	0.28
Marshall silt loam	Not cultivated, bare	4/18	1.50	5.37	3.58	0.11
Marshall silt loam	Cultivated, straw cover	8/10	2.00	6.92	3.46	1.20
Marshall silt loam	Cultivated, straw cover	8/17	13.00	22.62	1.74	0.48
Marshall silt loam	Cultivated, bare	8/26	1.00	1.53	1.53	0.80
Lancaster sandy loam	Cultivated, bare	10/4	1.00	1.63	1.63	0.32
Lancaster sandy loam	Cultivated, straw cover	10/5	1.00	3.41	3.41	0.92
Lancaster sandy loam	Straw removed	10/10	1.00	1.76	1.76	0.40

* Heavy subsoil.

Table 1 were made after preceding tests had supplied the soils with
relatively high percentages of moisture. Final rates of infiltration are
shown in the last column. Increased infiltration rates resulting from
respading the surfaces or maintaining straw covers are particularly
noticeable.

In the Nebraska investigations, water was applied at a practically
uniform rate during each test. On the bare cultivated plots, formations of thin dense coatings on the soil surfaces during early applications of water rapidly reduced rates of infiltration. Straw mulches
greatly retarded the development of such coatings. Rates of infiltra-

tion usually decreased to approximately constant values in 30 to 60 minutes on the bare cultivated plots, and in 2 to 8 hours on the straw-covered plots. During prolonged applications of water, some moisture may have moved laterally through the soil under the plot borders. Therefore, some of the final rates of infiltration in Table 1 may be slightly higher than the rates that would occur during natural rainfalls of similar intensity.

Tests on sod plots, not included in Table 1, showed that grass covers affected infiltration rates in about the same way as straw mulches. However, final rates of infiltration at the grass plots were lower than at the straw-covered plots. Similar effects of straw mulches on infiltration at silt loam plots in Ohio were observed by the Soil Conservation Service in 1940.[5]

Tube Tests of Infiltration. Tube tests of infiltration were made by the United States Department of Agriculture at 68 field sites throughout the country, where soil types varied from porous gravelly silt loams to relatively impervious heavy clay soils. The results of the investigations, including detailed data, were reported by Free, Browning, and Musgrave in 1940.[15]

In general, the sites were located in fields of row crops, not recently cultivated, but some were located in farm areas growing small grains. A few in the Southwest were on range lands sparsely covered with permanent grasses. All vegetation and accumulations of ground litter were removed from the soil surfaces before beginning the tests.

The infiltration measurements were made in 9-inch, galvanized steel tubes, 18 or 24 inches long, jacked into the soil until only 2 or 3 inches projected above the ground. A head of about $\frac{1}{4}$ inch of water was maintained on the surface within the tube during the infiltration observations. Initial runs, continuing for 3 hours, were made first, followed by similar 3-hour runs 24 hours later. The second runs were called wet runs. Soil-moisture contents to depths of 25 inches were determined by sampling before both runs. Mechanical analyses, volume weights, moisture equivalents, porosities, alkali-acidity reactions, and other soil properties were also determined.

Table 2 shows some infiltration rates observed during the third hour of wet runs on soils of different types, as reported by Free and his associates. Pertinent data on locations, porosities, and mechanical equivalents of the surface soils are also tabulated. Where several test sites were located on the same type of soil, the data tabulated are for sites showing maximum rates of infiltration. Much lower rates were observed at some sites on similar soils.

TABLE 2

INFILTRATION RATES ON WET SOILS OF DIFFERENT TYPES
TUBE MEASUREMENTS [15]

Soil type	Site no.	Location	Porosity, per cent by volume		Moisture equivalent, per cent by weight	Infiltration rate, in. per hr.*
			Total	Non-capillary		
Gravelly silt loam	17	Marcellus, N. Y.	54.9	28.1	25.0	4.96
Clay loam	140	Newberg, Ore.	61.1	36.3	27.0	3.98
Silt loam	144	Pullman, Wash.	57.0	32.0	25.0	2.09
Sandy loam	137	Gallup, N. Mex.	49.6	26.3	15.3	1.93
Clay (eroded)	123	Temple, Tex.	54.3	28.7	23.7	1.78
Sandy clay loam	136	Gallup, N. Mex.	48.8	27.7	12.0	1.42
Silty clay loam	19	Geneva, N. Y.	50.8	24.3	19.4	0.72
Stony silt loam	25	Ithaca, N. Y.	59.7	32.6	31.9	0.55
Fine sandy loam	129	Guthrie, Okla.	41.5	24.2	7.4	0.55
Very fine sandy loam	130	Elk City, Okla.	49.6	23.4	17.5	0.51
Loam	141	Newberg, Ore.	45.7	17.2	18.4	0.50
Sandy clay	125	Guthrie, Okla.	42.9	16.9	14.1	0.05
Heavy clay	132	Gallup, N. Mex.	57.8	27.0	34.8	0.02
Light clay	131	Gallup, N. Mex.	47.0	19.8	20.1	0.00
Clayey silt loam	112	New Concord, Ohio	49.4	17.6	26.5	0.00

* During third hour of wet runs.

The infiltration rates on the wet soils varied from zero on the clayey silt loam at New Concord, Ohio, and on the light clay at Gallup, New Mexico, to 4.96 inches per hour on the gravelly silt loam at Marcellus, New York.

Detailed tabulations of data in the original publication showed some correlations of infiltration rates on wet soils with certain soil properties, particularly noncapillary porosities and contents of organic matter. However, all correlations were too variable, interrelated, and complicated to supply means for accurate predictions of infiltration rates. The results of the tests show that definite information regarding infiltration rates on a particular soil must be obtained by actual measurements in the field.

Supplementary sprinkling tests in which rainfall was applied at rates of about 2.5 inches per hour were made on small plots at some of the sites. These tests showed infiltration rates somewhat lower than those observed by applying clear water through tubes. When turbid water was applied through the tubes, average infiltration rates were about the same by both methods.

Irrigation Infiltration Tests. Irrigation infiltration tests were made on soils of widely varying permeability at several locations in Idaho and Oregon during 1926 to 1935. The tests were conducted by the Idaho and Oregon Agricultural Experiment Stations in cooperation with the United States Department of Agriculture. Results of the tests were reported by Lewis in 1937.[27] In general, measurements were made in 18-inch rings set a few inches into the ground. Water was applied to the soil surfaces within the rings, and times required for infiltration recorded. Inasmuch as the rings held the water in place, no surface runoff could occur.

In some of the earlier investigations, the rings were set only 3 or 4 inches into the ground. However, tests in 1933 showed that, in order to prevent appreciable lateral movements of moisture through the soil to locations beyond the areas of application, the rings should be set to depths of 6 inches. Therefore, subsequent experiments were made with rings set to 6-inch depths.

Table 3 shows results of some infiltration measurements on loamy sand soils at the Umatilla Field Station, Hermiston, Oregon, during

TABLE 3

INFILTRATION TESTS ON LOAMY SAND SOILS AT UMATILLA
FIELD STATION, HERMISTON, OREGON [27]

Test numbers	Years irrigated	Surface vegetation	Apparent specific gravity	Initial moisture content, per cent	Time for infiltration of 2 in., min.
1, 2, 3	1	Rye	1.66	6.6–7.4	18.0–27.3
4, 6, 7	0	Dead grass	1.56	1.2–2.6	6.9–11.3
5	0	Dead grass	1.57	9.2	18.6
8, 9	0	Dead rye	1.63	1.6	7.0– 8.7
10, 11	4	Bare spot in alfalfa	1.68	7.0	17.2–22.8
12, 13	4	Heavy stand of alfalfa	1.57	4.8	39.0–44.8
15, 16	2	Heavy stand of sweetclover	....	3.3–4.3	17.0–18.2
14, 17	2	Dead rye	1.69	5.8–6.1	14.8–17.6

1935, compiled from data in the above-noted reference. Times required for the infiltration of 2 inches of irrigation water are given in the last column. Preceding columns give test numbers, years the soils had been irrigated, surface vegetation, apparent specific gravities, and initial moisture contents of the surface soils. Although the data show some variations in time of infiltration with differences in initial moisture contents, the most noticeable condition probably is the relatively long time required for 2 inches of water to infiltrate into the soil covered with heavy stands of alfalfa.

Figure 2 shows infiltration data observed on different soils as summarized and plotted by Lewis. Soil types varied from readily permea-

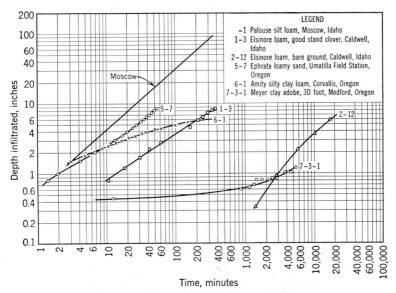

FIGURE 2. Infiltration during irrigation of different soils. (After Lewis.)

ble silt loams and loamy sands to highly impermeable clay adobe soils. Difficulties that may be encountered in securing adequate infiltration of irrigation water on impermeable soils are illustrated by the curves for the bare Elsinore loam at Caldwell, Idaho, and the Meyer clay adobe at Medford, Oregon.

On heavy clay soils that crack while drying, some penetration of irrigation water can be secured by applying water when the surface layers are dry and cracked. Light irrigations can be accomplished by such methods, but as soon as the soil formations adjoining the cracks become wetted they swell and close the cracks so that further infiltration is extremely slow. Mathews, in his investigations of gumbo soils on the Belle Fourche Project, western South Dakota, found that penetration of water took place rapidly to depths of about 2 feet when the soils were dry and cracked.[29]

Although infiltration rates are materially affected by soil texture, soils of the same textural type may have greatly different infiltration properties. Musgrave and Norton, in their investigations of water and soil relations near Clarinda, Iowa, found that rates of infiltration on the Marshall silt loam were from 7 to 10 times as rapid as on the Shelby silt loam.[36]

Factors Influencing Infiltration. Infiltration rates on irrigation soils may be influenced by cultural practices, tillage operations, or traffic over moistened soils too soon after irrigation. Early traffic over moistened soils may cause compaction and the formation of plow soles just below depths of cultivation. Such formations impede moisture movements during subsequent irrigations, thus reducing infiltration rates. Taylor observed such conditions in citrus orchards in southern California, where traffic had been concentrated in lanes between the trees. In some lanes, infiltration rates were only about one-third as great as in adjacent uncompacted soils.[55]

Investigations in southern California, reported by Huberty and Pillsbury in 1941, showed that permeabilities of surface soils may be altered and infiltration rates affected by the use of certain fertilizers.[23] Applications of calcium nitrate caused increases in permeability and infiltration, whereas applications of ammonium sulphate caused decreases. Infiltration rates on soils where ammonium sulphate had been applied were increased by adding organic matter or gypsum to the surfaces.

Investigations on a fine sandy loam growing date palms in the Coachella Valley near Indio, California, reported by Reitemeier and Christiansen in 1946, showed that infiltration rates could be doubled by applications of gypsum or chopped alfalfa.[38] The investigations also showed that, when the trees reduced the soil-moisture content to approximately the wilting range, the infiltration rates were increased even more than by the gypsum and alfalfa applications.

Inasmuch as the coefficient of viscosity of water decreases rapidly with increasing temperature, infiltration rates during irrigation may be affected by temperature conditions. Increases in water temperature from the coolest spring irrigation to the warmest summer irrigation probably seldom amount to as much as 36 degrees F. However, an increase from 50 to 86 degrees causes a decrease in the coefficient of viscosity from about 1.308 to 0.801, a decrease of about 39 per cent. The coefficient of viscosity of water is the tangential force necessary to move a unit area of a plane surface at unit speed relative to another parallel plane surface from which it is separated by a layer of water of unit thickness.

Rates of infiltration resulting from precipitation during different seasons of the year probably are also affected by temperature conditions. Tests conducted during summer and winter rainfalls of similar intensities and duration have shown greater quantities of infiltration during the summer rainfalls. Probably some parts of the differences in infiltration were due to differences in temperature and accompanying differences in viscosity.

Rates of infiltration during rainfalls, also during the melting of accumulated snowfalls, are affected by frost conditions in the ground. If a soil becomes frozen to an appreciable depth while wet, it may be so impervious that rates of infiltration are practically zero. If a soil becomes frozen while relatively dry, it may be even more permeable than when free from frost, so that increased rates of infiltration are possible. Soils containing small percentages of moisture, mostly held in the structural aggregates, may become fluffy and more porous when frozen.

Percolation. Percolation of moisture in soils takes place principally through openings between soil structures, through such passageways as may result from earthworm excavations, decaying plant roots, or other causes, and through noncapillary pore spaces in the soil. The moisture movements are caused primarily by gravity forces but are aided by hydrostatic pressures when water is present on the ground surfaces. Some percolation may take place through capillary pore spaces, especially when hydrostatic pressures are aiding the moisture movements.

Percolation is often defined as the movement of moisture through saturated soils due to gravity, hydrostatic pressures, or both. However, in considerations of moisture movements following irrigation, it is desirable to include also the downward movement of water caused by gravity as the moisture content of the wetted zone is drained from saturated conditions to field capacity.

Downward movements of moisture by percolation occur most rapidly when the soil is saturated and covered with water. After irrigation or rainfall has continued long enough to fill the surface storage and saturate the upper part of the soil profile, the rate of percolation through the saturated soil is essentially the same as the rate of infiltration.

When the rainfall ceases, or the supply of irrigation water is discontinued, and the ground surface becomes drained, the rate of percolation decreases rapidly. Water moves downward from the saturated soil to depths where capillary moisture can be stored, or to depths where free subsoil drainage is available. Within a few days, the moisture content of coarse- or medium-textured soils is reduced from saturated conditions to field capacity. In fine-textured soils, percolation takes place slowly, even under saturated conditions, and continues for relatively long periods of time. In the heavy soils of the Oregon pear orchards, discussed in Chapter 4, percolation rates after the soil became wet were less than ½ inch in 24 hours.

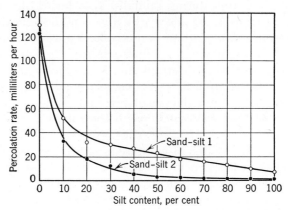

FIGURE 3. Rates of percolation through Yuma Mesa sand containing different percentages of Colorado River silt. (Plotted from data in reference 30.)

In some coarse-textured sandy soils, rates of percolation may be more rapid than are desirable. During the irrigation of such soils, objectionable amounts of water may percolate to depths beyond reach of the plant roots and may cause leaching of valuable mineral nutrients from the root zones as well as losses of irrigation water. Excessive rates of percolation through sandy soils can be reduced to more desirable values by irrigating the fields with silty water, provided the silt deposited on the field surfaces during irrigations can be thoroughly mixed with the sand before applying additional quantities of silty water.

Figure 3 shows reductions in percolation rates through Yuma Mesa sandy soils, resulting from the incorporation of different percentages of Colorado River silt. The two curves in the figure were plotted from laboratory data reported by McGeorge in 1941.[30] Both curves show that additions of only 10 to 20 per cent of silt caused considerable reductions in rates of percolation. The additions of silt also caused some reductions in rates of capillary-moisture movements.

Rates of percolation through a particular soil, like rates of infiltration, probably are affected by differences in water temperature, owing to the accompanying differences in viscosity. When other influences are the same, rates of percolation probably are higher during summer irrigations or summer rainfalls than during early spring irrigations or winter rainfalls. Rates of percolation during winter rainfalls are materially affected by frost conditions in the soil. In general, the factors that influence rates of percolation through soils are the same as those that influence rates of infiltration.

Percolation Tests. Table 4 shows percolation rates for some saturated soils of different texture, determined in laboratory tests reported

TABLE 4

PERCOLATION RATES FOR SATURATED SOILS OF DIFFERENT TEXTURE [49]

Soil	Depth, in.	Moisture equiva-lent, per cent	Volume weights		Percolation rate, in. per hr.	
			Tubes	Cores	Tubes	Cores
Manor clay loam	1–9	26.3	1.34	1.38	0.202	0.104
Manor clay loam	9–14	23.5	....	....	0.106	0.032
Leonardtown silty clay loam, A	1–9	22.9	1.38	1.40	0.057	0.069
Leonardtown silty clay loam, B_1	10–16	25.7	....	....	0.254	0.041
Leonardtown silty clay loam, B_2	18–24	21.5	....	....	0.108	0.025
Davidson clay	1–9	29.7	1.38	1.45	0.940	1.020
Davidson clay, subsoil	9–17	28.0	....	....	0.401	.....
Penn loam	1–9	20.1	1.42	1.45	0.238	0.247
Norfolk loamy sand	1–9	7.1	1.45	1.60	2.780	6.820
Iredell silt loam, A	1–9	19.4	1.50	1.60	0.062	0.030

by Slater and Byers.[49] The observations were made on undisturbed core specimens abstracted from field soils, also on tubes artificially packed with soil samples. Percolation rates determined by both methods are given in the last two columns of the table. Preceding columns give depths of samples, moisture equivalents, and volume weights. The Norfolk loamy sand was sparsely covered with bunch grass, weeds, and tree seedlings. The Manor clay loam samples were taken from an old pasture where the grass was thin and stunted. Locations where other samples were taken were all well sodded. Water depths of about 2 centimeters were maintained on the soil surfaces during the tests.

The data in Table 4 show the relatively large differences in percolation rates that may take place in soils of different texture. They also show how results obtained on artificially packed specimens may differ from results obtained on undisturbed field cores. Subsequent tests on Norfolk loamy sand showed that the unusually high rates of percolation measured on the cores were largely due to the presence of open passageways between the sand grains, free from silt and clay particles.

The rate of percolation through a saturated soil probably constitutes a fair indication of the amount of pore space that may be drained as the moisture content of the soil is reduced to field capacity. Laboratory tests reported by Bendixen and others showed a definite correlation between the rate of percolation and the amount of pore space drained under a water tension of 60 centimeters during 1 hour following saturation.[3] The relationship was nearly constant for soils of similar structure varying in texture from loamy sands to heavy clays but was shifted somewhat for soils of definitely different structure. The percolation rates produced by a tension of 60 centimeters were not much greater than those caused by normal gravity forces. On the basis of these tests, Bendixen and his associates proposed the permeability classification of soils briefly discussed in Chapter 2.

Percolation from Rainfall. Percolation from rainfall or snowfall on irrigated lands seldom is of sufficient magnitude to need consideration. However, percolation from precipitation on upstream drainage basins, where most water supplies for irrigation originate, may constitute an important hydrological factor.

In upstream drainage basins, large amounts of percolation during the late winter and early spring months usually are beneficial from the viewpoint of irrigation, inasmuch as they build up storage in the groundwater reservoir and thus tend to maintain streamflow during the summer months when water must be diverted to supply crop requirements. Proportions of the precipitation that percolate to the water table and can be stored underground tend to reduce the storage capacity that would be needed in costly above-ground reservoirs if the water reached the streams as surface runoff.

Table 5 shows monthly depths of percolation through two grass-covered, silt loam soils at the Soil Conservation Research Station, Coshocton, Ohio, as determined by weighing lysimeters. Depths of monthly water input are also shown in the table. Water input included direct condensation and absorption from the atmosphere as well as precipitation. Records are given for 1943 and 1944 at lysimeter Y 103, and for 1944 at lysimeter Y 102. The subsoil at Y 102 was more pervious and well drained than at Y 103. The data were reported by Harrold and Dreibelbis in 1945.[18]

TABLE 5

MONTHLY PERCOLATION THROUGH SOILS AT COSHOCTON, OHIO,
DETERMINED BY WEIGHING LYSIMETERS [18]

(Depths in inches)

Month	Lysimeter Y 103 1943		Lysimeter Y 103 1944		Lysimeter Y 102 1944	
	Water input *	Percola-tion	Water input	Percola-tion	Water input	Percola-tion
January	3.12	1.18	1.88	0.04	2.23	0.00
February	2.36	1.21	3.02	0.25	2.63	0.01
March	5.16	2.32	6.72	2.92	7.37	3.46
April	3.42	0.66	4.32	1.67	4.62	3.22
May	7.14	1.91	2.57	0.07	2.60	0.50
June	2.62	0.53	3.32	0.04	3.92	0.10
July	4.15	0.05	2.53	0.02	2.92	0.02
August	3.73	0.06	4.46	0.02	4.91	0.00
September	0.89	0.02	2.04	0.01	2.50	0.00
October	2.24	0.02	2.26	0.01	2.66	0.00
November	2.09	0.01	1.64	0.00	2.29	0.00
December	1.72	0.00	6.10	0.00	5.99	0.02
Yearly total	38.64	7.97	40.86	5.05	44.64	7.33

* Precipitation plus direct condensation and absorption from the atmosphere.

The Coshocton lysimeters consisted of vertical concrete side walls, with perforated steel plates at the bottoms to permit collection and measurement of percolation. They were 14 feet long, 6.22 feet wide, and 8 feet deep, and were installed without disturbing the soil blocks. Steel strips, projecting from the concrete walls into the soil blocks, were installed at different depths, to prevent the development of seepage planes along the inside faces. Details of the design and construction features were described by Garstka in 1937.[16]

Although the Coshocton investigations were made in a humid region, the results illustrate the portions of the precipitation that may percolate through the root zones in upstream drainage basins during different seasons of the year. In 1943, nearly all the percolation took place during January to May. About ½ inch percolated through the 8-foot depth during June, and only negligible amounts during the remainder of the year. In 1944, nearly all the percolation took place during March and April. Total depths of percolation at lysimeter Y 103 amounted to about 21 per cent of the water input during 1943, and to about 12 per cent of the input during 1944. The total depth of percolation at lysimeter Y 102 amounted to about 16 per cent of the water input during 1944.

Determinations of water input resulting from direct condensation and absorption of moisture from the atmosphere during the Coshocton tests were somewhat uncertain at times during the winter, owing to drifting snow. However, total yearly amounts for the observations reported appear to have been about 10 to 14 per cent of the total input. During May to August, monthly accretions from such sources did not exceed $\frac{1}{5}$ inch.

Percolation in Saturated Zones. Percolation in saturated zones below the water table takes place when the zones are under varying hydrostatic pressures or when the slopes of the water tables are great enough to cause movements of water through the pore passages in the earth formations. The water that fills the pores in earth materials below the water table is commonly known as groundwater.

Movements of groundwater have been studied for many years. Conditions of flow through capillary tubes and filter sands were studied by Hagen, Poiseuille, and Darcy about the middle of the nineteenth century. Relations of permeability to the porosity and mechanical composition of earth materials, together with other phases of groundwater problems, were studied by Hazen, King, and Slichter about the end of the nineteenth century. More recently, detailed investigations of groundwater have been carried on by various organizations engaged in hydrological work, particularly the Ground Water Division of the Water Resources Branch, United States Geological Survey.

The Geological Survey has published many water-supply papers on groundwater in the United States. These papers have discussed tests of water-bearing materials, methods of determining permeability, methods of estimating groundwater supplies, field measurements of groundwater, technical analyses of groundwater movements, and other aspects of groundwater problems. The outline of groundwater hydrology prepared by Meinzer [33] and the report on methods of determining permeability prepared by Wenzel [61] are especially pertinent in irrigation hydrology. Wenzel's report includes a lengthy bibliography on permeability and laminar flow prepared by Fishel.

Percolation of water through permeable materials in the zone of saturation takes place so slowly that the flow is free from eddies and therefore is laminar. Eddies sufficient to cause turbulent conditions of flow may sometimes occur in subsurface formations of large cobbles, boulders, or rock fragments, or through large subterranean passageways. Movements of water through large underground channels are usually called cavern flow. However, groundwater movements involved in irrigation work are principally those that take place as laminar flow.

Velocities of percolation through a particular permeable material vary directly with differences in hydrostatic pressure or differences in the slopes of the water table, that is, in accordance with Darcy's law. Amounts of flow through permeable materials are usually calculated by the formula

$$Q = ASK$$

where Q is the quantity of water moved through the cross section of permeable material per unit time, A is the area of the cross section, S is the hydraulic slope, and K is a constant depending on the particular characteristics of the permeable material.

Rates of percolation through saturated zones below the water table are usually slow. They may vary from a few feet per year through sandstone formations to 50 or 60 feet per day through sand and gravel strata where hydraulic gradients amount to 10 or 15 feet per mile. Higher rates have been measured in some formations. Relatively high rates of percolation are essential when water supplies for irrigation are to be obtained by pumping.

Analyses of percolation in zones of saturation may sometimes be desirable in considerations of water supply, drainage, return flow, seepage from canals, and other phases of irrigation work. Percolation analyses are especially pertinent in studying the quantities of groundwater that may be pumped from wells to supply water for irrigation. Percolation analyses may sometimes be needed in connection with the design of important structures that extend to considerable distances below the water tables.

Groundwater Flow Coefficients. The constant K in the above equation for groundwater flow through permeable materials is commonly called the coefficient of permeability. Different investigators have used different units in evaluating K, but all evaluations can be reduced to the same basis by applying proper conversion factors. Detailed data on conversion factors are given in Wenzel's report.[61]

The definition of the coefficient of permeability adopted by the Geological Survey, sometimes called Meinzer's definition, is the flow in gallons per day through a cross section of 1 square foot, caused by a hydraulic slope of 100 per cent when the temperature of the water is 60 degrees F.

Values of the coefficient of permeability for different materials may be obtained from permeameter tests in a laboratory or from data measured in the field. Field determinations of permeability usually are more reliable than laboratory determinations, inasmuch as some conditions that affect percolation in the field are difficult to duplicate in laboratory specimens. Field determinations may be made by measuring percolation rates with dyes, chemicals, or electrolytes, or by observing the drawdown of the water table in the vicinity of wells while pumping different quantities of water.

Laboratory tests of more than 2,000 materials, made by the Geological Survey in connection with groundwater investigations, have shown coefficients of permeability varying from less than 1 for fine silt and clay soils to about 90,000 for coarse gravel formations containing negligible proportions of fine soil particles. Methods of conducting laboratory tests and details of permeameter equipment have been described by Mrs. Stearns.[54]

Other coefficients that are sometimes used in considerations of groundwater flow include the field coefficient of permeability and the coefficient of transmissibility. The field coefficient of permeability is defined as the flow in gallons per day, under prevailing conditions, through a section of permeable material 1 foot deep and 1 mile wide, for each foot per mile of hydraulic gradient.

The coefficient of transmissibility, proposed by Theis in 1935, is the field coefficient of permeability multiplied by the thickness in feet of the formation through which the water percolates.[56] Thus, the coefficient of transmissibility varies with the thickness of the saturated aquifer. It represents the percolation capacity of the water-bearing formation, whereas the coefficient of permeability represents the permeability characteristics of the material.

Some engineers engaged on groundwater problems or on the design of filtration works have proposed formulas for computing permeabilities, velocities of percolation, or losses of head for flow through saturated sands. The formulas usually include factors representing the viscosity or temperature of the water and the porosity, mechanical analysis, or effective sizes of the permeable materials. Although such formulas may give reasonably reliable information for sands similar to those for which they were developed, they seldom prove satisfactory when applied to other formations.

Movements of Capillary Moisture. Movements of capillary moisture from wet soils to dry soils, often referred to as capillary movements, take place in accordance with capillary tensions. The movements take place principally through capillary pore spaces and through minute passageways between the smaller soil particles. They depend largely on soil texture but may be affected by the presence of organic matter, colloidal contents, composition of colloidal material, kinds of soluble salts in the soil, temperature, and other conditions.

Downward movements of capillary moisture are materially aided by gravity forces. Owing to gravity influences, movements of capillary moisture in a downward direction take place more rapidly and extend to greater distances than movements in an upward direction. Movements of moisture in horizontal and inclined directions take place at intermediate rates. When soil with a high moisture content is in contact with a dry soil, capillary movements take place rapidly at first, then decrease rapidly as the moisture becomes distributed and as the distances from the wet soil to the dry soil become greater. Increased percentages of moisture in the wet soil cause increased rates of capillary movements toward the dry soil.

Changes in soil temperature probably affect movements of capillary moisture only in so far as they cause freezing or thawing of the moisture contents, or in so far as they influence condensation or evaporation at the soil surfaces. Theoretically, variations in temperature cause variations in surface tension and therefore should cause variations in capillary movements. However, variations in surface tension through the usual range of temperatures are practically negligible. A rise in temperature from 32 to 86 degrees F. reduces the surface tension of water from 75.6 to 71.1 dynes per centimeter, a reduction of only about 6 per cent.

During furrow irrigations, capillary movements transfer moisture laterally through the dry soil between furrows as well as downward beneath the furrows. As the surface soil dries following an irrigation, they move moisture upward to replace the evaporated moisture and continue the evaporation. After the moisture content of the wetted zone is reduced to field capacity and percolation is practically completed, capillary movements continue the downward transference of moisture and thus increase the depths of penetration. As plant roots absorb moisture from the soil, capillary movements bring additional supplies from other parts of the wetted zone.

In irrigating lands where the water table is relatively deep, capillary movements of soil moisture are most important during the period just after irrigation. Later, as moisture becomes depleted by surface evaporation and plant transpiration, and after cultivation loosens the topsoil, capillary movements become too small to be effective. After cultivation, or after the surface soil dries to depths of 8 or 10 inches, very little moisture moves upward to maintain evaporation. When the moisture content of the root zone becomes reduced somewhat below field capacity, capillary movements become too small to supply the moisture required for plant growth. In order to maintain continuous growth, plants must extend their roots toward moist soil as adjacent moisture supplies become depleted and as capillary movements become too small to bring sufficient supplies to the roots.

The methods by which plants obtain moisture from the soil have been debated at length. Some scientists claim that plant roots always move to the moisture. Others claim that capillary movements bring moisture to the roots. Considerations of available data, including tests of capillary movements of moisture through soils, indicate that both methods are utilized to some extent and that both processes probably are going on at the same time, especially when the moisture contents of the root zones are at about field capacity. Both processes decrease in magnitude and become negligible as moisture contents approach the wilting coefficient. Opinions of different workers in the fields of soil moisture and plant growth were reviewed by Lewis in 1937.[26]

Capillary movements of soil moisture are especially important when the water table is relatively close to the ground surface. In natural subirrigation, where plant roots extend into the capillary fringe, upward capillary movements of moisture from the water table supply the moisture needed for plant growth. They also raise moisture from the water table to maintain evaporation at the soil surface.

Tests of Capillary Movements. Table 6 shows some test data on upward and downward movements of capillary moisture from wet soils of different initial moisture contents to adjoining dry soils of the same texture, as reported by McLaughlin.[31] Two soils are represented in the table, a heavy soil from Riverside, California, and a lava ash soil from central Idaho. The moisture equivalent was 14.1 per cent for the Riverside soil, and 18.3 per cent for the Idaho soil.

Upward movements of capillary moisture from the wet Riverside soil, for an initial moisture content of 20 per cent, reached 1.12 inches in one day, 3.00 inches in 3 days, 5.00 inches in 8 days, and 8.37 inches in 23 days. Downward movements were about 4 times as great during the first day, $2\frac{1}{2}$ times as great during the first 3 days, and a little

TABLE 6

MOVEMENTS OF CAPILLARY MOISTURE FROM WET TO DRY SOILS [31]

(Distances in inches)

Days from start of test	Riverside soil				Idaho lava ash soil			
	Upward movements		Downward movements		Upward movements		Downward movements	
	20 per cent *	10 per cent *	20 per cent	15 per cent	25 per cent	14 per cent	25 per cent	14 per cent
1	1.12	....	4.50	4.00	....	....	3.00	0.75
2	2.25	....	.....	5.75	1.00	....	5.25	....
3	3.00	1.25	7.50	6.37	....	1.25	.....	....
4	3.37	....	.....	7.00	....	....	.....	....
5	4.00	....	.....	.....	....	....	.....	1.75
6	4.50	....	.....	.....	....	1.83	.....	....
7	4.82	2.00	.....	.....	....	....	9.00	....
8	5.00	....	11.75	8.50	....	....	.....	....
9	5.37	....	.....	.....	4.50	....	.....	4.00
11	....	2.25	.....	.....	....	....	.....	....
12	....	....	.....	.....	....	2.75	.....	....
13	....	....	14.00	9.50	....	....	12.00	....
14	7.00	....	.....	.....	6.50	....	.....	....
16	....	....	15.75	10.75	....	....	.....	4.50
22	....	....	17.25	11.25	....	....	15.25	....
23	8.37	4.37	.....	.....	7.75	3.25	.....	....

* Initial moisture content of wet soil.

more than twice as great during 23 days. Somewhat similar movements of capillary moisture were shown by the observations on the lava ash soil.

In general, the data in Table 6 show that movements of capillary moisture from wet soils to dry soils take place at fairly rapid rates during the first 2 or 3 days, then gradually decrease as the moisture becomes distributed through increasing distances.

Figure 4 shows the moisture gradients that maintained certain rates of upward capillary flow through soil cores of different textures, as reported by Lewis in 1937.[26] Rates of flow and types of soil are shown in the lower right-hand portion of the figure. Figure 5 shows

similar data for tests in which the moisture moved downward instead of upward. Rates of flow maintained in the tests of downward
movements were somewhat higher than those maintained in the tests
of upward movements. Rates of flow are given in milligrams per
square centimeter per hour.

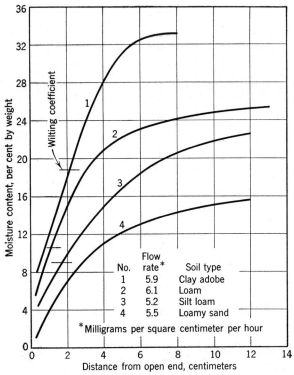

FIGURE 4.   Moisture gradients producing upward capillary flow through different
soils. (After Lewis.)

Soils used in determining curves 1 and 2 of Figure 5 were not the
same as those used in determining curves 1 and 2 of Figure 4. Field
capacities were practically the same, but wilting coefficients were
slightly different. Wilting coefficients are shown on the diagrams.
Field capacities of the soils for curves 1, 2, and 3 of both figures were
34, 27, and 24 per cent, respectively.

In conducting the tests illustrated by Figures 4 and 5, water was
added to the cores at one end, at predetermined rates, and moisture
that moved through the cores was evaporated by a current of air of
constant temperature and humidity maintained at the other end.

When rates of moisture evaporation became equal to rates of water supply, the cores were removed from their tube encasements and moisture contents determined at different sections along their lengths.

In the curves of Figures 4 and 5, the moisture-content gradient at any point is the slope of the curve at that point. All curves show

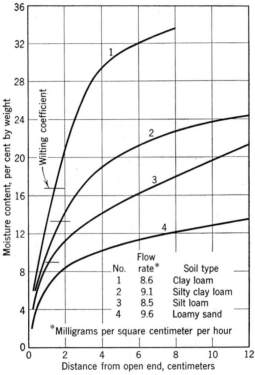

FIGURE 5. Moisture gradients producing downward capillary flow through different soils. (After Lewis.)

that for steady capillary flow of soil moisture the gradient increases as the moisture content at the source of supply decreases. Thus, when soils are wetted to field capacity, relatively low gradients are able to bring moisture to the plant roots. When the roots reduce the moisture contents at their particular locations, steeper moisture gradients are developed, so that capillary movements may continue to bring moisture to the roots. As moisture contents are reduced at increasing distances from the roots, moisture gradients decrease, movements of capillary moisture decrease, and plants can obtain adequate supplies of moisture only in so far as they are able to extend their roots into zones where moisture is available.

The investigations by Lewis, only briefly discussed above, showed that effects of soil texture on movements of soil moisture produced by capillary tensions are less pronounced than on movements of soil moisture produced by gravity, as in saturated soils. For moisture contents between about field capacity and the wilting point, different soil types were able to move 1 inch of water through 1 to 4 inches of soil in from 8 to 20 days.

Capillary Movements from Groundwater. Capillary movements of moisture from groundwater may raise appreciable quantities of water for plant use when the plant roots extend into the capillary fringe. Capillary movements may also raise appreciable quantities of water to maintain evaporation at soil surfaces when the water table is less than about 4 feet deep, the quantities raised increasing as the depth of the water table decreases.

Table 7 shows quantities of capillary moisture raised from free water surfaces into air-dry soils of different texture during some ex-

TABLE 7

QUANTITIES OF SOIL MOISTURE RAISED FROM FREE WATER
SURFACES BY CAPILLARY ACTION [31]

(Equivalent depths in inches on soil surfaces)

Days	Sandy soil (1)	Gravelly soil (2)	Decomposed granite (3)	Riverside heavy soil (4)	Lava ash soil (5)	Heavy clay soil (6)
1	2.59	2.44	5.49	4.27	4.88	4.88
2	2.74	3.05	6.10	6.10	6.71	6.10
3	2.82	4.27	6.71	6.45	8.54	6.71
4	2.89	4.47	6.86	6.71	9.72	7.32
10	....	5.49	7.78	7.42	12.81	9.00
15	....	5.86	8.24	8.08	14.34	10.62
20	....	6.24	8.62	8.54	14.95	11.35
30	3.36	7.17	9.06	9.36	16.17	12.21
40	....	7.48	9.31	9.70	17.39	12.57
50	3.86	....	....	10.00	18.37	13.06
60	....	....	....	.....	.....	13.42
M.E.*	4.7	6.6	7.9	14.1	18.3	38.3
Height †	23	35	42	31	55	24

* Moisture equivalent.
† Inches moisture was raised in 30 days.

perimental investigations reported by McLaughlin.[31] Quantities of moisture raised are given for different periods of from 1 to 60 days and are expressed in equivalent inches of water over the soil surfaces. Moisture equivalents of the different soils, also the heights moisture was raised in 30 days, are given at the bottom of the tabulation. The tests were made in wooden boxes, lined with galvanized iron, 10 by 10 inches in cross section and from 4 to 8 feet long. Plate-glass panels were provided in one side of the boxes, so that the advance of soil moisture could be observed.

All soils represented in Table 7 raised moisture rapidly during the first 2 or 3 days, especially during the first day, then at gradually decreasing rates as long as the measurements were continued. The lava ash soil from central Idaho, which raised moisture 55 inches in 30 days, produced the most effective capillary action. At the end of 30 days, quantities of moisture raised varied from 3.36 inches for the sandy soil to 16.17 inches for the lava ash soil.

Subsequent tests by McLaughlin, in which moisture contents of small columns were determined at different heights above free water surfaces, showed that moisture percentages did not diminish gradually with increasing height above the water.[32] Instead, the moisture was found to be distributed somewhat irregularly throughout the heights of the moistened columns. The maximum moisture content usually occurred a few inches above the water, rather than just above. The height of the maximum moisture content varied from about one-seventh to one-fourth of the height of moistened soil. However, all tests showed heights of several inches above the water in which moisture contents were almost uniform.

Discussions of amounts of capillary moisture that may be raised from groundwater storage to supply surface evaporation and plant transpiration are presented in a later chapter on land evaporation and transpiration.

Vapor Movements of Soil Moisture. Some moisture may be moved through the soil in the vapor stage when local changes in soil temperature or soil-moisture contents cause appreciable differences in vapor pressure. Such movements transfer moisture from zones of high vapor pressure to zones of low vapor pressure. They constitute the only type of moisture movements in soils when moisture contents are lower than the hygroscopic coefficient. They may, under certain conditions, account for some transference of capillary moisture from place to place when the moisture contents are higher than the hygroscopic coefficient.

Measurements at Odessa, Russia, reported by Lebedeff in 1927, indicated an upward transference of 2.60 inches of soil water by vapor movements during a 4-month period in the winter of 1914–1915.[25] Similar upward movements of soil moisture in the vapor stage, totaling about the same depth, were reported at Rostov for the winter of 1922–1923. The movements were believed to be due to differences in vapor pressure resulting from differences in soil temperature.

Laboratory tests of soil cores reported by Lewis in 1937 showed that soil moisture in the vapor stage moved across breaks in the cores when differences in moisture contents on the opposite sides of the breaks varied from about 12 to 17 per cent.[26]   From 8.5 to 12 milligrams of moisture per hour were moved across open spaces about 1 millimeter wide. These rates were equivalent to about 0.69 to 0.97 inch of moisture transference per month.   If upward movements of soil moisture in the vapor stage continued through the winter months at such rates, they would represent total depths of moisture transference somewhat greater than those reported in Russia.

Vapor movements of soil moisture are interesting from the scientific viewpoint. They may have some significance in hydrological studies of drainage basins where water supplies for irrigation projects originate. However, they probably do not exert appreciable influences on moisture conditions in the soils actually utilized in irrigation agriculture.

Movements following Irrigation.   In soils of uniform texture and adequate permeability, where the water table is several feet below the plant roots, movements of moisture during and following irrigations distribute water through zones of different depth, depending on the quantities of water applied and the field capacities of the soils.

When a field is flooded during irrigation, water first fills the available storage on the field surface, infiltrates into the surface soil, and produces saturated conditions in the upper soil layers.   As irrigation water is maintained on the field, water continues to infiltrate into the soil and produces downward percolation through the saturated soil, increasing the depth of saturation and increasing the moisture content of the soil below the saturated layers.   These movements continue until the supply of irrigation water is shut off.

When irrigation is discontinued, water on the field surface soon infiltrates into the soil or drains away as surface runoff, but percolation continues for some time.   Percolation continues to move moisture downward from the saturated soil and from the underlying soil where the moisture content is higher than field capacity, gradually extending the depth of penetration.   This continues until the moisture contents of the soil become approximately uniform and equal to field capacity throughout the entire depth of the wetted zone.

The downward distribution of moisture during irrigation by flooding, although aided by capillarity, is accomplished primarily by percolation. When water is supplied through corrugations or furrows, as in the production of row crops, the lateral distribution of moisture through the soil between corrugations or furrows is accomplished largely by capillary movements. Soil samples taken at different depths a few days after irrigation, or trenches excavated after furrow irri-

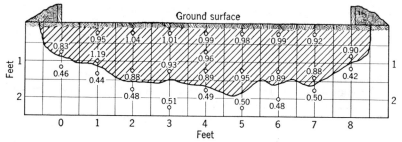

FIGURE 6. Distribution of moisture in clay loam four days after a 4-inch irrigation. (After Veihmeyer.)

gations, usually show that zones of penetration are uniformly wetted to field capacity and that the limits of the zones are sharply defined.

Gravity and capillary movements of moisture following the application of only a few inches of water to field surfaces do not wet the soil to uniform moisture contents less than field capacity. They simply wet shallow depths to field capacity. If the zones wetted are not deep enough to surround the principal mass of moisture-absorbing roots, greater quantities of water must be supplied during irrigations. Otherwise the plant roots will tend to congregate in the shallow depths where moisture supplies are available and consequently will not be able to utilize the mineral nutrients that can be secured at greater depths. When depths of moisture penetration resulting from large applications of irrigation water are greater than the depths of the root zones, deep percolation losses occur.

Figure 6 shows the distribution of moisture in a clay loam four days after a shallow irrigation, as reported by Veihmeyer.[59] A water depth of 4 inches, applied in a basin 8 feet wide, wetted the soil to a maximum depth of about 1.9 feet. The limits of the wetted zone are indicated by the irregular line. Quantities of moisture in the soil are expressed as ratios of moisture contents to field capacity and are shown as numbers on the cross section. Within the wetted zone, the ratios vary from 0.83 to 1.19. Just outside the irregular line, the ratios vary from 0.42 to 0.51.

REFERENCES

1. Alway, F. J., and Guy R. McDole, "Relation of the Water-Retaining Capacity of a Soil to Its Hygroscopic Coefficient," *Jour. Agr. Res.,* Apr. 9, 1917, pp. 27–71.
2. Baver, L. D., "Retention and Movement of Soil Moisture," Chapter IX–B in Meinzer's *Hydrology,* 1942, pp. 364–384 (see reference 23 in Chapter 1).
3. Bendixen, T. W., M. F. Hershberger, and C. S. Slater, "A Basis for Classifying Soil Permeabilities," *Jour. Agr. Res.,* Sept. 1, 1948, pp. 157–168.
4. Beutner, Edward L., Ralph R. Gaebe, and Robert E. Horton, "Sprinkled-Plat Runoff and Infiltration-Experiments on Arizona Desert-Soils," *Trans. Am. Geop. Union,* 1940, Part II, pp. 550–558.
5. Borst, Harold L., and Russell Woodburn, "Effect of Mulches and Surface Conditions on the Water Relations and Erosion of Muskingum Soils," *U.S. Dept. Agr. Tech. Bull.* 825, 1942.
6. Bouyoucos, G. J., "Effect of Temperature on Movement of Water Vapor and Capillary Moisture in Soils," *Jour. Agr. Res.,* Oct. 25, 1915, pp. 141–172.
7. Browning, G. M., and others, "Investigation in Erosion Control and the Reclamation of Eroded Land at the Missouri Valley Loess Conservation Experiment Station, Clarinda, Iowa, 1931–42," *U.S. Dept. Agr. Tech. Bull.* 959, 1948.
8. Buckingham, Edward, "Studies on the Movement of Soil Moisture," *U.S. Dept. Agr. Bull.* 38, 1907.
9. Cameron, Frank K., and F. E. Gallagher, "Moisture Content and Physical Condition of Soils," *U.S. Dept. Agr. Bull.* 50, 1908.
10. Darcy, Henri, *Les fontaines publique de la ville de Dijon* (The Water Supply of Dijon), Paris, France, 1856.
11. Davidson, J. M., "Infiltration of Water Into the Soil," *Soil Conservation Bibliography No. 3,* U.S. Dept. Agr., 1940 (mimeographed).
12. Duley, F. L., and L. L. Kelley, "Effect of Soil Type, Slope, and Surface Conditions on Intake of Water," *Nebr. Agr. Exp. Sta. Res. Bull.* 112, 1939.
13. —— "Surface Condition of Soil and Time of Application as Related to Intake of Water," *U.S. Dept. Agr. Cir.* 608, 1941.
14. Fletcher, Joel E., "Some Properties of Water Solutions That Influence Infiltration," *Trans. Am. Geop. Union,* August 1949, pp. 548–554.
15. Free, G. R., G. M. Browning, and G. W. Musgrave, "Relative Infiltration and Related Physical Characteristics of Certain Soils," *U.S. Dept. Agr. Tech. Bull.* 729, 1940.
16. Garstka, W. U., "Design of the Automatic Recording In-Place Lysimeters near Coshocton, Ohio," *Proc. Soil Sci. Soc. Am.,* Vol. 2, 1937, pp. 555–559.
17. Harris, F. S., and H. W. Turpin, "Movement and Distribution of Moisture in the Soil," *Jour. Agr. Res.,* July 16, 1917, pp. 113–155.
18. Harrold, L. L., and F. R. Dreibelbis, "An Accounting of the Daily Accretion, Depletion, and Storage of Soil-Water as Determined by Weighing Monolith Lysimeters," *Trans. Am. Geop. Union,* October 1945, pp. 283–292.

19. Horton, R. E., "The Role of Infiltration in the Hydrologic Cycle," *Trans. Am. Geop. Union,* 1933, pp. 446–460.

20. ——— "Determination of Infiltration-Capacity for Large Drainage-Basins," *Trans. Am. Geop. Union,* 1937, Part II, pp. 371–385.

21. ——— "Analysis of Runoff-Plat Experiments with Varying Infiltration-Capacity," *Trans. Am. Geop. Union,* 1939, Part IV, pp. 693–711.

22. Houk, Ivan E., "Rainfall and Runoff in the Miami Valley," *Miami Conservancy Dist. Tech. Rep.,* Part VIII, Dayton, Ohio, 1921.

23. Huberty, Martin R., and Arthur F. Pillsbury, "Factors Influencing Infiltration-Rates Into Some California Soils," *Trans. Am. Geop. Union,* 1941, Part III, pp. 686–694.

24. Kohnke, Helmut, F. R. Dreibelbis, and J. M. Davidson, "A Survey and Discussion of Lysimeters and a Bibliography on Their Construction and Performance," *U.S. Dept. Agr. Misc. Pub.* 372, 1940.

25. Lebedeff, A. F., "The Movement of Ground and Soil Waters," *Proc. First Intern. Cong. Soil Sci.,* Vol. I, 1927, pp. 459–494.

26. Lewis, M. R., "Rate of Flow of Capillary Moisture," *U.S. Dept. Agr. Tech. Bull.* 579, 1937.

27. ——— "The Rate of Infiltration of Water in Irrigation-Practice," *Trans. Am. Geop. Union,* 1937, Part II, pp. 361–368.

28. Lowdermilk, W. C., "Water-Intake of Saturated Soils," *Trans. Am. Geop. Union,* 1937, Part II, pp. 355–361.

29. Mathews, O. R., "Water Penetration in the Gumbo Soils of the Belle Fourche Reclamation Project," *U.S. Dept. Agr. Bull.* 447, 1916.

30. McGeorge, W. T., "Influence of Colorado River Silt on Some Properties of Yuma Mesa Sandy Soil," *Ariz. Agr. Exp. Sta. Tech. Bull.* 91, 1941.

31. McLaughlin, Walter W., "Capillary Movement of Soil Moisture," *U.S. Dept. Agr. Bull.* 835, 1920.

32. ——— "The Capillary Distribution of Moisture in Soil Columns of Small Cross Section," *U.S. Dept. Agr. Bull.* 1221, 1924.

33. Meinzer, Oscar E., "Outline of Ground-Water Hydrology with Definitions," *U.S. Geol. Sur. Water-Supply Paper* 494, 1923.

34. Meinzer, Oscar E., and Leland K. Wenzel, "Movement of Ground Water and Its Relation to Head, Permeability, and Storage," Chapter X–B in Meinzer's *Hydrology,* 1942, pp. 444–477 (see reference 23 in Chapter 1).

35. Musgrave, G. W., and others, "Report of Committee on Infiltration, 1945–46," *Trans. Am. Geop. Union,* October 1946, pp. 726–747; also preceding annual reports.

36. Musgrave, G. W., and R. A. Norton, "Soil and Water Conservation Investigations at the Soil Conservation Experiment Station, Missouri Valley Loess Region, Clarinda, Iowa, Progress Report 1931–35," *U.S. Dept. Agr. Tech. Bull.* 558, 1937.

37. Nelson, W. R., and L. D. Baver, "Movement of Water through Soils in Relation to the Nature of the Pores," *Procs. Soil Sci. Soc. Am.,* Vol. 5, 1940, pp. 69–76.

38. Reitemeier, R. F., and J. E. Christiansen, "The Effect of Organic Matter, Gypsum, and Drying on the Infiltration Rate and Permeability of a Soil Irrigated with a High Sodium Water," *Trans. Am. Geop. Union,* April 1946, pp. 181–186.

39. Reitemeier, R. F., and others, "Effect of Gypsum, Organic Matter, and Drying on Infiltration of a Sodium Water into a Fine Sandy Loam," *U.S. Dept. Agr. Tech. Bull.* 937, 1948.

40. Schiff, Leonard, and F. R. Dreibelbis, "Infiltration, Soil Moisture, and Land-Use Relationships with Reference to Surface Runoff," *Trans. Am. Geop. Union*, February 1949, pp. 75–88.

41. ——— "Movement of Water within the Soil and Surface Runoff with Reference to Land Use and Soil Properties," *Trans. Am. Geop. Union*, June 1949, pp. 401–411.

42. Scofield, Carl S., "The Movement of Water in Irrigated Soils," *Jour. Agr. Res.*, Mar. 1, 1924, pp. 617–694.

43. Sharp, A. L., and H. N. Holtan, "A Graphical Method of Analysis of Sprinkled-Plat Hydrographs," *Trans. Am. Geop. Union*, 1940, Part II, pp. 558–570.

44. Sherman, LeRoy K., "Derivation of Infiltration-Capacity (f) from Average Loss-Rates (f_{av})," *Trans. Am. Geop. Union*, 1940, Part II, pp. 541–550.

45. ——— "Infiltration and the Physics of Soil-Moisture," *Trans. Am. Geop. Union*, 1944, Part I, pp. 57–71.

46. Sherman, L. K., and L. C. Mayer, "Application of the Infiltration-Theory to Engineering Practice," *Trans. Am. Geop. Union*, 1941, Part III, pp. 666–677.

47. Sherman, L. K., and G. W. Musgrave, "Infiltration," Chapter VII in Meinzer's *Hydrology*, 1942, pp. 244–258 (see reference 23 in Chapter 1).

48. Slater, C. S., "The Flow of Water through Soils," *Agr. Eng.*, March 1948, pp. 119–124.

49. Slater, C. S., and H. G. Byers, "A Laboratory Study of the Field Percolation Rates of Soils," *U.S. Dept. Agr. Tech. Bull.* 232, 1931.

50. Slichter, Charles S., "Field Measurements of the Rate of Movement of Underground Waters," *U.S. Geol. Sur. Water-Supply Paper* 140, 1905.

51. Smith, R. M., D. R. Browning, and G. G. Pohlman, "Laboratory Percolation through Undisturbed Soil Samples in Relation to Pore-Size Distribution," *Soil Sci.*, Vol. 57, 1944, pp. 197–213.

52. Smith, W. O., "Thermal Transfer of Moisture in Soils," *Trans. Am. Geop. Union*, 1943, Part II, pp. 511–524.

53. ——— "Pedological Relations of Infiltration Phenomena," *Trans. Am. Geop. Union*, August 1949, pp. 555–562.

54. Stearns, Norah Dowell, "Laboratory Tests on Physical Properties of Water-Bearing Materials," *U.S. Geol. Sur. Water-Supply Paper* 596–F, 1927.

55. Taylor, C. A., "Water Penetration in Hardpan Citrus Soils," *Agr. Eng.*, June 1934, pp. 202–203.

56. Theis, Charles V., "The Relation between the Lowering of the Piezometric Surface and the Rate and Duration of Discharge of a Well Using Ground-Water Storage," *Trans. Am. Geop. Union*, 1935, Part II, pp. 519–524.

57. United States Department of Agriculture, "Influences of Vegetation and Watershed Treatment on Run-off, Silting, and Streamflow," *Misc. Pub.* 397, 1940.

58. Veihmeyer, F. J., "Report of the Committee on Physics of Soil-Moisture, 1937–38," *Trans. Am. Geop. Union*, 1938, Part I, pp. 326–342.

59. ——— "Evaporation from Soils and Transpiration," *Trans. Am. Geop. Union*, 1938, Part II, pp. 612–619.

60. Wenzel, Leland K., "The Thiem Method for Determining Permeability of

Water-Bearing Materials and Its Application to the Determination of Specific Yield," *U.S. Geol. Sur. Water-Supply Paper* 679–A, 1936.

61. Wenzel, Leland K., "Methods for Determining Permeability of Water-Bearing Materials with Special Reference to Discharging-Well Methods," *U.S. Geol. Sur. Water-Supply Paper* 887, 1942.

62. Wenzel, L. K., and A. L. Greenlee, "A Method for Determining Transmissibility and Storage Coefficients by Tests of Multiple Well Systems," *Trans. Am. Geop. Union*, 1943, Part II, pp. 547–564.

63. Werner, P. Wilh., "Notes on Flow-Time Effects in the Great Artesian Aquifers of the Earth," *Trans. Am. Geop. Union*, October 1946, pp. 687–708.

64. Widstoe, J. A., and W. W. McLaughlin, "The Movement of Water in Irrigated Soils," *Utah Agr. Exp. Sta. Bull.* 115, 1912.

65. Wilm, H. G., "Methods for the Measurement of Infiltration," *Trans. Am. Geop. Union*, 1941, Part III, pp. 678–686.

66. ––– "The Application and Measurement of Artificial Rainfall on Types FA and F Infiltrometers," *Trans. Am. Geop. Union*, 1943, Part II, pp. 480–487.

67. Woodward, Lowell, "Infiltration-Capacities of Some Plant-Soil Complexes on Utah Range Watershed-Lands," *Trans. Am. Geop. Union*, 1943, Part II, pp. 468–475.

Chapter 6

CLIMATIC FACTORS

The principal climatic factors involved in irrigation agriculture are precipitation and temperature. Crop growth on arable land requires moisture, heat, and light. In regions where irrigation is practiced, adequate amounts of light are commonly available wherever supplies of moisture and heat are sufficient for normal plant growth. Other weather phenomena, such as wind, relative humidity, evaporation, cloudiness, and fog affect soil-moisture conditions, available moisture supplies, choice of crops, crop yields, and even the quality of the crop products. However, precipitation and temperature are of primary importance.

Local conditions of precipitation determine the need for irrigation. Conditions of precipitation on upstream drainage areas influence streamflow and thus affect the possibility of securing water supplies during the irrigation season. Temperature conditions not only determine the feasibility of producing profitable crops on arable lands, if irrigated, but also exert important influences on hydrological processes in upstream watersheds.

The following sections present brief discussions of weather and climate, precipitation, temperature, and some additional climatic factors that affect irrigation. Some pertinent data are included for arid and semiarid regions in western United States. In general, such data have been abstracted from publications of the United States Weather Bureau. Because of space limitations, the various climatic factors cannot be treated in detail. A few publications that contain comprehensive treatments are listed at the end of the chapter. All statements regarding effects of climatic factors on irrigation agriculture assume satisfactory soil conditions.

WEATHER AND CLIMATE

Weather and climate deal with conditions of the earth's atmosphere. Weather denotes atmospheric conditions at a particular time or during a relatively short period of time. Climate refers to weather conditions during a comparatively long period of time. Climate includes departures from normal weather conditions, minimum and maximum data, and daily, monthly, seasonal, and annual variations during the entire period of record, as well as normal values. Climate applies particularly to elements of weather that affect animal and vegetable life.

Climatology is the branch of science that deals with climates, their causes, occurrences, characteristics, variations, and effects on life. Meteorology is the branch of science that deals with atmospheric phenomena and the basic laws that produce and control such phenomena. It is really a branch of physics and is sometimes referred to as physics of the atmosphere. Inasmuch as both climatology and meteorology deal with weather conditions, no definite line can be drawn between the two.

The term hydrometeorology has been proposed to designate the branch of science that deals with atmospheric moisture, precipitation, disposal of precipitation, and effects produced by precipitation. More recently, the term has been applied with particular reference to the meterorology and intensity of storms and the possible upper limits of storm rainfall.[3]

Elements of weather and climate include temperature, radiation, sunshine, wind, humidity, cloudiness, fog, precipitation, evaporation, and barometric pressure. Sometimes atmospheric electricity and the dust content of the air are important elements. Weather conditions depend primarily on atmospheric circulation. The development of areas of high and low barometric pressure and their movements across the country cause changes in weather. Low-pressure areas are often accompanied by widespread precipitation. The meeting of warm moist air with cold dry air along polar fronts constitutes a particularly significant cause of weather changes. Characteristics of atmospheric circulation and their effects on weather are too complex and variable to be discussed herein. Rossby has discussed them in considerable detail.[28]

In general, conditions that affect land climates are (1) latitude, (2) distances from large water surfaces, (3) proximity and direction of ocean currents, (4) elevations above sea level, (5) proximity and direction of high mountain ranges, (6) prevailing winds, and (7) location with respect to paths of major storm movements. Air temperatures and air movements over water and land areas are materially affected by the different heat properties of the two types of surfaces. Seasonal changes in climate occur because the axis of the earth's rotation is inclined at an angle of 66½ degrees with the plane of its path around the sun, so that the sun's rays enter the atmosphere at gradually changing inclinations throughout the year.

Climates of particular localities may be affected by major changes in surface conditions, whether produced by natural or artificial agencies. Draining of swamps, development of reclamation projects, deforestation, reforestation, or other general alterations in land use may cause changes in weather phenomena. In the Copper Basin of southeastern Tennessee, where vegetation was destroyed by fumes from smelter plants, measurements at meteorological stations showed that deforestation resulted in decreased rainfall, increased wind movements, increased annual evaporation, and increased ranges in soil temperature.[13]

Types of Climate. Climates have been classified on the basis of temperature, precipitation, humidity, prevailing winds, location with respect to oceans, topography, native vegetation, and various other conditions or combinations of conditions. Classifications according to location or topography may include such types as marine, coastal, continental, mountain, plain, or plateau. One classification on the basis of decreasing depths of precipitation includes superhumid, humid, subhumid, semiarid, and arid types.[5]

From the viewpoint of irrigation, a classification of climate on the basis of precipitation is logical. However, since irrigation is practiced principally in regions of low rainfall, one designation for moist climates is sufficient. Therefore, the climate of a region may be designated as humid, semiarid, or arid, as in one previous classification. Humid regions are those receiving more than 30 inches of precipitation annually; semiarid regions, those receiving from 15 to 30 inches; and arid regions, those receiving less than 15 inches.

The need for irrigation depends on the seasonal and monthly distribution of precipitation as well as on the total depth received annually. In general, irrigation is essential for crop production in arid regions, necessary to some extent in most semiarid regions, and not commonly required for usual types of farm crops in humid regions. For the production of valuable fruit and truck crops, irrigation often is desirable in humid regions, as well as in semiarid and arid regions, inasmuch as irrigation water can be applied to the crops when needed, without waiting for rainfall which is always more or less uncertain as to time of occurrence.

Weather Records. Some records of weather conditions in the United States were made prior to the beginning of the nineteenth century. Systematic weather observations were begun at the military posts in 1819 and continued under Army auspices until about 1890. The Smithsonian Institution collected weather data from about 1849 to 1874. Most early weather observations were confined to measurements of temperature and precipitation, with general notes on weather conditions.

In western United States, weather records were begun at Sacramento and San Francisco, California, in 1849; at El Paso, Texas, in 1850; at the New Mexico Agricultural College in 1851; and at Boise, Idaho, in 1864. Records were begun at Buford, North Dakota, in 1866, and at Tucson, Arizona, in 1867. Since about 1870, weather stations have been established in all parts of the West. Many long-time records are now available for use in irrigation studies.

In 1890, the Weather Bureau was organized as a branch of the Department of Agriculture and assigned the "taking of such meteorological observations as may be necessary to establish and record climatic conditions in the United States." Since its organization, the Bureau has established about 400 offices in key cities throughout the country. These offices, called first-order stations, maintain continuous records of weather phenomena. Some offices also maintain records of river stages. They issue forecasts of local weather and river conditions and conduct special investigations of meteorological and hydrological problems. Table 1 shows some first-order weather stations in western United States, where records have been maintained through comparatively long periods of years.

The Bureau also has established about 5,700 cooperative stations where temperatures, precipitation, and general weather conditions are observed and recorded daily. In 1940, the Bureau was transferred to the Department of Commerce, largely because of the increasing importance of meteorological data in connection with airline transportation. Many of the more recently established first-order stations are located at airports.

The more useful weather records for each state are published in monthly and annual issues of *Climatological Data*. Additional tabulations of weather data were formerly published in statistical sections of the annual reports of the Chief of the Weather Bureau. Since 1935, these additional tabulations have been published in the *United States Meteorological Yearbook*. Reports on meteorological studies and investigations are published in the *Monthly Weather Review* and

TABLE 1

SOME FIRST-ORDER WEATHER STATIONS IN WESTERN UNITED STATES

Station	Elevation	Years of record to 1945		Station	Elevation	Years of record to 1945	
		Temperature	Precipitation			Temperature	Precipitation
Arizona:				New Mexico:			
Flagstaff	6,907	54	54	Albuquerque *	5,314	44	75
Phoenix *	1,107	50	50	Raton	6,676	28	29
Tucson †	2,555	75	77	Roswell	3,566	52	68
Yuma	138	68	76	North Dakota:			
California:				Williston	1,878	67	67
Auburn	1,234	74	76	Oregon:			
Bakersfield	489	57	57	Baker	3,445	56	56
Fresno	277	58	64	Burns	4,143	34	34
Los Angeles ‡	312	68	69	Medford	1,314	35	35
Red Bluff	341	68	74	Pendleton	1,056	57	57
Sacramento	25	68	96	Portland *	30	75	75
San Diego	19	71	96	Roseburg	479	69	69
San Francisco *	52	75	96	Salem	195	54	54
Colorado:				South Dakota:			
Denver *	5,221	74	74	Rapid City	3,215	58	58
Grand Junction	4,668	55	56	Texas:			
Pueblo	4,808	53	67	El Paso	3,920	69	67
Idaho:				Utah:			
Boise *	2,858	79	79	Milford	4,962	36	38
Lewiston	738	44	44	Modena	5,460	45	45
Pocatello	4,446	45	45	Ogden	4,400	75	76
Montana:				Salt Lake City *	4,260	72	72
Billings	3,139	51	46	Washington:			
Butte	5,526	52	52	Ellensburg	1,727	53	55
Glasgow	2,086	50	50	La Crosse	1,546	38	55
Great Falls	3,657	55	55	Seattle ‡	14	55	68
Havre	2,488	66	66	Spokane	1,954	65	65
Helena *	3,893	66	66	Walla Walla	952	60	73
Kalispell	2,956	49	49	Yakima	1,068	37	37
Missoula	3,202	66	69	Wyoming:			
Nevada:				Casper	5,290	35	35
Elko	5,077	50	76	Cheyenne *	6,144	75	75
Las Vegas	2,033	36	41	Lander	5,351	53	53
Winnemucca	4,287	67	77	Sheridan	3,773	50	50

* Section center.
† Lengths of record at University Station.
‡ Regional office.

in special bulletins. Many comprehensive discussions of climate, also detailed tabulations of climatic data, are given in the 1941 *Yearbook* of the Department of Agriculture.

Weather records also are maintained by certain other federal agencies, state bureaus, municipalities, educational institutions, water districts, private corporations, and various organizations. However, such records usually are maintained in cooperation with the Weather Bureau, and the more important records usually are included in *Climatological Data*. Some state experiment stations have published special bulletins on the climates of their localities.[20]

Use of Weather Data. Data observed at weather stations are used in general studies of temperature and precipitation on irrigation projects, considerations of evaporation and transpiration during the growing season, evaluations of evaporation losses at lakes and reservoirs, analyses of hydrological conditions in upstream drainage basins, and other problems involved in planning, constructing, and operating irrigation projects as well as in maintaining profitable crop production on project lands.

In general, weather data observed at first-order stations can be used with confidence, usually without adjustments. First-order stations are supervised by experienced meteorologists, and the weather measurements are made by trained personnel. Changes in many weather elements are recorded continuously by automatic registering instruments, carefully installed and properly calibrated so as to maintain accurate records. Adjustments may be needed in some of the data, such as wind velocities, in order to obtain proper values for ground levels. First-order stations often have to be located in high office buildings, a hundred feet or more above street levels. Possible uncertainties in meteorological data due to obstructions, such as adjacent buildings, should also be considered.

Records at cooperative stations, which usually include only daily observations of temperature and precipitation, can be used without adjustment in most irrigation studies. In special studies of storm rainfall, some adjustments may be needed because of differences in times of measurement. Depths of precipitation published in the monthly issues of *Climatological Data* are for calendar days. In many cases, the rainfalls probably occurred in less than 24 hours. In some cases, rainfalls recorded on two consecutive days may have actually occurred in less than 24 hours.

Studies of excessive rates of rainfall during short periods of time must be based on data recorded at first-order stations. Times of beginning and ending of heavy rainfall are recorded at many cooperative stations, but such records usually are not suitable for careful studies of short-time precipitation. Data on excessive rainfalls of short duration are published in the meteorological yearbooks. Rates that are considered as lower limits of excessive rainfall in most states vary from 0.25 inch in 5 minutes to 2.00 inches in 3 hours. They are determined by the equation

$$A = t + 20$$

where A is the accumulated depth of rainfall in hundredths of an inch and t is the total time in minutes.

In some southern states, including Texas and Oklahoma, lower limits of excessive rainfall are determined by the equation

$$A = 2t + 30$$

Whether adjustments in published climatic data will be needed before proceeding with hydrological studies for irrigation projects depends on the particular nature and purpose of the studies. Procedures followed in conducting weather observations and compiling weather data should be carefully examined before beginning detailed analyses. Bulletins on measurements of climatic conditions have been published by the Weather Bureau.[38]

PRECIPITATION

Precipitation constitutes the basic source of all water used in crop production, whether it falls on farm lands where it replenishes soil moisture directly or on other areas from which it can subsequently be brought to the fields as irrigation water. When depths of precipitation on arable lands preceding and during the growing season are less than those needed for crop production, the deficiencies must be made up by irrigation. If depths of precipitation on upstream drainage areas exceed those required for evaporation, transpiration, and local uses, resulting accretions to streamflow may become available for irrigating downstream areas.

Studies of precipitation in connection with the development of an irrigation project should include a review of all records maintained at stations on and near the project lands and in the drainage areas from which water supplies may be obtained. The studies should include considerations of past experiences as recorded year by year, as well as considerations of average conditions for the entire period of record.

Data regarding average conditions of precipitation are valuable, especially when determined by a long series of continuous observations. They indicate in a general way the irrigation needs of the project lands and the possibility of securing water from upstream drainage basins. However, departures from average conditions are perhaps more valuable, particularly as regards years of subnormal precipitation and the number of subnormal years that may be experienced in succession. A series of consecutive years of low water supply may mean the failure of a project which would appear to be feasible when studied on the basis of average annual precipitation.

Precipitation studies should also include careful considerations of seasonal distribution. Arable lands that receive appreciable depths of rainfall during the growing season may need only relatively small quantities of irrigation water. During some years of more than normal precipitation, they may produce profitable crop yields without irrigation. Lands that receive spring rainfalls sufficient to fill the soil-moisture storage in the root zones may not require irrigation until the crop plants have attained considerable growth. Lands that receive only negligible depths of rainfall during the spring and summer months require the largest amounts of irrigation water. They must be supplied with the full depths needed for crop production.

From the viewpoint of streamflow that can be utilized in irrigation, heavy winter snowfalls on upstream drainage areas are particularly important. Most irrigated regions of western United States secure their water supplies from the late spring and early summer melting of winter snowfalls accumulated in the higher mountain basins. Low or negligible rainfall during the melting period is an advantage. Heavy spring rainfalls that accelerate snow runoff are a disadvantage when adequate surface reservoirs have not been constructed, because the water may pass down the stream channels before it can be diverted for irrigation use.

Forms of Precipitation. Precipitation results from the condensation of atmospheric water vapor. When particles of condensed moisture in the atmosphere above the surface of the earth become too heavy to be supported by the air, they fall toward the ground. If only limited condensation takes place, the small droplets of moisture may be reevaporated before reaching the earth's surface. If not reevaporated, they produce rain, snow, sleet, or hail, depending on conditions of air temperature and vertical air currents.

Rain occurs when air temperatures are above the freezing point. Snow occurs when condensation takes place at temperatures below the freezing point and air temperatures below the elevations of condensation are not high enough to melt the snowflakes before they reach the ground. Sleet occurs when raindrops pass through low-lying strata of cold air and freeze before they reach the ground. Hail occurs when raindrops are lifted repeatedly into air strata of freezing temperatures, by vertical air currents, until they finally become hailstones too heavy for further support. This type of frozen precipitation takes place almost exclusively during summer thunderstorms.

Rain, snow, sleet, and hail are the usual forms of precipitation. Although sleet and hail are familiar weather phenomena in many parts of the country, they seldom if ever make up appreciable portions of total annual precipitation. Depths of precipitation that replenish soil moisture in irrigated regions, or produce water supplies that become available for irrigation, are almost entirely rain and snow.

Conditions Causing Precipitation. Amounts of water vapor that can exist in the atmosphere decrease as air temperatures decrease. When temperatures reach the dew point, the point of saturation, condensation of moisture begins. Continued cooling results in continued condensation. Therefore, any condition of atmospheric circulation that causes continued cooling of moisture-laden air to the dew point causes continued condensation of moisture and produces precipitation.

The atmosphere obtains its load of water vapor by evaporation from water and moist soil surfaces and from transpiration by growing vegetation. Consequently, winds blowing from locations where such processes are in operation carry moisture supplies that may become available for precipitation. Air masses moving inland from ocean areas during the winter months, when the land is colder than the ocean, become cooled. If the cooling continues until temperatures reach the dew point, moisture condenses and precipitation takes place. Air masses moving inland from ocean areas during the summer months, when the land is warmer than the ocean, do not produce precipitation because their capacities for holding water vapor are increased by increasing air temperatures. However, such winds may produce precipitation if deflected up mountain slopes to elevations where sufficient cooling is attained.

When moisture-laden air moves up a mountain slope, it becomes cooled by expansion, moisture condenses, and precipitation occurs. This type of precipitation is called orographic. Orographic precipitation usually increases with elevation until altitudes are reached where the greater portions of the moisture loads have been precipitated.

During the summer months, air strata near ground surfaces become heated by the direct rays of the sun, rise to higher levels by convection, and become cooled by expansion. When the convectional currents continue long enough, moisture condenses, cumulo-nimbus clouds develop, rainfall begins, and a local thunderstorm is experienced. If the vertical currents become sufficiently pronounced, hailstones are formed and hail accompanies the rainfall. This type of precipitation may be called convective, convectional, or thermal convection.

The large areas of low barometric pressure that move across the United States in easterly directions, known as extratropical cyclones, are accompanied by spirally inblowing winds that often produce widespread and long-continued precipitation. This type of precipitation is called cyclonic. Continuous cyclonic rainfalls that often occur in the frontal zones of such barometric depressions are sometimes referred to as frontal precipitation.

Low-pressure areas may originate in the northwestern states or in adjoining sections of Canada, or they may enter the country from the west or northwest. They usually move in southeasterly, easterly, and northeasterly directions and pass out over the Atlantic Ocean in the general direction of the St. Lawrence Valley. Similar storms, known as West India hurricanes, may move inland through the South Atlantic or Gulf States, then progress in northwesterly, northerly, and northeasterly directions, passing out over the North Atlantic in the same general directions. Low-pressure areas that cause cyclonic precipitation may develop in other parts of the United States, but, unless soon dissipated, they usually move in easterly or northeasterly directions. Cyclones constitute important causes of precipitation along the North Pacific Coast and in the eastern states.

To summarize, causes of precipitation are classified as orographic, convectional, and cyclonic. In some locations, combinations of such causes may produce unusually heavy precipitation. For instance, heavy rainfalls in the Cascade Mountains of Washington and the Appalachian Mountains of the Carolinas may be produced by orographic and cyclonic precipitation.

Regional Precipitation. In general, the precipitation characteristics of a region depend on distances from sources of moisture supply, prevailing wind movements, altitude, locations with respect to paths of cyclonic storms, and locations with respect to high mountain ranges.

When several or all conditions are unfavorable for precipitation, arid or desert climates prevail. When several or all conditions are favorable, unusually heavy precipitation is experienced.

Depths of precipitation usually decrease with increasing distances from sources of moisture supply. In mountainous regions, areas of relatively high elevation commonly receive more precipitation than nearby areas of lower elevation. However, when moisture-laden winds approach the mountains in approximately normal directions, they deposit their moisture loads on the windward slopes and are comparatively dry as they move down the leeward slopes. Consequently, locations on the leeward slopes receive less precipitation than locations of equal elevation on the windward slopes.

The westward slopes of the Sierra Nevada and Cascade ranges in California, Oregon, and Washington receive heavier precipitation than the eastern slopes and the lands to the eastward, because the moisture supplies are depleted as the air moves up the westward slopes. Along the western slopes of the southern Sierras, precipitation increases with elevation up to altitudes of about 4,000 to 6,000 feet, then decreases with further increases in elevation.[19]

In the Pikes Peak region, Colorado, annual precipitation increases with altitude up to the summit of the peak, 14,110 feet. Other conditions also affect precipitation in mountainous regions. For western Colorado, Spreen found that only 30 per cent of the variations were due to altitude.[31]

The western slopes of the Cascades in Washington receive more precipitation than the western slopes of the Sierras in California because they are located more directly in the paths of cyclonic storms. Valley lands between these ranges and the Pacific Coast receive very little summer precipitation because the land is warmer than the ocean, so that air moving inland becomes warmer and does not precipitate its moisture. Therefore, these valleys have become known as regions of summer-dry climate. Except for the regions of summer-dry climate, the arid areas of western United States lie principally between the Sierra Nevada and Cascade ranges and the 102nd meridian.

Annual Precipitation. In the United States, depths of annual precipitation vary from about an inch in Death Valley, southeastern California, to more than 160 inches in the Pacific Northwest. Greenland Ranch, on the edge of Death Valley, has a mean annual rainfall of 1.58 inches. Glenora, Oregon, received 167.29 inches in 1896. Wynooche Oxbow, Washington, received an average of 150.73 inches a year during 13 years of measurements. Louisiana, the wettest state,

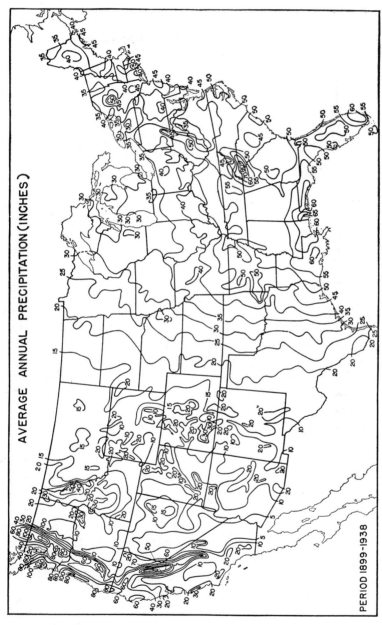

FIGURE 1. Average annual precipitation in the United States. (From *Yearbook of Agriculture*, 1941.)

receives about 55 inches a year. Nevada, the driest state, receives about 9 inches. The average annual precipitation over the entire United States is approximately 30 inches. Unless otherwise stated, all depths of precipitation include depths of melted snowfall as well as depths of rainfall.

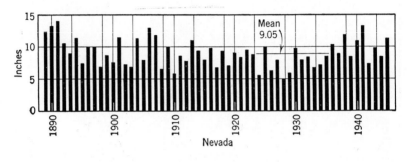

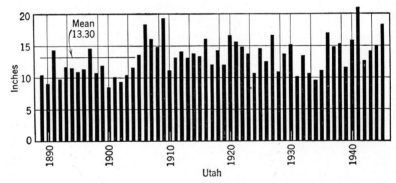

FIGURE 2.   Average annual precipitation in Nevada and Utah from 1889 to 1945. (Plotted from U.S. Weather Bureau data.)

Figure 1 shows the average annual precipitation in the United States during the period from 1899 to 1938. Lines of equal precipitation are shown for 5-inch increments of depth, except in a few regions of unusually heavy precipitation. Figure 1, also subsequent Figures 3 and 7, were prepared in the Weather Bureau, under the direction of J. B. Kincer. They were published in the 1941 *Yearbook* of the Department of Agriculture, and the Secretary of Agriculture has courteously granted permission for their use in this chapter.

Depths of annual precipitation in western United States decrease gradually from the Mississippi Valley to the eastern edge of the Rocky Mountains. From the Rockies to the Sierra Nevada and Cascade ranges, the depths vary from about 5 to 20 inches. The smaller depths are experienced in southwestern Arizona, southeastern California, and western Nevada. Depths of more than 30 inches occur at some of the higher altitudes in the Rockies, and much greater depths occur along the western slopes of the Cascade and Sierra Nevada ranges.

Figure 2 shows average annual precipitations over the states of Nevada and Utah during the period from 1889 to 1945, plotted from tabulations in the annual summaries of *Climatological Data* for 1945. Both diagrams show considerable variations in precipitation from year to year. For Nevada, the records do not indicate any general increase or decrease in precipitation during the 57-year period. For Utah, records since about 1904 show somewhat higher annual precipitations than the records for the earlier years.

A study of long-time precipitation records, published in 1936, showed a stationary or slightly upward trend in annual precipitation in the Southwest and the Great Basin, and a downward trend in the Northwest Interior, North Pacific Coast, and Central Pacific Coast areas.[12] Areas in which downward trends were indicated included the states of Washington, Oregon, Idaho, and Nevada, and the central and northern portions of California.

TABLE 2

MEAN, MINIMUM, AND MAXIMUM ANNUAL PRECIPITATION
IN WESTERN STATES, 1886 TO 1938 [40]

State	Mean annual precipitation, in.	Minimum year			Maximum year		
		Year	Precipitation, in.	Per cent of mean	Year	Precipitation, in.	Per cent of mean
Arizona	13.46	1900	7.83	58	1905	27.83	207
California	23.99	1898	10.35	43	1909	42.13	176
Colorado	16.49	1934	10.89	66	1923	21.23	129
Idaho	17.91	1935	12.40	69	1927	24.04	134
Kansas	26.55	1936	18.31	69	1915	40.77	154
Montana	14.88	1889	8.94	60	1927	20.63	139
Nebraska	22.30	1894	13.93	62	1915	35.58	160
Nevada	8.81	1928	4.87	55	1891	14.06	160
New Mexico	14.41	1910	9.46	66	1905	20.95	145
North Dakota	16.89	1936	8.83	52	1896	22.60	134
Oklahoma	31.94	1886	16.61	52	1908	47.73	149
Oregon	26.92	1930	19.22	71	1887	42.31	157
South Dakota	18.97	1936	10.93	58	1915	28.61	151
Texas	30.54	1917	16.21	53	1919	45.64	149
Utah	12.63	1887	6.35	50	1909	19.31	153
Washington	35.18	1929	23.74	67	1933	47.48	135
Wyoming	13.93	1887	8.02	58	1923	19.31	139

Table 2 shows mean, minimum, and maximum depths of annual precipitation over state areas in the West during the 53-year period from 1886 to 1938, also percentages of mean annual precipitation during years of minimum and maximum precipitation. In California, the average precipitation over the state during the driest year was only 43 per cent of the mean annual precipitation. In Arizona, the average precipitation over the state during the wettest year was 207 per cent of the mean annual precipitation. Data not tabulated show that in most western states the yearly precipitation may be 15 per cent or more below normal about one year in five, or similar percentages above normal about one year in five.[40]

Conditions of precipitation vary widely throughout state areas, as shown in Figure 1. Depths of annual precipitation at particular weather stations, or average depths over small areas, may be greatly different from the values shown in Table 2. Departures from mean values from year to year are also more variable and more pronounced. Table 3 shows mean, minimum, and maximum annual precipitations

TABLE 3

MEAN, MINIMUM, AND MAXIMUM ANNUAL PRECIPITATION
AT SOME WEATHER STATIONS IN THE WEST *

State	Station	Period of years	Mean annual precipitation, in.	Minimum year Precipitation, in.	Per cent of mean	Maximum year Precipitation, in.	Per cent of mean
Arizona	Phoenix	52	7.43	3.03	41	19.73	265
California	Sacramento	81	18.50	7.78	42	34.92	189
Colorado	Denver	59	14.21	7.75	54	22.96	162
Idaho	Boise	63	13.38	6.69	50	25.80	193
Kansas	Dodge City	56	20.51	10.12	49	33.55	163
Montana	Helena	49	13.31	6.71	50	20.04	151
Nebraska	North Platte	56	18.54	10.70	58	32.70	176
Nevada	Winnemucca	60	8.30	3.85	46	18.38	221
New Mexico	Albuquerque	60	8.06	3.29	41	16.30	202
North Dakota	Bismarck	56	16.34	11.03	67	30.92	189
Oklahoma	Lawton	53	31.53	16.07	51	50.08	159
Oregon	Umatilla	43	8.00	4.58	57	11.69	146
South Dakota	Pierre	39	16.65	7.82	47	23.57	142
Texas	El Paso	62	8.86	2.22	25	21.81	246
Utah	Salt Lake City	56	16.28	10.33	63	23.67	145
Washington	Ellensburg	41	9.12	3.71	41	13.58	149
Wyoming	Cheyenne	58	14.59	5.04	35	22.68	155

* Compiled from *Climatic Summary of the United States*, to 1930, U.S. Weather Bureau.

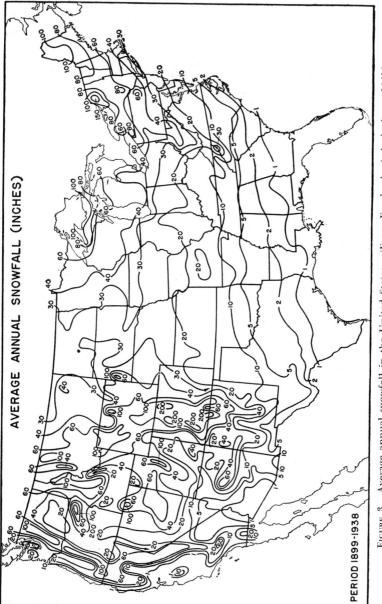

AVERAGE ANNUAL SNOWFALL (INCHES)

PERIOD 1899-1938

FIGURE 3. Average annual snowfall in the United States. (From *Yearbook of Agriculture*, 1941.)

as recorded at some weather stations in the West, also percentages of mean annual values during years of minimum and maximum precipitation. The minimum annual precipitation at El Paso, Texas, was only 25 per cent of the mean, and the maximum annual precipitation at Phoenix, Arizona, was 265 per cent of the mean.

The ratio of actual precipitation during a particular year to the mean annual precipitation, expressed as a percentage, is often called the index of wetness. When long records of precipitation are available, indices of wetness can be used as aids in extending streamflow records.

Annual Snowfall. Depths of annual snowfall in the mountains of western United States vary from less than 50 inches in Arizona and New Mexico to several hundred inches at some of the higher locations in the Sierra Nevada and Cascade ranges. A total of 884 inches fell at Tamarack, California, during the winter of 1906 and 1907.

TABLE 4

ANNUAL SNOWFALL AT SOME MOUNTAIN STATIONS
IN WESTERN UNITED STATES *

Station	Eleva- tion, ft.	Years of rec- ord	An- nual snow- fall, in.	Station	Eleva- tion, ft.	Years of rec- ord	An- nual snow- fall, in.
Arizona:				Nevada:			
Greer	8,500	18	86.2	Eureka	6,500	31	80.9
Bright Angel	8,400	6	119.3	Marlette Lake	8,000	9	254.7
California:				New Mexico:			
Bear Valley Dam	6,700	9	117.4	Anchor Mine	10,600	8	317.2
Bucks	5,515	10	361.3	Harvey's Upper Ranch	9,400	15	156.2
Norden	6,871	53	408.7	Oregon:			
Tamarack	8,000	21	451.4	Crater Lake	6,475	8	377.7
Colorado:				Government Camp	3,890	29	312.9
Hermit Lake	10,000	5	319.2	Greenhorn	6,250	5	288.1
Ruby	9,850	9	463.1	Musick	5,530	7	429.5
Savage Basin	11,522	15	400.2	Utah:			
Spruce Lodge	9,600	9	287.5	East Portal	7,606	12	142.0
Idaho:				Park City	7,100	22	163.5
Boulder Mine	4,830	15	169.7	Silver Lake	8,700	10	346.0
Cuprum	4,276	23	154.5	Washington:			
Lake	6,700	14	133.0	Mt. Baker Lodge	4,200	4	477.5
Roland	4,150	10	230.1	Monte Cristo	2,872	4	442.4
Montana:				Paradise Inn	5,550	11	591.3
Babb	4,461	20	88.0	Snoqualmie Pass	3,010	17	398.0
Elliston	5,041	10	137.3	Tye	3,126	11	365.8
Hebgen Dam	6,550	25	151.8	Wyoming:			
Mystic Lake	6,545	6	140.1	Dome Lake	8,821	20	218.6
Saltese	3,600	8	161.5	Elk Mountain	7,500	24	141.8
				Thumb	7,772	7	215.4

* Compiled from *Climatic Summary of the United States*, to 1930, U.S. Weather Bureau.

The average annual snowfall at Paradise Inn, on the slopes of Mount Rainier, Washington, amounts to 591 inches. Comparatively heavy snowfalls are also experienced at some of the higher locations in the Rocky Mountains.

Figure 3 shows the average annual snowfall in the United States during the period from 1899 to 1938. Because of the scale of the map, lines of equal snowfall are not shown for the relatively small areas where the greatest depths are recorded. Table 4 shows the average annual snowfall at some of the higher mountain stations where unusually heavy snows occur.

Fresh snow of average density generally contains about 1 inch of water to each 10 inches of snow. Light fluffy snows may require 20 inches or more to produce 1 inch of water when melted. Heavy wet snow may contain 1 inch of water for each 5 or 6 inches of depth. Snows that remain on the ground through the winter are gradually compacted by wind movements, fresh snowfalls, and partial melting and freezing. They may attain densities as high as 50 per cent by the time spring melting begins. Snow surveys, which measure quantities of water in accumulated snow covers, are discussed in Chapter 8.

Seasonal Precipitation. From the viewpoint of seasonal precipitation, the year may be considered to begin with December, instead of January, and to be divided into four 3-month periods, namely, winter, spring, summer, and fall. Thus, winter includes the months of December to February; spring includes March to May; summer, June to August; and fall, September to November.

Table 5 shows depths of average seasonal precipitation over the western states during the 53-year period from 1886 to 1938, also ranges in seasonal precipitation during the same period, expressed as percentages of the seasonal averages.[40] Minimum depths of precipitation for the four seasons occurred during different years in all cases. In California, the minimum fall precipitation occurred in 1929 and was only 8 per cent of the average for the 53 fall seasons.

Maximum depths of precipitation for the four seasons occurred during different years in nearly all cases. In Oregon, maximum winter and spring precipitations occurred in 1887, the year of maximum annual precipitation. In Arizona, maximum winter, spring, and fall precipitations occurred in 1905, also the year of maximum annual precipitation. The maximum spring precipitation in Arizona was 362 per cent of the average for the 53 spring seasons.

Depths of seasonal precipitation at particular weather stations, also average seasonal depths over small areas, may be considerably differ-

Table 5

SEASONAL PRECIPITATION IN WESTERN STATES, 1886 TO 1938 [40]

State	Average seasonal precipitation, in.				Range in seasonal precipitation, minimum to maximum, per cent of average			
	Winter, Dec. to Feb.	Spring, Mar. to May	Summer, June to Aug.	Fall, Sept. to Nov.	Winter, Dec. to Feb.	Spring, Mar. to May	Summer, June to Aug.	Fall, Sept. to Nov.
Arizona	3.82	1.95	4.74	2.95	19–237	18–362	33–184	19–266
California	13.10	6.40	0.48	4.01	37–202	32–220	19–311	8–237
Colorado	2.64	4.96	5.62	3.27	45–196	56–171	42–158	44–164
Idaho	6.03	4.88	2.61	4.39	55–168	36–140	24–212	24–215
Kansas	2.53	7.80	10.22	6.00	15–194	60–162	31–166	50–163
Montana	2.43	4.16	5.06	3.23	39–195	54–180	37–173	25–177
Nebraska	1.89	6.85	9.32	4.24	32–212	33–168	45–173	38–167
Nevada	3.25	2.58	1.36	1.62	38–291	24–213	24–297	21–187
New Mexico	2.00	2.77	6.15	3.49	20–196	31–234	45–175	37–184
North Dakota	1.50	4.40	7.89	3.10	41–183	29–225	44–162	43–220
Oklahoma	4.41	10.01	9.51	8.01	16–178	34–173	30–173	30–229
Oregon	11.31	6.66	2.13	6.82	53–200	36–167	33–257	17–177
South Dakota	1.69	6.02	8.00	3.26	43–202	35–179	44–170	26–186
Texas	5.94	8.70	8.09	7.81	32–208	53–177	50–172	43–192
Utah	3.56	3.72	2.44	2.91	37–170	32–194	24–211	22–179
Washington	14.37	7.82	3.13	9.86	59–161	31–163	38–219	27–170
Wyoming	2.29	4.75	4.04	2.85	40–249	45–145	49–161	34–209

ent from the values shown in Table 5. Normal depths of seasonal precipitation at particular stations, also actual depths during different years, can be computed from tabulations of precipitation published in the annual summaries of *Climatological Data.*

Monthly Precipitation. Figure 4 shows mean monthly precipitations at some weather stations in western United States, plotted from Weather Bureau records published in the *Climatological Data.* Mean annual precipitations are shown below the names of the stations. The diagram for Merced, California, illustrates the summer-dry climate between the Pacific Coast and the Sierra Nevada range. Summer rainfalls at Denver and Albuquerque supply some moisture for crop growth. At other locations represented on the figure, summer rain-

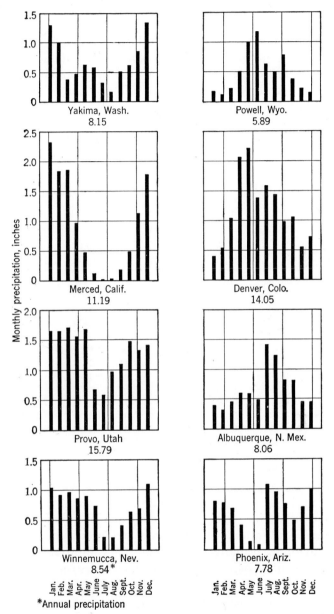

FIGURE 4. Mean monthly precipitation at some stations in western United States.
(Plotted from U.S. Weather Bureau data.)

falls are too small to be of much value in reducing irrigation requirements.

Summer showers of less than ½ inch, unless falling on moist soil, are rapidly evaporated as soon as the rain ceases, without contributing to soil-moisture storage. In fact, relatively large proportions of summer showers may be intercepted by crop foliage and evaporated without reaching the soil (see Chapter 10).

Table 6 shows mean, minimum, and maximum monthly precipitations at Boise, Idaho, during the period from 1868 to 1946, also monthly

TABLE 6

MEAN, MINIMUM, AND MAXIMUM MONTHLY PRECIPITATION AT
BOISE, IDAHO, 1868 TO 1946 *

Month	Mean precipita- tion, in.	Minimum precipitation		Maximum precipitation		Mini- mum year, 1868, in.	Maxi- mum year, 1871, in.
		In.	Yr.	In.	Yr.		
January	1.73	0.40	1924	5.29	1875	1.08	3.54
February	1.44	0.04	1889	6.49	1872	0.09	1.29
March	1.35	Trace	1895	7.66	1871	0.09	7.66
April	1.18	0.09	1885	4.73	1869	0.15	1.54
May	1.43	0.01	1928, 1931	4.90	1896, 1941	0.32	2.75
June	0.92	0.00	1895	3.41	1884	1.50	0.64
July	0.24	0.00	Several	2.01	1913	Trace	0.14
August	0.19	0.00	Several	1.65	1873	0.00	0.00
September	0.53	0.00	1869, 1870	2.32	1918	0.02	0.11
October	1.24	0.00	1869, 1895	4.06	1883	0.02	0.27
November	1.28	0.00	1890	4.43	1874	0.02	1.90
December	1.57	0.01	1877	5.96	1871	3.40	5.96
Year	13.10	....	....	....	....	6.69	25.80

* Compiled from *Climatological Data*, U.S. Weather Bureau.

precipitations during years of minimum and maximum annual precipitation. The columns of minimum and maximum monthly precipitation are particularly significant. They illustrate the extreme ranges in monthly precipitation that may be experienced at many locations in arid climates. Maximum precipitations of from 1.65 to 7.66 inches were recorded during the different months, sometime during the 79 years, but minimum precipitations were zero from June to November. Minimum precipitations were less than 0.10 inch during all months except January, and only 0.40 inch in January.

Storm Rainfall. Studies of storm rainfall may be needed as aids in determining spillway capacities to be provided at storage dams. Such studies are made for unusually heavy storms that cause excessive rates of surface runoff. When sufficient precipitation records are available, maps showing lines of equal rainfall can be prepared. Lines of equal

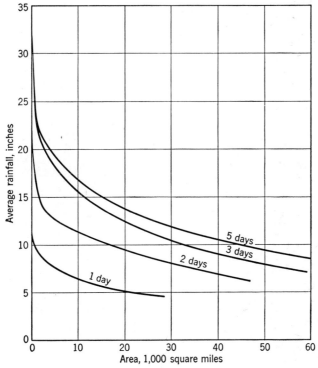

FIGURE 5. Time-area-depth curves for storm of June 27 to July 1, 1899, in eastern Texas. (Plotted from data in reference 22.)

rainfall are called isohyetals or isohyets. Isohyetal maps should be prepared for the day of maximum precipitation and for different combinations of consecutive days throughout the storm. Areas receiving different depths of rainfall during different time periods can be determined by planimeter measurements. Diagrams showing average depths of rainfall over different areas during different time periods can then be prepared. Such diagrams are often called time-area-depth curves.

Isohyetal maps and time-area-depth curves for most large storms that occurred in central and eastern United States during 1892 to

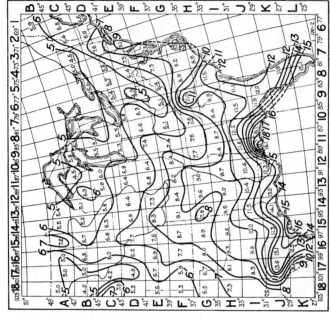

100-year period and 2-day rainfall

100-year period and 1-day rainfall

FIGURE 6. Isopluvial charts for 100-year rainfalls. (Courtesy The Miami Conservancy District.)

1933 were prepared by the Miami Conservancy District.[22] Although the area studied lies east of the arid and principal semiarid regions, some of the data may be pertinent in irrigation considerations.

Figure 5 shows time-area-depth curves for the storm of June 27 to July 1, 1899, in eastern Texas, plotted from data in the Miami report. This storm was caused by a semitropical hurricane that moved northward from the Gulf of Mexico. It precipitated 33 inches of rain over small areas near Turnersville, and relatively high average depths over areas up to more than 50 thousand square miles. It caused destructive floods in the Brazos River Valley, the loss of 24 lives, and property damages estimated at more than 8 million dollars.

The Miami investigations also included frequency studies for heavy rainfalls occurring in periods of from 1 to 6 days. Maximum rainfalls that may be equaled or exceeded, on the average, once in 15, 25, 50, and 100 years were determined for each 2-degree quadrangle east of the 103rd meridian. The studies were based principally on Weather Bureau records of daily precipitation, and the results were shown on special maps called isopluvial charts. Figure 6 shows the isopluvial charts for 1- and 2-day rainfalls that may be equaled or exceeded once in 100 years.

In most parts of central and eastern United States, maximum rainfalls shown in Figure 6 probably apply to all parts of the quadrangles they represent. Some uncertainties may be involved at locations near high mountain divides, where orographic processes have pronounced effects on precipitation.

In studying probable maximum rates of flood runoff, records of large storms that have occurred in certain drainage basins are sometimes moved bodily to adjacent or nearby drainage basins. This is done on the assumption that the storms might have occurred at the other locations. Although this procedure may be feasible to a limited extent in level or slightly rolling sections of the country, such as central United States, it can be used only with extreme caution in mountainous regions where orographic influences are present.

Intense Local Rainstorms. Intense local rainstorms or cloudbursts that cannot be absorbed by the soil may cause high rates of runoff, extensive soil erosion, and severe destructive effects in many irrigated regions. Such storms may destroy crops, either by washing away surface soils at locations of intense precipitation or by covering crops with mud, sand, gravel, or boulders, brought to the fields by runoff from adjacent areas. They also may cause serious damages to irrigation ditches, canals, canal structures, farm buildings, and local municipalities. In the Sevier Lake basin, Utah, more than 100 damaging cloudbursts were recorded during the 85 years from 1852 to 1936.[43]

Cloudbursts are characteristic phenomena in arid regions. They usually occur during the summer and fall months. In the Sevier Lake Basin, all but 8 of the recorded storms occurred during July and August. Fortunately, cloudbursts are local in nature, so that only relatively small areas are affected. Because of their local nature, maximum depths of rainfall are seldom recorded at weather stations.

Data on excessive rates of rainfall observed at first-order weather stations, also methods of defining lower limits of excessive rainfall, have been mentioned earlier in the chapter. A special report on the frequency of excessive rainfall as observed in different parts of the United States was prepared by Yarnell and published in 1935.[44] A special report, extending Yarnell's tabulations to 1945 and including data for different durations up to 24 hours, was prepared by Shands and Ammerman and published in 1947.[30] Characteristics of rainfall as related to soil erosion were analyzed by Blumenstock and published in 1939.[4]

TEMPERATURE

Temperature conditions on irrigation projects largely determine the types of crops most suitable for profitable production. Common types of farm crops grow in a temperature range from a few degrees above freezing to about 120 degrees F. Most rapid growth often takes place at temperatures of from 75 to 100 degrees. However, for satisfactory growth and ripening, different crops need different temperatures at different times during the growing season. They also need different lengths of growing season. Small grains are adapted to cool climates and relatively short growing seasons. Corn, sorghum, and cotton need warmer climates and longer growing seasons.

The growing season is the warm period between the last killing frost of spring and the first killing frost in the fall. When spring and summer rainfalls are negligible, the irrigation season is approximately the same as the growing season. When the winter and spring months are unusually dry, early irrigations may be needed to replenish soil moisture in the root zones before crops are planted.

Temperatures during the growing season affect rates of crop growth, amounts of moisture consumed by transpiration, and losses of moisture by evaporation at soil surfaces. Protracted periods of unusually low or high temperature may seriously reduce crop yields. Certain temperature conditions may favor the growth of destructive insects and the development of plant diseases. Soil temperatures, primarily dependent on air temperatures and sunshine, affect movements of soil moisture and solvent properties of soil solutions.

Temperature conditions in upstream drainage basins affect precipitation, infiltration, storage of moisture, evaporation, and runoff characteristics. Low winter temperatures mean precipitation in the form of snow, storage of congealed moisture on the ground surface until warmer weather, low evaporation losses, and spring runoff that can be diverted for irrigation at downstream locations. Temperatures also affect evaporation losses at lakes and reservoirs.

Regional temperatures are determined principally by latitude, elevation, distances from large bodies of water, and prevailing wind movements. At coastal locations, temperatures may be materially affected by the proximity and nature of ocean currents. In the mountains of western United States, temperatures at similar latitudes are determined principally by elevation. In the plateau region between the Rocky Mountains and the Sierra Nevada and Cascade ranges, temperatures at similar elevations are determined principally by latitude.

Temperatures as low as −66 degrees F. have been observed in Yellowstone National Park, northwest Wyoming, and temperatures as high as 134 degrees have been observed at the edge of Death Valley. In general, temperature conditions throughout the arid and semiarid regions of the West are suitable for some types of irrigation agriculture wherever topographic and soil conditions are satisfactory and adequate supplies of water can be obtained.

Annual Temperatures. Mean annual air temperatures in the United States, determined as averages for state areas, vary from 39.6 degrees F. in North Dakota to 70.9 degrees in Florida. All South Atlantic and Gulf states have relatively high annual temperatures. Texas has an average annual temperature of 66.3 degrees over its 267 thousand square miles. Brownsville, at the southernmost tip of the state, has a mean annual temperature of 73.1 degrees. Mean annual temperatures at weather stations in western United States vary from about 33 degrees at Lake Yellowstone, northwest Wyoming, to about 77 degrees in Death Valley, southeast California. The mean annual temperature for the entire United States is 53.7 degrees.

Table 7 shows some data on annual temperatures in the western states, compiled from annual summaries of *Climatological Data* to

TABLE 7

ANNUAL AIR TEMPERATURES IN WESTERN UNITED STATES *

(Degrees F.)

State	Mean annual state tempera- ture †	Station	Years of rec- ord	Eleva- tion, ft.	Mean annual temper- ature	Average temperature during year of	
						Mini- mum temper- ature	Maxi- mum temper- ature
Arizona	60.4	Phoenix	50	1,107	69.7	66.3	74.0
California	58.4	Fresno	58	277	62.2	61.0	65.4
Colorado	45.2	Denver	74	5,221	50.0	47.6	54.8
Idaho	45.6	Boise	79	2,858	49.8	48.4	55.8
Montana	43.0	Havre	66	2,488	41.6	37.9	47.2
Nevada	49.9	Winnemucca	67	4,287	48.4	46.1	53.2
New Mexico	52.7	Albuquerque	44	5,314	55.3	53.4	57.6
Oregon	51.7	Baker	56	3,445	45.3	42.9	50.2
Utah	48.1	Salt Lake City	72	4,260	51.6	48.5	56.5
Washington	49.6	Walla Walla	60	952	53.1	50.0	57.8
Wyoming	41.9	Cheyenne	75	6,144	44.7	42.7	48.9

* Compiled from *Climatological Data*, to 1945, U.S. Weather Bureau.
† Based on 49 to 58 years of records in the different states.

1945. Mean annual temperatures for state areas are given in the second column. Remaining columns give data for particular weather stations, including minimum and maximum yearly temperatures. Minimum yearly temperatures at the stations listed were from 2 to 9 per cent lower than mean annual temperatures. Maximum yearly temperatures were from 4 to 13 per cent higher. Maximum temperatures occurred during 1934 at most stations.

In the plateau region between the Rocky Mountains and the Sierra Nevada and Cascade ranges, mean annual temperatures at similar elevations decrease about 1.5 degrees per additional degree of latitude. In easterly directions through southern Arizona, mean annual temperatures at similar latitudes decrease about 3.5 degrees per 1,000 feet increase in elevation. In northern Montana, the rate of decrease with elevation on the western slopes of the Rockies is about the same as in southern Arizona. East of the divide, the rate of decrease is only about 0.5 degree per 1,000 feet of elevation.

In 1933, a study of long-time records at some American and foreign stations, reported by Kincer, showed that a general uptrend in seasonal and annual temperature had taken place during the preceding 100 years or more.[17] A supplemental study, reported in 1946, showed a continuation of the upward trend for several years, then a leveling off, with possibly a suggestion of an approaching reversal in trend.[18]

Monthly Temperatures. Table 8 shows mean monthly air temperatures at the stations listed in Table 7. In general, differences in

TABLE 8

MEAN MONTHLY AIR TEMPERATURES IN WESTERN UNITED STATES *

(Degrees F.)

Station	Jan.	Feb.	Mar.	Apr.	May	June	July	Aug.	Sept.	Oct.	Nov.	Dec.
Phoenix	51.2	55.1	60.7	67.0	75.0	84.5	89.8	88.5	82.7	70.6	59.7	52.0
Fresno	45.5	50.3	54.4	60.2	67.2	75.7	81.3	79.5	72.0	62.3	52.4	45.1
Denver	29.8	32.7	39.3	47.1	56.2	66.3	72.2	70.7	63.0	51.2	39.8	32.5
Boise	27.9	33.6	41.4	49.1	56.1	64.5	72.5	71.0	61.2	50.1	39.7	30.3
Havre	12.9	13.6	27.1	43.7	53.4	62.0	68.3	65.4	56.4	44.5	31.2	20.4
Winnemucca	28.6	33.5	40.0	46.7	53.9	62.8	70.6	69.3	59.2	48.3	38.4	30.0
Albuquerque	34.1	40.5	45.9	54.0	63.3	72.6	76.7	73.9	67.9	56.6	43.3	34.5
Baker	24.9	29.0	37.6	45.2	51.7	58.6	65.6	64.6	56.0	46.6	36.0	27.3
Salt Lake City	29.2	33.8	41.7	49.6	57.4	67.4	75.7	74.5	64.4	52.5	41.1	31.9
Walla Walla	32.7	37.1	46.1	53.1	59.6	66.5	74.0	72.7	63.8	53.5	42.8	35.5
Cheyenne	25.5	27.3	33.1	40.9	50.3	60.4	66.8	65.6	57.0	44.8	34.8	28.5

* Compiled from annual summaries of *Climatological Data*, 1945, U.S. Weather Bureau; see Table 7 for state locations, elevations, and years of record.

mean monthly temperatures at different locations are more pronounced in winter than in summer. All stations listed have summer temperatures high enough for crop growth. Phoenix and Fresno have relatively high temperatures throughout the year. Havre, Montana, the most northerly station listed, has low winter temperatures, but relatively high summer temperatures. Some stations south of Havre, located at higher elevations, have lower summer temperatures.

Table 9 shows some data on monthly temperatures at Pueblo, Colorado. Column 2 shows mean monthly temperatures, columns 3 and 4 show average temperatures during the coldest and warmest months of the 42 years of record, and columns 5 and 6 show monthly averages of minimum and maximum daily temperatures. Columns 7 and 8 show extreme minimum and maximum temperatures recorded during the different months.

Inasmuch as minimum daily temperatures usually occur during the night, and maximum daily temperatures during the day, columns 5 and 6 of Table 8 indicate the average temperatures that may be experienced at Pueblo during the nighttime and daytime hours in

TABLE 9

MONTHLY AVERAGES AND EXTREMES OF AIR TEMPERATURE
AT PUEBLO, COLORADO *

(Degrees F.)

Month	Monthly averages			Monthly averages of		Extreme temperatures	
	Mean monthly	Coldest month	Warm-est month	Mini-mum temper-atures	Maxi-mum temper-atures	Mini-mum recorded	Maxi-mum recorded
(1)	(2)	(3)	(4)	(5)	(6)	(7)	(8)
January	31	19	39	17	45	−25	74
February	33	19	43	19	47	−27	76
March	41	32	51	27	55	−13	86
April	50	44	57	36	64	12	88
May	59	53	64	46	73	23	95
June	69	64	74	54	84	32	103
July	74	70	77	60	88	41	102
August	73	68	76	59	87	39	104
September	65	57	69	50	80	28	98
October	52	47	56	37	68	−4	90
November	40	33	46	25	55	−17	81
December	31	20	42	17	46	−22	74
Year	52 †	19	77	37 †	66 †	−27	104

* Compiled from *Climatic Summary of the United States*, to 1930, U.S. Weather Bureau; elevation at station, 4,685 feet; length of record, 42 years.

† Yearly averages.

the different months. Such data may be valuable in considering crop growth. For example, satisfactory corn production requires warm nights as well as warm days.

Average temperatures during the coldest and warmest months at Pueblo, columns 3 and 4, differed from mean monthly values more in winter than in summer. Variations from mean monthly temperatures at Pueblo illustrate conditions that may be experienced in many parts of western United States. Temperature conditions along the Pacific Coast are commonly more uniform than at inland locations, due to the regulating effects of the ocean. At San Diego, California,

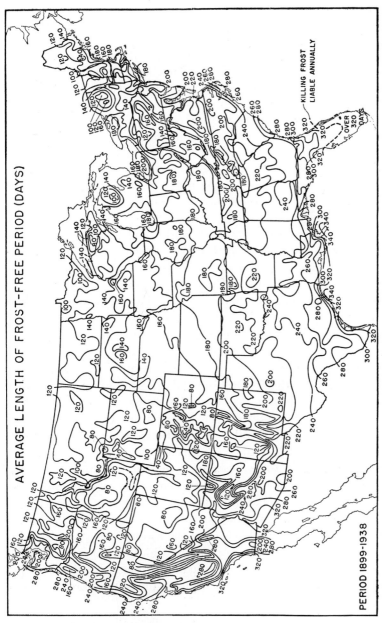

FIGURE 7. Average length of frost-free periods in the United States. (From *Yearbook of Agriculture*, 1941.)

monthly temperatures did not differ from mean values more than 5 degrees during the coldest or warmest weather in a period of 56 years.

Frost-Free Periods. Figure 7 shows average lengths of frost-free periods in the United States, determined by data recorded during the 40-year period from 1899 to 1938. In irrigated regions, average frost-free periods are as short as 40 days in some of the small basins at high altitudes in the Rocky Mountains. In southwestern Arizona, southeastern California, and along the coast in southern California, average frost-free periods are as long as 320 days. No irrigated section of the West is entirely free from the danger of frost damages, but the danger is least near Yuma, Arizona, in the Imperial Valley of southern California, and at some locations along the coast near San Diego.

Soil Temperatures. Soil temperatures in root zones vary throughout the year, principally in accordance with surface air temperatures and amounts of sunshine reaching the ground surface. Temperatures at shallow depths rise rapidly during the spring and early summer months, when but little shade is provided by crop foliage. Later in the irrigation season, after crops attain considerable growth, the ground is shaded and soil temperatures increase more slowly. At greater depths, temperatures rise more gradually, so that they lag behind the upper soil temperatures. Near the bottom of a 4-foot root zone, maximum temperatures may not be reached until a month or more after maximum temperatures are reached at the ground surface.

Evaporation of soil moisture following irrigation retards the warming of the soil. Cultivation following irrigation also retards warming. Loose earth impedes conduction of absorbed radiation, so that temperatures at shallow depths may be 5 to 10 degrees lower in cultivated soils than in undisturbed soils. In forest regions, warming of the soil is retarded by shading and by the insulating effects of forest litter. During the summer, soil temperatures at shallow depths may be 15 to 20 degrees lower in forests than in denuded areas. Minimum soil temperatures during the winter are not so different.[13] During the winter months, snow covers act as insulation and retard the cooling of the soil, in the open as well as in the forests.

Diurnal variations of soil temperature, which may amount to several degrees near the ground surface, usually become negligible at depths greater than about 1 foot. They seldom amount to more than about 1 degree at depths greater than 2 feet.

Table 10 shows some data on soil temperatures at Ames, Iowa, during 1938 to 1946, compiled from records published in the annual

TABLE 10

SOIL TEMPERATURES AT AMES, IOWA, DURING PERIOD
FROM 1938 TO 1946 *

(Degrees F.)

Temperature condition	Air temperature, Ames Weather Bureau Station	Soil temperatures † at depths in in. of					
		1	6	12	24	48	72
Mean temperatures:							
Annual	49.0	54.1	54.2	51.6	51.3	50.9	51.9
January	20.5	25.9	27.8	29.4	34.1	39.2	44.3
February	24.5	28.6	29.2	29.6	32.8	36.8	41.6
March	36.9	38.8	37.6	35.0	35.3	36.9	40.7
April	49.8	53.7	52.6	47.8	45.0	42.5	43.7
May	60.2	66.6	65.3	59.0	54.3	49.8	48.7
June	69.5	77.3	75.9	69.1	63.7	57.5	54.8
July	74.2	85.1	83.2	75.4	69.9	63.4	60.1
August	71.6	80.3	79.6	73.8	70.2	65.8	63.1
September	63.9	69.0	70.1	66.6	66.0	64.2	62.9
October	54.2	55.4	57.1	55.9	57.6	58.9	59.5
November	37.4	38.1	40.7	43.0	47.3	51.8	54.2
December	25.1	30.0	31.9	34.1	39.2	44.6	48.7
Highest observed temperature	102	106	95	82	75	68	65
Mean date of highest temperature	7/22	7/21	7/21	7/21	8/8	8/18	8/28
Lowest observed temperature	−25	−4	7	20	29	35	39
Mean date of lowest temperature	1/18	1/24	1/27	1/25	2/8	2/21	3/8

* Compiled from the annual summaries of *Climatological Data*, U.S. Weather Bureau.
† Average annual and monthly soil temperatures are for 7 P.M. observations.

summaries of *Climatological Data*. Maximum mean monthly temperatures occurred during July at depths of 1, 6, and 12 inches, and during August at depths of 24, 48, and 72 inches. The highest temperature observed at a depth of 1 inch was 4 degrees higher than the highest air temperature observed at the Ames Weather Bureau Station. The soil was kept free from vegetation and was loosened to a depth of 2 inches by raking. Figure 8 shows monthly averages of soil temperatures at different depths during 1946, as determined by observations made at 7 P.M. Average air temperatures 4 feet above the ground are shown at the top of the diagram.

Soil temperatures affect moisture movements and rates of moisture absorption by plant roots. Sudden reductions in soil temperature in the early fall, prior to the occurrence of killing frosts, may cause

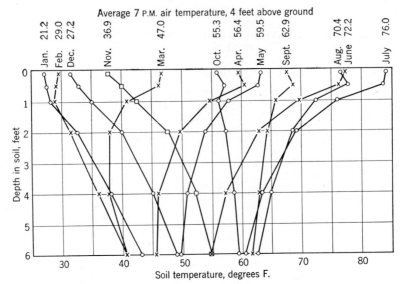

FIGURE 8. Monthly soil temperatures at Ames, Iowa, during 1946; averages of
7 P.M. observations. (Plotted from U.S. Weather Bureau data.)

wilting of shallow-rooted, warm-weather plants when moisture contents
of the root zones are well above the normal wilting point.

ADDITIONAL CLIMATIC FACTORS

Additional climatic factors that influence irrigation agriculture include light conditions, relative humidity, wind movements, and evaporation. Some of these factors are more or less interrelated in their
effects on crop growth. Some act in combination with special conditions of temperature or precipitation in causing desirable or undesirable effects on plant life. Therefore effects of particular climatic
factors on crop production often are difficult to segregate.

Certain storm phenomena may cause serious crop losses or even
crop failures. Sandstorms, duststorms, windstorms, hailstorms, and
severe electrical storms that may occur in arid and semiarid regions
may cause local damages to crops. Destructive tornadoes occur but
rarely in irrigated regions west of the Rocky Mountains.

The following sections present brief discussions of most additional
climatic factors that affect irrigation agriculture. Conditions of evaporation from water and land surfaces are taken up in Chapters 9 and 10.

Light Conditions. In general, light conditions throughout the western states are favorable for the production of most farm crops. At some locations along the Pacific Coast, quantities of sunshine available for plant growth are reduced by cloudiness and fogs. However, in most arid and semiarid regions, light intensities and proportions of sunshine that reach the earth's surface are greater than in the humid sections of the country. Since many crops amply supplied with water develop maximum quantities of dry matter under high light intensities, maximum crop yields are often secured on irrigated lands.

Except for a narrow strip along the coast, practically all parts of the West receive more than 70 per cent of possible sunshine during the principal crop-growing months of June to August. Some parts of central and southeastern California, also the southwestern parts of Arizona, where growing seasons are relatively long, receive more than 90 per cent of possible sunshine during the summer months and more than 80 per cent during the winter. These regions normally experience from 220 to 280 clear days each year.

Light conditions affect practically all stages of plant growth, including stem elongation, leaf development, photosynthesis, flowering, and seed maturity. Photosynthesis is the process by which chlorophyll, the green pigment of the leaves, converts water, carbon dioxide, and sunlight into plant food. Although all crop plants require light for proper growth, different plants need different light conditions. Some thrive in bright sunlight; others do better in the shade. Some need long days for flower development and seed maturity; others need short days. Still others develop normally during either long- or short-day seasons. Effects of light conditions and other climatic factors on crop growth have been discussed in the Department of Agriculture *Yearbook* for 1941.

Relative Humidity. Relative humidity is the actual moisture content of the atmosphere expressed as a percentage of the moisture that could be present if the water vapor content of the atmosphere were in a saturated condition at the existing air temperature. Absolute humidity is the actual amount of moisture in the air per unit volume. It is usually given in grains per cubic foot. Except during sudden changes in air mass movements, absolute humidities do not vary greatly throughout the day.

Inasmuch as the amount of water vapor that can be present in the atmosphere increases with temperature, relative humidities generally attain maximum values in the morning when air temperatures are low, and minimum values in the afternoon when air temperatures are high.   Observations of relative humidity are made at first-order weather stations three times a day, namely, morning, noon, and evening.   Averages determined by morning and evening observations probably are closely representative of mean daily relative humidities.

Obviously, relative humidities in arid and semiarid regions where irrigation is practiced are commonly lower than in humid regions. In most parts of western United States relative humidities are higher in winter than in summer.   Between the Rocky Mountains and the West Coast regions, January relative humidities vary from about 60 to 90 per cent in the morning, and from about 30 to 80 per cent at noon.   Noon values increase in northerly directions from Arizona to the Canadian border.   Morning values are lowest in southern Arizona and highest in southwestern Wyoming.

During July, relative humidities are lowest in Nevada and adjoining areas.   Noon values are about 20 per cent, and morning values about 50 per cent.   July relative humidities along the eastern edge of the irrigated regions are about 40 per cent at noon, and about 75 per cent in the morning.   Along West Coast regions, both noon and morning values of July relative humidities are somewhat higher.

Relative humidities, in combination with other climatic factors, have important effects on the growth and ripening of fruit and vegetable crops.   Dates need low relative humidities during the fruiting season. Some types of melons, such as the honeydew, grow best in climates of high temperature and low relative humidity.   Certain conditions of temperature and relative humidity may have important effects on the development of plant diseases and the growth of destructive insects.

Wind Movements.   Wind movements in irrigated districts vary widely from day to day, not only in velocity but also in direction. Some days may be practically calm.   Others may have comparatively high velocities.   During storm periods, comparatively high velocities may continue for several days.   However, the extremely high velocities that are recorded only occasionally during long periods of years seldom continue for more than a few minutes at a time.   Average velocities during different months, also during the entire year, are much less variable than daily velocities.

Table 11 shows some data on wind movements at a few weather stations in western United States.   Average annual wind velocities at the stations listed vary from 5.7 miles per hour at Phoenix to 11.0 miles per hour at Cheyenne.   Average velocities during the calmest months vary from 5.1 miles per hour at Phoenix to 8.9 miles per hour at

TABLE 11

WIND MOVEMENTS AT SOME WEATHER STATIONS IN WESTERN
UNITED STATES *

(Miles per hour)

State	Station	Years of record	Calmest month, average of records		Maximum wind recorded		Average annual wind	
			Month	Ve-locity	Month	Ve-locity	Pre-vailing direc-tion	Ve-locity
Arizona	Phoenix	35	Nov., Dec.	5.1	Aug.	41	e.	5.7
California	Fresno	43	Nov., Dec.	5.3	Jan.	41	nw.	6.9
Colorado	Denver	57	Aug.	7.3	Aug.	58	s.	8.0
Idaho	Boise	32	Oct.	5.4	June	43	nw.	6.0
Montana	Havre	40	Aug.	7.5	June	57	sw.	8.9
Nevada	Winnemucca	52	Aug.	7.5	Nov.	58	sw.	8.4
New Mexico	Albuquerque	12	Aug.	7.2	Mar.	63	s.	8.2
Oregon	Baker	40	June–Aug.	6.6	Dec.	40	se.	6.9
Utah	Salt Lake City	57	Dec.	6.9	Apr.	53	se.	8.2
Washington	Walla Walla	45	Oct.	5.7	June	51	s.	6.6
Wyoming	Cheyenne	59	Aug.	8.9	Jan.	63	nw.	11.0

* Compiled from *Climatic Summary of the United States*, to 1930, U.S. Weather Bureau.

Cheyenne. Maximum velocities during the entire periods of record vary from 40 miles per hour at Baker to 63 miles per hour at Cheyenne and Albuquerque.

The wind velocities in Table 11 may not be comparable at all stations, owing to differences in exposure and heights of anemometer installations. Wind velocities usually increase with increasing heights above ground levels.

Wind movements increase plant transpiration as well as evaporation losses from water and moist soil surfaces. Hot dry winds during the growing and maturing seasons may damage crop products. Continued high winds during certain seasons of the year may cause serious erosion of light loose soils that cannot be kept moist. In some districts, wind-breaks may be needed to protect crop plants and prevent the blowing away of topsoils. During high winds, crop damages may be caused by wind-borne materials as well as by wind velocities. Sand grains carried in the air may cut away plant foliage. Winds blowing from ocean areas sometimes carry enough salt particles to damage crops several miles inland.

Meteorologists have classified and named many types of winds that occur in different regions as results of special atmospheric or topographical conditions. Several types affect hydrological processes in irrigated regions. The type that causes the most sudden and pronounced effects is the chinook.

Chinook winds are the warm, dry, southwest winds that blow down the eastern slopes of the mountains after moisture loads have been depleted by upward movements along the western slopes. They become warmer and drier by compression as they descend and often cause sudden increases in temperature when they reach the plains. They may occur at any time, but their effects are most noticeable in winter. They may cause complete melting of deep snow covers in a few hours. For this reason they are sometimes called "snow eaters." In the Alps they are known as foehns.[32]

Storm Damages. Sandstorms, duststorms, windstorms, hailstorms, and electrical storms may cause serious damages to agriculture in some irrigated regions. Storm damages usually are local in nature, except during severe duststorms which may extend over large areas. Damages caused by cloudbursts or by intense local rainstorms have been mentioned in the preceding discussions of precipitation.

Sandstorms are really local phenomena in sandy desert regions, but the term is sometimes applied to duststorms. Duststorms are essentially the result of prolonged drought conditions. The most destructive storms occur during dry winter and spring months. They cause severe damages to winter wheat and other crops, by eroding topsoils, covering crop plants with drifting soil, or cutting away crop foliage. Large areas of seedlings may be wiped out in a few hours. Topsoils may be eroded to such an extent as to prevent crop production during one or more succeeding years. Several destructive duststorms occurred in the southwest plains during the thirties. In fact, this region is sometimes called the dust bowl of the United States.

Local windstorms may cause crop damages and soil erosion, as discussed in the preceding section. Hailstorms may cause crop damages any time during the growing season. Heavy hailstorms occurring when crops are approaching maturity may cause complete crop failures. In cotton-growing regions, electrical storms may cause local crop losses by starting fires in the cotton fields.

References

Although most storm damages are confined to local areas, total seasonal losses often amount to considerable sums. In 1942, total damages caused by hail amounted to more than 4 million dollars in Montana, and to nearly 18 million dollars in the entire United States. Damages to crops caused by a severe duststorm may run into millions of dollars in a single state. Compilations of data on annual losses caused by some types of storms are published in the meteorological yearbooks.

Air Drainage. Air drainage is the local movement of heavy surface air toward lower levels, caused by more rapid cooling and increased air densities at the higher elevations. Such air movements may take place during calm nights and may produce cold air pockets on adjacent lowlands. When temperatures are near freezing, frost may occur on the lowlands, but not on the hillsides. At most locations, air drainage causes only slow drifting movements of air strata along the ground surfaces. However, in mountainous regions, movements of cooled air down long steep valleys and canyons may develop appreciable or even high velocities. In such regions, the air movements are sometimes called mountain winds or canyon winds.

Air drainage should be carefully considered in planning irrigation agriculture. Whenever feasible, fruits, berries, vegetables, and other crops that may be damaged by frost should be grown on hillsides or sloping land where adequate air drainage is available. Orchards on lowlands near Yakima, Washington, are often damaged by frost when nearby orchards on sloping hillsides remain undamaged. Similar examples occur in fruit-growing sections of Oregon, California, and other western states.

REFERENCES

1. Bernard, Merrill, "Hydrometeorology—A Coordination of Meteorology and Hydrology," *Trans. Am. Geop. Union*, 1938, Part II, pp. 598–602.
2. ——— "Precipitation," Chapter II in Meinzer's *Hydrology*, 1942, pp. 32–55 (see reference 23 in Chapter 1).
3. ——— "The Role of Hydrometeorology in Planning the Water Economy of the West," *Trans. Am. Geop. Union*, April 1949, pp. 263–271.
4. Blumenstock, David I., "Rainfall Characteristics as Related to Soil Erosion," *U.S. Dept. Agr. Tech. Bull.* 698, 1939.
5. Blumenstock, David I., and C. W. Thornthwaite, "Climate and the World Pattern," *U.S. Dept. Agr. Yearbook*, 1941, pp. 98–127.
6. Choun, H. F., "Duststorms in the Southwestern Plains Area," *U.S. Dept. Agr. Monthly Weather Rev.*, June 1936, pp. 195–199.
7. Hepner, Frank E., "Forty Years of Weather Records," *Wyo. Agr. Exp. Sta. Bull.* 209, 1935.

8. Hildreth, A. C., J. R. Magness, and John W. Mitchell, "Effects of Climatic Factors on Growing Plants," *U.S. Dept. Agr. Yearbook,* 1941, pp. 292–307.

9. Holzman, Benjamin, "Sources of Moisture for Precipitation in the United States," *U.S. Dept. Agr. Tech. Bull.* 589, 1937.

10. Hoyt, John C., "Droughts of 1930–34," *U.S. Geol. Sur. Water-Supply Paper* 680, 1936.

11. ——— "Drought of 1936 with Discussion on the Significance of Drought in Relation to Climate," *U.S. Geol. Sur. Water-Supply Paper* 820, 1938.

12. Hoyt, W. G., and others, "Studies of Relations of Rainfall and Run-Off in the United States," *U.S. Geol. Sur. Water-Supply Paper* 772, 1936.

13. Hursh, C. R., "Local Climate in the Copper Basin of Tennessee as Modified by the Removal of Vegetation," *U.S. Dept. Agr. Cir.* 774, 1948.

14. Jarvis, C. S., "Rainfall Characteristics and Their Relation to Soils and Run-Off," *Trans. Am. Soc. C. E.,* Vol. 95, 1931, pp. 379–458.

15. Kincer, J. B., "Climate and Weather Data for the United States," *U.S. Dept. Agr. Yearbook,* 1941, pp. 685–699.

16. ——— *Normal Weather for the United States,* U.S. Dept. Com., Weather Bur., 1943.

17. ——— "Is Our Climate Changing? A Study of Long-Time Temperature Trends," *U.S. Dept. Agr. Monthly Weather Rev.,* September 1933, pp. 251–259.

18. ——— "Our Changing Climate," *Trans. Am. Geop. Union,* June 1946, pp. 342–347.

19. Lee, Charles H., "Total Evaporation for Sierra Nevada Watersheds by the Method of Precipitation and Runoff Differences," *Trans. Am. Geop. Union,* 1941, Part I, pp. 50–71.

20. Linney, Charles E., Fabian Garcia, and E. C. Hollinger, "Climate as It Affects Crops and Ranges in New Mexico," *N. Mex. Agr. Exp. Sta. Bull.* 182, 1930.

21. Linsley, Ray K., Jr., "Frequency and Seasonal Distribution of Precipitation over Large Areas," *Trans. Am. Geop. Union,* June 1947, pp. 445–450.

22. Miami Conservancy District, *Storm Rainfall of Eastern United States,* Dayton, Ohio, 1917, revised, 1936.

23. Namias, Jerome, and others, *An Introduction to the Study of Air Mass and Isentropic Analysis,* Am. Meteorological Soc., Milton, Mass., 1940.

24. Pagon, W. Watters, "Wind Velocity in Relation to Height above Ground," *Eng. News-Rec.,* May 23, 1935, pp. 742–745.

25. Platzman, George W., "Computation of Maximum Rainfall in the Willamette Basin," *Trans. Am. Geop. Union,* August 1948, pp. 467–472.

26. Potter, W. D., "Normalcy Tests of Precipitation and Frequency Studies of Runoff on Small Watersheds," *U.S. Dept. Agr. Tech. Bull.* 985, 1949.

27. Reichelderfer, F. W., "The How and Why of Weather Knowledge," *U.S. Dept. Agr. Yearbook,* 1941, pp. 128–153.

28. Rossby, C. G., "The Scientific Basis of Modern Meteorology," *U.S. Dept. Agr. Yearbook,* 1941, pp. 599–655.

29. Schaefer, Vincent J., "The Natural and Artificial Formation of Snow in the Atmosphere," *Trans. Am. Geop. Union,* August 1948, pp. 492–498.

30. Shands, A. L., and D. Ammerman, "Maximum Recorded United States Point Rainfall," *U.S. Dept. Com., Weather Bur. Tech. Paper* 2, 1947.

31. Spreen, William C., "A Determination of the Effect of Topography upon Precipitation," *Trans. Am. Geop. Union,* April 1947, pp. 285–290.

32. Thiessen, Alfred H., "Weather Glossary," *U.S. Dept. Com., Weather Bur., W.B.* 1445, 1946.
33. Thornthwaite, C. W., "Atlas of Climatic Types in the United States, 1900–1939," *U.S. Dept. Agr. Misc. Pub.* 421, 1941.
34. ——— "The Moisture-Factor in Climate," *Trans. Am. Geop. Union,* February 1946, pp. 41–48.
35. ——— "An Approach toward a Rational Classification of Climate," *The Geog. Rev.,* Vol. 38, No. 1, 1948, pp. 55–94.
36. United States Department of Agriculture, "Climatic Data, with Special Reference to Agriculture in the United States," *Yearbook,* 1941, Part 5, pp. 663–1228.
37. ——— *Atlas of American Agriculture, Part II, Climate,* 1922.
38. Weather Bureau, "Measurement of Precipitation," *U.S. Dept. Agr. Cir. E, Instrument Div.,* revised, 1936.
39. ——— "Instructions for Cooperative Observers," *U.S. Dept. Com. Cirs. B and C, Instrument Div.,* revised, 1941.
40. ——— "Maps of Seasonal Precipitation, Percentage of Normal by States, Fifty-Three Years, 1886–1938," *U.S. Dept. Com., W.B.* 1353, 1942.
41. ——— "Generalized Estimates of Maximum Possible Precipitation over the United States East of the 105th Meridian," *U.S. Dept. Com., Hydromet. Rep.* 23, 1947.
42. Weightman, Richard Hanson, "Forecasting from Synoptic Weather Charts," *U.S. Dept. Agr. Misc. Pub.* 236, 1936.
43. Woolley, R. R., "Utilization of Surface-Water Resources of Sevier Lake Basin, Utah," *U.S. Geol. Sur. Water-Supply Paper* 920, 1947.
44. Yarnell, David L., "Rainfall Intensity-Frequency Data," *U.S. Dept. Agr. Misc. Pub.* 204, 1935.

Chapter 7

RUNOFF AND STREAMFLOW

Runoff from precipitation in excess of local consumption constitutes the basic source of water supply for irrigation. When depths of precipitation are too great to be immediately evaporated, or to be stored in the root zones and subsequently returned to the atmosphere from the places of precipitation by evaporation from soil surfaces or plant transpiration or both, the excess depths run off and produce streamflow. Thus runoff is essentially a residual quantity. It is precipitation minus evapo-transpiration.

Excess depths of precipitation run off in two ways: (1) as movements of water along ground surfaces to stream channels, commonly referred to as direct runoff, overland runoff, surface runoff, or surface flow; and (2) as percolation of infiltrated water through permeable subsurface formations or underground passageways to stream channels, commonly referred to as groundwater runoff, groundwater flow, underground flow, sustained flow, or effluent seepage. Relative amounts of the two types of runoff from a particular area, also total quantities of runoff, depend on topographic and geologic conditions throughout the area, precipitation characteristics, and weather conditions preceding, during, and following precipitation.

In areas having certain geologic structures, some of the precipitation that infiltrates into the ground may percolate into inclined permeable strata and thence into deep water-bearing formations, overlaid by impermeable rock layers. Such quantities may remain in underground storage until released through artesian wells many miles away, sometimes many years after the precipitation took place. However, in most drainage basins such quantities do not amount to large percentages of the annual precipitation.

Runoff results from gravitational movements of precipitated moisture from places of precipitation toward lower levels. Small quantities of water moving along the ground surface constitute elements of surface runoff. Small quantities of water moving through subsurface formations are usually referred to as percolation, but when they emerge in stream channels they constitute elements of groundwater runoff.

When elements of runoff unite in stream channels in volumes sufficient to produce measurable discharges, they cause streamflow. Thus, streamflow is collected runoff. The terms runoff and streamflow are often used synonymously, but it seems better to think of runoff as movements of water from the land to the stream channels, and of streamflow as the subsequent movements of the collected runoff down the stream channels.

The flow of a stream at any location represents unused and unstored accumulated runoff from the drainage area above that location. Quantities of runoff from different drainage areas are determined by measuring the flow of the streams draining the different areas and correcting for the portions of the runoff that may have been diverted or stored above the gaging stations.

The following sections present brief discussions of runoff and streamflow data, runoff phenomena, streamflow characteristics, and flood characteristics, primarily from the viewpoint of irrigation. Runoff from melting snow and forecasts of runoff are taken up in the next chapter.

Runoff and Streamflow Units. Total quantities of runoff are usually expressed as inches of depth over the drainage area or as acre-feet. One acre-foot of water is the quantity required to cover an acre 1 foot deep; that is, 43,560 cubic feet. Rates of runoff may be given in inches per day, acre-feet per day, second-feet, or second-feet per square mile. Second-feet is an abbreviation for cubic feet per second. High rates of runoff from small drainage areas are often given in inches per hour. In runoff studies, the use of depths in inches is preferred since the results can be compared directly with depths of precipitation.

Total quantities of streamflow may be expressed as inches over the drainage area, acre-feet, or second-foot days. One second-foot day is the quantity of water represented by a flow of 1 second-foot for 1 day. Rates of streamflow are determined by discharge measurements and are computed in second-feet. Therefore, they are commonly given in second-feet. Maximum rates of streamflow during flood periods are often given in second-feet per square mile of drainage area. Table 1 gives some data that may be used in converting discharges to different units of runoff.

Records of total streamflow are compiled by days, months, and years. Daily and monthly quantities are not directly comparable with precipitation experienced during the same periods, because of dif-

TABLE 1

CONVERSION FACTORS FOR DISCHARGE AND RUNOFF QUANTITIES

Discharge, sec.-ft.		Runoff in 1 day		
	Acre-ft.	Millions of cu. ft.	Millions of U.S. gal.	In. on 1 sq. mile
1	1.983	0.0864	0.646	0.0372
2	3.967	0.1728	1.293	0.0744
3	5.950	0.2592	1.939	0.1116
4	7.934	0.3456	2.585	0.1488
5	9.917	0.4320	3.232	0.1860
6	11.90	0.5184	3.878	0.2231
7	13.88	0.6048	4.524	0.2603
8	15.87	0.6912	5.170	0.2975
9	17.85	0.7776	5.817	0.3347
10	19.83	0.8640	6.463	0.3719

ferences in soil-moisture, groundwater, stream-channel, and surface-reservoir storage. In compiling yearly totals, these differences are largely eliminated by using the water year ending September 30. By the end of September, crops in most sections of the United States have matured; stream stages have fallen to relatively low levels; and quantities of water held in storage are nearly the same as they were 12 months before.

Runoff and Streamflow Records. Runoff and streamflow records were begun in western United States during the latter part of the nineteenth century. The State Engineer of California established twelve gaging stations in the San Joaquin Valley in 1878. The State Engineer of Colorado installed a station on the Cache la Poudre River in 1883. Additional stations were subsequently installed on practically all important western streams. Early streamflow investigations in the western states were promoted by federal and state agencies, corporations, private companies, and other organizations, largely for use in developing irrigation.

In 1888, the Geological Survey, United States Department of the Interior, began streamflow measurements in the western states. The work was begun by a division known as the Hydrographic Survey. This division later became the Hydrographic Branch, then the Water Resources Branch. The work was soon expanded to include stream gagings in all parts of the country. It was also expanded to include investigations of groundwater, quality of water, and uses of water.[15a]

In 1948, the Water Resources Branch included four major divisions, namely, Surface Water, Ground Water, Quality of Water, and Water

TABLE 2

WESTERN OFFICES OF WATER RESOURCES BRANCH, UNITED STATES
GEOLOGICAL SURVEY, AS MAINTAINED IN 1948

Location of office	Resources division *	Location of office	Resources division *
Arizona:		Nevada:	
Flagstaff	SW	Boulder City	SW
Holbrook	QW	Carson City †	SW, GW
Phoenix	SW, GW	Ely	GW
Safford	SW	New Mexico:	
Tucson †	SW, GW	Albuquerque	GW, QW
Yuma	SW	Santa Fe †	SW
California:		North Dakota:	
Atascadero	SW	Bismarck †	SW, GW
Long Beach	GW	Dickinson	SW, QW
Log Angeles †	SW, WU	Grand Forks	GW
Merced	SW	Oklahoma:	
Oakland	SW	Norman	GW
Redding	SW	Oklahoma City †	SW
Sacramento	SW	Pryor	SW
San Bernardino	SW	Stillwater	QW
San Diego	SW	Oregon:	
San Francisco	SW	Medford	SW
Santa Barbara	GW	Portland †	SW, GW
Colorado:		Salem	SW
Denver †	SW, GW	South Dakota:	
Montrose	SW	Pierre †	SW
Idaho:		Rapid City	SW
Boise †	SW, GW	Texas:	
Idaho Falls	SW	Austin †	SW, GW, QW
Kansas:		Fort Worth	SW
Lawrence	GW	Houston	SW, GW
Norton	QW	Lufkin	SW
Topeka †	SW	San Angelo	SW
Montana:		Wichita Falls	SW
Billings	SW, WU	Utah:	
Helena †	SW	Logan	SW
Nebraska:		Salt Lake City	SW, GW, QW, WU
Cambridge	SW	Washington:	
Lincoln †	SW, GW, QW, WU	Tacoma	SW, WU
		Wyoming:	
		Cheyenne	GW
		Worland	QW

* SW—Surface Water.
  GW—Ground Water.
  QW—Quality of Water.
  WU—Water Utilization.
† Division Office.

Utilization. Activities were conducted through more than a hundred field offices, located in the larger cities. Table 2 shows the offices being maintained in the western states in 1948, also the divisions represented by each office.

In a 1949 reorganization, the Water Resources Branch became the Water Resources Division, and the three subdivisions, Surface Water, Ground Water, and Quality of Water, became branches instead of divisions. The Water Utilization organization was divided into two parts, Technical Coordination and Program Control, and both placed under the Chief of the Division.

During recent years, streamflow investigations have been greatly expanded, not only by the Geological Survey but also by other federal agencies, state bureaus, municipalities, corporations, and various organizations that utilize water supplies. However, most agencies that maintain gaging stations cooperate with the Geological Survey, so that the Survey is essentially a clearing house for all available data on streamflow. In 1949, about 6,000 gaging stations were being maintained in the United States.

Accuracy of Records. The accuracy of streamflow records at a particular station depends on (1) suitability of conditions at the station, (2) permanency of the control section, (3) precision and frequency of gage readings, (4) proper rating of the current meter, (5) accuracy and frequency of discharge measurements, and (6) adequate care in compiling the records. Probably the careful location of the station at a stable section with a permanent control, where the relation between stage and discharge remains constant, is of first importance. Detailed discussions of various factors involved in establishing stations, installing equipment, maintaining measurements, and compiling records have been adequately treated elsewhere.[9]

In general, current meter ratings should be accurate within 1 per cent. Under favorable conditions, discharge measurements should be accurate within 2 per cent, and daily streamflow records, within 5 per cent. Monthly and yearly records should be somewhat more accurate than daily records. The Geological Survey describes daily streamflow records as "excellent" when the errors are believed to be less than 5 per cent; "good" when less than 10 per cent; "fair" when less than 15 per cent; and "poor" when probably more than 15 per cent.

Streamflow records compiled during early years of measurements, when methods and procedures were being developed, were sometimes open to question. Some early records were recomputed as more reliable information became available. Later, investigations of conditions affecting streamflow, developments in measuring equipment, and better locations of gaging stations, particularly as regards permanent controls, led to improvements in accuracy. More recently, the increased use of recording gages, installation of artificial controls, development of a pigmy meter for measuring small flows, and use of heavy weights suspended from reels and cranes in measuring large rivers have resulted in still greater accuracy.[60]

Publication of Records. Runoff and streamflow records have been published in bulletins, water-supply papers, annual reports, and special reports of federal agencies, state governments, commissions, water districts, and other organizations. Early records collected by the Geological Survey were published in bulletins and annual reports. Since about 1900, the Survey records for each year have been published in water-supply papers.

Water-supply papers containing streamflow data are now published in 14 parts. Each part contains the records for a large drainage basin or a natural group of adjacent or related drainage basins. The different parts are as follows:

1. North Atlantic slope basins (St. John River to York River).
2. South Atlantic and eastern Gulf of Mexico basins (James River to Mississippi River).
3. Ohio River basin.
4. St. Lawrence River basin.
5. Hudson Bay and upper Mississippi River basins.
6. Missouri River basin.
7. Lower Mississippi River basin.
8. Western Gulf of Mexico basins.
9. Colorado River basin.
10. The Great Basin.
11. Pacific slope basins in California.
12. Pacific slope basins in Washington and upper Columbia River basin.
13. Snake River basin.
14. Pacific slope basins in Oregon and lower Columbia River basin.

Runoff and streamflow data now being published in water-supply papers include daily discharges, maximum, minimum, and mean monthly discharges, and total monthly and annual runoff. Descriptions of stations, lengths of record, extremes of stage and discharge, drainage areas, and notes on accuracy, regulation, diversions, and

other pertinent matters are also included. Tabulated indices of streamflow data are included, not only for records published by the Geological Survey but also for records published by other agencies. In some
cases, the indices include lists of unpublished data collected by other
agencies.

Streamflow records maintained along the Lower Rio Grande are
published in bulletins of the International Boundary and Water Commission, El Paso, Texas. Streamflow records maintained in Canada
are published in *Water Resources Papers,* prepared by the Dominion
Water and Power Bureau of the Department of Mines and Resources,
Ottawa, Canada.

RUNOFF PHENOMENA

A clear understanding of runoff phenomena is necessary in conducting hydrological studies for irrigation projects. Irrigation projects,
in order to produce profitable crops, must be supplied with adequate
quantities of water as needed during the growing season. The irrigation water, wherever and however secured, is a result of excess precipitation in some drainage basin. On most large irrigation projects,
water supplies are obtained from streamflow that originated as runoff
in upstream drainage areas. In arid regions of western United States,
nearly all streamflow is snow runoff from high mountain basins.
Surface runoff seldom results from rainfall in arid climates, except
during intense local storms of thunderstorm or cloudburst types.

Runoff conditions on lands included in irrigation projects are important in so far as they affect water supplies for beneficial use on
areas farther downstream. Groundwater runoff may be especially
important. Excessive applications of water to irrigated lands often
cause return flows that may be rediverted from streams for use on lands
at lower elevations.

Runoff Occurrence. Surface runoff occurs when rain falls, or snow
melts, faster than the water can infiltrate into the ground. Groundwater runoff occurs as previously infiltrated water reaches the streams
through springs or by percolation through the bed and banks of the
channels. When heavy continuous rainfall occurs on a drainage area,
the precipitated moisture is disposed of in the following manner (see
Figure 1):

1. Interception. Some of the precipitation, usually only a fraction of an inch, is intercepted by vegetation and held in temporary
storage on the plant foliage.

2. Temporary Surface Storage. A small portion of the precipitated moisture collects in depressions on the ground surface, in such surface litter as may be present, and in spaces between close-growing grasses. This is temporary surface storage, sometimes called surface detention. It seldom amounts to more than a small part of an inch.

3. Evaporation and Transpiration. Very small portions of the moisture, usually negligible during continued precipitation, may be reevaporated directly or returned to the atmosphere through plant transpiration.

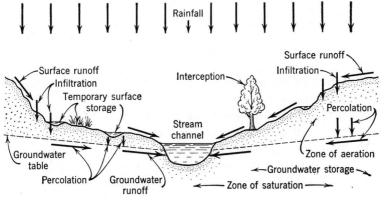

FIGURE 1. Disposal of moisture during heavy rainfall.

4. Infiltration. Some of the precipitated moisture, usually an appreciable portion, enters the ground through the surface soil. This portion saturates the soil in the upper parts of the zone of aeration and produces percolation downward toward the groundwater reservoir—the zone of saturation. Water reaching the zone of saturation raises the water table and thus increases the subterranean storage available for maintaining subsequent groundwater runoff.

5. Surface Runoff. The remainder of the precipitated moisture moves overland toward stream channels as surface runoff.

In hilly or mountainous regions, where water tables may not be continuous or may be at considerable depths, portions of the infiltrated water may be deflected toward stream channels by impervious subsurface strata or may enter perched bodies of groundwater that later contribute groundwater runoff. Portions of infiltrated water that reach stream channels through pervious formations in the upper parts of the zone of aeration, or through drainage tiles, are not greatly retarded. These portions, sometimes referred to as subsurface storm runoff, may be considered as parts of the surface runoff.

When the rain ceases and a period of fair weather begins, the following disposals of precipitated moisture take place:

6. Water held in temporary storage as plant interception usually evaporates within a few hours.

7. Surface runoff moving overland toward stream channels drains away more or less rapidly, depending on the slopes of the ground surface.

8. Water temporarily held as surface storage drains away, infiltrates into the soil, or evaporates, generally within a day or so after the end of the storm.

9. Infiltration ceases as soon as the field surfaces become free from water.

10. Water in the surface soil evaporates rapidly until the ground surface becomes dry.

11. If the rainfall occurred during the growing season, soil moisture in the root zones is reduced rapidly by plant transpiration.

12. Downward percolation of gravity water continues until excess moisture contents of the soil are reduced to field capacity.

13. Groundwater runoff continues at increased rates due to the higher water tables and steeper hydraulic gradients toward the stream channels.

Conditions during snowfall and subsequent snow melting are much the same as those discussed above, except that they usually take place more gradually and continue through longer periods. Rains of moderate intensity falling on deep snow covers may be wholly absorbed by the snow. Heavy rains on snow covers may accelerate melting and increase both runoff and infiltration. Infiltration rates, discussed in Chapter 5, are primarily dependent on soil conditions. They may be materially affected by the presence of frost. The different processes involved in runoff occurrence were described in greater detail by Hoyt, in an excellent contribution entitled "The Runoff Cycle."[31]

Factors Affecting Runoff. In a particular drainage basin, having definite physical characteristics, differences in runoff from season to season and from year to year are caused primarily by differences in weather conditions. Inasmuch as runoff is a residual quantity, precipitation minus losses by evaporation and transpiration, the factors that affect runoff are the factors that affect precipitation and losses.

Since precipitation is the source of runoff, variations in intensity, time distribution, and total amount of precipitation are of first importance. Temperature, which affects precipitation as well as evaporation, transpiration, and plant growth, is next in importance. Temperature conditions and resulting changes in plant growth affect seasonal runoff.

Factors that affect precipitation and temperature are discussed in the preceding chapter. Factors that affect evaporation and transpiration are discussed in Chapters 9 and 10.

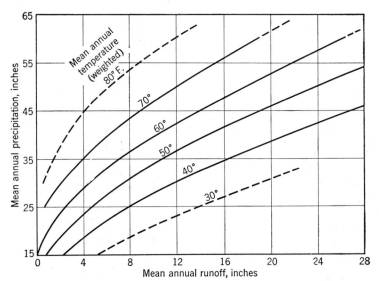

FIGURE 2. Relations between annual precipitation, temperature, and runoff. (After Langbein and others.)

In general, increased annual precipitation means increased annual runoff. For the same annual precipitation, increased temperature means increased losses, and increased losses mean decreased runoff. Figure 2 shows general relations between annual conditions of precipitation, temperature, and runoff as given by Langbein and others in a recent Geological Survey publication.[39]

Any major change in the physical conditions of a drainage basin that affects evaporation and transpiration, whether caused by man's activities or natural agencies, causes changes in runoff characteristics. Changes that affect evaporation and transpiration may include drainage of swamp lands, removal of forests, denudation of vegetation by fires or smelter fumes, or development of more luxuriant types of plant growth. Removal of forests on a test plot at Wagon Wheel Gap, Colorado, caused an increase of 15 per cent in annual runoff.[5]

Depths of runoff from drainage basins having different physical characteristics are affected by differences in physical characteristics, as well as by variations in weather conditions. In some drainage basins, different weather conditions may be due to variations in altitude. Therefore, altitude is one of the factors that affect runoff. Physical conditions that affect runoff are primarily topography, vegetation, root-zone soils, and subsurface geological formations. When physical and weather conditions are the same in two drainage basins, depths of runoff in inches during equivalent storms are not affected by differences in size and shape of the drainage basins.

Topography, vegetation, and soils affect infiltration and surface runoff during heavy rainfalls and periods of snow melting. They also affect amounts of soil moisture lost by evaporation and transpiration during intervals between precipitation. Soils and subsurface geological formations affect amounts of infiltration that reach the water table, percolation of groundwater toward stream channels, and characteristics of groundwater runoff.

Areas where topography and soils are favorable for plant growth have higher transpiration losses and therefore lower runoff than areas where conditions are unfavorable for plant growth. Low-lying flat lands, poorly drained, may lose relatively high percentages of their rainfall through evaporation from water and soil surfaces and transpiration by native vegetation. Consequently, they may yield relatively small amounts of runoff. Topographic characteristics of drainage areas that affect runoff have recently been classified for some valleys in northeastern United States.[38]

In mountainous regions, small drainage areas with northern exposures may yield more runoff than areas of similar size and elevation with southern exposures, because of decreased losses of moisture on the northern exposures.[11] Steep rocky slopes with scant vegetation may yield relatively high percentages of their precipitation as runoff. Due to easterly air movements, precipitation and runoff in the high mountain ranges of the West are commonly greater on the western slopes than on the eastern slopes.

Effects of Altitude. In mountainous regions, runoff commonly increases with altitude up to certain elevations, usually not far from timberline. This is due to decreasing temperatures, decreasing amounts of moisture consumed by evapo-transpiration, and increasing precipitation. As mentioned in the preceding chapter, precipitation generally increases with altitude up to elevations where the greater portions of the atmospheric moisture have been precipitated. Above these elevations, especially above timberline, different relations between altitude and runoff begin to develop.

Alpine zones above timberline have special hydrologic characteristics. In such zones, nearly all precipitation takes place in the form of snow, freezing temperatures occur during all months of the year,

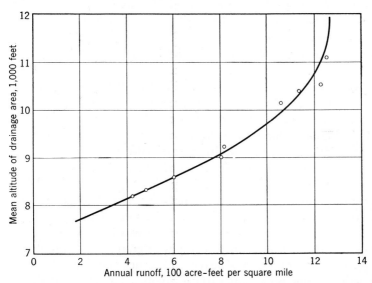

FIGURE 3.   Relation between mean altitude and runoff in San Juan basin, Colorado.

winter runoff is practically nonexistent, and snowmelt water is produced only during the warmer hours of midsummer days. At the higher altitudes, sunlight is unusually intense and dissipation of snow takes place largely by evaporation.[42]   Consequently, in the higher mountains of western United States, runoff often decreases with altitude at elevations above about 11,000 or 12,000 feet, depending on latitude.

Figure 3 shows relations between altitude and average annual runoff in the upper end of the San Juan River basin, southern Colorado, for 1916 to 1925, based on data reported by Hart.[21]   Plotted points are identified in the original publication.   A new curve has been drawn to indicate the relations between runoff and altitude that probably begin to develop at the higher elevations.   Comprehensive data on runoff from areas of different elevation in the Rocky Mountain region were published by Follansbee in 1922.[15]

Surface and Groundwater Runoff. During high stages of stream-flow, whether caused by heavy rains or melting snows, both surface and groundwater runoff pass down the stream channels. During rising stages and the early period of falling stages, surface runoff normally constitutes the larger portions of the flow. However, surface runoff usually drains away rapidly after the end of a storm, or the completion of melting, and decreases to small percentages of the total flow in a few days. During the time of falling stages, part of the flow is water draining out of the channel storage which had been filled by the preceding surface runoff.

Groundwater runoff, low at the beginning of a storm following a long interval of dry weather, probably does not begin to increase until after peak stages have occurred in the stream channel. In fact, groundwater runoff may decrease during the period of rising stages. In some places, stream stages may rise to levels higher than the water table in the bank formations, thus stopping effluent seepage and causing percolation into the adjoining materials.

During most storms, groundwater runoff probably reaches a maximum rate of flow rather late in the period of surface runoff. It then decreases gradually during the remainder of the flood, also during subsequent periods of dry weather. The rate of decrease, relatively rapid at first, becomes less and less as dry weather continues.

Figure 4 shows assumed hydrographs of groundwater and total runoff during and following a heavy rainstorm. The area between the two hydrographs represents surface runoff. The curve of decreasing total runoff during the later period of surface runoff is often called a recession curve. The curve of decreasing groundwater flow is commonly called a depletion curve. The portion under the flood hydrograph is sometimes called base flow.

Depletion curves, arbitrarily extended backward into periods of flood runoff, somewhat as shown in Figure 4, may be used in estimating proportions of groundwater and surface runoff during times of high streamflow. Thus far, no satisfactory method of accurately determining proportions of groundwater and surface runoff at times of combined runoff has been devised. Meinzer has suggested that groundwater flow during a period of falling stages, after surface runoff has ceased, might be evaluated by deducting channel-storage contributions from discharges measured at a gaging station.[43] In drainage basins where surface runoff is relatively pure and groundwater runoff has an appreciable salt content, chemical analyses of the flows may indicate the proportions of the two types of runoff.[41]

Although estimates of groundwater and surface runoff for particular times of high stages are only approximate, estimates of such quantities for entire water years probably can be made within reasonable limits of accuracy. Several years ago the author estimated annual depths of groundwater and surface runoff in the Miami Valley, southwestern Ohio, assuming groundwater flow to be represented by lines drawn through low points on the hydrographs.[27] The aim was to draw

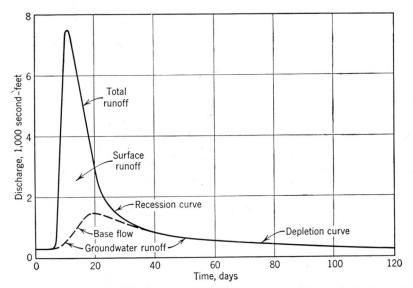

FIGURE 4. Assumed hydrographs of groundwater and total runoff during and following a heavy rainstorm.

the lines so that the drainage and other subsurface storm runoff would be included with surface runoff. No percolation was assumed to take place during the growing season. A few years later, Meinzer and Stearns made a similar study for Pomperaug Basin, Connecticut.[44]

In 1936, Hoyt reviewed different methods of separating groundwater runoff from surface runoff and published annual data for several drainage basins in central and eastern United States.[32] Table 3 shows some data abstracted from Hoyt's report. Annual depths of precipitation and precipitation minus total runoff are included in the table, as well as annual depths of surface, groundwater, and total runoff.

Annual groundwater runoff is usually much less variable from year to year than annual surface runoff. In the Miami Valley above Dayton, the maximum annual groundwater runoff in 26 years was only

TABLE 3

ANNUAL RUNOFF, PRECIPITATION, AND LOSSES IN SOME RIVER BASINS [32]

(Depths in inches)

River basin	Station	Years *	Pre-cipita-tion	Runoff			Precipi-tation — total runoff
				Total	Sur-face	Ground-water	
Red	Grand Forks, N. Dak.	1928–32	18.53	0.59	0.35	0.24	17.94
Minnesota	Mankato, Minn.	1930–32	22.22	0.69	0.42	0.27	21.53
St. Croix	Rush City, Minn.	1928–32	25.32	7.27	3.76	3.51	18.05
La Crosse	West Salem, Wis.	1928–32	30.35	9.92	2.64	7.28	20.43
Iowa	Wapello, Iowa	1928–32	32.83	7.00	4.28	2.72	25.83
Skunk	Augusta, Iowa	1928–32	35.85	7.84	5.47	2.37	28.01
Pecatonica	Freeport, Ill.	1928–32	31.95	10.01	4.77	5.24	21.94
Mississippi	Keokuk, Iowa	1928–32	28.64	5.98	3.36	2.62	22.66
Neosho	Iola, Kan.	1928–32	33.07	4.92	4.06	0.86	28.15
Miami	Dayton, Ohio	1894–1919	37.07	11.85	7.77	4.08	25.22
Pomper-aug	Bennetts' Bridge, Conn.	1914–16	44.48	20.66	11.90	8.76	23.82 †
Chatta-hoochee	West Point, Ga.	1928–32	59.65	23.14	11.59	11.55	36.51

* Water years ending September 30, except for Red, Mississippi, Neosho, and Chatta-hoochee rivers.

† Includes 0.62 inch added to groundwater storage.

3.14 times the minimum annual value, whereas the maximum an-nual surface runoff was 15.3 times the minimum annual value. In sand-hill regions such as certain parts of Nebraska, annual runoff may be almost entirely groundwater flow.

Proportions of rainfall that reach stream channels as surface runoff during particular storms are affected by both weather and physical conditions. In general, they are governed by variations in intensity and duration of the storm rainfall, vegetation, soil conditions that in-fluence infiltration, and topographic conditions that affect the over-land movement of water. Storm rainfalls occurring in close succes-sion, before previously accumulated soil moisture can be depleted, produce more surface runoff than storms of similar intensity and duration occurring less frequently. In hilly or mountainous drainage basins, overland movements of precipitated water are facilitated by the steeper ground slopes, so that higher rates and greater amounts of surface runoff are experienced.

Percentages of precipitation that ultimately reach stream channels as groundwater flow depend on the quantities of water that percolate to the water table or to impervious strata by which they are deflected toward stream channels. Rates at which they reach stream channels depend on permeabilities of the soil and underlying geological formations and on the increased elevations of the water table caused by the increased underground storage. Movements of water through the ground take place slowly. Groundwater runoff maintains streamflow at gradually decreasing rates after surface runoff ceases and during subsequent periods of deficient precipitation.

Annual Runoff. Depths of annual runoff in the United States vary widely from year to year and from place to place. The annual runoff for the entire country averaged about 8.7 inches during the 25 years from 1921 to 1945.[39] Variations in annual runoff from place to place in the central and eastern parts of the country, where humid climates prevail, are less pronounced than in the western states where climates vary from extremely arid to highly humid.

In western United States, depths of annual runoff vary from practically zero in local desert areas such as Death Valley, southeastern California, to about 200 inches in some mountain basins of the Northwest. Records for Baker River near Concrete, Washington, show a total runoff of 191 inches during the water year 1918, and an average annual runoff of 147 inches during 18 years of measurement up to 1931. Baker River drains an area of about 184 square miles heading on high mountain slopes near Mount Baker, where heavy rainfalls occur during the spring and fall months and deep snows accumulate every winter. Several gaging stations on streams draining mountain basins in Washington show average depths of runoff exceeding 100 inches annually.

Table 4 shows median streamflows in second-feet and median depths of runoff in inches for some drainage areas in western United States, as measured during the 25 years from 1921 to 1945. The table was compiled largely from Geological Survey data assembled by Harbeck and Langbein [20] but includes a few average discharges taken from water-supply papers giving streamflow data for 1945. Depths of runoff were computed from median discharges and drainage areas.

Depths of annual runoff in Table 4 vary from 0.15 inch for the drainage area of the Little Colorado River above Grand Falls, Arizona, to 84.2 inches for the drainage area of the South Fork of the

TABLE 4

MEDIAN ANNUAL RUNOFF IN SOME WESTERN RIVER BASINS,
1921 TO 1945 [20]

State	River and gaging station	Drainage area, sq. miles	Median flow, sec.-ft.	Median runoff, in.
Arizona	Colorado near Grand Canyon	137,800	18,500	1.82
	Gila near Solomonsville	7,950	350	0.60
	Little Colorado at Grand Falls	21,200	240	0.15
	Salt near Roosevelt	4,310	670	2.11
California	Kings at Piedra	1,694	2,070	16.6
	Santa Ana near Mentone	189	70	5.02
	Trinity at Lewiston	724	1,340	25.1
	West Walker near Coleville	182	243	18.1
Colorado	Roaring Fork at Glenwood Springs	1,460	1,350	12.5
	South Platte at Balzac *	17,700	374	0.29
	Arkansas at La Junta *	12,200	282	0.31
Idaho	Salmon at Whitebird	13,550	9,420	9.44
	Snake near Heise	5,740	6,210	14.7
	Clearwater at Spalding *	9,570	13,720	19.5
Montana	Judith near Utica	331	48	1.97
	Yellowstone at Corwin Springs	2,630	2,630	13.6
	Clark Fork near Heron *	21,800	18,290	11.4
Nevada	Humboldt at Palisade	5,010	285	0.77
New Mexico	Pecos below Alamogordo Dam *	4,390	264	0.82
	Rio Grande at Otowi Bridge	14,300	1,670	1.59
	San Juan at Farmington	6,580	2,650	5.47
Oregon	Columbia near The Dalles	237,000	165,000	9.45
	John Day at Service Creek	5,090	1,520	4.05
	Umqua near Elkton	3,680	6,300	23.2
Texas	Guadalupe at New Braunfels	1,666	333	2.71
	Neches at Evadale	7,908	6,780	11.6
Utah	Colorado near Cisco	24,100	8,220	4.63
	Green at Green River	40,600	5,980	2.00
	San Juan near Bluff	23,000	2,890	1.71
Washington	Columbia at Grand Coulee Dam	74,100	102,000	18.7
	Skykomish, South Fork, near Index	355	2,200	84.2
	Spokane at Spokane	4,350	5,550	17.3
Wyoming	North Platte at Saratoga	2,880	1,070	5.04
	Tongue near Dayton	204	177	11.8

* From water-supply papers on "Surface Water Supply of the United States, 1945."

Skykomish River above Index, Washington. Tabulated depths of
runoff for some drainage basins may be considerably lower than
actual depths of runoff, because of the consumption of water on irrigated lands above the gaging stations. The South Platte, Arkansas,
and Pecos rivers may be cited as examples.

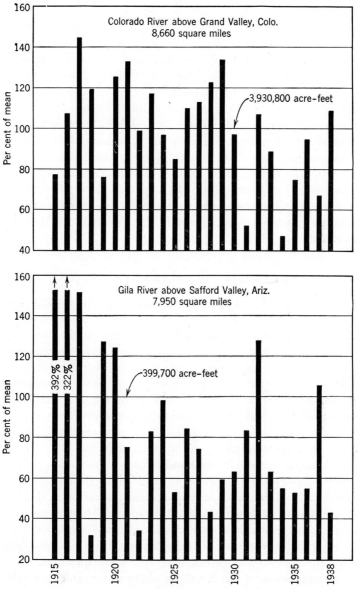

FIGURE 5. Annual runoff in Colorado and Gila River basins, water years 1915 to
1938, inclusive. (Plotted from data in *U.S. Geol. Sur. Water-Supply Papers* 918
and 1049.)

The period from 1921 to 1945 included some unusually wet years as well as the drought years that occurred during the thirties. Earlier records of streamflow indicate that depths of runoff during the preceding 25 years probably were higher than during 1921 to 1945.

Figure 5 shows yearly variations in runoff on two widely separated drainage areas of similar size, for the 24 water years from 1915 to 1938. Yearly quantities of runoff are plotted as percentages of mean annual runoff. Quantities of mean annual runoff in acre-feet are shown at the 100 per cent lines. The upper diagram shows runoff from 8,660 square miles drained by the Colorado River above diversions to the Grand Valley Project, western Colorado, where runoff comes principally from melting snow. The lower diagram shows runoff from 7,950 square miles drained by the Gila River above diversions to the Safford Valley, southeastern Arizona, where runoff comes largely from storm rainfalls. Some streamflow is diverted for irrigation in both drainage basins.

STREAMFLOW CHARACTERISTICS

After elements of runoff in the upstream portions of a drainage basin unite in the stream channel to produce streamflow, their further movements toward lower elevations are controlled largely by conditions along the stream channel. As the flow proceeds downstream, it is usually augmented by runoff from downstream areas, either as discharges brought to the channel by tributary streams, or as surface and ground-water flows entering the channel directly. At the same time, the flow is gradually diminished by evaporation from the stream surface, evaporation from moistened soil surfaces along the stream channel, transpiration by vegetation along the stream banks, and percolation into pervious materials along the bed and banks of the stream.

If the stream enters an arid region and passes through areas where no runoff takes place, the flow may gradually decrease in downstream directions, owing to losses along the channel. Many large rivers in western United States show such characteristics. Many small streams in the West dry up completely as they emerge from mountain canyons and pass through regions of but little or no precipitation.

When streams flow through valleys where water tables are relatively high, so that groundwater runoff percolates into the channels, they are known as effluent. When they flow through regions where water tables are relatively low, so that water percolates from the streams into formations along their beds and banks, they are known as influent.

Thus, many western streams are effluent in mountain basins where they originate and later become influent as they leave the mountains and flow through arid territories.

Factors Affecting Streamflow. The factors that affect streamflow throughout the length of a stream may be briefly summarized in three groups as follows:

1. Factors that affect intensities and depths of runoff on the tributary drainage areas as discussed on the preceding pages.
2. Factors that affect the time of arrival of the runoff at the main stream.
3. Such additional factors as may cause changes in flow along the location of the main stream.

For similar rates of surface runoff throughout different drainage basins, the principal factors that affect the time of arrival of the runoff at the main stream, also the rates of flow produced therein, include the following:

1. Size and shape of the drainage basin.
2. Arrangement and length of tributary channels.
3. Ground slopes toward tributary channels.
4. Size and gradients of tributary channels.
5. Natural or artificial storage along tributary channels.

The time required for surface runoff in the most remote part of a drainage basin to reach the main stream at the location under consideration is called the time of concentration. For a particular drainage basin, the time of concentration varies with the intensity of the surface runoff and the amount of water already held in surface storage along the tributaries. Considerations of time factors are especially important in studies of maximum rates of flood flow.

Factors that may cause changes in streamflow after runoff reaches a stream channel include various physical, hydrologic, and climatic conditions, as well as such artificial controls as may have been imposed by man through the construction of engineering works along the stream and the diversion or storage of water for beneficial uses. Some or all of these factors may affect flows in tributary channels as well as in the main stream.

Sizes, shapes, slopes, and other physical conditions along different lengths of a stream channel affect depths and rates of flow. Sizes of the channel at different locations determine the capacities that are available for channel storage. The nature of the soil and subsurface formations along the channel, particularly as regards permeability, affect capacities that may be utilized in bank storage. Materials along the bed and banks of the stream, together with climatic conditions, affect the growth of vegetation along the channel and losses of water by transpiration. Climatic conditions, especially temperature, affect rates of evaporation from the stream surface and from moist materials along the channel. Temperature conditions also affect rates of stream-flow.

During winter months, freezing temperatures may cause the formation of ice along the channel, thus retarding streamflow, affecting stage-discharge relations, and complicating streamflow measurements.[30] Small streams in regions of severe winter climate may be entirely frozen during protracted cold spells. Even when the streams remain free from ice, their flows may be slightly retarded by low temperatures, due to increased viscosity of the water. In the Kootenai River near Copeland, Idaho, temperature decreases down to 32 degrees F. reduced the flow about 3 per cent, according to Eisenlohr.[14] When snow covers are melting, freezing temperatures during the night cause diurnal fluctuations in streamflow, as discussed in the next chapter.

Rates of percolation into permeable formations along the channel are also reduced by decreases in temperature. Rates of percolation from underground storage into the stream channel are not materially influenced by changes in air temperature, inasmuch as temperatures of the groundwater remain approximately the same.

Rates and total quantities of streamflow at different locations along a stream may be materially affected by drainage improvements, direct diversions, return flow, or storage of water in surface reservoirs. Rates of flow may be affected by power dams or other regulatory structures. Since February 1935, the flow of the Colorado River at Black Canyon, near Las Vegas, Nevada, has been fully regulated by Lake Mead, the reservoir formed by Hoover Dam, where 2 years of normal runoff can be impounded. As streams pass through irrigated regions, their discharges may be augmented by return flow, either entering the channel directly as groundwater runoff or brought to the channel through natural drainage courses or artificial drainage ditches.

Channel Storage. Channel storage is the actual volume of water in a stream channel at any time. The capacity available for channel storage during different stages of flow in a particular length of channel can be computed from measurements of areas at representative cross sections. During flood flows that overtop the banks of a channel, the similar storage in the valley along the channel is called valley storage.

Channel storage is filled as the stream surface rises and emptied as the stream surface falls. Channel storage acts as any surface reservoir in that it tends to smooth out the hydrograph at the downstream end of the storage. It reduces initial discharges, reduces and retards the peak discharge, and increases and prolongs the smaller discharges toward the end of the high-water period.

Effects of channel storage on streamflow occur to some degree during all periods of rising and falling stages. They are most pronounced during sudden major changes in flow, as during the passage of a flash flood. Extremely high discharges caused by the sudden failure of dams are rapidly reduced by channel and valley storage as the released waters move downstream. When the Castlewood Dam, south of Denver, Colorado, failed on August 3, 1933, released storage started down the valley at a maximum rate of about 126,000 second-feet. By the time the flood reached Denver, 35 miles downstream, channel and valley storage had reduced the maximum rate of flow to about 15,000 second-feet.[29]

Bank Storage. Bank storage is the water that percolates into the banks of a stream channel when the stages rise above the water table in the bank formations, then returns to the channel as effluent seepage when the stages fall below the water table.

The capacity of the banks to hold influent seepage depends on the porosity and permeability of the bank materials. The actual amount of water that percolates into the banks during a period of high streamflow depends on the porosity and permeability of the materials, the height of the stream stages above the water table in the bank formations, and the time the stream continues to flow at high stages.

The approximate amount of bank storage that takes place in a length of channel can be estimated from continuous records of discharge at the upper and lower ends of the stream section during relatively long periods of time. Effects of bank storage on streamflow are similar to effects of channel storage, but much more gradual and prolonged. Contributions of bank storage to low-water flow in large rivers flowing through permeable materials, such as the Missouri, may be of considerable magnitude.[6]

Gains in Streamflow. Gains in streamflow in a particular length of channel occur when discharges entering the channel exceed those lost through natural processes or diverted for various uses. Discharges entering the channel may be runoff from adjoining drainage areas or returns of unused water diverted at upstream locations. They may enter the channel through natural drainage courses, through drainage ditches, as direct surface runoff from lands along the stream, or as effluent seepage along the bed and banks of the channel.

Groundwater runoff entering the channel as effluent seepage may be contributions from the underground reservoir, the draining out of water temporarily held in bank storage, or invisible return flows from irrigated areas where excess depths of water have been applied to the fields. In streams passing through irrigated regions, gains in flow

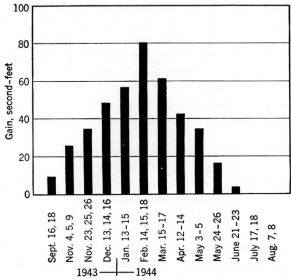

FIGURE 6. Streamflow gains, Gila River, Thatcher to Calva, Arizona. (Plotted from data in *U.S. Geol. Sur. Water-Supply Paper* 1009.)

during the summer and fall months often are caused principally by invisible return flows and drainage recoveries of excess irrigation water. Gains in groundwater flow sometimes occur at the end of the growing season, owing to reductions in amounts of soil moisture required for plant transpiration.

Figure 6 shows streamflow gains in the 46 miles of the Gila River between Thatcher and Calva, Arizona, as measured by the Geological Survey in 1943 and 1944. Although losses were observed in some intermediate sections of the 46-mile length, net results at Calva were gains on all dates except in July and August 1944, when practically no changes could be detected. Return flows and drainage recoveries are discussed at greater length in the chapter on irrigation water supplies.

Losses of Streamflow.   Losses of streamflow in a particular length of channel may be caused by diversions, percolation into adjoining pervious materials, direct evaporation from the stream surface, evaporation from moist materials along the channel, or transpiration by vegetation growing along the bed and banks of the stream.   In streams flowing through irrigated regions, the principal reductions in flow are caused by diversions of water for irrigation.   Such reductions are often referred to as streamflow depletion.

Streams flowing through alluvial valleys may lose appreciable quantities of water by percolation.   When adjoining water tables are above the bed of the channel, portions of the percolation that take place during relatively high stages may be held temporarily as bank storage and returned to the stream during subsequent low stages.   When water tables are below the bed of the channel, portions of the flow that enter the pervious materials may percolate to distances and depths from which they cannot return to the channel.   Percolation losses in a particular length of channel may be estimated from continuous records of discharge at the upstream and downstream ends of the section, proper allowances being made for the evaporation and transpiration losses that may occur within the section.

Losses of streamflow caused by direct evaporation from the stream surface seldom constitute appreciable portions of the flow.   However, total losses caused by evaporation and transpiration along the channel may be appreciable, especially in the smaller streams.   Investigations in a section of Coldwater Canyon near San Bernardino, California, in 1932, showed daily rates of evapo-transpiration averaging 0.42 acre-inch per day during July, 0.44 acre-inch during August, and 0.37 acre-inch during September, with a total loss of 64 acre-inches per acre for the 6 months from May to October.[8]   Similar investigations on Farmington Creek, northern Utah, showed that during the late summer of 1944 total losses by evaporation and transpiration amounted to about one-third of the streamflow.[12]

Losses of water by evaporation and transpiration along the channel sometimes cause small diurnal fluctuations in flow.   This is because the losses occur largely during daylight hours and are relatively small during the night.   Maximum stages usually occur late in the forenoon, and minimum stages late in the afternoon.   Troxell reported studies of such fluctuations in eight southern California streams of different sizes and characteristics.[55]   His hydrographs showed that total changes in stage varied from a few tenths of an inch to a little more than an inch. The fluctuations probably disappear rapidly as they move downstream.

Evapo-transpiration losses along stream channels are discussed in more detail in the chapter on land evaporation and transpiration.

Daily Streamflow.   In an unregulated stream, free from upstream diversions, the most pronounced changes in rates of streamflow from day to day usually are caused by changes in surface runoff during periods of storm rainfall.

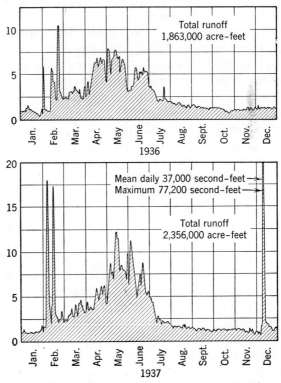

FIGURE 7.   Hydrographs of daily streamflow in San Joaquin River, Friant, California, during 1936 and 1937. (Plotted from data in *U.S. Geol. Sur. Water-Supply Papers.*)

Appreciable variations in streamflow from day to day sometimes are caused by variations in surface runoff during the spring melting of accumulated winter snowfalls, as when sudden increases in temperature cause increased rates of melting or sudden decreases in temperature cause freezing of the snowmelt water. Warm rains, falling when the snow is nearly gone, may cause pronounced increases in daily streamflow. During periods of continuous warm weather, free from heavy rainfall, snow runoff and resulting streamflow increase gradually and slowly to maximum rates, then decrease gradually and slowly until the ground surfaces become drained.

Changes in rates of groundwater runoff during times of storm rainfall or snow melting take place so slowly that their effects on daily

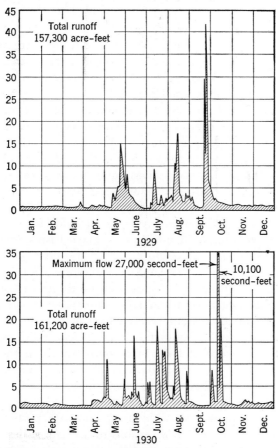

FIGURE 8. Hydrographs of daily streamflow in Pecos River near Alamogordo Dam, New Mexico, during 1929 and 1930. (Plotted from data in *U.S. Geol. Sur. Water-Supply Papers*.)

streamflow generally are small in comparison with effects produced by changes in surface runoff. The gradual decreases in daily streamflow that take place slowly during dry weather after surface runoff ceases are caused entirely by decreasing rates of groundwater runoff (see Figure 4).

In sand-hill regions, where nearly all the precipitation enters the ground, daily streamflows are primarily groundwater runoff. They may be almost uniform throughout the year. They usually increase gradually and slowly during periods of heavy rainfall, then decrease more gradually and more slowly during subsequent periods of no precipitation.

Figure 7 shows daily rates of streamflow in the San Joaquin River at Friant, California, where runoff results from both rainfall and melting snow. Figure 8 shows daily rates of streamflow in the Pecos River near Alamogordo Dam, New Mexico, where more runoff results from rainfall. Both figures are merely illustrative. They are for certain years, selected at random, and therefore cannot be considered as representing average conditions. Several reservoirs have been constructed in the San Joaquin drainage basin above Friant, and some diversions for irrigation are made in the Pecos drainage basin above Alamogordo Dam. Drainage areas total about 1,600 square miles above Friant, and about 4,400 square miles above Alamogordo Dam.

In 1949, Lane and Kai Lei proposed the standard deviation of streamflow, based on duration curves, as an index for comparing the variability of streamflow in different drainage basins.[37] Low values of the index mean low streamflow variability, and high values, high variability. They studied streamflow variability by this method in more than 220 drainage basins, mostly in northeastern United States. The basins included areas where streamflow records had been maintained 10 years or longer, and where effects of artificial controls were negligible. The studies showed that geologic conditions, including soils, and the presence of lakes or swamps constitute the most pronounced influences on variability. Values of the index were especially low in sections of Nebraska, where the watersheds include large areas of sand hills.

Monthly Streamflow. Monthly streamflow at a particular station, unless modified by upstream diversions or storage, varies with runoff conditions in the drainage basin above the station. At most gaging stations, months of high streamflow are months of high surface runoff in the upstream drainage area. Sometimes high surface runoff occurring late in the month does not reach the gaging station and become recorded as streamflow until the beginning of the succeeding month. Natural flows may be materially changed by storage regulation, diversions, or return flow.

Streams supplied principally by runoff from melting snow covers commonly experience high monthly streamflow during the spring and

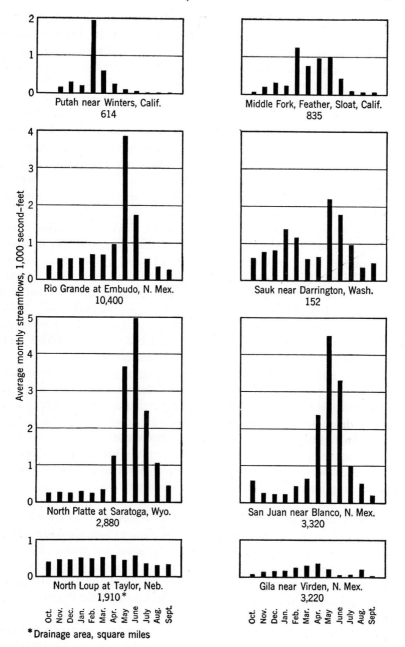

FIGURE 9. Monthly distributions of flow in some western streams during water
year 1945. (*Plotted from data in U.S. Geol. Sur. Water-Supply Papers.*)

early summer months. Streams supplied principally by runoff from rainfall commonly experience high monthly streamflow during months of heavy precipitation. Streams supplied by both types of runoff experience high monthly flows during the spring and early summer and may experience high monthly flows during other seasons of the year. Monthly streamflows in most sections of the country are normally low during the late summer and early fall. In some regions, above normal monthly streamflows during the late summer and early fall may be caused by storm rainfalls or by return flow from irrigation projects.

Figure 9 shows monthly distributions of flow in some western streams during 1945, plotted from records published in the Geological Survey water-supply papers. Average rates of flow during each month of the water year are shown by the vertical bars.

The diagram for the North Loup River at Taylor, Nebraska, shows the approximately uniform conditions of flow that may occur when the drainage basin includes large areas of sand hills. Some storage and relatively large irrigated areas exist in the upper Rio Grande basin, which includes parts of northern New Mexico and southern Colorado. The 10,400 square miles above Embudo include 2,940 square miles in a closed basin that comprises part of the Colorado area. Drainage areas above the other stations include no appreciable storage and only relatively small areas of irrigated land.

Average monthly streamflows at most gaging stations vary widely from year to year as well as during the different months of the year. In general, minimum average flows for particular months occur during the driest years, and maximum average flows during the wettest years. In irrigated regions, all summer flows are sometimes diverted and consumed in crop production, so that minimum streamflows at the gaging stations may be practically zero. Maximum average streamflows during particular months are commonly caused by floods.

Table 5 shows ranges in average monthly streamflow during several years of record at some gaging stations in Washington, compiled from data published in Bartholet's report.[4] Maximum and minimum average flows in percentage of mean monthly flows are shown for each month of the water year. Minimum monthly flows were sometimes lower than 20 per cent of the mean, and maximum monthly flows, sometimes higher than 300 per cent of the mean. The Palouse River shows the greater ranges in monthly flow.

The Palouse and Colville rivers are in the eastern part of Washington, where the annual precipitation is about 20 inches. The Methow River drains an area on the eastern slopes of the Cascades, and the

TABLE 5

RANGES IN MONTHLY STREAMFLOW AT SOME STATIONS
IN WASHINGTON [4]

Stream Station	Sauk Darrington		Lewis Near Amboy		Methow Pateros		Colville Meyer Falls		Palouse Hooper	
Area, sq. miles	293		665		1,810		. . . .		2,210	
Years	16		20		17		11		15	

Month	Monthly flow, in per cent of mean monthly discharge									
	Max.	Min.	Max.	Min.	Max.	Min.	Max.	Min.	Max.	Min.
October	233	33	347	35	190	75	315	37	208	18
November	220	24	216	17	178	73	301	37	316	20
December	300	34	289	37	179	74	294	42	373	9
January	242	32	216	38	153	77	268	25	333	6
February	215	19	190	31	156	79	245	36	297	14
March	189	33	193	53	260	58	189	39	303	16
April	150	51	138	53	242	18	226	20	306	27
May	145	50	147	53	189	35	199	20	214	46
June	159	34	200	33	148	45	237	20	160	44
July	217	38	276	46	204	43	233	26	253	39
August	179	58	183	68	190	60	220	24	294	26
September	307	48	301	54	166	60	343	33	270	30

Sauk and Lewis rivers drain areas on the western slopes. No appreciable regulation of streamflow was being made in any of the drainage basins during the years represented by the table. Some percentages of the summer flows were diverted for irrigation above the Colville and Methow stations.

In some of the smaller rivers of western United States, ranges in average monthly streamflow during long periods of years may be even greater than those shown in Table 5.

Annual Streamflow. Annual streamflows, as recorded for water years ending September 30, usually represent unused annual runoff in the drainage basins above the gaging stations. Exceptions may occur when appreciable surface runoff takes place late in September, so that it does not reach the gaging stations and become recorded as streamflow until early in October. Variations in annual streamflow throughout the country, also from year to year at particular stations, are substantially the same as variations in annual runoff (see preceding section on annual runoff).

Annual streamflows from year to year often are less variable in regions where runoff comes largely from melting snows than in regions where runoff comes mostly from storm rainfalls. Median annual streamflows at some stations in western United States, for the 25-year period from 1921 to 1945, are given in Table 4. Average discharges for entire periods of record at stations maintained 10 years or longer are given in the Geological Survey water-supply papers on "Surface Water Supply of the United States."

FLOOD CHARACTERISTICS

Studies of flood characteristics often are needed in planning irrigation projects, particularly in designing the larger and more important project structures. Storage dams, diversion dams, intakes, bridges, and other structures located along the paths of floods must be designed to pass flood flows safely, without damages to the structures and without producing backwater or other conditions that may damage upstream or downstream lands and property.

The principal flood characteristic that requires consideration in most designs is the maximum rate of flow that may be expected to occur in the future. Other characteristics that may need consideration include the total volume of flow above a normal flood stage and the probable frequency of flood flows of different magnitude.

Total volumes of flood flow may materially affect the design of spillways at storage dams where freeboard storage is to be utilized as an aid in controlling maximum reservoir levels. Total flood volumes and probable times of occurrence may also affect the water supplies that can be made available for use on project lands. When flood flows can be impounded in surface reservoirs, they can be released later, as needed, to maintain streamflow at downstream locations while diversions of water are required for irrigation.

Frequencies of flood flows of different magnitude may affect the design of costly structures where partial failures would not cause calamities. For some structures, the payment of damages once in a long period of years may be more economical than construction to provide for an ultimate maximum flood that may not occur more than once in a thousand years.

Floods are high stages of streamflow, produced by high rates of surface runoff. Any pronounced increase in streamflow, where contributions from surface runoff are considerably greater than the prevailing groundwater runoff, may be called a flood. For most rivers, no definite limits are established above which streamflows become flood flows. At some Weather Bureau stations, rivers are said to reach flood stage when they rise to elevations at which flooding of low lands and damage to property begin. Floods that require consideration in irrigation designs are those that reach relatively high or maximum stages, so that they cause serious damages to property and sometimes losses of life.

Flood Data. Flood data for streams in the United States are now becoming voluminous. Today, flood records for considerable periods of years are available at some stations on most important rivers. Within a few years, similar records should become available on many additional streams.

During the earlier years of the present century, only limited data on maximum flood discharges were available for use in planning engineering works. Since the destructive Ohio Valley floods of 1913, investigations of floods and the assembling of flood data have been receiving more and more attention. Municipal governments, flood districts, and special flood commissions have studied regional flood problems. Several state and federal agencies have begun new flood investigations or have intensified and amplified investigations already under way.

Flood data assembled during recent years have been published in special reports, state bulletins, and federal documents, particularly the Geological Survey water-supply papers. The Miami Conservancy District, organized to plan and construct flood-control works in the Miami Valley, southwestern Ohio, following the flood of March 1913, published a series of technical reports containing comprehensive data on floods and flood problems. Many papers on floods have been published in engineering periodicals, scientific journals, and engineering society proceedings. Only a few of the more valuable contributions are listed in the references at the end of the chapter. The comprehensive report by Jarvis and others, published in 1936, contains a list of more than 200 sources of information on flood flows, intense rainfalls, and frequencies.[35]

In general, data on past floods in most drainage basins can be obtained from the Geological Survey water-supply papers, either from annual issues on "Surface Water Supply of the United States" or from special reports on particular regions or particular floods.

Causes of Floods. Floods are commonly caused by storm rainfall, by the rapid melting of deep snows accumulated during the winter months, or by combinations of storm rainfall and melting snow. Storm rainfall is the principal cause of severe floods. However, surface runoff during the storm period often is augmented by snowmelt water in regions subject to heavy snowfalls, especially when the rainfall occurs near the end of the melting season.

General conditions affecting surface runoff are discussed in preceding sections of this chapter. Special conditions affecting snow runoff are taken up in the next chapter.

In streams draining the higher mountain regions of western United States, annual spring and early summer floods are caused by melting snow or combinations of melting snow and rainfall. Rates of flood flow caused by melting snow alone are usually low, particularly in the smaller drainage basins, but total volumes of flood runoff may be greater than those produced solely by storm rainfall. When maximum rates of snow runoff from tributary drainage basins reach the main stream simultaneously, relatively high rates of flood flow may be produced in the main stream.

Rates of flood flow caused by snow runoff increase slowly to maximum values, then decrease slowly, so that flood periods are prolonged. Rates of flood flow caused by storm rainfall increase and decrease more rapidly, so that flood periods are shorter. During both types of floods, rates of flow often increase more rapidly during rising stages than they decrease during falling stages.

In Figure 7, the hydrographs for the San Joaquin floods of April to June, although probably affected by storage regulation, show the general characteristics of floods produced by snow runoff. Hydrographs for the floods of February and December, also most of the flood hydrographs in Figure 8, show general characteristics of floods produced by storm rainfall.

In rivers draining relatively large areas, major floods usually are caused by heavy rainfalls occurring either continuously or intermittently throughout periods equaling or exceeding the time of concentration. Severe floods of this type occur in some parts of the United States practically every year. A few noteworthy floods include those that occurred in the Ohio River Valley in March 1913, in the upper Arkansas River Valley in June 1921, in the upper Republican River Valley in May and June 1935, in northern California in December

1937, and in southern California in March 1938. Many others could be mentioned.

During the northern California floods of December 1937, melting snow probably contributed small amounts of surface runoff in some of the higher drainage basins. During the Columbia River Valley floods of May and June 1948, melting snow contributed large proportions of the runoff in some basins and nearly all the runoff in a few basins. Melting snow and storm rainfall caused the severe floods in New England in March 1936. The Missouri River flood of March 1943 was caused almost entirely by snowmelt runoff.

On small drainage areas, sudden high rates of flood runoff are often caused by unusually intense or cloudburst rainfalls of relatively short duration. Floods caused by cloudburst rainfalls are often called cloudburst floods. Cloudburst floods, also other sudden floods that rise and fall at rapid rates, are frequently called flash floods.

Cloudburst Floods. Cloudburst floods usually occur during the summer and fall months. Many cloudburst floods occur along the southern and western slopes of the Wasatch Mountains in Utah, along the Front Range of the Rockies in Colorado, in parts of Texas, and to some extent in other parts of the country. Along the Colorado Rockies, they generally originate at elevations below 7,500 feet. One of the earliest and most disastrous cloudburst floods recorded in the West was the one that nearly destroyed the town of Heppner, Oregon, in June 1903.

Damages to irrigation projects caused by cloudbursts and cloudburst floods are mentioned in the preceding chapter. Floods caused by cloudbursts and other intense rainfalls of short duration sometimes transport heavy loads of mud, sand, gravel, and even boulders, especially in arid regions or denuded mountain valleys. They sometimes carry such heavy loads of mud that they are really flows of mud, rather than flows of water, and are accordingly referred to as mud flows. The flood of January 1, 1934, in La Cañada Valley, southern California, washed more than 600 thousand cubic yards of debris from denuded mountain slopes.[57]

Table 6 shows some data on cloudburst floods in Colorado, compiled from the report by Follansbee and Sawyer.[16] Only floods that produced maximum rates of runoff greater than 1,000 second-feet per square mile are included. The Hogans Gulch flood flow was estimated by the Denver and Rio Grande Railroad. The others were determined by slope-area measurements after the floods had passed,

TABLE 6

MAXIMUM DISCHARGES DURING SOME CLOUDBURST FLOODS
IN COLORADO [16]

Stream and location	Drainage area, sq. miles	Date	Sec.-ft.	Maximum discharge Sec.-ft. per sq. mile
Cold Spring Gulch	4.48	Sept. 2, 1938	9,000	2,010
Tributary of Cold Spring Gulch	0.63	Sept. 2, 1938	2,050	3,250
Dixon Gulch	2.15	Sept. 1, 1938	3,620	1,680
Missouri Canyon near mouth	2.4	June 15, 1923	4,350	1,810
Spring Creek, tributary of Dry Creek	7.31	Sept. 2, 1938	11,600	1,590
Osteen Arroyo	7.8	June 3, 1921	9,060	1,160
Cameron Arroyo	7.3	June 3, 1921	13,900	1,900
Unnamed Arroyo	1.8	June 3, 1921	1,910	1,060
Blue Ribbon Creek	6.7	June 3, 1921	9,130	1,360
Hogans Gulch near Eden	6.1	Aug. 7, 1904	9,640	1,580
Skyrocket Gulch at Ouray	1	July 20, 1923	2,000	2,000

similar to the measurements made in the Miami Valley, Ohio, following the floods of March 1913.[26]

Although rates of flood runoff shown in Table 6 are unusually high,
they do not necessarily represent the maximum conditions that may
be experienced during cloudburst floods. Probably even higher rates
of runoff have already been experienced during other cloudburst
floods in Colorado or elsewhere.

Special Types of Floods. Special types of floods may be caused by
log jams, ice jams, failure of storage dams, overtopping and washing
out of natural barriers formed by snowslides or landslides, or other
unusual conditions.

Backwater caused by ice jams may raise upstream river surfaces to
levels above flood stages. Backwater flooding may cause considerable
damages to property but seldom loss of life. When the jams break
and suddenly release the impounded water, resulting floods may cause
severe damages and losses of life at downstream locations. Damaging
floods produced by ice conditions occurred in the Ohio River during
the winter of 1917 and 1918. Severe damages were also caused by ice
during the New England floods of March 1936.

Effects of ice on stream stages and discharges often are pronounced
in long rivers flowing in northerly directions, inasmuch as the debacle,

the breaking up of ice covers, begins in the headwaters and progresses in downstream directions.

The Gros Ventre flood of May 1927, which caused property damages and some loss of life in western Wyoming, was caused by the washing out of a natural dam formed by a landslide from Sheep Mountain. Floods of this type have been experienced in Canada, Switzerland, Italy, India, and other countries. Several have been experienced in the Himalaya Mountains. Probably the most noteworthy landslide flood was the one that originated near Gohna Lake, northern India, in August 1894. This flood was caused by storage water cutting through the upper 400 feet of a landslide dam more than 900 feet high.

Floods caused by the sudden failure of storage dams cause calamities when the valleys below the dams are thickly populated. The failure of the Castlewood Dam, previously mentioned, did not cause disastrous damages because the valley was thinly populated and the flood was greatly reduced by channel and valley storage before it reached Denver. The failure of an earth dam a few miles above Johnstown, Pennsylvania, in 1889, caused the historic Johnstown disaster in which several thousand lives were lost and several million dollars' worth of property destroyed. Other dam failures that caused disastrous floods include the Mill River Dam, Massachusetts, in 1874, the Hatfield Dam, Wisconsin, in 1911, and the St. Francis Dam, southern California, in 1928.

At Britannia Beach, British Columbia, combinations of unusual conditions in the drainage basin of Britannia Creek caused the disastrous flood of October 28, 1921. Heavy rainfall, saturated snow on the mountain slopes, snowslides, landslides, washing out of snowslide and landslide dams, erosion of railroad fills, failure of diversion dams, and large quantities of debris moved by the flood waters, especially logs and trees, caused the destruction of the village and the loss of many lives.[18]

Peak Discharges during Floods. Peak discharges during floods usually are higher than maximum discharges shown in tables of daily streamflow. Daily discharges, as commonly tabulated, represent average daily flows. Therefore, maximum flows given in such tables usually are lower than peak flows. Moreover, they may be recorded on days preceding or following the dates on which the peak flows actually took place.

Crest stages at downstream stations on large rivers such as the Mississippi sometimes remain stationary for 24 hours or longer, but crest stages at stations on small rivers continue only a few hours or a few minutes, depending principally on the size of the drainage basin and the time of concentration in the tributary elements of the basin. For very small basins, crest stages may occur only momentarily. In some flood reports, discharges at times of crest stage have been designated momentary flood peaks. However, the qualification "momentary" seems superfluous. Sometimes it may actually be misleading.

Ratios of peak discharge to maximum average daily discharge may vary from approximately unity for unusually large rivers to 15 or more for flash floods in small drainage basins. Detailed tabulations for many streams draining areas of different size have been published.[35] A ratio of 17.6 has been reported for a stream draining an area of 250 square miles in New Mexico. Other high ratios reported for streams in New Mexico include 9.76 for 1,160 square miles, 7.63 for 6,400 square miles, and 4.63 for 11,200 square miles.

In water-supply papers containing tables of daily streamflow, maximum peak discharges for the year reported, also maximum peak discharges for entire periods of record, are given in the station descriptions, under the heading "Extremes."

Maximum Recorded Floods. Table 7 shows maximum flood discharges in some western rivers as recorded by the Geological Survey up to 1945. Drainage areas and years of record are also shown. Additional data, including dates of occurrence, are given in the original publications. The table was compiled principally from the reports on "Surface Water Supply of the United States, 1945." Some records were taken from Paulsen's report on the Columbia Basin floods of 1948,[47] and a few from an earlier report on maximum discharges.[59]

Table 7 shows maximum discharges at a few stations where records have been maintained through relatively long periods. It does not show the most intense rates of runoff that have occurred on areas of different size throughout the West. For more detailed data on floods in particular drainage basins, the reader should consult the above noted water-supply papers and such additional reports on floods of unusual magnitude as may be available for the particular basins.

Most flood discharges in Table 7 were caused by storm rainfall or by combinations of storm rainfall and melting snow. The maximum discharges in the Methow River at Twisp, Washington, and the Clearwater River at Spalding, Idaho, occurred during the floods of 1948 and were produced largely by melting snow.

The most remarkable flood record shown in Table 7 is the 1,440 second-feet per square mile from the 402 square miles drained by the West Nueces River near Bracketville, southern Texas. This flood

TABLE 7

MAXIMUM DISCHARGES IN SOME WESTERN RIVERS AS SHOWN BY U.S. GEOLOGICAL SURVEY WATER-SUPPLY PAPERS

Stream and location	Drainage area, sq. miles	Years	Maximum discharge Sec.-ft.	Sec.-ft. per sq. mile
Missouri River Basin				
Missouri at Fort Benton, Mont.	24,600	64	140,000	5.7
Yellowstone at Corwin Springs, Mont.	2,630	35	26,500	10.1
Big Horn at Thermopolis, Wyo.	8,080	40	29,800	3.7
North Platte at Saratoga, Wyo.	2,880	38	18,000	6.2
South Platte at Denver, Colo.	3,840	50	22,000	5.7
Republican at Max, Neb.	7,740	17	190,000	32.5 *
Lower Mississippi River Basin				
Arkansas near Pueblo, Colo.	4,730	53	103,000	21.8
Canadian at Logan, N. Mex.	11,200	15	278,000	24.8
Red near Colbert, Okla.	38,330	22	201,000	6.1 *
Western Gulf of Mexico Basins				
Sabine at Logansport, La.	4,858	42	92,000	18.9
Neches near Rockland, Tex.	3,539	42	49,800	14.1
Trinity at Dallas, Tex.	6,001	42	184,000	30.7
Brazos at Seymour, Tex.	14,490	22	95,400	18.2 *
Colorado at Austin, Tex.	38,160	47	481,000	18.3 *
Concho near Paint Rock, Tex.	5,538	30	301,000	57.2 *
West Nueces near Brackettville, Tex.	402	6	580,000	1440
Rio Grande at San Marcial, N. Mex.	27,700	50	50,000	2.0 *
Pecos below Alamogordo Dam, N. Mex.	4,390	15	42,800	9.7
Colorado River Basin				
Colorado at Glenwood Springs, Colo.	4,560	45	30,100	6.6
Colorado at Yuma, Ariz.	242,900	43	250,000	1.0
Roaring Fork at Glenwood Springs, Colo.	1,460	39	17,600	12.1
Gunnison near Grand Junction, Colo.	8,020	35	35,700	4.5
Green at Green River, Utah	40,600	46	68,100	1.7
San Juan at Ship Rock, N. Mex.	12,800	24	150,000	11.7
Little Colorado at Grand Falls, Ariz.	21,200	20	120,000	5.7
Virgin at Virgin, Utah	934	36	13,500	14.5
Bill Williams at Planet, Ariz.	5,140	17	92,500	18.0
Gila near Dome, Ariz.	58,100	43	230,000	4.0
The Great Basin				
Bear at Alexander, Idaho	3,840	31	4,590	1.2
Weber at Devils Slide, Utah	1,100	40	6,000	5.5
Sevier near Juab, Utah	5,120	34	2,140	0.4
Carson near Fort Churchill, Nev.	1,450	34	6,300	4.3
Humboldt at Palisade, Nev.	5,010	38	6,250	1.2
Pacific Slope Basins in California				
San Gabriel near Azusa, Calif.	211	51	65,700	311

* Based on contributing area.

TABLE 7 (*Continued*)

MAXIMUM DISCHARGES IN SOME WESTERN RIVERS AS SHOWN BY U.S.
GEOLOGICAL SURVEY WATER-SUPPLY PAPERS

| | Drainage area, sq. | | | Maximum discharge |
Stream and location	miles	Years	Sec.-ft.	Sec.-ft. per sq. mile
Kern near Bakersfield, Calif.	2,420	49	21,700	9.0
Kings at Piedra, Calif.	1,694	50	80,000	47.2
San Joaquin below Friant, Calif.	1,675	38	77,200	46.1
Tuolumne above La Grange Dam, Calif.	1,540	50	60,300	39.2
Sacramento near Red Bluff, Calif.	9,300	50	291,000	31.3
Pit at Big Bend, Calif.	4,920	35	34,200	7.0
Feather near Oroville, Calif.	3,611	43	230,000	63.7
Eel at Scotia, Calif.	3,070	34	345,000	112
Klamath at Somesbar, Calif.	8,480	18	73,700	8.7
Washington and Upper Columbia Basins				
Skagit at Newhalem, Wash.	1,160	31	63,500	54.7
Columbia at Trinidad, Wash.	89,700	54	740,000	8.2
Kootenai at Libby, Mont.	10,240	38	130,000	12.7
Clark Fork near Plains, Mont.	19,900	38	134,000	6.7
Flathead near Polson, Mont.	6,990	41	82,100	11.7
Spokane at Spokane, Wash.	4,350	57	49,000	11.3
Okanogan near Tonasket, Wash.	7,250	33	40,900	5.6
Methow at Twisp, Wash.	1,330	25	40,800	30.7 †
Puyallup at Puyallup, Wash.	948	31	57,000	60.1
Snake River Basin				
Snake near Blackfoot, Idaho	11,700	38	46,200	3.9
Owyhee above Owyhee Reservoir, Ore.	10,400	19	16,000	1.5
Salmon at Whitebird, Idaho	13,550	54	120,000	8.9
Clearwater at Spalding, Idaho	9,570	22	177,000	18.5 †
Oregon and Lower Columbia Basins				
Columbia near The Dalles, Ore.	237,000	70	1,240,000	5.2
Umatilla near Umatilla, Ore.	2,290	45	19,600	8.6
John Day at McDonald Ferry, Ore.	7,580	54	33,000	4.4
Deschutes at Moody, Ore.	10,500	44	43,600	4.2
Crooked near Culver, Ore.	4,330	31	8,260	1.9
Willamette at Salem, Ore.	7,280	87	500,000	68.7
Umqua near Elkton, Ore.	3,680	40	172,000	46.7
Rogue at Raygold, Ore.	2,020	40	91,500	45.3

† Largely snow runoff.

occurred on June 14, 1935. It was described by Dalrymple and others in a report published in 1939.[13] Other unusually high rates of flood runoff that have been experienced in southern and southeastern Texas are given in this report and in subsequent special reports on floods in Texas.

Rates of flood runoff vary widely throughout the West, not only for areas of similar size in different river valleys but also for areas of different size in the same river valley. Rates of flood runoff in the same river valley decrease more or less rapidly with increasing size of drainage area.

Maximum Flood Curves. Maximum flood curves for particular drainage basins, or for regions having similar conditions of precipitation and runoff, are useful in planning hydraulic structures. The curves are commonly determined by plotting maximum recorded floods on logarithmic paper and drawing a line through the higher points. Maximum rates of flow in second-feet per square mile are usually plotted as ordinates, and drainage areas in square miles. as abscissas. Curves determined in such a manner are sometimes called enveloping curves. When additional factors of safety are considered essential, a somewhat higher curve can be drawn, paralleling the envelope curve.

Figure 10 shows a maximum flood diagram and enveloping curve for the Columbia River basin, prepared by Rantz and Riggs and originally published in Paulsen's report.[47] The curve is practically a straight line for areas up to about 50,000 square miles. For areas up to about 10,000 square miles, the line is approximately represented by the equation

$$q = \frac{3,000}{\sqrt{M}}$$

where q is the maximum rate of flow in second-feet per square mile, and M is the drainage area in square miles.

Maximum flood curves for different regions often can be represented by the equation

$$q = \frac{C}{\sqrt{M}}$$

where C is a coefficient having different values for regions experiencing different hydrological conditions. Thus, for Columbia basin areas up to about 10,000 square miles, C appears to be about 3,000. For

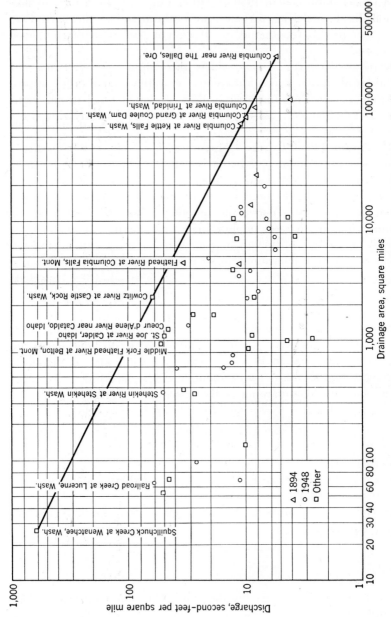

FIGURE 10. Maximum flood discharges in the Columbia River basin. (After Rantz and Riggs.)

areas of similar size in the upper Tennessee River Valley, C is about 5,000. For areas in southern Texas, C may be considerably higher. In western United States, values of C for some California drainage basins probably are higher than the general value for the Columbia River basin. For most drainage areas in the Great Basin, they probably are lower.

Inasmuch as the maximum rate of flood discharge at any station is q times M, the maximum discharge according to the above equation is

$$Q = C\sqrt{M}$$

The preparation of a maximum flood curve for a large river basin is desirable whenever sufficient records of major floods are obtainable. However, the curve must be used intelligently. Some tributary drainage areas may have special features that are unfavorable for high rates of flood runoff, as when considerable natural or artificial storage capacities are available. Others may have special topographic or geologic features that are conducive to high rates of flood runoff. Therefore, special features on particular areas should be carefully studied and flood rates taken from the curve modified accordingly.

All regions subject to cloudbursts require special considerations. Curves and equations of the nature discussed above usually need some modifications before they can be applied to areas that may experience cloudburst rainfalls. In general, the curves should be used with extreme caution where areas smaller than about 100 square miles are involved.

Maximum Flood Formulas. A formula for maximum flood discharge, similar to the above equation for Q, was proposed by Myer in 1879. In 1926, Jarvis proposed a modified type of the equation which may be written in the form

$$Q = 100p\sqrt{M}$$

The factor p, sometimes called the Myer rating, is a percentage varying with the flood-producing potentialities of the drainage area.[34] Its value would be 30 for the smaller Columbia basin areas, and 50 for the upper Tennessee Valley region. A map showing values of p determined from flood experiences in various parts of the country has been published.[58] Such values of p, like maximum flood curves, must be used with caution.

Many empirical formulas for computing maximum flood discharges were developed in the past, when records of maximum floods were much more limited than they are today. Some were similar to the above equation, except that they assumed different variations of discharge with size of drainage area. Exponents of M in the various equations varied from 0.5 to as much as 1. Some included factors for width, length, or shape of drainage area. Others, usually developed for very small areas or for use in storm-sewer design, included factors for rainfall intensity.

Early flood formulas were useful in preliminary studies of flood possibilities but seldom gave more than approximate indications of maximum flood flows. They have gradually been discarded and need not be considered further. Jarvis discussed some of the more pertinent equations in his report on floods.[35] Some of the formulas developed for aid in designing culverts or storm sewers may still be useful, but such formulas are beyond the scope of this chapter. One method used in sewer design that sometimes can be used to obtain approximate estimates for relatively small rural areas is commonly called the rational method.

The Rational Method. The rational method assumes that the maximum rate of flow at a particular point on a stream is reached when all parts of the drainage area are contributing surface runoff during a period of maximum rainfall intensity. Thus, in order to produce maximum flood conditions, the intense rainfall must continue through a period equaling or exceeding the time of concentration. The proportion of the rainfall that reaches the stream as surface runoff is estimated according to the topographic and geologic conditions throughout the drainage area and the amount of moisture already held by the surface soil at the time of the storm.

The rational method of computing maximum flood flow may be represented by the equation

$$Q = CIA$$

where Q = maximum rate of flow in second-feet.
   C = ratio of maximum runoff in second-feet per acre to average rate of rainfall in inches per hour during the time of concentration.
   I = average intensity of rainfall in inches per hour during the time of concentration.
   A = drainage area in acres.

The expression of rainfall intensity in inches per hour and drainage area in acres is an advantage, because an average rate of runoff of

1 inch per hour from 1 acre is practically equal to 1 second-foot of streamflow.

In applying the rational method, difficulties are encountered in estimating the value of C and in determining the time of concentration. The time of concentration varies with the intensity of surface runoff and other conditions as previously mentioned. Probable maximum rates of rainfall during different periods of duration can be estimated from records maintained at first-order Weather Bureau stations. Assumed periods of maximum rainfall should not be longer than probable times of concentration, inasmuch as average rainfall intensities decrease rapidly with increasing periods. The value of C is always more or less uncertain. It probably can be estimated more accurately for urban areas than for rural areas.

Where a drainage basin contains two or more principal tributary elements, the rational method can be applied to the tributary streams and the resultant flood flow in the main stream estimated by combining tributary flows according to time of arrival. Detailed discussions of the rational method may be consulted in a published report.[58]

The Unit Hydrograph. The unit-hydrograph method of analyzing and computing surface runoff from storm rainfall was proposed by Sherman in 1932.[52] It was later amplified by others, particularly Bernard, who introduced the use of the distribution graph.[7] Briefly, it supplies a procedure for calculating the hydrograph of surface runoff on a given drainage area that might be caused by an assumed or transposed storm of unusual intensity. It is based on analogies with actual storm rainfalls and resultant surface runoff already recorded in the same drainage basin.

The unit-hydrograph method of calculating surface runoff is based on the following hypotheses, now fairly well established:

1. Different storm rainfalls on a particular drainage area, occurring in the same unit of time and distributed uniformly over the area and within the unit time, produce hydrographs having approximately equal bases.

2. The ordinates of the hydrographs resulting from rainfalls in the same unit of time are directly proportional to the total surface runoff resulting from such rainfalls; that is, to net rainfall, recorded rainfall minus infiltration and incidental losses.

3. The volumes of surface runoff occurring in successive intervals of time during the period of surface runoff caused by a storm rainfall in a unit of time, expressed as percentages of the total volume of

surface runoff, make up the distribution graph. They total 100 per cent.

4. The distribution graph of surface runoff for a particular drainage area is the same for different storm rainfalls occurring in the same unit of time.

In compiling a distribution graph of surface runoff for a particular drainage area, increments of flow caused by groundwater runoff should be estimated and deducted from the recorded discharges. Runoff caused by precipitation before or after the selected time unit of storm rainfall, if any, should also be deducted. The unit of time is usually taken as 1 day. In analyzing flood runoff caused by severe storms of short duration, it may be taken as a fraction of a day, or even as short as 1 hour.

The computation of a hydrograph for a particular storm rainfall involves the following steps:

1. List the rainfall in each successive time unit during the storm period.

2. Estimate the infiltration and incidental losses during each time unit, and deduct from the listed rainfall to obtain the net rainfall that produces surface runoff.

3. Apply the distribution graph to the net rainfall in each time unit, thus obtaining increments of surface runoff for each time unit during the total period of surface runoff.

4. Summate the increments of surface runoff for each time unit, thus obtaining the total ordinates that make up the hydrograph of surface runoff.

5. Add the estimated groundwater flow to each ordinate, thus obtaining the ordinates needed to plot the hydrograph of total flow.

Items 2 and 5 involve estimated quantities. During flood flows of considerable magnitude, groundwater runoff is normally low in comparison with surface runoff, so that it can be estimated within reasonable limits of accuracy. Depths of infiltration and total incidental losses are more difficult to estimate.

If the ground surface is impervious and weather conditions such that infiltration and incidental losses can be assumed to be negligible throughout the flood period, the resulting flood hydrograph is the maximum that could be produced by the assumed storm rainfall. Bernard called this the pluviagraph. It is useful in studying maximum possible floods.

Unfortunately, from the viewpoint of unit-hydrograph studies, infiltration and incidental losses are seldom, if ever, negligible. They may amount to more than half the total rainfall, even during unusual storms that precipitate more than 20 inches of water in a few days. Therefore, item 2, which requires the estimating of such amounts, is the most uncertain step in unit-hydrograph calculations.

The unit-hydrograph method is not applicable in determining flood flows produced by the melting of accumulated snow covers. However, in studying maximum floods that may occur in regions subject to heavy snowfalls as well as heavy rainfalls, assumed amounts of snow runoff can be added to hydrographs computed from storm rainfalls. Samples of detailed tabulations required in analyses by the unit-hydrograph method have been published.[53]

Runoff and Retention. Depths of runoff and retention during floods vary widely for different storms in the same drainage basins, also for similar storms in different drainage basins. Storms occurring during the winter and early spring months usually cause more runoff and less retention than similar storms occurring during the summer and early fall months when conditions are more favorable for infiltration.

The occurrence of runoff has been discussed earlier in the chapter. In considering flood runoff caused by storms, retention usually is assumed to equal total precipitation minus total runoff. Thus, it includes not only infiltration but also incidental losses such as evaporation and transpiration. During most major storms, infiltration comprises the greater portion of the retention.

Total depths of runoff and retention during storm periods in a particular drainage basin vary with (1) intensity, time distribution, and duration of the rainfall, and (2) weather, vegetal, and soil conditions throughout the basin at the time of the storm. When other factors are the same, increased intensities, continuity, and duration of rainfall mean increased flood runoff. Conditions stated in item 2 affect incidental losses and amounts of water that can infiltrate into the soil. Thus, they affect the portions of the precipitation that must be disposed of by surface runoff. Surface runoff is often considered as a residual quantity, that is, as the excess of precipitation over infiltration plus incidental losses.

When surface soils are dry and loose, as often happens in the summer, appreciable portions of initial storm rainfalls are utilized in saturating the soil. Some writers have assumed that all rainfall occurring after the soil becomes saturated appears in the streams as surface runoff. However, infiltration usually continues at relatively high rates after conditions of saturation are attained. Investigations in the Miami Valley, discussed in Chapter 5, showed that rates of infiltration into saturated soils increased as rainfall intensities increased. Therefore increased storm rainfalls generally mean increased retention as well as increased surface runoff.

Table 8 shows some data on total rainfall, runoff, and retention, also maximum 24-hour runoff, in several southern California drainage basins during the floods of February 27 to March 3, 1938, as reported

TABLE 8

RAINFALL, RUNOFF, AND RETENTION DURING SOUTHERN CALIFORNIA
FLOODS OF FEBRUARY 27 TO MARCH 3, 1938 [56]

Stream and location	Drain-age area, sq. miles	Average rainfall, Feb. 27 to Mar. 3, in.	Runoff, in.			Reten-tion, in. to 12 P.M., Mar. 10
			Maxi-mum, 24 hr.	Feb. 27 to Mar. 3	Mar. 4 to 10	
San Vicente at Foster	75	8.96	1.25	1.88	0.77	6.31
Santa Ysabel near Mesa Grande	58	15.10	1.77	2.91	1.26	10.93
Temecula near Temecula	592	8.51	0.83	1.43	0.25	6.83
Murrieta at Temecula	220	8.42	1.48	2.14	0.14	6.14
Mill near Craftonville	42.9	25.86	6.67	8.17	3.94	13.75
Santa Ana near Mentone	144 *	24.63	5.41	6.56	2.01	16.06
Lytle near Fontana	47.9	27.33	7.69	10.24	3.76	13.33
Day near Etiwanda	4.8	25.27	9.51	13.43	3.63	8.21
Cucamonga near Upland	10.1	25.38	8.91	12.14	3.18	10.08
San Antonio near Claremont	16.9	28.58	10.14	11.84	3.96	12.78
West Fork, San Gabriel near Camp Rincon	40.4	23.62	8.26	12.06	3.01	8.55
Fish near Duarte	6.5	21.77	4.80	8.70	2.82	10.25
Dalton near Glendora	4.5	17.85	3.83	5.93	2.08	9.84
Arroyo Seco near Pasadena	16.4	21.86	6.83	10.10	2.69	9.07
Santa Anita near Sierra Madre	10.8	25.76	6.84	11.06	3.52	11.18
Piru near Piru	432	12.35	1.16	2.18	0.66	9.51
Ventura near Ventura	187	13.32	3.90	5.78	2.00	5.54
Santa Ynez near Montecito	16.0	14.69	3.32	4.67	2.14	7.88
Cuyamo near Santa Maria	902	5.31	0.22	0.24	0.19	4.88

* Excluding Bear Valley.

by Troxell.[56] Although storm rainfalls exceeding 20 inches fell on mountainous areas, total depths retained in several basins were more than half the total precipitation. In the San Antonio basin, near Claremont, where the average rainfall was 28.58 inches, the maximum 24-hour runoff was 10.14 inches; the total runoff, 15.80 inches; and the total retention, 12.78 inches.

Additional data on rainfall, runoff, and retention during floods may be consulted in several Geological Survey water-supply papers on floods. A special report on flood volumes was published by The Interstate Commission on the Delaware River basin in 1940.[25]

Flood Frequencies and Probabilities. Frequencies of flood flows of different magnitude and probable maximum rates of discharge that may be expected to occur once in extremely long intervals, such as 100, 1,000, or even 10,000 years, have been studied intensively at many river stations where continuous records are available for long periods.

Frequency studies often are needed in planning control works of a temporary nature, such as cofferdams for use during the building of permanent structures. They are also needed in planning permanent control works where partial or even complete failures would not cause disasters. For such structures, the payment of damages once in a considerable number of years may be more economical than permanent construction designed for complete safety.

Probability studies of unusually large floods that may occur at long intervals of time often are made in considering flood provisions needed at high dams or at other major structures located in densely populated regions, where failures would cause disastrous losses of life and property. They constitute useful aids in studying flood problems but cannot be accepted as reliable.

Frequency and probability studies are usually made by one of two methods: (1) for maximum annual floods, or (2) for all floods exceeding a peak discharge selected so as to give at least one flood in each year. The first method has the objection that some major floods may be omitted. Some years may include additional floods almost as high as the maximum, possibly higher than the maximum in other years. The second method sometimes involves difficulties in selection. Two or more floods may occur in close succession and therefore may not constitute events that could properly be included as separate items. A flood array used in the second method is generally called a partial duration series. Detailed procedures by both methods, also by certain additional methods, are described in the report by Jarvis.[35]

In general, peak discharges are arranged in order of magnitude, plotting positions are calculated, and the points are plotted on logarithmic, semilogarithmic, probability, or other specially designed plotting paper. A type of paper that has been found useful in studying floods by the Gumbel theory was proposed by Powell in 1943.[50] In most procedures, curves are drawn through the plotted points and extended to frequency intervals for which no data are available. Such curves are commonly called frequency curves or probability curves. When successive points are connected by straight lines, the charts may be designated recurrence diagrams.

Flood discharges, discharges per square mile, or ratios of flood discharge to the mean annual flood discharge are commonly plotted as ordinates. Percentages of time, frequency of occurrence per 100 years, or recurrence intervals in years are plotted as abscissas.

Plotting positions as regards recurrence are determined in different ways. The Hazen method, which is often used and which the author prefers, determines the recurrence interval by the ratio

$$\frac{N}{M - 0.5}$$

where N is the number of floods, and M the number assigned according to magnitude, beginning with 1 for the largest flood. Others have used the ratio N/M, the ratio $(N + 1)/M$, or values computed by special formulas. Rantz and Riggs used the ratio $(N + 1)/M$ in their studies of the Columbia basin floods.[47]

Arguments have been advanced in favor of all methods of determining plotting positions. Recurrence intervals obtained by the various methods do not differ greatly for the smaller floods. Hazen's method gives relatively high values for the larger floods, especially for the largest. This may be logical inasmuch as the maximum recorded flood often has a recurrence interval somewhat longer than the period of record. Sometimes a fairly accurate estimate of the probable recurrence interval for the maximum recorded flood can be determined from past history at the station, even though continuous data on discharges are not available during the earlier periods.

Figure 11 shows recurrence diagrams for floods in the John Day River at McDonald Ferry, Oregon, as prepared by Rantz and Riggs. The diagrams were based on the 44-year record from 1904 to 1948. The upper diagram was based on maximum annual floods; the lower, on all floods exceeding 7,000 second-feet. In both diagrams, plotted

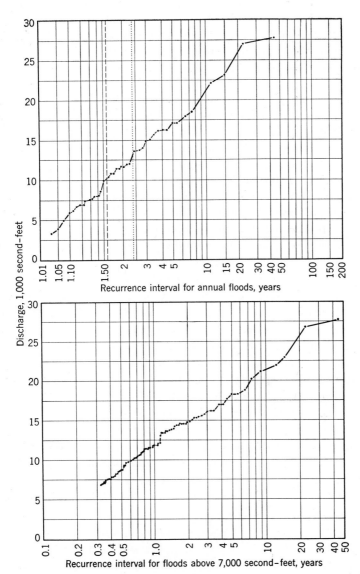

FIGURE 11.   Recurrence diagrams for floods in John Day River at McDonald Ferry, Oregon, 1904 to 1948. (After Rantz and Riggs.)

points are connected by straight lines. Apparently, continuous straight lines could be drawn to balance the points, at least up to recurrence intervals of about 15 years. If recurrence intervals were determined by the Hazen method, the larger floods would plot at increasing distances to the right, and curves balancing the points would show greater increases in recurrence intervals with increasing flood discharges.

Various methods have been used in analyzing flood data, drawing curves through points on frequency diagrams, and extending the curves to long recurrence intervals. Some have been based on probability theories, equations used in statistical studies, or other mathematical functions. Lengthy discussions of such methods have been published. The Jarvis report contains some discussions and many references.[35] Inasmuch as the plotted points represent the only known data, curves drawn by eye probably are fully as reliable as those drawn by precise mathematical procedures.

One objection to probability studies based on either annual floods or floods exceeding a fixed discharge is that the data are not homogeneous. Floods caused by snow runoff, storm rainfall, intense rainfalls of the cloudburst type, and combinations of storm rainfall and snow runoff are all included in one array. Probably separate studies should be made for each type of flood phenomena.

Horton and VanVliet, in their studies of Delaware basin floods, analyzed the data by seasons and found that the limiting flood probably would occur during the spring. Their studies indicated that the limiting flood during the spring might be twice as great as the limiting flood during the summer, and about 1.4 times as great as the limiting flood during the fall or winter.[25]

Comments on Frequency Studies. Frequency studies, based on available flood records, usually constitute an adequate basis for planning temporary control works such as cofferdams, establishing minimum highway grades along river channels, or designing structures where only limited damages would result from failure. Where records have been maintained 50 years or longer, frequency studies supply fairly reliable information regarding the size of floods that may be expected to occur, on the average, once in 5, 10, or 15 years. Elements of uncertainty increase as the recurrence interval increases.

All frequency studies, including those dealing with short recurrence intervals, are uncertain. They merely indicate average conditions to be anticipated. Floods of long recurrence intervals may occur during any particular period of short duration. A 100-year flood, or even one of greater magnitude, may occur this year, next year, or any year.

The Arkansas River flood of June 1921 produced a maximum discharge of 103,000 second-feet at Pueblo, Colorado, a discharge about 2.6 times the greatest that had been experienced in the preceding 36 years. Hazen, in his book, *Flood Flows*, estimated that this may have been a flood that would occur once in 2,872 years. Many similar examples where flood discharges have greatly exceeded earlier recorded discharges could be cited.

In 1939, Creager discussed the fact that curves of maximum recorded flood flows, revised as additional records became available, were continually showing greater flood discharges.[10] Frequency or probability curves for particular river stations, prepared before and after the occurrence of record-breaking floods such as the 1921 flood at Pueblo, show similar increases, especially when extended to indicate the maximum floods that may be probable at long intervals of time. Considering the relatively short streamflow records at most river stations in the United States, the gradually increasing magnitude of recorded floods seems natural. Obviously, such trends will not continue indefinitely, unless pronounced changes in climate take place in the future. When 50 or 100 years of additional records become available, trends in maximum flood discharges should be materially modified.

With streamflow records of 150 years or more, flood magnitudes should be fairly well defined. Recurrence diagrams should furnish reliable information regarding floods that may be expected to occur, on the average, once in different periods of time up to 50 or 75 years. Probability curves should show fair estimates of maximum 100-year floods, and extensions of the curves should indicate, within reasonable limits, the magnitude of floods that may occur at somewhat longer intervals. Studies by the Miami Conservancy District based on records in Europe, reported by Woodward, indicated that maximum floods occurring in several centuries are not much greater than 100-year floods.[62]

Probability curves based on short records of streamflow may be misleading. Even when based on 50 or 75 years of record, they often are not reliable as regards 100-year floods. Therefore, they cannot be recommended as a satisfactory basis for the design of high dams or other structures of unusual size and importance.

REFERENCES

1. Adams, Frank, Paul A. Ewing, and M. R. Huberty, *Hydrologic Aspects of Burning Brush and Woodland-Grass Ranges in California*, Calif. Dept. Natural Resources, Div. of Forestry, 1947.
2. American Geophysical Union, "Symposium on Floods," *Trans. Am. Geop. Union*, 1939, Part II, pp. 143–234.
3. Bailey, Paul, "Flow in California Streams," *Calif. Dept. Pub. Works Bull.* 5, 1923.
4. Bartholet, Charles J., "Monthly and Yearly Summaries of Hydrometric Data in the State of Washington to September, 1933," *Wash. Water-Supply Bull.* 5, 1935.
5. Bates, C. G., and A. J. Henry, "Forest and Stream-Flow Experiment at Wagon Wheel Gap, Colo.," *U.S. Weather Bur. Monthly Weather Rev. Suppl.* 30, 1928.
6. Beckman, H. C., "Bank Storage-Loss and Recovery of Missouri River Discharge during Drought of 1934," *Trans. Am. Geop. Union*, 1935, Part II, pp. 513–515.
7. Bernard, Merrill M., "An Approach to Determinate Stream Flow," *Trans. Am. Soc. C. E.*, No. 100, 1935, pp. 347–395.
8. Blaney, Harry F., Harold C. Troxell, and others, "Water Losses under Natural Conditions from Wet Areas in Southern California," *Calif. Dept. Pub. Works Bull.* 44, 1933.
9. Corbett, Don M., and others, "Stream-Gaging Procedure, A Manual Describing Methods and Practices of the Geological Survey," *U.S. Geol. Sur. Water-Supply Paper* 888, 1945.
10. Creager, William P., "Possible and Probable Future Floods," *Civ. Eng.*, November 1939, pp. 668–670.
11. Croft, A. R., "Some Recharge and Discharge Phenomena of North and South Facing Watershed Lands in the Wasatch Mountains," *Trans. Am. Geop. Union*, 1944, Part VI, pp. 881–889.
12. ——— "Water Loss by Stream Surface Evaporation and Transpiration by Riparian Vegetation," *Trans. Am. Geop. Union*, April 1948, pp. 235–239.
13. Dalrymple, Tate, and others, "Major Texas Floods of 1935," *U.S. Geol. Sur. Water-Supply Paper* 796–G, 1939.
14. Eisenlohr, Wm. S., Jr., "Effect of Water Temperature on Flow of a Natural Stream," *Trans. Am. Geop. Union*, April 1948, pp. 240–242.
15. Follansbee, Robert, "Some Characteristics of Run-Off in the Rocky Mountain Region," *U.S. Geol. Sur. Water-Supply Paper* 500–C, 1922.
15a. ——— *A History of the Water Resources Branch of the United States Geological Survey to June 30, 1919* (published privately).
16. Follansbee, Robert, and Leon R. Sawyer, "Floods in Colorado," *U.S. Geol. Sur. Water-Supply Paper* 997, 1948.
17. Gumbel, E. J., "Simplified Plotting of Statistical Observations," *Trans. Am. Geop. Union*, August 1945, pp. 69–82.
18. Haggen, E. A., "The Britannia Disaster," *Mining and Eng. Rec.*, November 1921, pp. 229–235.
19. Hall, L. Standish, "The Probable Variations in Yearly Run-Off as Determined from a Study of California Streams," *Trans. Am. Soc. C. E.*, Vol. 84, 1921, pp. 191–257.

20. Harbeck, G. E., Jr., and W. B. Langbein, "Normals and Variations in Runoff, 1921–1945," *U.S. Geol. Sur. Water Resources Rev. Suppl.* 2, 1949.

21. Hart, F. C., "Precipitation and Run-Off in Relation to Altitude in the Rocky Mountain Region," *Jour. Forestry*, November 1937, pp. 1005–1010.

22. Holland, Wm. T., and C. S. Jarvis, "Inventory of Unpublished Hydrologic Data," *U.S. Geol. Sur. Water-Supply Paper* 837, 1938.

23. Hoover, M. D., "Effect of Removal of Forest Vegetation upon Water-Yields," *Trans. Am. Geop. Union*, 1944, Part VI, pp. 969–977.

24. Horton, R. E., "Surface Runoff Phenomena, Part I—Analysis of the Hydrograph," *Horton Hydrological Laboratory Pub.* 101, 1935.

25. Horton, R. E., and Richard VanVliet, *Flood Volumes*, The Interstate Commission on the Delaware River Basin, Philadelphia, Pa., 1940.

26. Houk, Ivan E., "Calculation of Flow in Open Channels," *Miami Conservancy Dist. Tech. Rep.*, Part IV, Dayton, Ohio, 1918.

27. ——— "Rainfall and Runoff in the Miami Valley," *Miami Conservancy Dist. Tech. Rep.*, Part VIII, Dayton, Ohio, 1921.

28. ——— "Hydraulic Design of Bridge Waterways," *Eng. News-Rec.*, June 29, 1922. pp. 1071–1075.

29. ——— "Failure of Castlewood Rock-Fill Dam," *West. Constr. News and Highways Builder*, September 1933, pp. 373–375.

30. Hoyt, W. G., "The Effects of Ice on Stream Flow," *U.S. Geol. Sur. Water-Supply Paper* 337, 1913.

31. ——— "The Runoff Cycle," Chapter XI–D in Meinzer's *Hydrology*, 1942, pp. 507–513 (see reference 23 in Chapter 1).

32. Hoyt, W. G., and others, "Studies of Relations of Rainfall and Run-off in the United States," *U.S. Geol. Sur. Water-Supply Paper* 772, 1936.

33. Hoyt, W. G., and H. C. Troxell, "Forests and Stream Flow," *Trans. Am. Soc. C. E.*, No. 99, 1934, pp. 1–111.

34. Jarvis, C. S., "Flood Flow Characteristics," *Trans. Am. Soc. C. E.*, Vol. 89, 1926, pp. 985–1104.

35. Jarvis, C. S., and others, "Floods in the United States, Magnitude and Frequency," *U.S. Geol. Sur. Water-Supply Paper* 771, 1936.

36. Kinnison, H. B., and B. R. Colby, "Flood Formulas Based on Drainage Basin Characteristics," *Trans. Am. Soc. C. E.*, No. 110, 1945, pp. 849–904.

37. Lane, E. W., and Kai Lei, "Stream Flow Variability," *Trans. Am. Soc. C. E.*, Vol. 115, 1950, pp. 1084–1134.

38. Langbein, Walter B., and others, "Topographic Characteristics of Drainage Basins," *U.S. Geol. Sur. Water-Supply Paper* 968–C, 1947.

39. ——— "Annual Runoff in the United States," *U.S. Geol. Sur. Cir.* 52, 1949.

40. Lee, Charles H., "Total Evaporation for Sierra Nevada Watersheds by the Method of Precipitation and Runoff Differences," *Trans. Am. Geop. Union*, 1941, Part I, pp. 50–71.

41. Lenz, Arno T., and Clair N. Sawyer, "Estimation of Stream-Flow from Alkalinity-Determinations," *Trans. Am. Geop. Union*, 1944, Part VI, pp. 1005–1011.

42. Matthes, François E., "Evaporation and Runoff from Snow in the Alpine Zone of Our Western Mountains," *Trans. Am. Geop. Union*, 1938, Part II, p. 662.

43. Meinzer, Oscar E., "Occurrence, Origin, and Discharge of Ground Water," Chapter X–A in Meinzer's *Hydrology*, 1942, pp. 385–443 (see reference 23 in Chapter 1).

44. Meinzer, Oscar E., and N. D. Stearns, "A Study of Ground Water in the Pomperaug Basin, Connecticut," *U.S. Geol. Sur. Water-Supply Paper* 597–B, 1929.

45. Meyer, Otto H., "Analysis of Run-off Characteristics," *Trans. Am. Soc. C. E.*, No. 105, 1940, pp. 83–141.

46. Musgrave, G. W., "Some Climatic Factors That Affect Run-off," *U.S. Dept. Agr. Yearbook*, 1941, pp. 536–545.

47. Paulsen, C. G., and others, "Floods of May–June 1948 in Columbia River Basin," *U.S. Geol. Sur. Water-Supply Paper* 1080, 1949.

48. Pickels, George W., "Magnitude and Frequency of Floods on Illinois Streams," *Ill. Eng. Exp. Sta. Bull.* 296, 1937.

49. Potter, W. D., "Effect of Rainfall on Magnitude and Frequency of Peak Rates of Surface Runoff," *Trans. Am. Geop. Union*, October 1949, pp. 735–751.

50. Powell, Ralph W., "A Simple Method of Estimating Flood Frequency," *Civ. Eng.*, February 1943, pp. 105–107.

51. Rowe, P. B., "Some Factors of the Hydrology of the Sierra Nevada Foothills," *Trans. Am. Geop. Union*, 1941, Part I, pp. 90–101.

52. Sherman, L. K., "Streamflow from Rainfall by Unit-Graph Method," *Eng. News-Rec.*, Apr. 7, 1932, pp. 501–505.

53. ——— "The Unit Hydrograph Method," Chapter XI–E in Meinzer's *Hydrology*, 1942, pp. 514–525 (see reference 23 in Chapter 1).

54. Snyder, Franklin F., "A Conception of Runoff-Phenomena," *Trans. Am. Geop. Union*, 1939, Part IV, pp. 725–738.

55. Troxell, Harold C., "The Diurnal Fluctuation in the Ground-Water and Flow of the Santa Ana River and Its Meaning," *Trans. Am. Geop. Union*, 1936, Part II, pp. 496–504.

56. Troxell, Harold C., and others, "Floods of March 1938 in Southern California," *U.S. Geol. Sur. Water-Supply Paper* 844, 1942.

57. Troxell, Harold C., and John Q. Peterson, "Flood in La Cañada Valley, California, January 1, 1934," *U.S. Geol. Sur. Water-Supply Paper* 796–C, 1937.

58. Water Resources Committee, subcommittee report, *Low Dams, A Manual of Design for Small Water Storage Projects*, Natl. Resources Comm., Washington, D. C., 1938.

59. Williams, G. R., L. C. Crawford, and W. S. Eisenlohr, Jr., "Maximum Discharges at Stream-Measurement Stations," *U.S. Geol. Sur. Water-Supply Paper* 847, 1940.

60. Wood, G. K., "Accuracy of Stream-Flow Records," *Trans. Am. Geop. Union*, 1944, Part VI, pp. 985–989.

61. Wood, Horace W., Jr., "Flood Flow on Missouri Streams," *Mo. Eng. Exp. Sta. Bull.* 30, 1942.

62. Woodward, Sherman M., "Hydraulics of the Miami Flood Control Project," *Miami Conservancy Dist. Tech. Rep.*, Part VII, Dayton, Ohio, 1920.

63. Woolley, Ralf R., "Cloudburst Floods in Utah, 1850–1938," *U.S. Geol. Sur. Water-Supply Paper* 994, 1946.

Chapter 8

SNOW MELTING
AND RUNOFF FORECASTING

In most sections of western United States, runoff available for irrigation comes principally from the spring and early summer melting of winter snowfall accumulated in the higher portions of the drainage basins. Therefore, melting of snow and characteristics of snow runoff are perhaps more important than conditions of runoff caused by heavy rainstorms.

Quantities of runoff produced by melting snow covers, although variable from year to year, are generally more dependable than runoff produced by rainfall. Furthermore, volumes of snow runoff that may reach irrigation projects as streamflow during early periods of the growing season, or that may become available for storage in surface reservoirs, can be fairly well determined from snow surveys made some time before snowmelt water begins to appear in the streams.

During recent years, many investigations of snow problems have been made by meteorologists, hydrologists, and engineers actively engaged in measuring and recording snow data and in utilizing streamflow produced by melting snow. The investigations have covered practically all the more important phases of snowfall. They have included development of better equipment for measuring snowfall, snow depths, and snow densities throughout the drainage basins, studies of snow melting in the field as well as in the laboratory, technical analyses of the physics of snow melting, analyses of snow runoff, improvement of methods of forecasting snow runoff, and considerations of other aspects of snow science, sometimes referred to as the science of cryology.

The following pages discuss various phases of snow melting, snow runoff, snow surveying, and runoff forecasting, primarily from the viewpoint of the irrigation engineer. Scientific processes involved in snow melting are not covered in detail. References to publications containing lengthy treatments are given at the end of the chapter.

213

Articles on snow phenomena published since about 1930, particularly on the forecasting of snow runoff, are so numerous that only a few of the more important contributions can be listed. Discussions of runoff forecasting include some considerations of streamflow produced by rainfall as well as streamflow produced by melting snow.

SNOW MELTING

In mountainous regions where deep snows accumulate during the winter, melting that produces runoff begins with the arrival of warm spring weather. In such regions, the intermittent melting that takes place on relatively warm days during the winter compacts the snow and increases the snow density, but does not produce appreciable runoff. At lower elevations, winter melting may accomplish early removal of fresh snowfalls or shallow snow covers and may produce limited amounts of runoff. When warm rains follow fresh snowfalls at the lower elevations, high rates of flood runoff may be produced.

The melting of accumulated snow covers usually begins earlier and takes place more rapidly in open areas than in forests. In dense forests, melting is retarded by shading and by the protection the trees provide against wind movements. Melting takes place more rapidly along southern exposures than along northern exposures, owing to increased solar radiation and temperature.

In some parts of the West, unusually rapid rates of snow disappearance may be caused by chinook winds blowing down the eastern slopes of the mountains. Such winds are so warm and dry that appreciable portions of the snow are directly evaporated, melting is accelerated, and rates of infiltration into the soil are increased. Consequently, amounts of surface runoff are decreased.

As mentioned in the preceding chapter, snow melting in Alpine zones above timberline takes place only during the warmer hours of midsummer days and therefore seldom produces appreciable runoff. The wasting away of snow and ice by evaporation and melting at high altitudes is scientifically referred to as ablation. Lofty Alpine zones usually can be ignored in estimating quantities of runoff that may result from snow melting in mountainous regions. Matthes was unable to find evidence of snow runoff at elevations above 12,000 feet in the central Sierras. He concluded that on the glaciers of Mount Rainier melting sufficient to produce runoff does not take place at altitudes higher than about 7,500 feet.[49]

Conditions during Melting. In a region subject to deep winter snowfalls, the spring melting season begins when the mean daily air temperature rises above 32 degrees F. and continues at above-freezing levels. In snowmelt studies, the mean daily air temperature is usually assumed to equal the average of the observed maximum and minimum temperatures.

Air temperatures are commonly measured at about head height above the ground. Tests show that melting at the snow surface does not begin until the air temperature at head height rises to about 40 degrees or higher; also that congealing of snowmelt water at the snow surface begins when the temperature at head height falls to about 40 degrees or lower. Therefore, melting usually begins late in the morning and ceases early in the evening. Temperatures below the snow surface usually remain practically uniform at 32 degrees, or slightly lower, throughout the melting season.[13]

As the snow melts, water percolates downward through the snow, in much the same manner as through a pervious soil. Some water is retained in the snow column by capillarity. If the snow has accumulated on an unfrozen soil, the percolating water tends to continue into the soil. If the soil is frozen, or if snowmelt water reaches the ground faster than infiltration can take place, water accumulates at the bottom of the snow cover until it can begin moving toward drainage channels as surface runoff. Thus, an appreciable lag occurs between the beginning of melting and the beginning of runoff.

Data obtained at the Soda Springs Laboratory by Gerdel "indicated that the free water-holding capacity of a ripe snow pack was usually below ten per cent, and that under conditions where melt water or rain was not being added to the pack at a rate greater than the transmission capacity, the water-holding capacity of a deep, ripe snow pack was approximately 0.4 inch per foot of snow of 50 per cent density." The observations also showed that free-water transmission rates varied between 0.5 and 5.0 inches per foot per hour, the variations probably being due to the presence of ice planes in the snow.[13]

Most melting of a deep snow cover takes place at or close to the snow surface. When the snow has accumulated on an unfrozen soil, some melting may take place at the ground surface, owing to conduction of heat upward from warmer depths in the soil. Under such conditions, some melting may take place at the contact plane between the snow and the soil before the beginning of the melting season.

When snow is deposited on a thinly frozen ground surface, heat from the earth may thaw out the frozen soil soon after the snow falls.

When the snow cover is relatively shallow, sunlight may penetrate the snow and cause some melting at the ground surface. Light can penetrate dry dense snow to depths as great as 2 or possibly 3 feet. However, when the snow becomes wet or is reduced to slush, the depth of penetration is greatly reduced. The presence of slush at the snow surface results in increased absorption of light but decreased transmission to the lower layers.[30]

In the removal of deep snow covers, melting at the ground surface due to effects of light penetration from above and heat conduction from below probably constitutes only a small part of the total melting.

Ripening of Snow. During early stages of melting, snow crystals tend to become granular, spaces between the crystals become filled with water, and the water content of the snow tends to become uniform at all depths. This process is often referred to as ripening. When the snow becomes still more dense and begins to lose water, it is sometimes referred to as overripe.

Actual densities of ripe snow observed in the central Sierra Nevada Mountains varied from about 30 to 48 per cent. Densities of overripe snow varied from about 35 to 56 per cent. Densities of overripe snow seldom exceed densities of ripe snow by more than about 10 per cent.[11]

Ripe snow covers, containing appreciable percentages of water, need less heat to complete the melting than equivalent covers of dry snow. The amount of heat required to melt snow or ice is 144 British thermal units per pound or 80 calories per gram. When snow contains 40 per cent water, only 60 per cent as much heat is needed to complete the melting. Thus, sudden pronounced increases in temperature or warm moist winds following a long period of ripening may rapidly complete the melting and cause relatively high rates of snow runoff.

The condition of snow as regards heat needed to complete melting is sometimes called the quality of snow. For instance, snow containing 40 per cent water requires 60 per cent as much heat as dry snow and is said to have a quality of 60 per cent. Measurements of fresh snow in New York, reported by Bernard and Wilson, showed qualities varying from 89 to 130 per cent.[6] Values higher than 100 per cent were due to initial subfreezing temperatures not allowed for in the tests. The authors concluded that coarse-grained snow may have minimum qualities of 70 or 80 per cent, and that qualities of fresh, finer-grained snow may be less than 50 per cent.

Conditions That Cause Melting. Inasmuch as melting is caused by heat, conditions that cause the melting of snow covers are the conditions that bring heat to the snow. Heat may be supplied to snow covers by the following processes, listed approximately in the order of importance:

1. Convection from turbulent air above the snow.
2. Release of heat by condensation of moisture in overlying air.
3. Absorption of solar radiation.
4. Warm rain falling on the snow.
5. Conduction from underlying soil.
6. Conduction from still air above the snow.

The effectiveness of items 1 and 2 depends on the presence of wind and on temperature conditions. Amounts of heat supplied by both processes increase as wind velocities increase. Amounts supplied by turbulent convection increase as air temperatures increase. Amounts supplied by condensation increase as vapor pressure differences increase. Vapor pressures increase as dew-point temperatures increase. Inasmuch as the latent heat of condensation is 600 calories per gram and the heat of fusion of snow only 80 calories per gram, the condensation of 1 gram of atmospheric moisture releases enough heat to melt 7.5 grams of snow.

Amounts of heat supplied by solar radiation during the spring melting season depend principally on exposure conditions, latitude, cloudiness, and the albedo of the snow surface. Since the albedo is the ratio of reflected light to total light received, amounts of radiation absorbed by snow covers increase with decreasing albedos. Clean snow surfaces may have albedos as high as 90 per cent. Snow surfaces darkened by dust, soot, or other foreign materials may have albedos as low as 60 per cent. The average albedo of the earth's surface is 43 per cent. In dense forests, amounts of solar radiation received at snow surfaces are materially reduced by shading.

Amounts of heat supplied by warm rains during the melting season depend on depths and temperatures of the precipitated water. Temperatures of the rain may be assumed to equal wet-bulb air temperatures as regularly observed at weather stations. Although warm rains are not particularly effective in supplying heat needed for melting, they may have pronounced effects on snow runoff, especially when they occur about the time melting is completed.

Amounts of heat brought to the snow blanket by conduction from underlying soils are so small in comparison with items 1 to 4 that they are usually ignored in snowmelt studies. Amounts of heat supplied by item 6 are negligible.

Studies reported by Wilson, freely drawn upon in preparing the preceding paragraphs, indicate that relative magnitudes of heat supplied by different processes during the melting of snow are about as shown in Table 1.[56]

TABLE 1

RELATIVE MAGNITUDES OF HEAT SUPPLIED BY DIFFERENT
PROCESSES [56]

Heat supply	Extreme conditions	Approximate heat supplied *
Convection from turbulent air	70° dry bulb, 20-mile wind	600
Condensation of atmospheric moisture	60° dew point, 20-mile wind	600
Absorption of solar radiation	Very moist air, cloudy at night	200
Warm rain	4 inches, 50° wet bulb	100
Conduction from soil	New snow	20

* Calories per square centimeter per day.

Evaluations of Melting Factors. The following equations, proposed by Wilson, may be used as a means of evaluating effects of different melting factors:

For convection from turbulent air:

$$D = KV(T - 32) \qquad (1)$$

where D = depth of water melted in 6 hours, in inches.

V = wind velocity, in miles per hour.

T = dry-bulb air temperature, in degrees Fahrenheit.

K = a constant having a value dependent on the latent heat of ice, exposure of instruments, conversion of units, air density, and air turbulence. Weather Bureau tests at three locations in Yellowstone Park, Wyoming, indicated a value of about 0.001 for K.

For release of heat by condensation of atmospheric water vapor overlying the snow surface:

$$D = K_1V(e - 6.11) \qquad (2)$$

where D = depth of water melted in 6 hours, in inches, plus condensate.

V = wind velocity, in miles per hour.

e = vapor pressure, in millibars.

K_1 = a constant, similar to and related to K. For basins at elevations up to about 3,000 feet, when e and T are measured at the same height, the value of K_1 is about $3.2K$.

The second term in parentheses is the vapor pressure at the snow surface, where the temperature is 32 degrees. When the quantity $(e - 6.11)$ is negative, evaporation and cooling take place at the snow surface.

For melting by warm rains:

$$D = \frac{P(T - 32)}{144} \tag{3}$$

where D = depth of water melted from the snow, in inches.

P = depth of rainfall, in inches.

T = temperature of rain, assumed to equal the wet-bulb temperature.

An equation for depth of water melted by absorbed solar radiation would involve expressions for total radiation received at the snow surface and the value of the albedo. Unfortunately, but few data are available on these factors. Wilson made some computations and presented some curves for an assumed albedo of 75 per cent. He used a function of cloud cover to represent incoming radiation. His diagram shows a snowmelt depth of 0.42 inch in a half-day period in April, free from clouds, in latitudes of from 40 to 48 degrees north.

Light presented additional analyses of technical factors involved in snow melting, including some discussions of variations in different drainage basins caused by surface roughness and the presence of forests. He stated that "it seems reasonable to expect that the influence of forest cover exceeds that of surface roughness and, in general, the actual snow melt should be less than the theoretical melt." For drainage basins in the upper Ohio River Valley, he found that observed melting was about 65 per cent of the theoretical melting.[46]

Analyses of different processes involved in snow melting by equations 1 to 3 or similar theoretical expressions are valuable in studies of snow questions. However, because of their complexity and the lack of data on constants and other factors, they are seldom applicable in practical problems of snow disappearance during spring melting seasons.

Degree-Day Estimates. Inasmuch as temperature conditions constitute the principal factors involved in snow melting, estimates of daily melting and time required for snow disappearance are often based on degree days; that is, on the excess of actual mean daily air temperatures above the mean daily temperature at which melting begins.

The mean daily temperature at which melting begins is somewhat uncertain. It probably varies in different localities and under different weather conditions. It probably is a little lower than 32 degrees F. The report on floods prepared by a committee of the Boston Society of Civil Engineers adopted a base value of 27 degrees.[9] Their diagrams showed melting rates of 0.01 to 0.03 inch per degree day above the base temperature. Grover's studies of the New England floods of March 1936 indicated negligible snow runoff for mean daily temperatures of 31 degrees, and from 0.03 to 0.05 inch of melting per degree day above 31 degrees.[32]

For most degree-day estimates of snow melting, a base temperature of 32 degrees probably is adequate. The number of degree days for any particular day is the mean daily temperature minus 32 degrees. The total degree days for the melting period is the summation of the daily values for all days during the melting period. The calculation of daily melting may be represented by the equation:

$$D = K_m(T - 32) \tag{4}$$

where D = the depth of snow water melted during the day, in inches.

T = the mean daily temperature in degrees Fahrenheit.

K_m = the melting constant, that is, the depth of melting per degree day as previously determined for the drainage basin under consideration.

The total depth melted during the period of snow disappearance is the summation of the daily depths.

Average values of the melting constant as determined for the spring melting season in different drainage basins may vary from about 0.03 to 0.15 inch per degree day. Values may be considerably higher for small local areas, or for relatively short intervals during the melting season. Tests on small plots near Crater Lake, Oregon, reported by Work, showed an average value of 0.15 inch per degree day from March 3 to June 9, 1941, and an average value of 0.66 inch per degree day from May 26 to June 2, 1941.[58]

Unusual care must be exercised in working out values of the melting constant from previous records of temperature and snow runoff in the basin under study, also in transposing values from other drainage basins where topography, range in altitude, and other characteristics may be different.

Rates of Melting. Rates of snow melting have been determined by laboratory tests of cores or cylinders, observations at small field plots, and studies of total precipitation and snow runoff in different drainage basins during periods of flood flow. Results of such investigations are commonly given as values of the melting constant.

Table 2 shows some determinations of the melting constant for different localities in the United States, also an average value for all drainage basins in Finland from 1934 to 1937. Melting constants for

TABLE 2

SOME DETERMINATIONS OF THE MELTING CONSTANT

Location	Descriptive notes	Melting period	Melting constant *	Ref. no.†
Albany, N. Y.	Tests of small cylinders	8–12 hours	0.04–0.06	36
Donner Summit, Calif.	Observations in 1917	Apr. 1–May 6	0.071	11
Gooseberry Creek, Utah	Field measurements	Apr. 23–May 9	0.091	17
Gooseberry Creek, Utah	Tests of cores	6–9 hours	0.05–0.07	17
Finland	All basins, 1934–1937	April	0.108	11
Soda Springs, Calif.	Average, 1936–1941	April	0.051	11
New England floods	Studies by Boston Soc. C. E.	1–14 days	0.01–0.04	9
N. Y. and Pa. basins	Flood runoff studies	March or April	0.04–0.07	44
La Grange Brook, N. Y.	Basin area, 36 acres	Mar. 28–Apr. 6	0.09	45
New England floods, 1936	Geol. Sur., average values	Mar. 9–22	0.03–0.05	32
Pemigewasset Basin, N. H.	Flood of March 1936	Mar. 17–20	0.16	44
Crater Lake, Ore.	Small test plots	Mar. 3–June 9	0.153	58
Crater Lake, Ore.	Small test plots	May 26–June 2	0.658	58

* Depth of water melted in inches per degree day.
† See references at end of chapter.

New England floods, determined by the Boston Society of Civil Engineers, were based on degree days above 27 degrees Fahrenheit, as previously mentioned. Melting constants for the New England floods of March 1936 were based on degree days above 31 degrees. Other values were based on degree days above freezing temperature. Except for the late period of melting at Crater Lake, melting constants in Table 2 vary from 0.01 to 0.16 inch per degree day.

Actual depths of snow water melted per day probably depend to some extent on night temperatures as well as on mean daily temperatures. When air temperatures remain above freezing during the night, melting may continue without interruption and higher daily rates of melting may be experienced.

In the Gooseberry Creek basin, Utah, the average depth of water melted per day during the 16-day melting season was 1.07 inches.[17] At Soda Springs, California, average depths of water melted per day during the spring melting season varied from 0.338 inch in 1938 to

0.728 inch in 1939. The average daily depth of melting for six seasons was 0.455 inch.[11] In Finland, the average depth of melting per day is about 0.53 inch.

At high altitudes, melting and evaporation during the warmer months may accomplish considerable reductions in depths of snow and ice. Observations reported from Russia show that ablation at the Karaugom glacier took place at rates as high as 14.0 centimeters per day during August 1933, with a mean rate of 9.1 centimeters per day for the entire month. The computed depth of ablation at the Bashkara glacier during the 6 months from May to October was 7.3 meters, about 27 feet.[41]

Rates of recession at several glaciers in British Columbia were discussed by Webb in 1948. Observations maintained at the Illecillewaet glacier in the Selkirk range since 1887 showed a mean annual rate of recession of 79 feet. Although measurements at other glaciers showed different rates of recession, some higher and some lower, the investigations in general indicated comparatively rapid rates of retreat during the last half-century.[54]

Gooseberry Creek Investigations. In 1931, Clyde reported the results of some snowmelt investigations in a small, fan-shaped basin at the head of Gooseberry Creek, near the north end of the Wasatch Plateau, Utah.[17] The basin is about 4.5 miles long, covers an area of 6.1 square miles, and has elevations ranging from 8,700 to 9,500 feet above sea level. Vegetation consists of grass and sagebrush at the lower elevations, and aspens and conifers at the higher elevations. The investigations included measurements of temperature, precipitation, water content of the snow cover, snow evaporation, soil-moisture contents, quantities of snow runoff, and some laboratory tests of snow melting. The following items, renumbered, are some of the conclusions:

1. The field studies showed that the density of the snow cover increased to a maximum of 49.4 per cent and then decreased to about 37 per cent where it remained during the remainder of the melting period. A rapid decrease in temperature caused a decrease in melting, but the accumulated storage of water in the snow continued to drain out even after the temperature decreased.

2. Before melting begins the density of a snow column is not uniform, but after melting starts, the density becomes uniform throughout its depth, except for the zone of capillary storage.

3. The major portion of the early melting seemed to take place at the snow surface.

4. Fluorescein was placed on the snow to trace the path of the water through the snow. During melting temperatures the color quickly passed through the snow to the bottom; during freezing weather, however, it remained in the snow surface.

5. Snow does not melt at the same rate that water drains out of the snow. The melting is more rapid at the beginning and less rapid at the end of melting than the drainage. The total melting equals the total drainage plus the evaporation from the snow during melting.

6. Field measurements showed that the water drained from the snow at a uniform rate throughout the melting season. Snow cores melted in the laboratory also drained out at practically a uniform rate.

7. There was a marked fluctuation in the stream discharge, due to temperature changes in spite of the fact that the rate of snow drainage was constant.

8. Temperature affects materially the rate of melting, but unless prolonged periods of low temperatures occur, it has little effect on the rate of drainage.

9. Field measurements of temperature and melting indicate that one day degree Fahrenheit of temperature will melt 0.091 inch depth of water. Laboratory measurements varied from 0.053 to 0.075 inch depth of water per day degree Fahrenheit of temperature.

10. The lag between beginning of melting and the appearance of runoff varies widely but seems to increase with an increase in the initial density of the snow.

11. Snow increases in density as melting progresses, the increase being most rapid in snow having a low initial density.

12. The rate of melting and drainage increases slightly, with an increase in the initial density of the snow.

13. The rate at which the water leaves the snow during the melting period is nearly constant during the forepart of the melting period but increases slightly with increase in density near the end of the melting season.

14. A cold backward spring which causes slow melting induces a lower but a better distributed runoff.

15. A warm early spring which causes rapid melting induces a higher but a more undesirable distribution of runoff.

16. The ability of the earth mantle to absorb water as fast as it leaves the snow cover governs largely the runoff characteristics.

17. Snow-melting characteristics govern to a large extent the losses, rapid melting reducing the losses, and slow melting increasing the losses.

18. Evaporation, transpiration, and seepage losses increase with a decrease in rate of melting.

Conclusions 10 to 13, inclusive, were based on laboratory tests of nine snow cores. In connection with item 8 it might be noted that, although the rate of snow drainage was but slightly affected by temperature changes, the snow runoff reaching the creek channel was materially affected. Clyde attributed this to differences in ground and surface storage caused by temperature changes. His hourly hydrograph of Gooseberry Creek showed a close correlation between temperature and gage height.

Crater Lake Investigations. Work recently reported the results of some intensive snow investigations conducted cooperatively by the United States Soil Conservation Service, the United States National Park Service, and the Oregon Agricultural Experiment Station, Corvallis, Oregon, during the winter of 1940–1941.[58] The observations were made on a small experimental plot, 25 feet square, located at an elevation of 6,450 feet near Crater Lake. The plot was established in an open clearing, where it was protected by nearby timber. The soil was a pervious pumice, with a slight surface slope. It was unfrozen during the melting season and probably absorbed the most of the snow water. Work's summary and conclusions were as follows:

1. The customary April 1 final spring snow survey date, for all practical purposes, measured the peak accumulation of snow-stored water at Crater Lake in 1941 and was almost an exact measure of total precipitation there from the time snow first remained on the ground in late October of 1940.

2. Rain falling on shallow snow of relatively low density may pass through to the ground beneath and contribute but little in transit to the snow-stored water.

3. Rain falling on moderately deep snow of low or intermediate density may be retained in the snow.

4. Snow density cannot accurately be estimated from measurements alone, any more than density of one portion of the snow cover can be computed from known density of another portion of the total layer.

5. Snow settling is a continuous process from the time snow first remains on the ground. Diminishing snow depth early in the winter is due more to settling and less to melting at the surface, but diminishing snow level later in the season is due nearly altogether to melting away of the surface snow, rather than to snow settling.

6. Density of snow generally increases consistently from the time snow is deposited until it disappears.

7. Density of new-fallen snow increases more rapidly in any given time period than density of older snow.

8. There is no single relationship between elapsed time after deposition and mature snow density.

9. When important melting began, the water did not leave the snow at a constant rate, but rather at a rate generally accelerated with time and

decreasing snow depth. A general upward air temperature trend accompanied it.

10. Short periods of density decrease, after melting begins, may be due to continued water drainage from the snow without replenishment from surface melting.

11. Density is directly related to the size and arrangement of the ice crystals comprising snow. In general, snow of fine texture having rounded crystals, and lubricated by melt-water from above, will have a higher density than snow of equal or older age but having coarser texture or very open structure.

12. Snow does not necessarily become homogeneous in texture after melting begins. Its density may similarly lack homogeneity.

13. Ultimate density of any long-lived, deeply buried snow layer may be partly dependent upon the atmospheric conditions under which the snow crystals are first formed. Ultimate density of any particular snow layer may, accordingly, be partly determined before its flakes reach the ground.

14. There appears to be no relationship between weight of overlying snow and density of lower layers.

15. In this series of observations, it was definitely determined that practically all snow melting occurred at the snow surface and only insignificant melting occurred at the snow-earth plane.

16. Water melting from snow and including surface evaporation at elevation 6,540 ft. averaged 0.153 inch per day-degree Fahrenheit temperature above freezing at Crater Lake in 1941.

17. Melt values are not constant per day-degree of temperature above 32 degrees F.

18. The maximum water-holding capacity of any snow layer of given depth is not constant, but varies with structure and texture of the snow. In general, its maximum water-holding capacity increases with age.

19. The density and water content of any snow layer after melting begins may be increased by the presence of an ice layer immediately below or within the layer.

20. Two common types of ice layers are those found at the snow surface and later buried within the snow body by new-fallen snow, and those formed within the snow body through freezing fixation of percolating meltwater. A secondary form of the first type is the ice layer which escapes observation until the surrounding snow changes its texture.

21. Frost will penetrate a snow cover at least 24 inches thick to freeze the earth beneath.

22. Frozen soil beneath the snow may thaw from upward conduction of heat stored in the deeper ground and not necessarily from direct radiant heat conducted through the snow.

23. Light sufficient to form chlorophyll in newly sprouted grass pene-trated at least 35 to 40 inches of dense snow.

Snow Runoff. Snow runoff does not reach stream channels and affect streamflow until some time after melting begins. The lag repre-sents time needed for snowmelt water to percolate downward through the snow column, attain a percolation rate greater than the rate at which water can enter the soil, fill the capillary storage in the lower part of the snow cover, and build up pressures at the ground surface sufficient to move water toward the drainage courses as surface flow. In general, appreciable snow runoff does not reach tributary streams until 2 or 3 days after the beginning of melting.

In the Gooseberry Creek basin, snow runoff during the spring of 1928 did not reach the stream channel until the third day after melt-ing began, after 14 degree days of melting temperatures had accumu-lated.[17] In the Driftwood Branch of Sinnemahoning Creek, Sterling Run, Pennsylvania, snow runoff in the spring of 1936 did not arrive until the fourth day after melting began, after 25 degree days of melt-ing temperatures had accumulated.[44]

At high altitudes in the western mountains, temperatures during the melting season often are below freezing during the night and above freezing during the day. In such regions, hydrographs of snow runoff show diurnal fluctuations. The fluctuations are pronounced in streams draining small areas but may be observed in streams draining as much as 5,000 square miles. They decrease in magnitude as the size of the drainage area increases, because runoff from different parts of the basin reach the main stream at different times. Figure 1 shows the magnitude of the diurnal fluctuations as observed in some Colo-rado streams during May 25 to 29, 1919, plotted from data reported by Follansbee.[25]

The portion of the water content of a snow cover that reaches the stream as runoff during the melting season depends principally on the rate of melting and the rate at which snowmelt water can be absorbed by the soil. When melting takes place slowly, depths of infiltration are increased and depths of runoff decreased. When melting takes place rapidly, depths of infiltration are decreased and depths of run-off increased. If the surface soil becomes frozen while wet and does not thaw out before melting begins, infiltration may be negligible and runoff almost equal to the total water content.

Total depths of evaporation and transpiration during the melting season seldom constitute large proportions of the total snowmelt water. Some water that infiltrates into the soil is evaporated from the wet soil surfaces after the snow disappears, some is transpired by vegetation, and some subsequently reaches the stream channel as groundwater runoff.

In the Gooseberry Creek basin, where deep seepage losses were believed to be small, 73.7 per cent of the snowmelt ultimately appeared as runoff in 1928, and 63.4 per cent appeared in 1929. In other

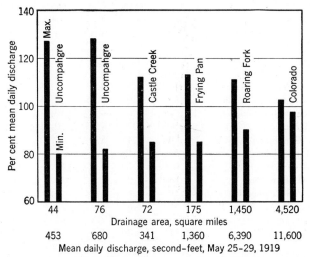

FIGURE 1. Diurnal fluctuations in Colorado rivers caused by freezing and melting of snow runoff. (Plotted from data in *U.S. Geol. Sur. Water-Supply Paper* 500–C.)

Wasatch Plateau basins, where some losses were believed to take place by deep seepage, total snow runoff varied from 15.8 to 56.5 per cent of the snowmelt. In the Logan River basin, 57.2 per cent of the snowmelt appeared as runoff in 1928, and 43.2 per cent appeared in 1929.[17]

Moderate rainfalls early in the melting season increase the water content of the snow cover and thus increase the subsequent volume of snow runoff. Heavy rainfalls near the end of the melting season, after the snow has been largely reduced to slush, may complete the melting and cause the sudden runoff of nearly all the snowmelt water remaining on the ground, together with the greater part of the added precipitation. When such conditions occur, sudden intense floods may be produced in the stream channels.

Table 3 shows depths of snow runoff that occurred in some of the larger drainage basins in northeastern United States during the floods of March 1936, when heavy rains fell on relatively deep snow covers.

TABLE 3

TOTAL PRECIPITATION AND SNOW RUNOFF IN NORTHEASTERN
UNITED STATES, FLOODS OF MARCH 1936 *

(Depths in inches)

River and location of measurement	Basin area, sq. miles	Water in snow cover, Mar. 9	Storm rain-fall, Mar. 9–22	Total pre-cipita-tion	Total run-off	Snow run-off
Penobscot, West Enfield, Me.	6,600	8.6	5.3	13.9	8.75	3.45
Kennebec, Waterville, Me.	4,270	9.2	6.6	15.8	9.20	2.6
Androscoggin, Auburn, Me:	3,257	9.9	9.0	18.9	12.87	3.85
Merrimack, Lowell, Mass.	4,424	4.0	8.2	12.2	11.53	3.45
Connecticut, Holyoke, Mass.	8,284	6.5	6.35	12.85	11.42	5.05
Housatonic, Stevenson, Conn.	1,545	4.0	5.45	9.45	8.42	2.95
Winooski, Essex Junction, Vt.	1,079	6.3	4.5	10.8	9.84	5.35
Hudson, Mechanicville, N. Y.	4,500	5.2	4.95	10.15	6.95	2.0
Sacandaga, Conklingville, N. Y.	1,004	6.4	5.4	11.8	8.46	3.05
Mohawk, Little Falls, N. Y.	1,348	5.1	3.6	8.7	6.39	2.8
Delaware, Port Jervis, N. Y.	3,076	4.2	6.0	10.2	9.91	3.9
Lehigh, Bethlehem, Pa.	1,280	4.0	6.4	10.4	8.90	2.5
Schuylkill, Philadelphia, Pa.	1,893	1.6	4.8	6.4	5.68	0.9
Susquehanna, Wilkes-Barre, Pa.	9,960	2.6	5.7	8.3	8.03	2.35
Juniata, Newport, Pa.	3,354	3.4	7.4	10.8	9.05	1.65
Oswego, Oswego, N. Y.	5,121	3.2	4.7	7.9	7.10	2.4

* See references 32 and 33.

Data on basin areas, water contents of the snow, total storm rainfall, and total runoff are also shown. The rains occurred principally in two storm periods, and practically all the snow had disappeared by the end of the second storm.[32] Inasmuch as quantities of snow runoff cannot be segregated accurately during such floods, the depths were estimated by deducting total rainfall from total runoff. In some drainage basins, depths of snow runoff probably were greater proportions of the snow water plus rainfall than would be indicated by the tabulated values.

Runoff that reaches stream channels as a result of melting at permanent snow fields or glaciers in the high mountains of the West comes primarily from the lower limits of the snow and ice formations. Inasmuch as such sources of supply are not exhausted by early summer melting, maximum rates of runoff take place during periods of maximum temperature, usually in July. Melting that occurs during ablation of new snow at high elevations on ice sheets contributes but little if any runoff. The water percolates downward during the day, as the surface snow melts, then freezes during the night, adding more ice to the glaciers.

RUNOFF FORECASTING

The forecasting of runoff is essential in order to conserve irrigation water supplies and utilize streamflow in the most economical manner. Accurate forecasting of spring and summer runoff is especially important on projects where surface reservoirs have not been constructed to store fall and winter runoff.

Runoff forecasting is now practiced to some extent in all parts of the country, even in humid regions where rainfall normally can be expected to maintain adequate stream discharges. Forecasts of runoff furnish information needed in operating municipal water-supply systems, hydroelectric power plants, and various industrial activities that utilize streamflow, as well as in operating irrigation enterprises. They also supply data needed in considering possible stream pollution during periods of low flow.

Inasmuch as runoff is produced by excess precipitation, forecasts of runoff must be based on precipitation, or on snow covers accumulated as a result of precipitation. Since predictions of excess precipitation can be made only a few days in advance of occurrence, and then only very approximately, accurate forecasts of runoff can be made only after the precipitation takes place. Thus, in regions where excess precipitation occurs principally as storm rainfall, forecasts of runoff have only immediate and limited value, because they cannot be made much in advance of runoff. In regions where winter precipitation occurs in the form of snow and the snow remains on the ground until warm spring weather, fairly accurate forecasts of spring and early summer runoff can be made several days or even weeks before the runoff takes place. Such forecasts usually are based on water contents of the snow as determined by snow surveys.

In western United States, where runoff is produced largely by the spring melting of deep snow covers accumulated in mountainous regions, forecasts of runoff based on snow surveys are utilized in planning irrigation procedures. When water shortages are indicated, steps sometimes can be taken to secure supplemental supplies. If supplemental supplies cannot be secured, crop acreages can be limited to areas on which crops can be matured with the supplies that are anticipated. When severe droughts seem imminent, planting can be drastically reduced, livestock can be moved or sold, and other measures can be taken to reduce drought losses. Early forecasts of severe water shortages in Utah, made during the drought year of 1934, permitted the adoption of measures that were estimated to have saved more than 5 million dollars.[19]

Snow Surveys. Snow surveys, to determine quantities of water held on the ground in the form of snow, are now being made periodically during the winter and spring months in most regions where spring melting contributes large proportions of the annual runoff. Results of the surveys are used in preparing forecasts of the spring and summer runoff that may be expected to become available for beneficial uses, particularly irrigation.

In general, snow surveys are made along carefully selected courses, where depths and water contents are representative of average snow conditions throughout the drainage basin. Vertical snow cores at intervals along the courses, down to the full depth of the snow cover, are taken with specially designed snow samplers, provided with a cutting edge at one end. Water contents of the core samples are accurately determined by weighing at the time of removal. Spring-balance scales are used in weighing. Detailed descriptions of survey methods, core samplers, weighing scales, and incidental items of equipment have been published in state and federal bulletins.[48]

Snow surveys are usually made along the more important courses about the first of each month from January to May, inclusive, and along all established courses in each watershed about the first of March, April, or May, depending on the particular latitude and probable time of melting. Tentative forecasts of probable runoff are generally made after each survey, and a final forecast, following the completion of the final survey. Final forecasts require revision when additional heavy snows or storm rainfalls occur after the last survey is made.

Most snow surveys are now conducted cooperatively by federal and state agencies, municipalities, power companies, irrigation districts, and other organizations that use streamflow. Data are made available to all interested parties, and regional snow conferences are arranged to facilitate the exchange of information and promote the development of more reliable methods of forecasting runoff.[54]

Snow-measurement researches now in progress may ultimately simplify the securing of snow data. If radioactive materials can be placed along the courses, modified Geiger counters installed, and radio transmission systems established, determinations of water contents in snow covers may be possible without conducting field surveys. Moreover, if the researches are successful, stations can be established and data secured at locations that are accessible in the summer but not in the winter.[31]

Establishing Snow Courses. Snow courses should be established in protected open areas or forests, where they can be reached during the winter months. Locations where snowslides disturb the snow cover or where wind movements cause pronounced drifting should be avoided. Stations along the courses should be definitely located and plainly marked, so that they can be easily found and measurements made at the same points during all subsequent surveys.

Usually, the more important courses should be established at altitudes high enough to prevent impairment of the data by winter melting. Locations with northern exposures often are an advantage from the viewpoint of avoiding winter melting. Some courses at lower altitudes may be desirable for use in evaluating winter melting and forecasting runoff during early stages of spring melting.

An altitude of 7,000 feet has been found adequate on the western slopes of the Sierra Nevada Mountains in California, but somewhat higher altitudes are more satisfactory on the eastern slopes.[10] In Utah, most snow courses are established at altitudes higher than 8,000 feet, but some are established at lower levels.[18]

In general, the snow courses should be long enough to permit observations at 30 or more stations, located from 50 to 100 feet apart. Where rugged mountain topography prevents the establishment of straight courses of such length, the courses may be laid out as crosses, triangles, or with two or more branching elements. Fallen trees, logs, brush, and other obstructions along the courses should be cleared away, especially at the measuring points. All courses and measuring points should be accurately located by surveying methods, and ground elevations should be determined along the courses. Suitable maps and profiles can then be plotted for record purposes and future considerations.

The number of snow courses needed in a particular drainage area depends on the extent of the mountainous area, the different separate basins contributing snow runoff to the main stream, and the relations of snow cover to runoff in the different basins. For a relatively small stream, draining a single segregated mountain basin, one or two properly established courses may be sufficient. In the headwater drainage area of a large river, several snow courses may be needed in each principal contributory element of the mountainous area. In the spring of 1945, snow surveys were made along 78 courses in the upstream drainage basins contributing runoff to the Colorado River. **Forecasts of Snow Runoff.** Forecasts of total snow runoff from high mountainous areas are made on the basis of snow surveys conducted along representative snow courses. When snow surveys and runoff measurements have been made for several years, so that normal relationships have become well established, such forecasts are usually reliable. Naturally, they are most reliable in regions where deep snow covers accumulate during the winter months and spring melting continues to completion, unaffected by the occurrence of heavy rainfalls.

For streams where adequate storage reservoirs have been constructed and streamflow can be properly regulated, forecasts of total spring runoff provide the principal data needed in allotting irrigation water supplies. For streams uncontrolled by storage, where streamflow must be utilized as it reaches the projects, forecasts of actual discharges throughout the irrigation season are desirable. Fairly reliable forecasts of actual discharges sometimes can be made after peak rates of snow runoff have developed. They seldom can be made before the beginning of melting. Continuous hydrographs at downstream locations are difficult to predict prior to melting, because of uncertainties regarding soil conditions, future temperature conditions, probable times and rates of melting, and rainfalls that may occur during the progress of melting.

In Utah, where precipitation during the summer months is normally low, some success has been attained in predicting summer discharges. The predictions are made after peak flows have been reached. They are based on characteristic shapes of the hydrographs during periods of decreasing discharges, as established during preceding years of observation. Inasmuch as peak discharges normally occur early in the irrigation season, the predictions can be made in time to be of material assistance in planning the distribution of available water supplies.[19]

Methods of Forecasting. In general, forecasts of total snow runoff are made by two methods: (1) the percentage method, which assumes that total runoff is proportional to the percentage of normal water content in the snow cover; and (2) the quantitative method, which assumes that total runoff equals the total quantity of snow water in the basin minus the total losses that occur during melting. The first method is commonly used in western United States.

Both methods of forecasting are based on snow surveys that determine actual water contents of snow covers at the time melting begins.

Therefore, the accuracy of both methods depends on the representativeness of the snow courses utilized in making the snow surveys. In large mountainous drainage basins, both methods may require divisions of basin areas into zones of different elevations and appropriate weighting of the different zones in making the forecast computations. In some basins, divisions into zones according to differences in precipitation characteristics may be desirable.[24]

During the earlier years of forecasting snow runoff, some fairly reliable forecasts were based on measurements of snow depths along representative courses. However, such methods have been largely discontinued. When snow courses are surveyed to measure depths of snow, only small additional costs are involved in accurately determining water contents, principally the costs of purchasing sampling and weighing equipment.

In the quantitative method of forecasting snow runoff, the average depth of water held on the watershed in the form of snow at the beginning of runoff is calculated from snow survey data, and an estimated depth of total water losses is deducted to obtain the total depth of anticipated snow runoff. This method has been used with some success in eastern United States, and to a limited extent for relatively small drainage areas in the West. For large and rugged mountainous areas in the West, where snow covers commonly attain considerable depths on inaccessible portions of the watershed, accurate quantitative determinations are not feasible.

Most forecasts of snow runoff in western United States are made by the percentage method. This method, developed by Church and sometimes called the Nevada system, assumes (1) that, in a particular watershed, snow courses can be located where the snow depths and water contents are representative of average conditions throughout the watershed; and (2) the average water content of the snow cover along representative snow courses at the beginning of the melting season bears a definite relationship to the total depth of snow runoff that will occur when the snow melts. Thus, when sufficient records become available for a particular drainage area, a diagram can be prepared showing the relation between the water content of the snow cover and the resultant snow runoff.

Figure 2, based on Boardman's data, shows the relation between the water content of the snow cover on April 1 and the resulting April to July runoff for the Tuolumne River basin above Hetch Hetchy, California.[7] Water contents of the snow were measured along 14 courses, 8 between altitudes 5,700 and 7,500 feet, 2 between

7,500 and 9,000 feet, and 4 above 9,000 feet. The drainage area above Hetch Hetchy includes 461 square miles above altitude 4,000 feet, of which 255 square miles are above 9,000 feet. The lower limits of the snow line on April 1 are at about altitude 4,000 feet. In working out the average water content of the snow cover throughout the basin, results of snow surveys along different courses were weighted according to zones of different elevation.

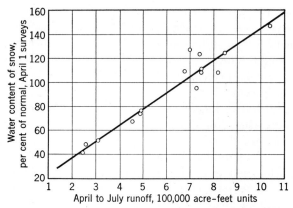

FIGURE 2. Relation between snow cover and April to July runoff, Tuolumne River, Hetch Hetchy, California, 1930 to 1944. (After Boardman.)

Forecasting from Photographs. Sometimes photographic surveys of snow cover on inaccessible mountain areas can be used as aids in forecasting summer runoff. In the winter, when the mountains are covered with snow, photographs show no information except the presence of snow. In the spring, after depths of snow on the more exposed slopes have melted, photographs taken at definite intervals show the portions of the areas still covered and the rates at which snow is disappearing from such areas.

A method of utilizing photographs in conjunction with precipitation measurements was developed by Potts in forecasting South Platte River runoff for municipal use at Denver, Colorado.[51] Summer flows in the South Platte are caused by runoff from rainfall combined with snow runoff from the higher basin areas. Forecasts made early in the summer involve the use of a normal precipitation curve. Consequently, they usually require some revision after rainfall takes place. Figure 3 shows seasonal runoff curves for the Middle Fork of the South Platte, plotted against percentages of snow cover in the upstream mountain areas. A scale of seasonal precipitation is shown along the 100 per cent line.

The use of vertical aerial photographs by the Corps of Engineers in studying snow conditions in the upper Columbia River basin, particularly as regards effects of topography and vegetation on snow cover and snow melting, was discussed by Daniels in 1948.[54]

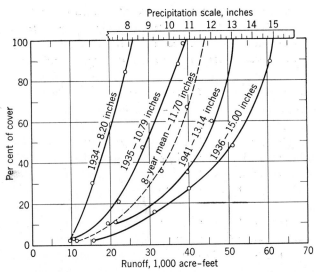

FIGURE 3. Relations between snow cover, precipitation, and runoff, Middle Fork of South Platte River, May 1 to November 1. (After Potts.)

Other Forecasting Methods. Other methods have been used in forecasting total spring and summer runoff. For some drainage basins, forecasts have been based on depths of precipitation accumulated prior to the melting season. For others, forecasts of summer and fall runoff have been based on observed winter and early spring flows and characteristics of the hydrographs that usually follow such flows, as observed for similar conditions recorded during preceding years.

For the Colorado River basin above Hoover Dam, where the drainage area is about 167,800 square miles, Stanley and Kennedy found that total depths of fall and winter precipitation at thirteen selected stations constituted fair indices of the volumes of subsequent spring and summer runoff. In the Colorado River basin above Hoover Dam, about two-thirds of the annual runoff comes from the melting of snow at the higher altitudes. Analyses based on data supplied by snow surveys gave less accurate indications of total runoff than those based on total fall and winter precipitation.[52]

Somewhat different conclusions were reached in studying methods of forecasting Tuolumne River flows, where the drainage area is much smaller than the Colorado River basin. Boardman found that forecasts of Tuolumne River runoff based on snow surveys were more accurate than those based on accumulated winter precipitation.[7]

For unusually large rivers, forecasts of summer and fall flows are sometimes formulated by methods variously referred to as pattern sequence, pattern repetition, or pattern behavior. Such methods assume that similar patterns of runoff during the winter and early spring months of different years are followed by similar patterns of runoff during the succeeding summer and fall months. Detailed pattern-behavior analyses of flows in the Columbia River at Cascade Locks, Oregon, were described by Wahle in 1943.[53]

Pattern-behavior methods have been used to some extent in forecasting other than spring flows in the Colorado River. The procedure followed in forecasting summer flows in Utah streams, described by Clyde in 1939, is essentially a pattern-repetition method.[19]

Various factors that affect snow runoff have been studied more or less intensively in efforts to improve forecasts of total runoff. Such factors include fall precipitation, spring precipitation, rainfall during the melting period, temperatures during the melting period, and soil-moisture contents at the time melting begins. Additions of moisture to snow covers caused by spring precipitations that do not cause immediate runoff affect the water contents of the snow covers as determined by the final surveys. Additions of moisture to surface soils produced by fall precipitations may materially affect rates of infiltration during spring melting.

Aside from rainfalls during the melting period, which constitute direct additions to the quantities of water available for runoff, soil-moisture conditions at the time melting begins probably constitute the most important influences on proportions of snowmelt water that reach stream channels as runoff.

Runoff from Rainfall. Where appreciable rainfall commonly occurs during or following the melting period, forecasts of total runoff based on snow surveys should include allowances for anticipated subsequent rainfall and resulting runoff. Usually, such allowances can be based on assumptions of normal spring precipitation, and the forecasts modified later, after the rainfall takes place. Where storm rainfall constitutes the principal source of streamflow, reliable forecasts of total runoff are not feasible until data on actual storm precipitations become available.

Rainfall occurring about the end of the melting season or within one or two days following the completion of melting, while the surface is still saturated, usually can be assumed to produce from 50 to 75 per cent runoff. Such rainfalls may materially increase the total runoff as forecast on the basis of the final snow survey. In studies of forecasting runoff from a small drainage basin in the Wasatch Mountains, Utah, Croft found that rainfalls after the final survey might account for as much as 40 per cent of the total runoff.[23]

In large river basins, where some time elapses between the occurrence of storm rainfall and the arrival of runoff at downstream locations, forecasts of total runoff sometimes can be based on the runoff measured from small elemental areas. When rainfall intensities and time distributions are fairly uniform throughout the drainage basins, forecasts based on runoff from elemental areas may be reasonably reliable. When rainfall conditions vary considerably throughout the basins, forecasts of total runoff require adjustments in accordance with observed variations in precipitation. This method of forecasting runoff, sometimes designated the index-area method, was discussed by Leach and others in 1933.[45]

An index-area method of forecasting runoff in the Salt River basin above Roosevelt Reservoir, Arizona, was described by Cooperrider and others in 1945.[21] Salt River drains a mountainous area of about 4,310 square miles, with altitudes varying from about 2,500 to 12,000 feet above sea level. Some winter precipitation occurs as snowfall at the higher elevations, but ordinarily snow covers do not accumulate on as much as 15 per cent of the area. Total March to May flows into the reservoir were determined on the basis of total October to February runoff at a small elemental area near the reservoir. The determinations were fairly reliable for years of high runoff but more uncertain for years of low runoff.

REFERENCES

1. Alciatore, Henry F., "Growth, Settling, and Final Disappearance of a Snow Cover in the Sierra Nevada, 1915–16," *U.S. Dept. Agr. Monthly Weather Rev.*, March 1917, pp. 109–113.
2. Alps, H. F., "Foot-Layer Densities of Snow," *U.S. Dept. Agr. Monthly Weather Rev.*, September 1922, pp. 474–475.
3. Bartell, M. J., "The Relation of Runoff to Precipitation in the Sierra Nevada, California," *Trans. Am. Geop. Union*, February 1949, pp. 89–97.

4. Bernard, Merrill, "The Expanded Program of the United States Weather Bureau in Snow-Work," *Trans. Am. Geop. Union,* 1938, Part II, pp. 673–685.

5. ——— "The Long Term Precipitation-Runoff Relation as the Basis for Forecasting Water Supply," *Trans. Am. Geop. Union,* June 1949, pp. 386–395.

6. Bernard, Merrill, and Walter T. Wilson, "A New Technique for the Determination of Heat Necessary to Melt Snow," *Trans. Am. Geop. Union,* 1941, Part I, pp. 178–181.

7. Boardman, H. P., "Snow Survey versus Winter Precipitation for Forecasting Runoff of the Tuolumne River, California," *Trans. Am. Geop. Union,* October 1947, pp. 752–765.

8. ——— "Snow Surveys for Forecasting Stream Flow in Western Nevada," *Nev. Agr. Exp. Sta. Bull.* 184, 1949.

9. Boston Society of Civil Engineers, "Report of the Committee on Floods," *Soc. Jour.,* September 1930, pp. 285–464.

10. Church, J. E., "Principles of Snow Surveying as Applied to Forecasting Stream Flow," *Jour. Agr. Res.,* July 15, 1935, pp. 97–130.

11. ——— "Snow and Snow Surveying; Ice," Chapter IV in Meinzer's *Hydrology,* 1942, pp. 83–148 (see reference 23 in Chapter 1).

12. ——— "Snow-Study Program at Soda Springs near Donner Summit of Central Sierra Nevada," *Trans. Am. Geop. Union,* 1943, Part III, pp. 77–90.

13. Church, J. E., and others, "Research Committee on Snow, Western Snow Conference, 1945," *Trans. Am. Geop. Union,* June 1946, pp. 412–440.

14. Church, Phil E., "Ice-Crusts and Snow-Settling, Snoqualmie Pass, Winter of 1940–1941," *Trans. Am. Geop. Union,* 1941, Part III, pp. 793–796.

15. Clyde, George D., "Change in Density of Snow Cover with Melting," *U.S. Dept. Agr. Monthly Weather Rev.,* August 1929, pp. 326–327.

16. ——— "Establishing Snow Courses and Making Snow Surveys," *Utah Agr. Exp. Sta. Cir.* 91, 1930.

17. ——— "Snow-Melting Characteristics," *Utah Agr. Exp. Sta. Tech. Bull.* 231, 1931.

18. ——— "Establishing Snow-Courses for Representativeness, Permanence, and Continuity of Record," *Trans. Am. Geop. Union,* 1937, Part II, pp. 618–631.

19. ——— "Forecasting Stream Flow from Snow Surveys," *Civ. Eng.,* April 1939, pp. 237–239.

20. Clyde, George D., and R. A. Work, "Precipitation-Runoff Relationships as a Basis for Water-Supply Forecasting," *Trans. Am. Geop. Union,* 1943, Part III, pp. 43–55.

21. Cooperrider, C. K., H. O. Cassidy, and C. H. Niederhof, "Forecasting Stream-Flow of the Salt River, Arizona," *Trans. Am. Geop. Union,* October 1945, pp. 275–282.

22. Criddle, Wayne D., "Value of Midwinter Snow Surveys," *Trans. Am. Geop. Union,* December 1947, pp. 888–898.

23. Croft, A. R., "Some Factors That Influence the Accuracy of Water-Supply Forecasting in the Intermountain Region," *Trans. Am. Geop. Union,* June 1946, pp. 375–388.

24. Elges, Carl, "Improvements in the Methods of Forecasting Stream-Flow," *Trans. Am. Geop. Union,* 1939, Part I, pp. 62–67.

25. Follansbee, Robert, "Some Characteristics of Run-Off in the Rocky Mountain Region," *U.S. Geol. Sur. Water-Supply Paper* 500–C, 1922.

26. Ford, Perry M., "Multiple Correlation in Forecasting Seasonal Runoff," *U.S. Bur. Recl. Eng. Monog.* 2, 1949.

27. Forsling, C. L., "Snow Melt," *U.S. Dept. Agr. Yearbook,* 1941, pp. 557–560.

28. Garstka, Walter U., "Interpretation of Snow Surveys," *Trans. Am. Geop. Union,* June 1949, pp. 412–420.

29. Gerdel, R. W., "Snow-Temperature Studies and Apparatus at the Soda Springs, California, Cooperative Snow-Research Project," *Trans. Am. Geop. Union,* 1944, Part I, pp. 118–122.

30. ——— "Penetration of Radiation into the Snow Pack," *Trans. Am. Geop. Union,* June 1948, pp. 366–374.

31. Gerdel, R. W., B. L. Hansen, and W. C. Cassidy, "The Use of Radioisotopes for the Measurement of the Water Equivalent of a Snow Pack," *Trans. Am. Geop. Union,* June 1950, pp. 449–453.

32. Grover, Nathan C., "The Floods of March 1936, Part 1, New England Rivers," *U.S. Geol. Sur. Water-Supply Paper* 798, 1937.

33. ——— "The Floods of March 1936, Part 2, Hudson River to Susquehanna River Region," *U.S. Geol. Sur. Water-Supply Paper* 799, 1937.

34. Henry, A. J., "The Disappearance of Snow in the High Sierra Nevada of California," *U.S. Dept. Agr. Monthly Weather Rev.* March 1916, pp. 150–153.

35. ——— "The Density of Snow," *U.S. Dept. Agr. Monthly Weather Rev.,* March 1917, pp. 102–109.

36. Horton, R. E., "The Melting of Snow," *U.S. Dept. Agr. Monthly Weather Rev.,* December 1915, pp. 599–605.

37. ——— "Phenomena of the Contact Zone between the Ground Surface and a Layer of Melting Snow," *Intern. Assoc. Hydrol. Sci. Bull.* 23, 1938, pp. 545–561.

38. Horton, R. E., and H. R. Leach, "Snow-Surface Temperature," *U.S. Dept. Agr. Monthly Weather Rev.,* April 1934, pp. 128–130.

39. Jaenicke, A. J., and M. H. Foerster, "The Influence of a Western Yellow Pine Forest on the Accumulation and Melting of Snow," *U.S. Dept. Agr. Monthly Weather Rev.,* March 1915, pp. 115–126.

40. Kaitera, Pentti, *On Snow Melting in Springtime,* Intern. Comm. Snow and Glaciers, Washington, D. C., 1939.

41. Kalesnik, S. V., "Fluctuation of Glaciers in USSR and Measurement of Their Ablation," *Intern. Assoc. Hydrol. Sci. Bull.* 23, 1938, pp. 669–689.

42. Kohler, M. A., and R. K. Linsley, Jr., "Recent Developments in Water Supply Forecasting from Precipitation," *Trans. Am. Geop. Union,* June 1949, pp. 427–436.

43. Kuhnel, John W., "A Reference Plane of Flood Volumes in the Sacramento-San Joaquin Basin, California," *Trans. Am. Geop. Union,* February 1949, pp. 98–115.

44. Langbein, Walter B., and others, "Major Winter and Nonwinter Floods in Selected Basins in New York and Pennsylvania," *U.S. Geol. Sur. Water-Supply Paper* 915, 1947.

45. Leach, H. R., H. L. Cook, and R. E. Horton, "Stream-Flow Prediction," *Trans. Am. Geop. Union,* 1933, pp. 435–446.

46. Light, Phillip, "Analysis of High Rates of Snow-Melting," *Trans. Am. Geop. Union,* 1941, Part I, pp. 195–205.

47. Light, Phillip, and Max A. Kohler, "Forecasting Seasonal Runoff by Statistical Methods," *Trans. Am. Geop. Union,* 1943, Part II, pp. 719–735.

240   Snow Melting and Runoff Forecasting

48. Marr, James C., "Snow Surveying," *U.S. Dept. Agr. Misc. Pub.*, 380, 1940.
49. Matthes, François E., "Ablation of Snow-Fields at High Altitudes by Radiant Solar Heat," *Trans. Am. Geop. Union*, 1934, Part II, pp. 380–385.
50. Piper, Arthur M., "Runoff from Rain and Snow," *Trans. Am. Geop. Union*, August 1948, pp. 511–524.
51. Potts, Harry L., "A Photographic Snow-Survey Method of Forecasting Runoff," *Trans. Am. Geop. Union*, 1944, Part I, pp. 149–153.
52. Stanley, J. W., and R. E. Kennedy, "Forecasting Colorado River Flow," *Trans. Am. Geop. Union*, October 1947, pp. 766–779.
53. Wahle, Rolla H., "Stream-Flow Forecasting by Pattern-Behavior," *Trans. Am. Geop. Union*, 1943, Part III, pp. 13–28.
54. Western Snow Conference, *Proceedings of the Western Snow Conference, Reno, Nevada, Meeting, April 15–17, 1948*, Fort Collins, Colo., 1949.
55. Wilm, H. G., "The Influence of Forest Cover on Snow-Melt," *Trans. Am. Geop. Union*, August 1948, pp. 547–557.
56. Wilson, W. T., "An Outline of the Thermodynamics of Snow-Melt," *Trans. Am. Geop. Union*, 1941, Part I, pp. 182–195.
57. Work, R. A., "Adjusting Forecast Curves for Abnormal Spring and Summer Temperatures," *Trans. Am. Geop. Union*, 1944, Part I, pp. 126–140.
58. ——— "Snow-Layer Density Changes," *Trans. Am. Geop. Union*, August 1948, pp. 525–546.

Chapter 9

EVAPORATION FROM WATER
SURFACES

Evaporation from water surfaces causes losses of water that otherwise would be available for beneficial use. In humid regions, depths of rainfall usually are high enough to satisfy local requirements. In such regions, losses by evaporation are important, but seldom critical. In arid regions, where depths of rainfall are too low to maintain crop growth, evaporation losses at lakes and reservoirs often constitute critical factors in irrigation developments. Consequently, evaporation losses must be carefully considered in all irrigation studies.

In irrigation, depths of water evaporated from the surfaces of ponds, lakes, reservoirs, seeped areas, rivers, canals, and other open conduits constitute losses of water that otherwise could be delivered to the fields. Depths evaporated from flooded fields during irrigation and from moist soil surfaces after deliveries of irrigation water are shut off constitute losses of water that otherwise could be stored in the root zones and used in crop production. Quantities of water lost by evaporation in the western states, if they could be prevented, could be utilized in producing crops on many areas now lying idle because of lack of water.

Probable losses of water that may occur by evaporation after an irrigation project is developed can best be evaluated from available data on evaporation under similar climatic conditions. Several formulas for computing evaporation on the basis of weather records have been proposed. A few have sufficient merit to warrant their consideration in hydrological studies. However, until their reliability is more definitely established, estimates of evaporation losses on contemplated irrigation projects had better be based on actual measurements of evaporation in adjoining regions.

In hydrological studies for irrigation, evaporation is commonly considered to be the natural process by which any form of water, liquid

241

or solid, is changed into water vapor. Thus, the sublimation of frozen moisture such as snow and ice, directly from the solid to the gaseous state, is included in the definition.

After infiltration ceases, following irrigation, rainfall, or snow melting, land surfaces are dried by evaporation. When the water table is relatively close to the ground surface, subsequent capillary movements may raise appreciable quantities of moisture to the surface to continue the evaporation process. The evaporation of moisture at the ground surface is generally referred to as soil evaporation or land evaporation. Transpiration, the emission of water vapor from plant foliage, is really a special type of evaporation. Evaporation from water and land surfaces, together with transpiration, constitute total evaporation, the first element in the hydrologic cycle of evaporation, precipitation, and runoff.

Basic principles involved in evaporation are usually discussed from the viewpoint of conditions at water surfaces. The following pages present brief treatments of the more important aspects of evaporation phenomena, together with some discussions of the measurement of evaporation at water surfaces and the large amount of data that have been accumulated by such measurements. Some data on evaporation from snow and ice surfaces are included. Land evaporation and transpiration are taken up in the next chapter. Evaporation losses are commonly expressed as inches of depth over the evaporating areas.

EVAPORATION PHENOMENA

Evaporation phenomena have been studied more or less intensively for 150 years. Dalton set forth the basic laws governing evaporation in 1802.[11] Since that time many scientists have studied evaporation processes on the basis of physical laws. Since about the end of the nineteenth century, several research workers have conducted elaborate field and laboratory tests and carefully analyzed the results of their observations. Federal, state, and municipal agencies, private corporations, irrigation districts, and other organizations have measured evaporation in the field and have accumulated a large amount of data on actual evaporation losses under different weather conditions.

Only a few of the more important evaporation investigations can be discussed herein. Sources of information regarding many comprehensive studies of evaporation are listed in the references at the end of the chapter.

Evaporation Theory. Evaporation phenomena are usually explained on the basis of molecular activity. Molecules of water are in continuous states of agitation. Some of the more rapidly moving molecules at the surface of the water pass into the overlying atmosphere and are retained in the air. Particles of water vapor in the air above the water also are in continuous states of agitation. Some of the vapor molecules pass into the water and are retained in the water. When the moisture particles leaving the water exceed those entering the water, evaporation losses result. When the moisture particles entering the water exceed those leaving the water, condensation gains result.

The average velocity of the molecules increases with temperature. Since some of the more rapidly moving molecules pass from the water to the air during evaporation, the average velocity of those remaining in the water is reduced and the water temperature lowered. Thus, evaporation is a cooling process. The addition of heat to a water surface increases its temperature, increases the molecular activity, and increases the rate of evaporation.

Briefly, the fundamental theory of evaporation, generally credited to Dalton, is that evaporation rates are proportional to the difference between the vapor tension corresponding to the temperature of the water at its surface and the actual pressure of the water vapor in the air just above the water surface. In other words, evaporation rates vary as the quantity

$$(V_s - V_a) \tag{1}$$

where V_s = the vapor tension of the water.

V_a = the pressure of the water vapor in the overlying air.

Inasmuch as the presence of vapor in the overlying atmosphere is affected by air movements, evaporation rates are also affected by wind velocities. Dalton recognized the effects of air movements as well as the effects of vapor pressure difference. Many comprehensive laboratory tests and field measurements have confirmed the Dalton theory, and it is now generally accepted.

For convenience in discussion, the term vapor tension is used for the water, and vapor pressure for the aqueous vapor in the air above the water. Actually they are similar quantities. Both are determined by temperature. The vapor tension of the water is the vapor pressure corresponding to the temperature of the water. The vapor pressure in the air is the vapor pressure corresponding to the dew-point temperature of the air, the temperature at which the aqueous vapor is in a state of saturation.

Dew-point temperatures are regularly observed at first-order weather stations. They are determined by psychrometer measurements, as described in a Weather Bureau bulletin.[47] Table 1 shows aqueous

TABLE 1

AQUEOUS VAPOR PRESSURES AT DIFFERENT TEMPERATURES [47]

(Inches of mercury)

Temp., °F.	0	1	2	3	4	5	6	7	8	9
−30	0.0069	0.0065	0.0061	0.0057	0.0054	0.0051	0.0048	0.0046	0.0044	0.0041
−20	0.0126	0.0119	0.0112	0.0106	0.0100	0.0094	0.0089	0.0083	0.0078	0.0074
−10	0.0222	0.0210	0.0199	0.0188	0.0178	0.0168	0.0159	0.0150	0.0141	0.0133
−0	0.0383	0.0363	0.0344	0.0325	0.0307	0.0291	0.0275	0.0260	0.0247	0.0234
+0	0.0383	0.0403	0.0423	0.0444	0.0467	0.0491	0.0515	0.0542	0.0570	0.0600
10	0.0631	0.0665	0.0699	0.0735	0.0772	0.0810	0.0850	0.0891	0.0933	0.0979
20	0.103	0.108	0.113	0.118	0.124	0.130	0.136	0.143	0.150	0.157
30	0.164	0.172	0.180	0.187	0.195	0.203	0.211	0.219	0.228	0.237
40	0.247	0.256	0.266	0.277	0.287	0.298	0.310	0.322	0.334	0.347
50	0.360	0.373	0.387	0.402	0.417	0.432	0.448	0.465	0.482	0.499
60	0.517	0.536	0.555	0.575	0.595	0.616	0.638	0.661	0.684	0.707
70	0.732	0.757	0.783	0.810	0.838	0.866	0.896	0.926	0.957	0.989
80	1.022	1.056	1.091	1.127	1.163	1.201	1.241	1.281	1.322	1.364
90	1.408	1.453	1.499	1.546	1.595	1.645	1.696	1.749	1.803	1.859
100	1.916	1.975	2.035	2.097	2.160	2.225	2.292	2.360	2.431	2.503
110	2.576	2.652	2.730	2.810	2.891	2.975	3.061	3.148	3.239	3.331
120	3.425	3.522	3.621	3.723	3.827	3.933	4.042	4.154	4.268	4.385
130	4.504	4.627	4.752	4.880	5.011	5.145	5.282	5.422	5.565	5.712

vapor pressures in inches of mercury for different temperatures from −39 to 139 degrees F.

In Chapter 6, absolute and relative humidities of the air are defined on the basis of amounts of aqueous vapor present per unit volume. Inasmuch as vapor pressure varies directly as vapor density during any given temperature, they could just as well be defined on the basis of vapor pressure. Thus, actual vapor pressure is relative humidity times the pressure the vapor would exert at the same temperature if it were in a state of saturation.

Occurrence of Evaporation. According to the Dalton theory, evaporation takes place when the vapor tension of the water is higher than the vapor pressure in the overlying air; in other words, when the temperature at the water surface is higher than the dew-point temperature of the air. When the vapor tension equals the vapor pressure, that is, when the water temperature is the same as the dew-point temperature, no evaporation losses take place. When the vapor tension is lower than the vapor pressure, that is, when the water temperature is lower than the dew-point temperature, condensation of aqueous vapor takes place and condensed moisture is added to the water.

As evaporation takes place, water vapor is added to the air above the evaporating surface. If the air is still and the temperature at the dew point, the added vapor condenses, forming fog particles—a phenomenon often observed during the winter. Usually the fog particles rise to drier air and are reevaporated. When the air is in motion over a lake, they have been known to form snowflakes and produce light snowfalls along the lake shores.

When the air temperature is above the dew point, the added vapor gradually increases the vapor pressure V_a and decreases the quantity $(V_s - V_a)$. Thus, if no air movements take place above the evaporating surface, the rate of evaporation gradually decreases. In order for evaporation to continue at a relatively high rate from a lake or reservoir surface, the overlying atmosphere must be in a state of motion whereby air containing evaporated moisture is continuously removed and replaced by drier air.

Evaporated moisture may be moved from the evaporating surface by diffusion of vapor particles, convection currents in the air, or wind movements. Diffusion may be an effective means of vapor removal at a small evaporation pan, but it is much less effective at a large lake or reservoir. Convection currents may be appreciable in the absence of wind movements, inasmuch as air masses containing large proportions of water vapor tend to rise. Water vapor is only about 62 per cent as heavy as ordinary dry air. However, still air, favorable for the development of convection currents, seldom exists over large water surfaces.

Turbulent wind movements are most effective in removing moist air, bringing in dry air, and thus producing conditions favorable for the continuance of high rates of evaporation at large lake and reservoir surfaces.

Conditions Affecting Evaporation. Conditions that affect rates of evaporation from water surfaces are principally those that affect the vapor pressure difference $(V_s - V_a)$, together with those that affect the removal of evaporated moisture from the region above the evaporating surface. Thus, the major influencing factors are:

1. Temperature of the water at the water surface.
2. Dew-point temperature of the air above the water.
3. Wind movements above the water.

Any climatic, meteorological, or physical conditions that affect the three items listed above also affect rates of evaporation from water surfaces. General alterations in watershed conditions that cause changes in weather and climate cause changes in evaporation. The development of an irrigation project in a desert region may cause changes in evaporation rates, particularly during the growing season when crops are transpiring large amounts of moisture. The removal of forests may increase evaporation rates. In the Copper Basin, south-eastern Tennessee, where smelter fumes destroyed the vegetation on about 7,000 acres, annual evaporation losses measured at small pans amounted to 56.95 inches in the denuded area and 17.76 inches in the surrounding hardwood forest.[37]

In general, temporary changes in air temperature and relative humidity, unaccompanied by changes in dew-point temperature, affect evaporation rates only in so far as they are accompanied by changes in water temperature. Relative humidity is involved in evaporation only in that, together with air temperature, it constitutes a means for determining the vapor pressure in the air. When the air temperature is the same as the water temperature, the quantity $(V_s - V_a)$ becomes $V_s(1 - R)$, where R is relative humidity expressed as a ratio.

Increasing rates of air movement over the evaporating surface, through the range of wind velocities ordinarily experienced, cause increasing rates of evaporation.

Inasmuch as the dry gases in the atmosphere exert some retarding influences on the diffusion of aqueous vapor, differences in barometric pressure at greatly different altitudes may cause slight differences in rates of evaporation.

Other factors that may affect rates of evaporation from water surfaces include physical conditions at the water surface and chemical contents of the water. Rates of evaporation from the surfaces of flowing water may be higher than those at the surfaces of still water. Sleight found that for velocities lower than about 1.5 feet per second the evaporation from flowing water was from 7 to 8.5 per cent higher than the evaporation from still water.[59] His investigations did not include tests for higher velocities.

Accumulations of foreign materials on the surfaces of stagnant water, such as films of oil, scums of dust, insect secretions, or other substances, may cause reductions in rates of evaporation.[56] Appreciable concentrations of soluble salts in the water may cause considerable reductions in rates of evaporation, as discussed later.

Temperature Factors. Temperature factors, items 1 and 2 in the preceding section, exert the most important influences on evaporation, because they determine the pressure gradient between the water surface and the aqueous vapor in the overlying atmosphere; that is, the value of $(V_s - V_a)$. Low water temperatures and high dew-point temperatures mean low rates of evaporation, or even condensation. High water temperatures and relatively low dew-point temperatures, commonly experienced in warm dry climates, mean high rates of evaporation.

Table 1 shows that for each 20-degree rise in water temperature from 30 to 110 degrees F. the vapor tension of the water is approximately doubled. Similarly, for each 20-degree rise in dew-point temperature the vapor pressure in the air is approximately doubled. However, since water temperatures are usually higher than dew-point temperatures, increases in water temperature, even when accompanied by increases in dew-point temperature, usually mean increased rates of evaporation. Increases in average monthly air temperature usually mean increased rates of evaporation because they are accompanied by increases in water temperature. Inasmuch as reliable records of air temperature are available for most locations, whereas corresponding records of water temperature seldom are available, observed rates of evaporation usually are studied on the basis of air temperature.

Figure 1 shows average depths of monthly evaporation measured at a Bureau of Plant Industry pan at Lubbock, Texas, plotted against mean monthly air temperatures.[40] Figure 2 shows similar data for the Weather Bureau pan at Davis, California. Figure 3 shows mean depths of monthly evaporation from a floating pan at Encino Reservoir, Los Angeles County, California, plotted against both air and water temperatures.[67]

Figures 1, 2, and 3 show that mean monthly depths of evaporation for similar mean monthly air temperatures are higher during the spring and early summer than during the late summer and fall. This condition, sometimes referred to as the temperature loop, is generally found in plotting evaporation measured at land pans and pans floating on shallow bodies of water. It is usually explained by seasonal differences in weather factors and resultant water temperatures. Figure 3 shows that for the floating pan at Encino Reservoir the loop is less pronounced when the evaporation observations are plotted against water temperatures instead of air temperatures. At deep reservoirs, the loop usually is reversed, as discussed later.

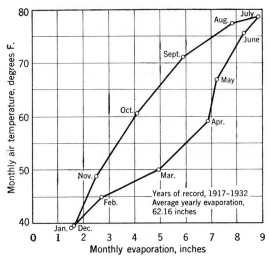

FIGURE 1. Monthly evaporation from Bureau of Plant Industry pan at Lubbock, Texas.

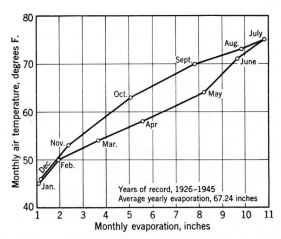

FIGURE 2. Monthly evaporation from U. S. Weather Bureau pan at Davis, California.

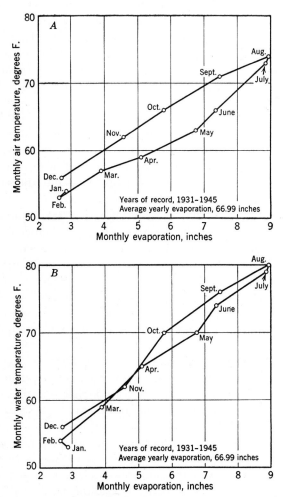

Water Temperatures. Water temperatures in evaporation pans and at the surfaces of shallow bodies of water lag behind air temperatures; but, when averaged for daily, weekly, or monthly periods, they usually are not greatly different from air temperatures.

At Weather Bureau evaporation stations, where the pans are set on timber grillages above the ground, average daily temperatures of the water in the pans are about the same as average daily air temperatures. The water warms rapidly during the day and cools rapidly during the night. At land pans, set in the ground, average daily water temperatures may be a few degrees higher or lower than average daily air temperatures, depending on pan dimensions, methods of installation, and prevailing weather conditions. At floating pans, where water surfaces in the pans are maintained at or below the lake surfaces, water temperatures in the pans are about the same as the temperatures of the adjacent lake water.

During the season when most evaporation takes place, average monthly temperatures at the surfaces of shallow bodies of water are within a few degrees of average monthly air temperatures, often a few degrees higher. At Marston Lake, a small municipal reservoir near Denver, Colorado, average monthly surface temperatures varied from about 2 degrees below to 2 degrees above average monthly air temperatures during the period from March to November.[34] Marston Lake covers an area of about 650 acres and has a maximum depth of 65 feet.

At Encino Reservoir, where the average depth is about 40 feet when the reservoir is full, mean monthly water temperatures for 14 years of record were from 2 to 8 degrees higher than mean monthly air temperatures during the season from March to October. At a shallow 64-acre lake in Baton Rouge, Louisiana, water temperatures averaged about 6.5 degrees higher than air temperatures during October 1938, and about 1.7 degrees higher during March 1939.[6]

During the summer months, surface temperatures along the shores of a lake, where the water is relatively shallow, may be a few degrees higher than in the center of the lake, where the water is deeper. Kennedy observed such conditions at Devils Lake, North Dakota, in 1932.[41] Water temperatures at different depths in deep bodies of water are discussed in a subsequent section.

The Wind Factor. Wind movements above a water surface aid evaporation in that they continuously remove the evaporated moisture and bring in air capable of holding additional aqueous vapor. When the wind velocity becomes high enough to remove the evaporated moisture as fast as it can be emitted from the evaporating surface, the maximum value of the wind factor is reached and further increases in velocity cause but little if any further increases in evaporation.

At a small evaporation pan installed on a land area, a slight breeze may be sufficient to remove the moisture as fast as it can evaporate, even when the air movement is laminar. At large bodies of water, turbulent air movements of higher velocity usually are necessary in order to permit maximum rates of evaporation. At a large lake or reservoir, the maximum value of the wind factor probably is not attained until the velocity reaches about 20 or 25 miles an hour.

Horton, in his studies of evaporation, adopted a variable wind factor represented by the equation

$$\psi = 2 - e^{-Kw} \tag{2}$$

where w = wind velocity at the ground level, in miles per hour.
K = a constant, usually given a value between 2 and 3.
e = the base of Naperian logarithms.

Rates of increase in the wind factor ψ gradually decrease with increasing values of w and become negligible for wind velocities higher than about 20 miles an hour.[27]

Rohwer, in his field and laboratory tests, found that for the usual range in wind velocities the wind factor could be represented by the quantity

$$(0.44 - 0.118w) \tag{3}$$

where w is the same as in equation 2, and quantity 3 is applied as a coefficient to the vapor pressure difference $(V_s - V_a)$.[55]

Meyer, in evaporation studies conducted prior to 1915, adopted a wind-factor coefficient represented by the quantity

$$(1 + 0.10W) \tag{4}$$

where W is the wind velocity in miles per hour as observed by the Weather Bureau at heights about 30 feet above ground levels.[48]

Observations of wind velocity maintained at evaporation stations are commonly made only a foot or two above the ground surface, whereas observations at first-order weather stations may be made 50 feet or more above ground levels, depending on station locations. First-order Weather Bureau stations often have to be located in high office buildings, so that the instruments have to be installed at considerable heights above the ground. Consequently, evaporation studies for irrigation projects may require reductions of available wind data to equivalent ground-surface values.

Table 2, prepared by Horton on the basis of experimental observations, shows approximate ground velocities for wind measurements at

TABLE 2

GROUND WIND VELOCITIES FOR WIND MEASUREMENTS
AT DIFFERENT HEIGHTS ABOVE THE GROUND [32]

(Miles per hour)

Measured wind velocity	Equivalent velocities 1 ft. above ground level when heights of anemometers are								
	10 ft.	20 ft.	30 ft.	40 ft.	50 ft.	75 ft.	100 ft.	150 ft.	200 ft.
2	1.85	1.73	1.62	1.58	1.53	1.44	1.37	1.28	1.22
3	2.68	2.48	2.32	2.23	2.18	2.05	1.90	1.78	1.68
4	3.48	3.18	2.97	2.88	2.75	2.55	2.38	2.22	2.08
5	4.25	3.84	3.58	3.45	3.30	3.05	2.84	2.65	2.48
6	5.00	4.50	4.18	4.00	3.80	3.54	3.28	3.04	2.83
7	5.86	5.08	4.75	4.52	4.30	4.00	3.68	3.42	3.18
8	6.42	5.75	5.30	5.05	4.78	4.42	4.06	3.78	3.50
9	7.10	6.35	5.82	5.55	5.30	4.82	4.45	4.10	3.82
10	7.75	6.90	6.38	6.05	5.70	5.28	4.85	4.45	4.12
12	9.08	8.00	7.35	6.95	6.60	6.02	5.55	5.10	4.70
14	10.30	9.00	8.30	7.90	7.40	6.75	6.25	5.70	5.30
16	11.60	10.00	9.20	8.75	8.20	7.50	6.85	6.30	5.85
18	12.80	10.90	10.05	9.55	8.95	8.10	7.50	6.85	6.35
20	13.90	11.80	10.85	10.40	9.70	8.80	8.10	7.35	6.80
25	16.60	14.25	13.00	12.40	11.45	10.40	9.55	8.65	7.95
30	19.30	16.35	15.00	14.20	13.20	11.85	10.85	9.90	9.10

different heights above the ground.[32] Although rates at which wind velocities increase with increasing heights above the ground vary widely at different locations and under different conditions of exposure, the values shown in Table 2 may be used when actual data are not available for the location under consideration.

Altitude Effects. Pronounced changes in altitude in mountainous regions may affect evaporation, not only because of changes in barometric pressure but also because of changes in other atmospheric conditions. Barometric pressures decrease as altitude increases. Mean air and water temperatures usually decrease as altitude increases. Vapor pressure in the air may be different at different elevations.

Wind velocities often are higher on exposed mountain slopes than in adjoining valleys. Reductions in barometric pressure accompanying increases in altitude tend to increase evaporation rates, because of diminished obstructions to diffusion of water vapor. However, such increases in evaporation usually are more than offset by decreases resulting from decreased temperatures. Therefore, actual evaporation rates in mountainous regions usually are lower at high altitudes than at low altitudes.

Measurements of evaporation at different elevations on the eastern slopes of Mt. Whitney, California, made by Frank Adams during the summer of 1905, showed reductions in daily rates from about 0.38 inch at elevation 4,515 feet to about 0.23 inch at elevation 10,000. Above elevation 10,000, the daily rate of evaporation remained approximately the same for further increases in altitude up to the summit of the peak, about elevation 14,500 feet.[16] Rohwer's measurements in the Rocky Mountains showed a daily evaporation of 0.161 inch at Victor, Colorado, elevation 10,089 feet, during 8 days in August 1927, and a daily rate of 0.139 inch at Pikes Peak, elevation 14,109, during 12 days in August 1928.[55]

Rohwer's measurements of evaporation at different altitudes were made primarily to determine effects of changes in barometric pressure. Careful measurements were made at 7 locations, varying in elevation

TABLE 3

SUMMARY OF ROHWER'S MEASUREMENTS OF EVAPORATION
AT DIFFERENT ALTITUDES [55]

Location	Time	No. of days	Elevation, ft. above sea level	Mean barometric pressure, in. of mercury	Ground wind velocity, mi. per hour	Temperature, °F. Air	Temperature, °F. Water	Vapor pres. diff. $(V_s - V_a)$ in. of mercury	Evaporation in. per 24 hr.
Imperial, Calif.	May 1928	14	− 68	29.86	1.93	81.6	78.7	0.641	0.383
Fort Calhoun, Neb.	September 1927	9	1,160	28.77	1.35	67.1	70.1	0.301	0.174
Logan, Utah	June–July 1928	14	4,778	25.06	1.89	68.0	70.0	0.470	0.288
Fort Collins, Colo.	September–October 1928	35	5,000	25.02	1.01	55.0	58.2	0.267	0.149
Lake Tahoe, Calif.	June 1928	13	6,300	23.76	1.02	55.0	61.8	0.365	0.221
Victor, Colo.	August 1927	8	10,089	20.8	3.06	50.5	54.9	0.186	0.161
Pikes Peak, Colo.	August 1928	12	14,109	18.07	6.28	40.5	42.3	0.116	0.139

from 68 feet below sea level to 14,109 feet above sea level. His investigations included accurate observations of all meteorological conditions affecting evaporation. A summary of the data obtained at the 7 locations is shown in Table 3. As a result of his investigations, Rohwer found that effects of variations in barometric pressure on evaporation rates calculated for different altitudes could be allowed for by applying a coefficient determined by the quantity

$$(1.465 - 0.0186B) \tag{5}$$

where B is barometric pressure in inches of mercury at a temperature of 32 degrees F. The value of the coefficient varies from 0.91 at sea level to 1.14 at an elevation of 15,000 feet. It becomes unity at 5,000 feet, the altitude at Fort Collins.

Effects of Salt Contents. When water contains appreciable concentrations of soluble salts, as in some western lakes, evaporation rates

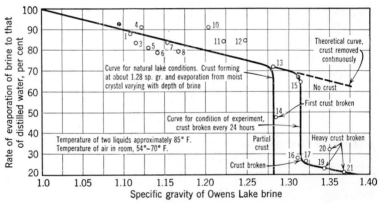

FIGURE 4. Effects of salt contents on evaporation rates, Owens Lake brine. (After Lee.)

are decreased. Tests with brine from Owens Lake, California, reported by Lee in 1927, showed that the evaporation rate decreased about 1 per cent for each 1 per cent increase in specific gravity, until the concentration became great enough to cause the formation of a crust at the water surface.[43] This took place at a specific gravity of about 1.275. When a crust formed, evaporation became negligible. Figure 4 shows the results of the observations as plotted by Lee.

Pan measurements of evaporation from sodium chloride and sodium sulphate solutions, reported by Rohwer in 1933, showed reductions somewhat similar to those at Owens Lake.[56] Investigations of evaporation at Great Salt Lake, Utah, reported by Adams in 1934, indicated that the lake evaporation was about 75 per cent as great as at a similar body of fresh water.[1] A sample of lake water taken near Saltair in June 1932 had a salt content of 25.1 per cent.

Reductions in evaporation rates and actual concentrations of salts at the time of crust formation probably vary somewhat with the kind of salts in solution. Times of crust formation on open bodies of concentrated salt water probably vary with wind and wave conditions. However, the decreases in evaporation with increasing salt contents shown by Figure 4 furnish a general basis for estimating evaporation rates at salt-water lakes in western United States.

Evaporation Formulas. Several formulas for computing evaporation from weather records have been proposed. Some of the earlier equations included corrections for barometric pressure, but not for wind velocity. Others included corrections for wind velocity, but not for barometric pressure. Some of the more recent equations have been based on considerations of solar radiation and stored heat utilized in evaporation. Most evaporation formulas that have been received favorably by irrigation engineers have been based on considerations of vapor pressure differences; that is, the quantity $(V_s - V_a)$.

Only three evaporation formulas need discussion. These are the equations proposed by Meyer, Horton, and Rohwer. The Rohwer formula for computing depths of evaporation in inches per day, as derived from measurements at small pans, is

$$E = (1.465 - 0.0186B)(0.44 + 0.118w)(V_s - V_a) \qquad (6)$$

where the first quantity in parentheses is the previously discussed factor for barometric pressure, the second quantity is the factor for wind velocity, and the third is the vapor pressure difference as before.[55] In computing lake and reservoir evaporation, an additional coefficient of 0.77 is applied, to allow for the greatly increased area of the evaporating surface.

The Horton formula, which contains the previously discussed wind factor ψ is

$$E = C(\psi V_s - V_a) \qquad (7)$$

where C is a constant depending on the area of the evaporating surface and the time interval for which the evaporation E is computed.[27] The value of C is usually taken as 0.4 when evaporation from small pans is computed in inches per day. V_s and V_a represent vapor pressures, as before.

The Meyer formula, originally proposed in 1915 and later discussed in a bulletin on evaporation,[49] is

$$E = C(1 + 0.10W)(V_s - V_a) \qquad (8)$$

where C is a constant depending on the size and character of the water body and on the time for which the evaporation is computed, W is the wind velocity in miles per hour, and $(V_s - V_a)$ the same as before. In his bulletin, Meyer specifies that the water temperature should be measured about 1 foot below the surface; that the vapor pressure should be determined about 25 feet above the water or above the surrounding land; and that the wind velocity should be observed about 25 feet above the water, above the surrounding land, or above the tops of trees or buildings. The equation does not contain a factor for barometric pressure, but in computing evaporation from small lakes and reservoirs he increased the calculated depths about 1 per cent for each 1,000-foot increase in altitude. He gives the following values for C:

C = 15 for monthly evaporation from fully exposed pans, small puddles of water, and intercepted rainfall on the surface of soil and vegetation while moisture is available.

C = 11 for monthly evaporation from small lakes and reservoirs when the actual vapor pressure in the air is determined from the mean of the daily maximum and minimum temperatures and the mean of the morning and evening relative humidity measured about 25 feet above the surface of the water or the ground.

C = 10 for monthly evaporation from small lakes and reservoirs when the actual vapor pressure in the air is the mean of the morning and evening or of more frequent, equally spaced, determinations of actual vapor pressure measured about 25 feet above the surface of the water or ground.

The Meyer bulletin, published by the Minnesota Resources Commission in 1942, contains maps showing computed depths of monthly, summer, and annual evaporation at shallow lakes and reservoirs in the United States; also detailed data on temperatures, vapor pressures, wind velocities, precipitation, and other climatic conditions.

Evaporation formulas developed from considerations of solar radiation, sometimes called heat-balance equations, are theoretically sound but are more complicated than formulas based on the Dalton theory. Solutions of such formulas require evaluations of incoming solar radiation, return radiation, heat storage in the water, heat leakage from the water body, and Bowen's ratio.[54]   Data for the accurate determination of these factors are seldom available.   Furthermore, the evaluation of Bowen's ratio requires data on temperatures, vapor pressures, and barometric pressures, the most of the factors included in formulas based on the Dalton theory.   Therefore, heat-balance equations do not at present constitute practicable methods for determining evaporation data needed in irrigation investigations.

In 1939, Thornthwaite and Holzman proposed a method for computing land and water surface evaporation from considerations of the vertical distribution of moisture in the lower air strata and the intensity of turbulent mixing.[62]   This method, which could be used in determining rates of transpiration as well as evaporation, requires simultaneous observations of vapor pressure and wind velocity at two levels within the turbulent layer.   Inasmuch as such observations have not been maintained regularly in the past, the method cannot be utilized in computing evaporation from existing weather records.

EVAPORATION MEASUREMENTS AND DATA

Evaporation losses from water surfaces may be determined in two ways: (1) by observations at evaporation stations, where actual losses are measured in small pans or tanks; and (2) by measurements of inflow, outflow, precipitation, surface elevations, and changes in storage at lakes and reservoirs where no losses take place by seepage.

Evaporation rates determined by the first method usually are larger than rates that would take place at large bodies of water in the same locations, because of differences in area of the evaporating surfaces. Therefore, appropriate coefficients or conversion factors must be applied to records at evaporation stations in order to obtain equivalent evaporation rates for large lakes and reservoirs.   When evaporation pans are maintained on the surfaces of large bodies of water, instead of on land areas, conversion factors are more nearly equal to unity.

Determinations of evaporation by the second method give actual losses at the bodies of water where the measurements are made.   Unfortunately, conditions suitable for determinations by the second method do not occur at many locations.   At a few lakes where conditions are favorable, determinations of evaporation have been made by both methods and have supplied data on proper conversion factors to be used in computing lake evaporation from pan measurements.

Evaporation Stations.   The installation of evaporation stations, mostly in western states, was begun by the United States Bureau of

Plant Industry about 1907 and by the Weather Bureau about 1916. The Bureau of Reclamation, Geological Survey, and certain other branches of the federal government have maintained evaporation stations, either independently or in cooperation with other agencies. Evaporation stations also have been maintained by state engineering departments, municipal bureaus, educational institutions, water districts, and other public or private organizations.

Some early measurements of evaporation were made at Boston, Massachusetts, by Fitzgerald, 1876 to 1887; at Kingsbury, California, by Grunsky, 1881 to 1885; at Reno, Nevada, and the Salton Sea, California, by Bigelow, 1907 to 1910; in Owens Valley, California, by Lee, 1908 to 1911; and by other investigators working in different sections of the country. Evaporation measurements were begun at Fort Collins, Colorado, by Carpenter, in 1887, and have been maintained continuously since that time.

Evaporation stations may be of land or floating types, depending on whether the measuring pan is installed on a land area or floated on a water surface. At land stations where measuring pans are set in the ground, the pans are often referred to as ground pans, buried pans, sunken pans, or sunken land pans.

Evaporation stations are generally equipped with hook gages, rain gages, anemometers, and maximum and minimum thermometers, so that evaporation, precipitation, wind velocity, and mean air temperatures can be determined daily. Measurements of relative humidity, which can be made with a sling psychrometer, are desirable and are sometimes made. Measurements of water temperature also are desirable. They can be made when an additional set of maximum and minimum thermometers is provided. Observations of water temperature were made at many Bureau of Plant Industry stations prior to 1916. Methods of installing equipment at Weather Bureau stations are described in a government bulletin.[38]

Accessory weather instruments at evaporation stations usually are satisfactory as regards accuracy, standardization, and installation; but evaporation pans often are of different shapes and sizes and are installed in different ways. Recommendations regarding standard equipment for evaporation stations were made by a subcommittee of engineers in 1934.[60]

Evaporation Pans. At a floating evaporation station, the measuring pan usually is placed in the center of a raft, so as to reduce wave troubles. It is installed with the rim projecting a few inches above the lake surface, and the water surface in the pan usually is maintained at or just below the surrounding lake surface. At a land station, the pan may be set on a grillage above the ground, or in an excavated site with the rim projecting a few inches above the ground. When the pan is installed above the ground, the water surface usually is maintained about 2 inches below the rim. When set in the ground, the water surface usually is maintained at about ground surface level.

The five more common types of evaporation pans were discussed in detail by Rohwer in 1934.[57] A sixth type of pan which is used at some stations in California was described by Young in 1947.[66] These six types of pans may be briefly described as follows:

1. Weather Bureau land pan, 4 feet in diameter by 10 inches deep, set on a timber grillage with the bottom of the pan about 6 inches above the ground. This is the standard pan used at Weather Bureau Class A evaporation stations and is often referred to as the Class A pan.

2. Bureau of Plant Industry ground pan, 6 feet in diameter by 2 feet deep, set with the rim projecting 4 inches above the ground. Prior to about 1917, some of the Bureau of Plant Industry ground pans were 8 feet in diameter.

3. Colorado sunken pan, 3 feet square by 18 inches deep, set with the rim projecting 3 or 4 inches above the ground. The pan is often made 3 feet deep, but satisfactory records are secured with the shallower pans.

4. Geological Survey floating pan, 3 feet square by 18 inches deep, mounted with the rim projecting about 3 inches above the lake surface. Diagonal diaphragms, perforated with 1-inch holes, are placed in the pans to reduce surging during windy weather.

5. Circular floating pan, 4 feet in diameter by 10 inches deep, installed with the rim projecting about 3 inches above the lake surface. This is the standard Weather Bureau pan adapted to floating stations. Cellular baffles sometimes are installed to reduce surging.

6. Circular sunken land pan, 2 feet in diameter by 3 feet deep, set with the rim projecting about 3 inches above the ground. This pan is commonly used at evaporation stations maintained by the Los Angeles County Flood Control District. It has also been installed at some additional stations. Some of the pans have recently been modified by the addition of $\frac{1}{4}$-inch mesh screens above the water, aimed to reduce evaporation losses to equivalent lake evaporation.[66]

Several additional types of pans have been used in measuring evaporation, particularly in detailed tests of an experimental nature. Sleight, in his tests at Denver, Colorado, used round and square pans of different sizes, depths, and methods of installation. His largest pan was a 12-foot circular tank, 3 feet deep, set in the ground with the rim projecting 3 inches above the ground surface.[59] Rohwer, in his investigations at Fort Collins, used an 85-foot circular reservoir, 7 feet deep, together with several small pans of standard types.[55] White, in his investigations near Milford, Utah, used a Class A pan and a 12-foot circular ground pan 3 feet deep.[64] Young, in his reports on evaporation in California, gives some data for small screened pans, insulated pans, and ground pans from 1 to 12 feet in diameter, also detailed data for the more usual types of installations.[67]

Evaporation losses are usually determined by hook gages, but sometimes by adding measured quantities of water until the surface rises to a fixed level. All types of pans have some disadvantages. Problems of rim effects, splashing during high winds, surging in floating pans, absorption of solar radiation, and maintenance of proper conditions are difficult to solve. Such problems have been discussed.[19]

Pans made of different materials or painted different colors absorb variable amounts of solar radiation and show variable rates of evaporation. Tests of four galvanized steel pans, three painted white, gray, and black, were reported by Hickox in 1946. Total evaporation losses measured for about 1 year varied from 49.63 inches at the white pan to 54.87 inches at the black pan.[25] Similar tests of nine pans at Fullerton, California, reported by Young, showed total February to December evaporation losses varying from 59.54 inches at a white enamel pan to 76.13 inches at a black enamel pan and 76.83 inches at an untreated copper pan.[68]

Thus far, an ideal type of evaporation pan has not been developed. Type 6 in the preceding list, with a screen installed above the water, seems promising. In establishing new evaporation stations on irrigation projects, one of the more common measuring pans should be installed, so that measured losses will be comparable with those determined at other locations.

Conversion Coefficients. Conversion coefficients for reducing pan evaporation to lake evaporation have been determined at several locations, for several sizes and types of pans, including the six previously listed. The determinations have been made by two methods: (1) by comparing pan evaporation with reservoir evaporation computed from inflow, outflow, and changes in storage; and (2) by comparing evaporation measured at small pans with evaporation measured at relatively large pans believed to represent reservoir evaporation without application of coefficients.

Some investigations indicate that rates of evaporation at circular ground pans, 3 feet deep and 12 feet or more in diameter, are substantially the same as rates of evaporation at large bodies of water in the same locations.

Conversion coefficients determined by the above-stated methods vary considerably, not only for different pans but also for the same pan at different locations. They also vary for the same pan during different seasons of the year. Some of the variations may be due to discrepancies in observations, but others probably are due to differences in installation, rim effects, exposure, and prevailing weather conditions.

Table 4 shows conversion coefficients for reducing monthly evaporation at pans 1, 3, 4, and 6 to equivalent reservoir evaporation, as

TABLE 4

CONVERSION COEFFICIENTS FOR REDUCING MONTHLY PAN
EVAPORATION TO EQUIVALENT RESERVOIR EVAPORATION

Month	Type 1 pan coefficients based on			Type 3 pan coefficients based on 85-ft. reservoir [57]	Type 4 pan coefficients based on 85-ft. reservoir [57]	Type 6 pan, screened, coefficients based on	
	Lake Elsinore [66]	12-ft. pan, Fullerton [66]	85-ft. reservoir, Fort Collins [57]			Lake Elsinore [66]	12-ft. pan, Fullerton [66]
January	0.82	0.65	....	....	....	0.96	0.83
February	0.63	0.77	....	....	....	0.77	0.93
March	0.68	0.76	....	....	....	0.92	1.06
April	0.66	0.80	0.60	0.75	0.77	0.87	1.03
May	0.68	0.81	0.63	0.76	0.76	0.90	1.02
June	0.77	0.82	0.69	0.77	0.76	0.99	1.02
July	0.74	0.81	0.69	0.76	0.76	0.95	1.01
August	0.78	0.81	0.71	0.75	0.77	1.02	0.99
September	0.87	0.76	0.82	0.86	0.80	1.10	0.96
October	0.93	0.75	0.72	0.82	0.76	1.12	0.91
November	0.97	0.72	0.77	0.99	0.82	1.12	0.86
December	0.95	0.66	....	....	....	1.03	0.87
Mean	0.77	0.77	0.70	0.79	0.77	0.98	0.975

determined at Fort Collins, Colorado, at Lake Elsinore, California, and at Fullerton, California. Average coefficients are shown at the bottom of the table. Average ratios of evaporation at the 12-foot pan to evaporation at the type 1 pan, determined near Milford, Utah, were

0.67, a little lower than the ratio determined by the 85-foot reservoir at Fort Collins.

Table 5 shows a summary of conversion coefficients for reducing pan evaporation to equivalent reservoir evaporation, as determined

TABLE 5

SUMMARY OF CONVERSION COEFFICIENTS FOR REDUCING PAN
EVAPORATION TO EQUIVALENT RESERVOIR EVAPORATION

Data by	Basis for coefficients	Conversion coefficients for evaporation pans of types						Ref. no.
		1. Land, circular, 4 ft. by 10 in.	2. Ground, circular, 6 ft. by 2 ft.	3. Sunken, square, 3 ft. by 18 in.	4. Floating, square, 3 ft. by 18 in.	5. Floating, circular, 4 ft. by 10 in.	6. Sunken, circular, 2 ft. by 3 ft.	
Sleight	12-foot pan	0.70	0.94	0.79	0.89	....	0.78	59
Rohwer	East Park Reservoir	0.69	....	0.75	....	0.78	....	55
Rohwer	85-foot reservoir	0.70	....	0.79	0.77	....	....	57
Subcommittee	Various data	0.70	....	0.78	0.80	....	....	60
Young	Lake Elsinore	0.77	....	....	....	....	0.98 †	66
Young	12-foot pan	0.77	0.94	0.89 *	....	....	0.975 †	66
White	12-foot pan	0.67	....	....	....	....	....	64
Hall	Various data	0.69	0.91	0.81	0.80	0.88	....	20
Follansbee	Various data	0.69	0.94	....	0.83	0.83	....	14

* Rim 4 inches above the ground.
† Screened.

during different periods of observation at different locations or as recommended by different investigators. Coefficients are given for the six more common types of pans. In some of the investigations, measurements were confined to the months experiencing the greater evaporation losses.

Lake and Reservoir Evaporation. In evaluating lake and reservoir evaporation from pan records, engineers may select appropriate conversion coefficients from Tables 4 and 5. Coefficients for type 1 pans determined at low elevations in southern California are somewhat higher than those determined at altitudes of about 5,000 feet in Colorado. As Young suggests, the Colorado coefficients probably apply to the higher locations in the western states, where subfreezing temperatures are experienced during the winter.[66] The southern California coefficients probably apply to the warmer coastal regions and the interior valleys of relatively low altitude in the Southwest, where mild weather prevails during the winter.

Table 6 shows monthly and annual evaporation losses at some lakes in California and Nevada, compiled from data reported by Harding

TABLE 6

EVAPORATION LOSSES AT SOME CALIFORNIA AND NEVADA LAKES

Lake	Buena Vista	Tulare	Elsinore	Eagle	Walker	Pyramid	Tahoe
State	California	California	California	California	Nevada	Nevada	California-Nevada
County	Kern	Kings	Riverside	Lassen	Mineral	Washoe	......
Elevation, ft.	290	200	1,260	5,100	4,030	3,830	6,230
Reference no.	66	21	66	21	21	21	21
Month	Evaporation loss, in.						
January	1.2	1.4	1.8	1.8 *	2.4	3.0	1.2 *
February	1.8	1.6	1.6	1.8 *	1.8	3.0	1.2 *
March	2.9	3.0	2.9	2.4 *	2.4	3.6	1.9 *
April	4.3	3.6	4.4	3.0 *	2.4	3.6	2.9
May	6.0	6.0	5.8	3.6	3.0	4.2	3.8
June	6.2	8.4	6.7	4.8	4.8	4.8	4.3
July	8.5	9.6	7.8	6.0	6.0	4.8	5.6
August	10.2	7.2	7.9	5.4	6.6	4.8	5.8
September	7.8	7.2	6.6	5.4	7.8	5.4	4.2
October	4.6	3.6	5.2	3.6	5.4	4.8	2.6
November	2.5	2.4	3.2	2.4	4.8	4.2	1.8
December	1.7	1.2	2.3	1.8	3.0	3.6	1.4 *
ANNUAL	57.7	55.2	56.2	42.0	50.4	49.8	36.7

* Estimated.

and Young. At Lake Tahoe, evaporation losses were determined by applying a coefficient of 0.9 to floating pan records. At the other lakes, evaporation losses were determined from records of inflow, outflow, and storage, so that the use of coefficients was not required.

Figure 5 shows monthly evaporation losses from a floating pan at Pardee Reservoir, California, plotted against monthly air temperatures. Pardee Reservoir is located on the Mokelumne River, in Calaveras County. It has a maximum surface elevation of 568 feet, and a maximum depth of about 350 feet. Evaporation and temperature data are available in Young's compilation.[67] The diagram does not show a pronounced temperature loop. Evaporation losses for similar air temperatures are higher in May and June than in September and October, but lower in January, February, and March than in November and December.

Figure 6 shows evaporation losses at Walker Lake, Nevada, plotted against air temperatures at Schurz, a weather station near the north end of the lake. Walker Lake is a deep natural lake, located about

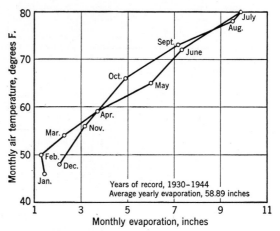

FIGURE 5.   Monthly evaporation from floating pan at Pardee Reservoir, Calaveras County, California.

70 miles southeast of Reno. It has an elevation of about 4,030 feet, as shown in Table 6. The diagram shows a pronounced temperature loop of the reversed type. Monthly evaporation losses for similar air temperatures are from 2 to more than 3 inches higher during September to November than during February to June. Evaporation losses at Pyramid Lake, about 30 miles north of Reno, show a somewhat similar loop of the reversed type.[22]

Reversed temperature loops at deep lakes and reservoirs are due to the pronounced lag between air temperatures and water surface temperatures. Water surface temperatures are materially affected by the gradual absorption and release of heat at considerable depths and the vertical currents that accompany such phenomena.

Temperatures in Deep Lakes. Surface temperatures in deep lakes and reservoirs depend on heat released from storage at different depths below the surface as well as on surface air temperatures and incoming solar radiation. Temperatures at different depths depend principally on absorption of solar radiation, agitation produced by waves, temperatures of inflowing water, and vertical currents caused by different densities of the lake water. Small changes in temperature along a lake bed, usually negligible, may be caused by flow of heat from the earth.

In general, seasonal temperature changes in deep bodies of water have maximum values at the water surface and decrease rapidly with

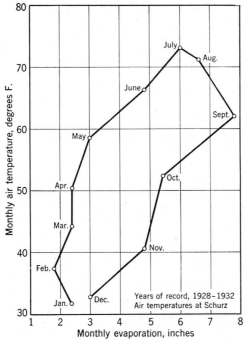

FIGURE 6. Monthly evaporation at Walker Lake, Nevada.

increasing depths below the surface. They usually become negligible at depths of about 175 to 200 feet.

In regions where protracted periods of cold weather occur during the winter, temperatures in the lower portions of deep lakes and reservoirs remain approximately uniform throughout the year, at 39.2 degrees F., the temperature of maximum density. In tropical and subtropical regions, temperatures at the lower levels remain approximately uniform at somewhat higher values. In tropical and subtropical regions, temperatures at the lower levels are about the same as the lowest surface temperature experienced during the winter, or the lowest temperature of the inflowing water. Streamflow entering a lake at a temperature lower than the temperature of the surface water promptly descends to the level of its density.

Water densities increase with decreasing temperatures down to 39.2 degrees, then decrease with further decreases in temperature down to 32 degrees, when formation of ice begins. After an ice cover melts in the spring, the surface water becomes warmer, sinks to lower levels, and is replaced by cold water rising from below. This phenomenon, known as the spring turnover, continues until temperatures at different depths become uniform at 39.2 degrees. During subsequent increases in temperature at the lake surface, the density of the water decreases and the water tends to remain at the surface. Increased temperatures below the surface are then caused by wave agitation and by the penetration of some solar radiation through the surface water.

As surface temperatures in northern lakes decrease in the fall, cold water sinks and is replaced by warm water rising from below. This phenomenon, known as the fall turnover, continues until the temperatures at different depths become uniform at 39.2 degrees. During further cooling at the surface, the density of the water decreases and the water tends to remain at the surface. Decreased temperatures at depths below the surface are then produced primarily by wave agitation. At a tropical or subtropical lake, the turnover ceases as soon as the water becomes uniformly cooled to the minimum temperature experienced in the lower portion of the lake.

Thus, surface temperatures at deep lakes and reservoirs lag behind air temperatures. In general, the lag is more pronounced during the fall and early winter than during the spring and early summer. The relatively low surface temperatures during the spring mean decreased rates of evaporation, whereas the relatively high surface temperatures during the fall mean increased rates. This accounts for the reversed temperature-evaporation loop shown in Figure 6.

Figure 7 shows seasonal temperature variations at different depths in Grand Lake, northern Colorado, during the year 1942, as measured by the Bureau of Reclamation. Grand Lake is a deep natural lake, with a surface at about elevation 8,365. It is located in a mountainous region near the Continental Divide, where the mean annual air temperature is about 40 degrees. The spring turnover was completed in May, and the fall turnover, about the end of November. Surface temperatures were about 10 degrees lower than air temperatures at the end of May, and about 12 degrees higher than air temperatures in September.

Figure 8 shows seasonal temperature variations at different depths in Lake Mead, as measured by the Bureau of Reclamation during 1944. The lake is an artificial reservoir, formed by the construction of Hoover Dam on the Colorado River near Las Vegas, Nevada. It is located in a region where the mean annual air temperature is about 72 degrees. The maximum surface elevation is about 1,220 feet, and the maximum depth, about 530 feet. Winter temperatures and streamflow do not produce deep-water temperatures lower than about 52

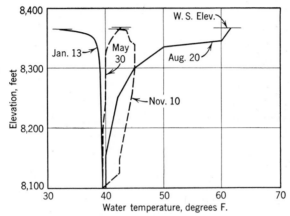

FIGURE 7. Seasonal temperature variations in Grand Lake, Colorado, during 1942. (Plotted from Bureau of Reclamation data.)

degrees. Only about half the measurements made during 1944 are shown in the figure.

The 1944 observations showed that surface temperatures at Lake Mead, as compared with mean weekly air temperatures at Boulder City, were higher during January to March, about the same in April, lower during May to September, slightly higher in October, and from 10 to 20 degrees higher during November and December. During July, surface temperatures were sometimes 10 to 15 degrees lower than mean weekly air temperatures.

The fall turnover at Lake Mead continues several months. It usually is not completed until the following January or February. Figure 8 shows that temperatures were nearly the same at all depths on January 31, 1944, at about 54 to 55 degrees. On November 30, 1944, the fall turnover had been completed to a depth of about 145 feet.

The increased temperatures near the bed of Lake Mead, shown on all diagrams in Figure 8, were primarily due to abnormal densities produced by heavy suspended loads of colloidal clay. Flow from warm salt springs in the bottom of the canyon may have had some influences on densities and temperatures.[35]

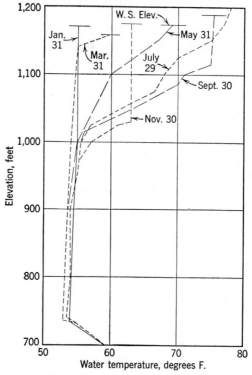

FIGURE 8. Seasonal temperature variations in Lake Mead during 1944. (Plotted from Bureau of Reclamation data.)

Evaporation Records. Detailed records of evaporation from water surfaces as measured at evaporation stations are seldom published but usually are available for inspection at the offices maintaining the stations. Some records at Class A stations are published regularly in the Weather Bureau *Climatological Data.* Monthly and annual records at some stations in the Lower Rio Grande Valley are published in water bulletins issued by the International Boundary and Water Commission, United States and Mexico, El Paso, Texas.

Mean monthly evaporation losses at a few stations in western United States are shown in Figures 1, 2, 3, and 5. Similar data for some lakes in California and Nevada are shown in Table 6. Mean monthly, seasonal, and annual evaporation measured at some additional stations

TABLE 7

MEAN MONTHLY, SEASONAL, AND ANNUAL EVAPORATION AT
SOME STATIONS IN WESTERN UNITED STATES

Station	Yuma Citrus	Elephant Butte	Utah Lake	Fallon	Fall River Mills
State	Arizona	New Mexico	Utah	Nevada	California
Elevation, ft.	181	4,265	4,497	3,965	3,340
Pan type	1	1	1	1	1
Years	1921–1944	1916–1938	1935–1947	1938–1947	1930–1945
Reference	67	23	*	*	67

Month	Evaporation losses, in.†				
January	4.04	2.88	.....	0.84	1.26
February	5.05	4.39	.....	1.53	1.52
March	8.25	7.81	2.98	3.47	2.81
April	10.67	10.32	5.74	4.97	4.13
May	13.98	13.13	8.72	6.49	5.72
June	15.28	14.48	10.07	7.58	7.07
July	16.60	12.50	10.98	8.10	8.62
August	14.56	10.90	9.87	7.34	7.75
September	11.58	8.79	7.15	5.06	5.38
October	8.33	7.24	4.01	3.15	3.01
November	5.43	4.27	1.34	1.70	1.68
December	3.90	2.85	.....	0.73	1.08
Total	117.67	99.56	60.86	50.96	50.03

Station	Akron	Moro	Moscow	Havre	Sheridan
State	Colorado	Oregon	Idaho	Montana	Wyoming
Elevation	4,650	1,800	2,628	2,505	3,790
Pan type	2	2	1	2	2
Years	1921–1932	1920–1931	1939–1947	1921–1932	1921–1932
Reference	31	31	*	31	31

Month	Evaporation, in.†				
April	5.16	4.51	.....	4.22	3.66
May	6.84	6.78	4.33	6.08	4.71
June	8.05	8.13	5.24	6.40	5.92
July	9.52	10.79	7.74	7.61	7.68
August	8.52	8.99	6.33	6.60	7.05
September	6.43	5.30	3.46	4.13	4.83
October	.....	2.59	2.36	.....	.....
Total	44.52	47.09	29.46	35.04	33.85

* U.S. Weather Bureau, *Climatological Data.*
† Coefficients must be applied to obtain reservoir evaporation.

in the West are shown in Table 7. Coefficients must be applied to the
data in Table 7 to obtain reservoir evaporation.

Several compilations of monthly, seasonal, and annual evaporation,
together with pertinent weather data, have been published in technical
journals and special reports. Table 8 lists some of the more valuable

TABLE 8

COMPILATIONS OF EVAPORATION DATA PUBLISHED SINCE 1927

Locations	Type of data	No. of sta- tions	Year pub- lished	Compiled by	Ref. no.
California	Monthly and annual	249	1948	Young	67
California	Mean annual	249	1947	Young	66
United States	Summer, winter, and annual	159	1943	Horton	30
New Mexico	Monthly and annual	10	1939	Hardy and others	23
Canada	Seasonal and annual	121	1939	Millar	51
United States and foreign	Seasonal and annual	310	1934	Follansbee	14
Western United States	Monthly and seasonal	28	1934	Horton and Cole	31
Texas	Monthly and annual	21	1933	Karper	40
Reclamation projects	Mean monthly and annual	50	1927	Houk	33
Southwest United States	Mean monthly and annual	14	1927	Linney	44

compilations published since 1927, arranged according to years of publication, beginning with the most recent. Brief notes regarding types
of evaporation data, general location of stations, and number of stations included in the compilations are also listed.

Variations in Evaporation. Inasmuch as rates of evaporation from
water surfaces depend on local conditions of temperature, vapor pressure, and wind, evaporation losses vary widely from place to place
and time to time. At a particular location, rates of evaporation vary
throughout the day, month, and year, also from year to year.

Daily evaporation losses take place largely during the daylight
hours. Daily and monthly evaporation losses increase during the
spring and summer and decrease during the fall and winter, in accordance with usual temperature trends. Annual evaporation losses vary
from year to year, in accordance with weather differences.

In the northern states, or at high elevations in mountainous regions,
minimum daily rates of evaporation may be practically zero, or only
a few hundredths of an inch. At low elevations in the arid Southwest,
maximum daily losses may be 0.75 inch or more. At the Yuma Citrus
Station, southwestern Arizona, a total evaporation loss of 20.36 inches

was measured in July 1924, an average loss of 0.66 inch per day. During 24 years of observations at the Yuma Station, 1921 to 1944, annual evaporation losses varied from 103.72 to 135.70 inches, averaging 117.67 inches or nearly 10 feet a year.[67]

Variations in normal summer and annual evaporation throughout the United States are shown in Figures 9 and 10. The maps were prepared by Horton and published by the American Geophysical Union in 1943.[30] They are based on records at Weather Bureau Class A stations. Figure 9 shows lines of equal evaporation for the 6 months from May to October. Figure 10 shows lines of equal annual evaporation. Data on evaporation taken from Figures 9 and 10, or from other summaries of pan records, may be reduced to equivalent lake evaporation by applying coefficients as previously discussed.

Snow and Ice Evaporation. Evaporation losses from snow and ice surfaces cannot be measured with instrumental equipment commonly installed at evaporation stations. Therefore, daily observations at regular stations in cold and temperate climates are discontinued during the winter months. Some data on snow and ice evaporation have been obtained from special investigations in which losses were determined by weighing.

In general, monthly rates of evaporation from snow surfaces during subfreezing weather may vary from about 0.5 to 2.0 inches. Rates of evaporation from solid ice surfaces, free from snow, are usually a little lower. Losses from both snow and ice surfaces may take place at higher rates during periods of melting temperatures when films of water are present. Rates of evaporation from snow intercepted by trees may be twice as great as rates of evaporation from snow on the ground. In the mountainous regions of western United States, daily rates of evaporation from snow and ice may be multiplied ten times or more during the occurrence of warm dry winds known as chinooks, sometimes popularly called "snow-eaters."

In the central Sierra Nevada range, Church found the average monthly evaporation from snow during the 5 months from December 1915 to April 1916 to be 1.395 inches at Lake Tahoe, elevation 6,225 feet, and 1.336 inches at Marlette Lake, elevation 8,000 feet.[5] Observations near Lake Tahoe during 1911 to 1917 showed an average March evaporation from snow equal to 0.469 inch in a fir forest; 0.666 inch in a pine and fir forest; 0.788 inch in a pine forest; and 1.303 in a meadow. Rohwer measured daily rates of ice evaporation varying from 0.0032 to 0.0291 inch in still air, and from 0.0182 to 0.1423 inch during wind velocities of from 5 to 16 miles per hour.[55]

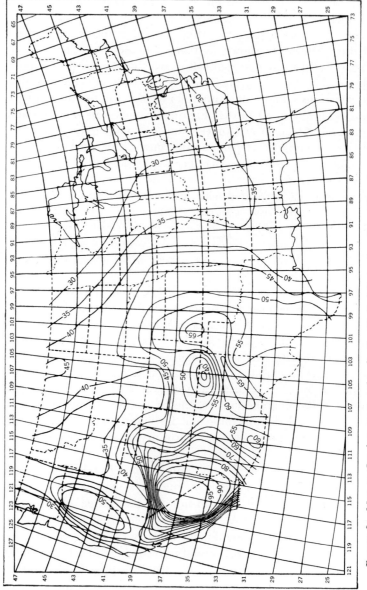

FIGURE 9. May to October evaporation in the United States based on Class A pan records. (After Horton.)

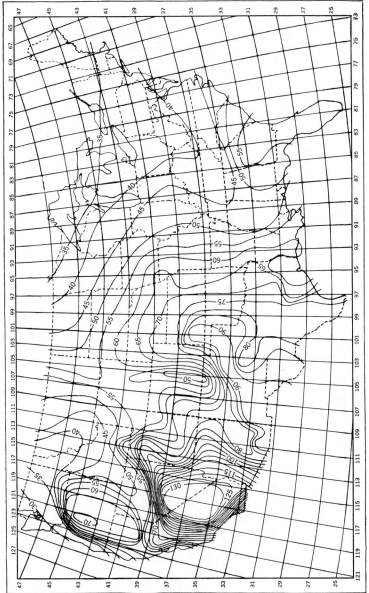

FIGURE 10. Annual evaporation in the United States based on Class A pan records. (After Horton.)

Evaporation from Water Surfaces

Table 9 shows some data on snow and ice evaporation observed on the Milk River Project, Montana, from 1922 to 1926.[33] Daily rates of

TABLE 9

EVAPORATION FROM SNOW AND ICE SURFACES,
MILK RIVER PROJECT, MONTANA [33]

Period of observation, year, month and days	Evaporation observed		Equivalent evaporation rates		
	No. of days	Loss, in.	In. per day	In. per month	Mean air temperature, °F.
1922, November	16	1.12	0.070	2.10	31.1
1922, December	13	0.17	0.013	0.40	28.1
1923, January	20	0.20	0.010	0.31	9.6
1923, February	28	0.41	0.015	0.41	9.8
1923, March	10	0.56	0.056	1.73	26.6
1924, January	31	0.56	0.018	0.56	4
1924, February 14–26	13	0.36	0.028	0.78	13
1924, March	31	1.43	0.046	1.43 *	26
1924, December 15–31	17	0.37	0.028	0.67 †	−8
1925, January 1–17	17	0.17	0.010	0.31 †	7
1925, January 18–23	6	0.32	0.053	1.65 *	33
1925, January 24–29	6	0.11	0.018	0.57	13
1925, February 11–28	18	0.61	0.034	0.95 †	14
1925, March 9–17	9	0.29	0.032	1.00 †	12
1925, March 18–22	5	0.21	0.042	1.30 *	31
1925, November 22–30	9	0.67	0.074	2.23 *	25
1926, January 1–9	9	0.84	0.093	2.89 †	20
1926, January 10–17	8	0.72	0.090	2.79 *	30
1926, January 18–31	14	0.52	0.037	1.15	19
1926, February 13–21	9	0.15	0.017	0.47	25
1926, March 7–14	8	0.31	0.039	1.20 *	34

* Water around edges of pan at times.
† Thin layer of snow on ice.

evaporation varied from 0.010 to 0.093 inch. The data apply to ice surfaces, except as indicated by the footnotes. On some dates, rates of evaporation were increased by the presence of water around the edges of the pan.

REFERENCES

1. Adams, Thomas C., "Evaporation from Great Salt Lake," *Bull. Am. Met. Soc.,* February 1934, pp. 35–39.
2. Baker, Frederick S., "Some Field Experiments on Evaporation from Snow Surfaces," *U.S. Dept. Agr. Monthly Weather Rev.,* July 1917, pp. 363–366.

3. Bigelow, Frank H., "Studies on the Phenomena of the Evaporation of Water over Lakes and Reservoirs," *U.S. Dept. Agr. Monthly Weather Rev.*, 1907, pp. 311–316; 1908, pp. 24–39, 437–445; 1910, pp. 307–313.

4. Bowen, I. S., "The Ratio of Heat Losses by Conduction and by Evaporation from Any Water Surface," *Physical Rev.*, June 1926, pp. 779–787.

5. Church, J. E., "Evaporation at High Altitudes and Latitudes," *Trans. Am. Geop. Union*, 1934, Part II, pp. 326–351.

6. Cox, Glen N., "A Summary of Hydrologic Data, Bayou Duplantier Watershed, 1933–1939," *La. State Univ. Bull.* 7, 1940.

7. Croft, A. R., "Evaporation from Snow," *Bull. Am. Met. Soc.*, October 1944, pp. 334–337.

8. Cummings, N. W., "The Evaporation-Energy Equations and Their Practical Application," *Trans. Am. Geop. Union*, 1940, Part II, pp. 512–522.

9. ——— "The Reliability and Usefulness of the Energy Equations for Evaporation," *Trans. Am. Geop. Union*, February 1946, pp. 81–94.

10. Cummings, N. W., and Burt Richardson, "Evaporation from Lakes," *Physical Rev.*, Vol. 30, 1927, pp. 527–534.

11. Dalton, J., "Experimental Essays on the Constitution of Mixed Gases . . . ," *Mem. Manchester Lit. and Phil. Soc.*, Vol. 5, 1802, pp. 535–602.

12. Duryea, Edwin, Jr., and H. L. Haehl, "A Study of the Depth of Annual Evaporation from Lake Conchas, Mexico," *Trans. Am. Soc. C. E.*, Vol. 80, 1916, pp. 1829–2060.

13. Fitzgerald, Desmond, "Evaporation," *Trans. Am. Soc. C. E.*, Vol. 15, 1886, pp. 581–646.

14. Follansbee, Robert, "Evaporation from Reservoir Surfaces," *Trans. Am. Soc. C. E.*, No. 99, 1934, pp. 704–715, 738–746.

15. Folse, J. A., "A New Method of Estimating Stream-Flow Based upon a New Evaporation Formula," *Carnegie Inst. Pub.* 400, Washington, D. C., 1929.

16. Fortier, Samuel, "Evaporation Losses in Irrigation," *Eng. News*, Sept. 19, 1907, pp. 304–307.

17. Freeman, John R., *Regulation of Elevation and Discharge of the Great Lakes*, The Sanitary District of Chicago, 1926.

18. Grunsky, C. E., "Evaporation from the Salton Sea," *Eng. News*, Aug. 13, 1908, pp. 163–166.

19. ——— "Evaporation from Lakes and Reservoirs," *U.S. Dept. Agr. Monthly Weather Rev.*, January 1932, pp. 2–6.

20. Hall, L. Standish, "Evaporation from Water Surfaces," *Trans. Am. Soc. C. E.*, No. 99, 1934, pp. 724–730.

21. Harding, S. T., "Evaporation from Large Water-Surfaces Based on Records in California and Nevada," *Trans. Am. Geop. Union*, 1935, Part II, pp. 507–512.

22. ——— "Evaporation from Free Water Surfaces," Chapter III in Meinzer's *Hydrology*, 1942, pp. 56–82 (see reference 23 in Chapter 1).

23. Hardy, Erle L., and others, "Precipitation and Evaporation in New Mexico," *N. Mex. Agr. Exp. Sta. Bull.* 269, 1939.

24. Hickman, Harold C., "Evaporation Experiments," *Trans. Am. Soc. C. E.*, No. 105, 1940, pp. 807–817.

25. Hickox, G. H., "Evaporation from a Free Water Surface," *Trans. Am. Soc. C. E.*, Vol. 111, 1946, pp. 1–66.

26. Holzman, Benjamin, "The Heat-Balance Method for the Determination of Evaporation from Water-Surfaces," *Trans. Am. Geop. Union,* 1941, Part III, pp. 655–660.

27. Horton, R. E., "A New Evaporation Formula Developed," *Eng. News-Rec.,* Apr. 26, 1917, pp. 196–199.

28. ——— "Results of Evaporation Observations," *U.S. Dept. Agr. Monthly Weather Rev.,* October 1921, pp. 553–566.

29. ——— "Water-Losses in High Latitudes and at High Elevations," *Trans. Am. Geop. Union,* 1934, Part II, pp. 351–379.

30. ——— "Evaporation-Maps of the United States," *Trans. Am. Geop. Union,* 1943, Part II, pp. 743–753.

31. Horton, R. E., and John S. Cole, "Compilation and Summary of the Evaporation Records of the Bureau of Plant Industry, U.S. Department of Agriculture, 1921–32," *U.S. Dept. Agr. Monthly Weather Rev.,* March 1934, pp. 77–89.

32. Horton, R. E., in collaboration with C. E. Grunsky, "Hydrology of the Great Lakes," *Rep. of Eng. Board of Review,* Part III, Appendix II, The Sanitary District of Chicago, 1927.

33. Houk, Ivan E., "Evaporation on United States Reclamation Projects," *Trans. Am. Soc. C. E.,* Vol. 90, 1927, pp. 266–378.

34. ——— "Temperatures in Denver Reservoirs," *Public Works,* November 1927, pp. 405–408.

35. ——— "Water-Temperatures in Reservoirs," *Trans. Am. Geop. Union,* 1937, Part II, pp. 523–527.

36. Humphreys, W. J., "Temperature of Deep Water," *U.S. Dept. Agr. Monthly Weather Rev.,* December 1924, pp. 586–587.

37. Hursh, C. R., "Local Climate in the Copper Basin of Tennessee as Modified by the Removal of Vegetation," *U.S. Dept. Agr. Cir.* 774, 1948.

38. Kadel, Benjamin C., "Instructions for the Installation and Operation of Class A Evaporation Stations," *U.S. Weather Bur. Instrument Div. Cir.* L, 1915.

39. Kaitera, Pentti, *The Evaporation from Snow,* Intern. Comm. Snow and Glaciers, Washington, D. C., 1939.

40. Karper, R. E., "Rates of Water Evaporation in Texas," *Tex. Agr. Exp. Sta. Bull.* 484, 1933.

41. Kennedy, Robt. E., "Evaporation from Devils Lake in North Dakota," *N. Dak. State Eng. Dept.,* 1933.

42. Lee, Charles H., "An Intensive Study of the Water Resources of a Part of Owens Valley, California," *U.S. Geol. Sur. Water-Supply Paper* 294, 1912.

43. ——— "Evaporation on Reclamation Projects," *Trans. Am. Soc. C. E.,* Vol. 90, 1927, pp. 330–343.

44. Linney, C. E., "Ten Years of Evaporation in the Southwest," *U.S. Dept. Agr. Monthly Weather Rev.,* July 1927, pp. 320–322.

45. Livingston, Grace J., "An Annotated Bibliography of Evaporation," *U.S. Dept. Agr. Monthly Weather Rev.,* 1908 and 1909.

46. McEwen, G. F., "Results of Evaporation Studies," *Scripps Inst. Oceanography Tech. Ser.,* Vol. 2, 1930, pp. 401–415.

47. Marvin, C. F., "Psychrometric Tables for Obtaining the Vapor Pressure, Relative Humidity, and Temperature of the Dew-Point," *U.S. Weather Bur. W.B.* 235, 1941.

48. Meyer, Adolph F., "Computing Run-off from Rainfall and Other Physical Data," *Trans. Am. Soc. C. E.*, Vol. 79, 1915, pp. 1056–1224.
49. —— *Evaporation from Lakes and Reservoirs, A Study Based on Fifty Years' Weather Bureau Records*, Minn. Resources Comm., St. Paul, Minn., 1942.
50. Meyer, Adolph F., and A. S. Levens, "Determining Evaporation Losses from Weather Bureau Data," *Eng. News-Rec.*, Apr. 1, 1937, pp. 481–483.
51. Millar, F. Graham, *The Present State of Evaporation Studies in Canada*, Intern. Comm. Snow and Glaciers, Washington, D. C., 1939, pp. 1–19.
52. Parshall, Ralph L., "Evaporation on Reclamation Projects," *Trans. Am. Soc. C. E.*, Vol. 90, 1927, pp. 318–326.
53. Powell, R. W., "The Evaporation of Water from Saturated Surfaces," *Engineering*, Sept. 20 and Oct. 4, 1940, pp. 238–239, 278–280.
54. Richardson, Burt, "Evaporation as a Function of Insolation," *Trans. Am. Soc. C. E.*, Vol. 95, 1931, pp. 996–1019.
55. Rohwer, Carl, "Evaporation from Free Water Surfaces," *U.S. Dept. Agr. Tech. Bull.* 271, 1931.
56. —— "Evaporation from Salt Solutions and from Oil-Covered Water Surfaces," *Jour. Agr. Res.*, Apr. 15, 1933, pp. 715–729.
57. —— "Evaporation from Different Types of Pans," *Trans. Am. Soc. C. E.*, No. 99, 1934, pp. 673–703.
58. Russell, T., "Depth of Evaporation in the United States," *U.S. Dept. Agr. Monthly Weather Rev.*, September 1888, pp. 235–239.
59. Sleight, R. B., "Evaporation from the Surfaces of Water and River-Bed Materials," *Jour. Agr. Res.*, July 30, 1917, pp. 209–261.
60. Special Committee on Irrigation Hydraulics, Report of Subcommittee, "Standard Equipment for Evaporation Stations," *Trans. Am. Soc. C. E.*, No. 99, 1934, pp. 716–718.
61. Thornthwaite, C. W., and Maurice Halstead, "Note on the Variation of Wind with Height in the Layer near the Ground," *Trans. Am. Geop. Union*, 1942, Part II, pp. 249–255.
62. Thornthwaite, C. W., and Benjamin Holzman, "The Determination of Evaporation from Land and Water Surfaces," *U.S. Dept. Agr. Monthly Weather Rev.*, January 1939, pp. 4–11.
63. —— "Measurements of Evaporation from Land and Water Surfaces," *U.S. Dept. Agr. Tech. Bull.* 817, 1942.
64. White, Walter N., "A Method of Estimating Ground-Water Supplies Based on Discharge by Plants and Evaporation from Soil, Results of Investigations in Escalante Valley, Utah," *U.S. Geol. Sur. Water-Supply Paper* 659–A, 1932.
65. Young, Arthur A., "Some Recent Evaporation Investigations," *Trans. Am. Geop. Union*, April 1947, pp. 279–284.
66. —— "Evaporation from Water Surfaces in California, A Summary of Pan Records and Coefficients, 1881 to 1946," *Calif. Dept. Pub. Works Bull.* 54, 1947.
67. —— "Evaporation from Water Surfaces in California, Basic Data," *Calif. Dept. Pub. Works Bull.* 54–A, 1948.
68. —— "Evaporation," *Trans. Am. Soc. C. E.*, Vol. 111, 1946, pp. 43–50.

Chapter 10

LAND EVAPORATION AND TRANSPIRATION

Quantities of moisture evaporated from land surfaces and transpired by vegetation constitute important factors in irrigation. Quantities transpired by farm crops constitute beneficial uses of water, but those transpired by nonuseful plants or evaporated from bare soil surfaces constitute losses of water that otherwise might be used in crop growth. Precipitations intercepted by vegetation and subsequently evaporated without reaching the ground constitute additional losses. In forest regions, snowfall intercepted and directly evaporated may amount to considerable portions of the annual snowfall.

Depths of precipitation intercepted by vegetation can be measured in the field. Depths of moisture evaporated from bare soils can be determined by field and laboratory measurements. Depths transpired by plants can be measured accurately in the laboratory, but not very precisely in the field. Total depths transpired by plants and evaporated from soils surrounding the plants can be determined during special investigations, either in the laboratory or in the field. Inasmuch as evaporation from soils surrounding plants cannot be prevented under field conditions, either for crop plants or native vegetation, determinations of total transpiration and soil evaporation are more pertinent than separate measurements of transpiration.

The more important items of land evaporation and transpiration involved in irrigation hydrology may be briefly stated as follows:

1. Precipitation intercepted and directly evaporated.
2. Moisture evaporated from bare soil surfaces.
3. Moisture transpired and evaporated on areas of natural vegetation.
4. Moisture transpired and evaporated on cropped areas.
5. Moisture transpired and evaporated on large areas including different types of surface cover.

Information on the above items is useful in estimating depths of irrigation water needed on agricultural lands in order to insure profitable crop production. Most items also are useful in considering the hydrology of upstream drainage basins where the water supplies originate. Depths of water required for crop production are discussed in the next chapter.

Nomenclature. As stated in the preceding chapter, the evaporation of moisture at the ground surface is generally referred to as soil evaporation or land evaporation. However, for detailed considerations of evaporation on land areas, it seems better to make a distinction between the two terms and to adopt a specific definition for each. Therefore, the terms are defined as follows:

1. Soil evaporation is the moisture actually evaporated at the ground surface.

2. Land evaporation is the moisture evaporated at the ground surface plus moisture intercepted by vegetation and evaporated without reaching the ground; in other words, soil evaporation plus interception.

3. In discussing total evaporation on large areas, land evaporation is considered to include evaporation at the surfaces of such bodies of water as may exist within the areas, as well as soil evaporation and interception on the net land areas.

Depths of water consumed by evaporation and transpiration on land areas are often referred to as evapo-transpiration. In western United States, where many investigations of combined evaporation and transpiration have been made in connection with irrigation developments, total depths consumed are commonly referred to as consumptive use. In this chapter, the term evapo-transpiration is generally used in discussing results of pot, tank, or plot measurements, and the term consumptive use, in discussing results of investigations on relatively large areas of native growths, agricultural crops, or mixed vegetation.

In discussing land evaporation, hydrologists often use such terms as evaporativity, evaporative capacity, potential rate of evaporation, evaporation power, and evaporation opportunity. The first three terms are practically synonymous. They are commonly defined as the rate of evaporation that existing atmospheric conditions would maintain at a water surface when wind is moving parallel to the water, the water is chemically pure, and the temperature at the water surface is the same as the temperature of the overlying air.

The term evaporation power is sometimes used as the equivalent of evaporativity, but often as the actual depth of water evaporated at a water surface under prevailing weather conditions. The last term stated above, evaporation opportunity, is the only one that needs discussion.

Evaporation Opportunity. Evaporation opportunity is usually defined as the ratio of actual land evaporation, under existing atmospheric, soil, and vegetal conditions, to the potential rate of evaporation, that is, to evaporativity. It is generally expressed as a percentage of evaporativity. Some authors have included transpiration in their considerations of evaporation opportunity, but it seems better to include only soil evaporation and interception, the items that constitute land evaporation. Evaporation opportunity is sometimes referred to as relative evaporation.

The evaporation opportunity on a particular land area depends primarily on the amount of moisture available for evaporation and the manner in which the moisture is exposed to evaporation. Thus, conditions that affect moisture quantities and their exposure to the atmosphere also affect the evaporation opportunity.

The principal conditions that affect the evaporation opportunity include depth, character, and time distribution of precipitation; depth, method, and frequency of irrigation; soil characteristics that control rates of infiltration, percolation, and capillary movements of soil moisture; and depths to the water table. The type, density, and stage of development of existing vegetation may have some effects on evaporation opportunity. However, investigations on small experimental areas in North Carolina, reported by Hoover, showed that when forest vegetation was removed decreases in evaporation of intercepted moisture were approximately balanced by increases in soil evaporation.[27]

In regions where precipitation occurs largely as storm rainfall, the evaporation opportunity is reduced, owing to decreased total interception, greater surface runoff, increased infiltration, and more percolation. The combined effects of these conditions mean smaller quantities of water available for land evaporation. In regions where the same total precipitation occurs principally in showers of low intensity and short duration, the evaporation opportunity is higher, because greater quantities of water are available for evaporation. In open areas where heavy snowfalls occur and the snow remains on the ground until spring, the evaporation opportunity during the winter may be practically 100 per cent.

In dense evergreen forests subject to heavy snowfalls, the evaporation opportunity at times in the winter may exceed 100 per cent. Evaporation rates on snow surfaces below the trees are lower than in open areas, but the large quantities of snowfall intercepted and held in the tree canopies experience high rates of evaporation.

In irrigated regions, the evaporation opportunity is higher when water is supplied to the fields in shallow frequent irrigations, inasmuch as such methods tend to increase losses by soil evaporation. When water is supplied in heavy, less frequent irrigations, moisture penetrates to greater depths in the soil, some moisture may percolate to depths below the root zone, and greater proportions of the moisture in the root zone are utilized by the crop plants. In fields of close-growing vegetation, the evaporation opportunity is reduced, not only because the plants transpire large proportions of the soil moisture, but also because they shade the soil and thus reduce soil evaporation.

The evaporation opportunity may be relatively high in regions where the water table is close to the ground surface. In such regions, capillarity can raise moisture to the surface to maintain soil evaporation.

In general, soils favorable for capillary movements of moisture tend to increase soil evaporation. Soils favorable for percolation tend to decrease soil evaporation. Drainage tiles and ditches remove moisture from the soil and therefore decrease the quantities available for evaporation at the ground surface. Evaporation opportunities are similarly affected by these changes in soil evaporation.

INTERCEPTION

Depths of precipitation intercepted by plant foliage are called interception, sometimes canopy interception. Quantities of water that reach the ground by running down the stems, branches, and trunks of trees are called stemflow. Stemflow becomes available for infiltration and soil evaporation. Canopy interception, unless dislodged by wind, is held in storage above the ground until evaporated. Stemflow usually is only a small percentage of precipitation. Total interception losses sometimes amount to considerable proportions of annual precipitation.

The maximum depth of precipitation a particular vegetal cover can intercept and retain under most favorable conditions of rainfall intensity and wind velocity is sometimes referred to as interception capacity. The actual depth of precipitation intercepted and held above the ground during any particular storm is often referred to as interception storage.

In western United States, where crop production depends largely on irrigation, interception losses are important in so far as they affect water supplies. Since water supplies usually come from the melting of snow covers in upstream drainage basins, interception of snowfall is especially pertinent. In semiarid regions, where precipitation on farm lands supplies some of the moisture needed for crop growth, interception losses during rainfalls may be important.

Interception by Farm Crops. Farm crops approaching maturity probably intercept as much rainfall as densely forested areas. Depths of interception during single storms of an inch or more may amount to a third or even half an inch. Total interception losses during the growing season may amount to 20 per cent or more of the total rainfall.

On an average farm, producing corn, small grains, and forage crops, interception losses increase gradually during the growing season, as the plants develop and become capable of holding increased quantities of moisture in their foliage. Investigations in Nebraska, reported by Clark, showed that prairie grasses, weeds, and crop plants intercepted from 20 to 70 per cent of the rainfall. Quantities of precipitation reaching the ground as stemflow were relatively small.[14]

Measurements near Clarinda, Iowa, reported by Musgrave and Norton, showed that during a rainfall of 2.11 inches on September 26, 1935, 0.50 inch was intercepted by corn, 0.58 inch by alfalfa, and 0.49 inch by clover. These were the greatest depths intercepted during single storms from August 10 to December 6. Total depths intercepted from August 10 to October 7, just before the corn was harvested, amounted to 1.74 inches for corn, 1.68 inches for alfalfa, and 1.47 inches for clover. These depths corresponded to 22.0, 21.2, and 18.6 per cent, respectively, of the total rainfall of 7.92 inches during the same period.[47]

Laboratory tests reported by Stoltenberg and Wilson in June 1950 indicate that depths of rainfall intercepted by mature corn plants and held in storage until evaporated may be lower than those heretofore estimated.[66]

Rainfall Intercepted by Trees. Depths of rainfall intercepted by trees vary with (1) conditions of tree growth and (2) conditions of rainfall. Conditions of tree growth that affect interception include species, age, development, density of stand, and state of foliage. Conditions of rainfall that affect interception include intensity, duration, time between showers, and accompanying wind velocities.

Isolated trees and open woods intercept relatively small proportions of the rainfall when the storms or showers are accompanied by strong winds. When the rainfalls are not accompanied by wind, or in dense forests where the trees are protected from wind movements, interception losses during similar rainfalls are greater. During light summer showers, unaccompanied by wind, interception by trees may be almost 100 per cent of the rainfall, especially when the showers are separated by time intervals long enough to permit complete evaporation of intercepted moisture.

Interception losses in forests are increased by the presence of weeds, bushes, shrubs, and other types of underbrush. Deciduous trees intercept more rainfall during the warmer months, when in full leaf, than during the colder months, after the leaves have fallen. Conifers usually intercept greater proportions of annual rainfall than deciduous trees, because they retain their foliage throughout the year. Trees of middle age intercept more rainfall than either young or old trees.

Only relatively small depths of rainfall take place before some water drips to the ground under the trees. Such depths, sometimes referred to as initial storage, seldom exceed a few hundredths of an inch. As rain continues, the foliage intercepts additional moisture until the interception storage is filled. Further rain then passes through the tree canopies as fast as it falls. Depths of interception storage during heavy showers may amount to 0.50 inch or more. Horton measured depths of interception greater than 0.50 inch during showers of more than 1.0 inch at Albany, New York, in 1918.

Many investigations of rainfall intercepted by trees have been made in the past. Usually, total depths of interception during periods of measurement are given as percentages of total rainfall. Horton summarized the results of some European investigations in 1919.[28] Table 1 gives some data on seasonal interception during rainfall as measured for different trees in various sections of the United States. The items for chaparral and ponderosa pine in southern California are for annual periods. Other items are for rainfall seasons.

In general, quantities of water that reach the ground as stemflow constitute only small proportions of the rainfall. Investigations at a plantation of Canary Island pine near Berkeley, California, reported by Kittredge and his associates in 1941, showed that stemflow began to reach the ground when the rainfall exceeded about 0.20 or 0.25 inch.[38] During some rainfalls of more than 1 inch, stemflow amounted to as much as 13 per cent of the rainfall. However, total seasonal stemflow amounted to only about 1 per cent of the rainfall. Meas-

Table 1

SEASONAL RAINFALL INTERCEPTED BY TREES AS MEASURED
IN THE UNITED STATES

Trees	Location	Year	Seasonal interception		Reported by	Ref. no.
			Depth, in.	Per cent of rainfall		
Mature ponderosa pine *	Southern California	Before 1944	7.5–9.0	15.0–	Rowe	77
Young ponderosa pine	Colorado	1941	2.54	16.5	Johnson	33
Mature lodgepole pine	Fraser, Colo.	1938–1940	2.21	30.5	Wilm	76
Canary Island pine	Berkeley, Calif.	1932–1939	4.64	20.5	Kittredge	38
Douglas fir	Pacific Northwest	About 1930	....	43.0 †	Simson	36
Chaparral *	Southern California	Before 1944	1.5–2.0	4–8	Rowe	77
Spruce, fir, and paper birch	Maine	Before 1933	....	26	Forest Service	18
Spruce and fir	Maine	Before 1933	....	37	Forest Service	18
White pine and hemlock	Massachusetts	Before 1933	....	24	Forest Service	18
Virgin white pine and hemlock	Idaho	Before 1933	....	21	Forest Service	18
Second-growth oak and hard pine	New Jersey	Before 1933	....	13	Forest Service	18
Jack pine and hardwood hemlock	Wisconsin	Before 1933	....	22, 19	Forest Service	18
Hardwoods in leaf	Wisconsin	Before 1933	....	25	Forest Service	18
Hardwoods not in leaf	Wisconsin	Before 1933	....	16	Forest Service	18
Hackberry	Dayton, Ohio	1919	3.28	30.5	Houk	30
Linden	Peru, Neb.	1927	3.75	27.2	Holch	26
Maple	Albany, N. Y.	1918	4.73	33.0	Horton	28
Elm	Albany, N. Y.	1918	6.42	44.7	Horton	28
Willow	Albany, N. Y.	1918	5.81	40.4	Horton	28
Ash	Albany, N. Y.	1918	5.62	39.1	Horton	28
Beech	Albany, N. Y.	1918	5.20	36.2	Horton	28
Hemlock	Albany, N. Y.	1918	6.63	46.2	Horton	28
White pine	Albany, N. Y.	1918	6.90	48.1	Horton	28
Oak	Albany, N. Y.	1918	4.26	29.6	Horton	28
Hickory	Albany, N. Y.	1918	2.38	19.8	Horton	28
Oak	Peru, Neb.	1927	2.22	16.1	Holch	26

* For annual periods.
† Maximum reported.

urements of interception in chaparral stands, southern California, reported by Rowe in 1944, showed total stemflow averaging from 15 to 20 per cent of the total precipitation.[77]

In regions that experience dense fogs, interception may be negative. Measured precipitation may be greater under the trees than in the open. Fog particles collect on the foliage and drip to the ground in measurable amounts at times when no precipitation can be measured beyond the trees. Kittredge reported the results of some measurements under a dense stand of sitka spruce and western hemlock, 150 feet high, located near the Oregon coast.[79]   During 142 foggy days, they showed a total precipitation of 25.19 inches in the open and 36.42 inches under the trees, a total fog drip of 11.23 inches or nearly 0.08 inch per day.

Snowfall Intercepted by Trees. Amounts of moisture intercepted by trees during snowstorms vary with tree characteristics and weather conditions, as in rainfall interception. In general, proportions of winter snowfall that can be intercepted by tree canopies and evaporated without reaching the ground vary from about 10 to 40 per cent of the total snowfall.

Amounts of moisture intercepted during particular storms and held until evaporated depend largely on temperatures and wind movements accompanying and following the storms. Heavy loads of snow intercepted during a snowfall unaccompanied by wind may be blown free and deposited on the ground if strong winds develop after the storm has passed. Wet snows, which cling to the trees more tenaciously than dry snows, may become frozen to the foliage as temperatures decrease after the storm. Later, as temperatures increase and wind movements develop, some of the intercepted snow may become detached and dislodged. Warm periods following snowstorms may cause some melting and dripping of snowmelt water from the intercepted snow.

Forest Service measurements in Idaho showed that up to the time of maximum storage 27 per cent of the winter snowfall was intercepted by a good stand of virgin ponderosa pine containing an undergrowth of young trees; 22 per cent by similar mature timber without undergrowth; and 8 per cent by a somewhat open stand of ponderosa and lodgepole pine about 20 to 30 feet high.[18]

Measurements in the South Platte Valley, Colorado, reported by Johnson, showed that young ponderosa pine intercepted 30 per cent of the snowfall during the winter of 1940 to 1941.[33]   Morey, in his discussion of Johnson's paper, reported an interception of 0.08 inch of water by 60-year northern hardwood and 0.36 inch by 30-year red spruce, in central Vermont, during a spring snowstorm in which the total precipitation was 0.82 inch. His measurements were made after some snow had blown from the tree crowns.

Because of their exposed positions above the ground, intercepted snowfalls show considerably higher rates of evaporation than snow surfaces on the ground, possibly twice as high as stated in the preceding chapter. In the Wagon Wheel Gap investigations, winter evaporation of intercepted snowfall on the forested area was about 2.5 inches. The elimination of snow interception by the trees may have accounted for a large part of the increased water yield that developed on the area where the forest had been removed.[4]

EVAPORATION FROM SOILS

Evaporation from soils takes place principally at the ground surface. When sufficient air circulation is possible, a small amount of evaporation may take place in soil interstices close to the surface. In heavy clay soils that crack during drying, some evaporation takes place along the cracked surfaces.

Rates of soil evaporation depend on quantities of moisture at the ground surface and prevailing weather conditions. When the ground is saturated, rates of soil evaporation depend on the same laws that control evaporation from water surfaces. When the ground is not saturated, rates of soil evaporation depend on the rates at which soil moisture can move to the surface to maintain evaporation.

Some investigations of soil evaporation under saturated conditions have indicated rates of evaporation higher than at water surfaces in standard measuring pans. The excess rates probably were due to heating of the ground, so that soil-moisture temperatures were higher than water temperatures in the pans.

Losses of water by soil evaporation vary widely, not only in different parts of the country but also at different times and under different conditions in the same locality. In general, appreciable wind movements, high temperatures, and low humidities mean high rates of soil evaporation whenever sufficient quantities of moisture are available for evaporation. Shading of the ground surface reduces soil evaporation. In fields of close-growing crops approaching maturity, daily evaporation losses may be less than half the losses in areas devoid of vegetation. In dense forests, where wind movements are reduced, surface litter acts as a mulch, and the ground is continuously shaded, annual depths of soil evaporation may be less than one-third of the losses in open areas.

On some irrigated lands in western United States, soils may contain enough alkali compounds to affect rates of evaporation. On such lands, salts are dissolved by the soil water, the vapor tension of the soil solution is reduced, and rates of soil evaporation are decreased. Tests at the Utah Agricultural Experiment Station, reported by Harris and Robinson, showed that rates of evaporation from Greenville loam were decreased about 50 per cent when 5 to 7 per cent of sodium chloride was mixed with the soil.[24]

On lands where the water table is relatively close to the ground surface, so that capillary tensions can raise moisture from the ground-water reservoir, annual depths of soil evaporation may be several times as great as on lands where the water table is naturally deep or has been lowered by drainage improvements. On lands where the water table is too deep to permit upward movements of moisture to the ground surface, soil evaporation depends on moisture supplied by precipitation or irrigation.

Evaporation following Precipitation. Soil evaporation following precipitation takes place at varying rates, depending on weather conditions, the amount of moisture available at the ground surface, and the quantities of soil moisture that capillarity can raise to the ground surface. Immediately following cessation of rainfall or completion of snow melting, soil evaporation takes place more or less rapidly, according to prevailing temperatures, humidities, and wind velocities.

As the ground surface dries during subsequent periods of no precipitation, previously infiltrated moisture is brought to the surface by capillary action to maintain soil evaporation. As soil evaporation continues and soil moisture becomes depleted at gradually increasing depths, rates at which moisture can be raised and resultant rates of soil evaporation decrease rapidly and soon approach negligible values.

Forest Service measurements at bare soil plots in southern California, reported by Colman, indicated that losses of moisture by soil evaporation extended to depths as great as 5 feet. Similar measurements in the Bass Lake area of the Sierra Nevadas showed that most of the moisture lost by soil evaporation came from the upper 2 feet of soil.[78]

The Santa Ana investigations in southern California indicated that immediately after winter rains the rate of soil evaporation was about the same as the rate of water surface evaporation; that after the soil moisture was reduced to field capacity the rate of evaporation from sandy soils was about 0.024 inch per day; and that after each rainstorm the average total loss by evaporation from the topsoil was about 0.5 inch.[54]

Direct measurements of soil evaporation have been made by periodic weighing of tanks filled with soil, initially supplied with definite quantities of moisture. Indirect measurements have been made using lysimeters to measure percolation following precipitation and computing soil evaporation as the difference between precipitation and percolation. Indirect measurements also have been made by sampling the soil at different depths at intervals following rainfall and calculating evaporation losses from moisture contents of the samples.

All three methods involve difficulties and uncertainties. The removal of soil layers from their natural positions and the placing of the layers in tanks or lysimeters is difficult to accomplish in such a manner as to insure an accurate representation of field conditions. Local variations in soil composition and moisture contents often are so pronounced as to throw doubt on interpretations made from soil samples. However, despite these objections, results of such investigations are worthy of consideration.

Table 2 gives some data on soil evaporation from precipitation as determined by a few of the more recent investigations, together

TABLE 2

DATA ON SOIL EVAPORATION FROM PRECIPITATED MOISTURE
DETERMINED BY SOME RECENT INVESTIGATIONS

Location	Soil	Observation period	Precipitation, in.	Soil evaporation, in.	Evaporation, per cent of precipitation	Ref. no.
Clarinda, Iowa	Marshall silt loam	Annual, 1935–1941	29.75	16.7	56.2	13
Clarinda, Iowa	Shelby silt loam *	Annual, 1935–1941	29.75	20.2	67.9	13
Anaheim, California	Fine sandy loam	Rainy season, 1927–1928	12.39	6.0	48.4	7
Ontario, California	Sand over silt loam	Rainy season, 1927–1928	7.79	2.99	38.4	7
Ontario, California	Sand	Rainy season, 1927–1928	7.13	4.1	57.5	7
Glen Avon Heights, California	Compact loam	Rainy season, 1927–1928	5.49	5.3	96.5	7
San Dimas, Experimental Forest, California	Denuded chaparral	Annual, 1940–1943	36.3	18.0	49.6	1
Coweeta Experimental Forest, North Carolina †	Red brown loam	April 1941–March 1942	62.4	18.2	29.2	78
San Fernando Valley, California	Tujunga sand	Sept. 23, 1939–Mar. 6, 1940	16.49 ‡	3.77	22.9	80
San Fernando Valley, California	Diablo clay adobe	Sept. 23, 1939–Mar. 6, 1940	16.09 ‡	4.15	25.8	80
San Fernando Valley, California	Yolo sandy loam	Sept. 23, 1939–Mar. 6, 1940	22.36 ‡	4.55	20.3	80
San Fernando Valley, California	Hanford fine sandy loam	Sept. 23, 1939–Mar. 6, 1940	28.82 ‡	5.13	17.8	80

* Relatively impermeable as compared with Marshall soil.
† Cut vegetation left as surface mulch.
‡ Includes irrigation.

with pertinent descriptive information. References to sources of information are given in the last column. Measurements were made with lysimeters at Clarinda, Iowa, and by soil sampling at the California locations. A similar tabulation, showing results of some earlier measurements in Europe, was presented by Lee in 1942.[43]

The addition of peat to sand and clay soils seems to prolong the evaporation period following saturation and thus to increase the total evaporation loss. Laboratory tests conducted by Feustel and Byers, using different peat and soil mixtures, showed that evaporation rates were unaffected by the peat for several days following saturation, then were gradually increased during succeeding periods.[17]

In temperate regions, winter and early spring losses of moisture by soil evaporation may be increased by repeated freezing and thawing. Soil sampling tests and analyses made by Anderson indicate that during periods of daily freezing and thawing, soil moisture is drawn upward to the frozen layer, the ground surface remains wet during the day, and soil evaporation is increased.[2] He reported a total loss of 1.02 inches by soil evaporation at North Fork, California, during the 10-day period from January 9 to 19, 1939. His investigations showed that surface freezing was accompanied by upward movements of soil moisture from depths as great as 36 inches.

Evaporation following Irrigation. Soil evaporation following irrigation takes place rapidly until the topsoil dries. When the irrigation supply is discontinued, rates of evaporation from the wet soil are about the same as from water surfaces of the same temperature. As moisture in the topsoil is depleted, rates of evaporation decrease rapidly. Subsequent rates of evaporation are affected by mulching, cultivation, and other tillage operations.

Total depths of water evaporated at field surfaces between successive irrigations depend principally on weather conditions, texture and structure of the topsoil, method, frequency, and depth of irrigation, type of crop and stage of plant growth, and time and method of tillage.

In general, depths of soil evaporation during the growing season decrease with increased depths of water applied per irrigation and decreased frequencies of irrigation. They are lower when water is supplied through deep furrows than when it is supplied through shallow furrows or by surface flooding. Depths evaporated between successive irrigations during a particular growing season decrease as the crop plants develop and shade increasing proportions of the soil surfaces.

Cultivation and mulching reduce soil evaporation. Cultivation loosens the topsoil and impedes capillary movements that bring moisture to the ground surface to maintain evaporation. Applications of suitable mulches following irrigation cause similar effects on soil evaporation. Tillage operations that compact the soil facilitate capillary movements of moisture and increase soil evaporation. Except

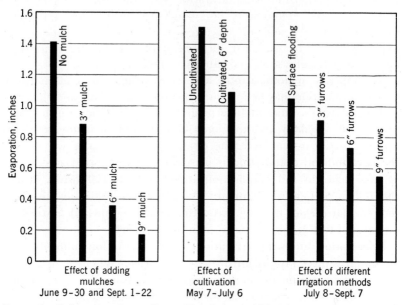

FIGURE 1. Soil evaporation at Reno, Nevada, as modified by mulches, cultivation, and different irrigation methods. (Plotted from data by Fortier and Beckett.)

where tillage operations compact the soil, moisture to maintain evaporation at the field surface is seldom raised from depths greater than about 10 or 12 inches.

Opinions differ regarding effects of cultivation on soil evaporation. Data obtained from tank measurements, reported by Fortier and Beckett, showed appreciable reductions in evaporation resulting from both cultivation and mulching.[19] Subsequent data reported by Veihmeyer showed negligible reductions resulting from cultivation to 6- and 8-inch depths, and only small reductions resulting from cultivation to 10-inch depths.[72]

Probably beneficial effects obtained by cultivation vary with the texture of the topsoil and the moisture content at the time of cultivation, as well as with the depth of cultivation. Some soils can be cultivated with higher moisture contents than others, but considerable drying must always take place before cultivation. Therefore, appreciable proportions of the soil evaporation following an irrigation take place before cultivation is possible.

Although reductions in soil evaporation obtained by cultivation may be relatively small in some fields, total effects on the conservation

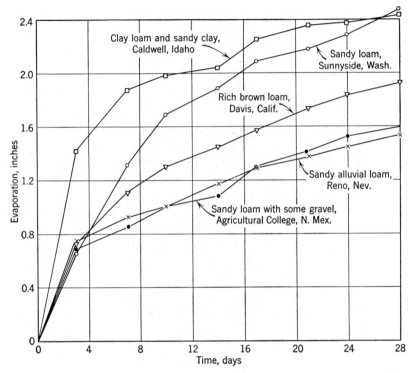

FIGURE 2. Soil evaporation following 6-inch irrigations, uncultivated soils of different texture. (Plotted from data by Fortier and Beckett.)

of soil moisture usually are important, inasmuch as weed growths are retarded and wasteful transpiration reduced. Cultivation also aerates the topsoil, facilitates absorption during subsequent irrigation, and reduces subsequent surface runoff.

Figure 1 shows effects of mulches, cultivation, and irrigation methods on soil evaporation at Reno, Nevada, as determined from tank measurements reported by Fortier and Beckett.[19] The soil was a sandy alluvial loam, containing considerable proportions of sand and small rock fragments. Measurements were made following 6-inch irrigations. Data for mulching tests are averages for two 21-day periods. Data for cultivation and irrigation-method tests are averages for two 28-day periods. Cultivations were made to 6-inch depths. In the tests of different irrigation methods, soil surfaces were cultivated a few hours after irrigation.

Figure 2 shows soil evaporation during 28-day periods following 6-inch irrigations, for some uncultivated soils of different texture, plotted from data in the same report. Rates of evaporation during the first 3 days were about the same, except at Caldwell, Idaho, where the relatively impermeable soil held more moisture near the surface and thus facilitated evaporation. The tests were made during different periods between early May and late July.

Lysimeter measurements of seasonal percolation and evaporation were made near Umatilla, Oregon, during 1915 to 1931, and reported by Hastings and Dean.[25] During the 10 years from 1922 to 1931, the average seasonal evaporation, April to October, was 16.94 inches or 28 per cent of the water applied by irrigation and natural rainfall. During the entire period of investigation, the average seasonal evaporation was 17.14 inches. This was 54 per cent of the average annual evaporation from a water surface. The soil was a virgin sandy type, which had a relatively low water-holding capacity. Weeds were removed from the lysimeter surfaces, but the soil was not mulched or cultivated.

Evaporation from Groundwater. Soil evaporation from groundwater takes place when the water table is high enough that capillarity can raise water to maintain evaporation. Many measurements of soil evaporation from groundwater have been made in the irrigated sections of western United States. The results of the investigations warrant the following general conclusions:

1. When the water table is at the ground surface, the rate of evaporation from a sand or sandy loam may be equal to, or slightly greater than, the rate of evaporation from a water surface in a standard measuring pan.

2. Rates of soil evaporation decrease rapidly with increasing depths to the water table, particularly in the first 2 feet of depth.

3. In most soils, rates of evaporation from groundwater supplies become negligible when the water table falls to a depth of more than about 4 feet.

Table 3 shows some data on evaporation from sand and water surfaces at Los Griegos, New Mexico, observed by the Bureau of

TABLE 3

EVAPORATION FROM SAND AND WATER SURFACES
AT LOS GRIEGOS, NEW MEXICO [31]

(Depths in feet)

Month	Year ending September 1927			Year ending September 1928		
	Pan 1, water	Pan 3, soil	Pan 7, soil	Pan 1, water	Pan 3, soil	Pan 7, soil
October	0.31	0.19	0.26	0.32	0.12	0.32
November	.24	.10	.23	.21	.08	.18
December	.08	.12	.08	.09	.13	.11
January	.08	.02	.12	.09	.03	.13
February	.20	.10	.20	.16	.08	.17
March	.38	.17	.40	.36	.09	.35
April	.48	.17	.47	.50	.10	.43
May	.77	.16	.68	.45	.16	.44
June	.57	.16	.57	.72	.06	.58
July	.65	.11	.63	.62	.15	.57
August	.55	.20	.54	.61	.20	.47
September	.41	.14	.40	.44	.13	.37
Year	4.72	1.64	4.58	4.57	1.33	4.12
Percentage	100.0	34.8	97.1	100.0	29.1	90.2
Depth to water	......	2.34	0.33	......	2.07	0.29

Reclamation.[31] The sand was a rather fine river wash material, with traces of silt. Measuring pans were standard farm stock tanks, approximately 4 feet in diameter, set in the ground with rims projecting about 3 inches. Pans 1 and 7 were 2 feet deep; pan 3, 4 feet deep. Depths to groundwater in the sand pans were maintained approximately constant by adaptations of the Mariotte system used by Parshall.[50] Mean ratios of soil evaporation to water surface evaporation, expressed as percentages, were 93.6 for a depth of 0.31 foot to the water table, and 32.0 for a depth of 2.20 feet to the water table.

Table 4 shows some data on evaporation from saturated sandy loam soil and water surfaces at Garnett, Colorado, observed by Tipton and Hart.[48] Measurements were made at 3-foot circular tanks, 3 feet deep, set in the ground with rims nearly at ground levels. Observed depths of evaporation were reduced to field conditions by applying

TABLE 4

EVAPORATION FROM SATURATED SOIL AND WATER SURFACES
AT GARNETT, COLORADO [48]

(Depths in feet)

Month	1927		1928		1930		1931	
	Soil	Water	Soil	Water	Soil	Water	Soil	Water
April	.....	......	0.27	0.32	.....	......	0.47	0.36
May	.....	......	.39	.39	0.52	0.52	.56	.47
June	0.47	0.48	.47	.55	.53	.56	.58	.54
July	.37	.44	.53	.47	.44	.44	.55	.51
August	.41	.35	.44	.42	.32	.35	.42	.46
September	.29	.29	.36	.33	.31	.35	.32	.33
October	.22	.22	.26	.27	.16	.24	.26	.27
Period	1.76	1.78	2.72	2.75	2.28	2.46	3.16	2.94
Percentage	98.9	100.0	98.9	100.0	92.7	100.0	107.5	100.0
Inches to water	0	......	0	......	0.25	......	0	......

a coefficient of 0.85. Evaporation from the soil was slightly less than
from the water, except during 1931 when the soil tank showed an
excess of 7.5 per cent.

Figure 3 shows variations in soil evaporation with depths to groundwater as determined by some investigations. Depths of evaporation
are plotted as percentages of water surface evaporation. Reference
numbers identify sources of information, as listed at the end of the
chapter, as well as particular curves in Figure 3. A similar diagram,
showing additional data on evaporation from sand surfaces, was presented in an earlier publication.[31]

In plotting observations made at Davis, California, soil evaporation
measured with the water table at the ground surface was assumed to
equal the evaporation at a water surface. Data plotted for the investigations at Santa Ana, California, and Milford, Utah, were obtained
on undisturbed soils. Companion tests on similar disturbed soils at
both locations showed higher rates of evaporation, only slightly higher
at Milford but more than three times as high at Santa Ana.

Parshall's investigations at Fort Collins, Colorado, confirmed some
earlier conclusions that rainfall, by cooling the soil and increasing

capillary tensions, or by reducing salt concentrations in the soil solution, may increase rates of soil evaporation from groundwater supplies.[50]

Ridgaway's tests at Laramie, Wyoming, showed that stirring the
surface soil to simulate cultivation reduced evaporation rates.[57] With
the water table 22 inches below the ground, evaporation was reduced

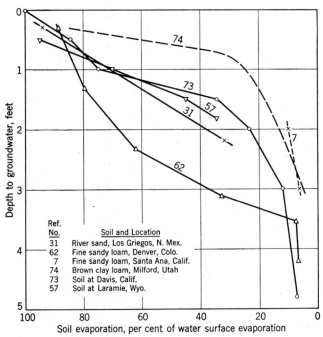

FIGURE 3.   Variations of soil evaporation with depths to groundwater.

19 per cent by stirring to a 2-inch depth, 23 per cent by stirring to a
4-inch depth, and 45 per cent by stirring to a 6-inch depth. Cultivation probably is more effective in reducing soil evaporation when
moisture is supplied from groundwater than when it is supplied by
rainfall or irrigation.

TRANSPIRATION

Transpiration usually is defined as the process by which water vapor
is released to the atmosphere through surface pores in plant foliage,
mainly through stomatal openings.   In irrigation studies, transpiration
includes liquid water that sometimes oozes from plant surfaces, a

process known as guttation. Most transpiration takes place at the plant leaves. A small portion of the emitted moisture, generally less than 10 per cent, comes from the younger plant stems. Transpiration is similar to evaporation in that it adds moisture to the air. Since it is a process involved in plant growth, it is sometimes referred to as physiological evaporation.

Release of moisture by transpiration occurs principally during the daylight hours of the growing season. Probably not more than 5 to 10 per cent of the daily transpiration takes place during the night. The rate of transpiration usually reaches a maximum value shortly after noon, and a minimum value just before sunrise. Trees, shrubs, and other perennials transpire some moisture during dormant seasons, but the amounts emitted usually are so small that they can be ignored in irrigation studies.

Transpiration takes place because of weather influences, physical conditions of plant structure, and characteristics of plant growth. Transpiration may reduce leaf temperatures slightly during warm weather. It also may facilitate delivery of nutrients to plant tissues through increased absorption of soil water. However, detrimental effects that result from transpiration at times may be greater than beneficial effects. Transpiration hastens the exhaustion of soil moisture. If additional water is not supplied to the soil by rainfall, or cannot be supplied by irrigation, crop losses may result.

During hot weather, especially when hot winds are blowing over the fields, transpiration may take place more rapidly than moisture can be absorbed by the plant roots, even when the soil contains ample moisture supplies. At such times, crop foliage may be dried to degrees beyond recovery. In the Plains states, hot winds continuing for only a few hours have caused almost complete destruction of corn crops.

Moisture is necessary for plant growth, but transpiration, from a theoretical viewpoint, may or may not be necessary. Some scientists have considered transpiration as an essential process. Others have concluded that transpiration, although unavoidable because of the nature of plant growth, is not essential. Many of the more recent discussions have favored the latter statement. Inasmuch as transpiration is unavoidable, conditions under which it takes place, rates at which moisture may be released from plants, and the various factors that affect rates of transpiration are matters that need consideration in irrigation studies.

Conditions Affecting Transpiration. Conditions that affect transpiration are the nature of the vegetation, suitability of soils for plant growth, and prevailing weather characteristics. Practically all conditions that cause variations in these items also cause variations in transpiration, either directly or indirectly. Many factors are more or less interrelated in their influences on transpiration. Therefore, effects of particular conditions often are difficult to determine separately.

Rates of transpiration and total depths of water transpired during the growing season vary widely for different types of plants. They also vary considerably for different varieties of the same type. Density of growth and stages of development affect transpiration rates. Conditions of shading may reduce transpiration. Plant diseases and applications of chemicals to control insect pests may have some effects on transpiration. Plants growing in arid regions, adequately supplied with irrigation water, transpire more moisture than similar plants growing in humid regions.

Soil conditions, particularly texture and moisture contents, affect rates at which moisture can be absorbed by plant roots, raised through plant structures, and made available for transpiration. Applications of fertilizers cause changes in transpiration. Plants growing on poor soils consume more moisture than similar plants growing on fertile soils. Differences in time and methods of tillage have some effects on seasonal transpiration.

Weather conditions that control rates of evaporation, primarily temperature, humidity, and wind, affect rates of transpiration. During daylight hours, when most transpiration takes place, rates of transpiration follow rates of evaporation closely. Light conditions, which influence plant temperatures and the opening and closing of the stomata, affect rates at which moisture can be released from plant foliage. Diurnal changes in atmospheric conditions probably are largely responsible for diurnal changes in transpiration rates. Annual changes in weather conditions during different growing seasons probably account largely for yearly differences in total amounts of moisture transpired by the same crops at the same locations.

Changes in rates of transpiration during a particular growing season are caused by developments in plant growth and variations in available moisture supplies, as well as by changes in weather conditions. When adequate supplies of moisture are available, daily rates of transpiration by small grains usually increase until about the middle of the growing season, then decrease gradually until the crops are harvested. Daily rates of transpiration by alfalfa usually increase up to the time of cutting.

Transpiration Measurements. Measurements of transpiration rates have been made by cutting plants or twigs and weighing at intervals until transpiration ceases. Continuous measurements of transpiration have been made by weighing quantities of water consumed by plants growing in pots or tanks, with the top surfaces sealed to prevent soil evaporation. Most of the more recent investigations of moisture consumed by plants growing in containers have determined total quantities used by transpiration and evaporation rather than by transpiration alone.

Many investigations of plant transpiration have been made in western United States and certain foreign countries. Lawes conducted measurements at Rothamsted, England, in 1850. A review of transpiration data obtained during some of the more important early investigations has been published.[10]

Comprehensive measurements of plant transpiration were begun by Briggs and Shantz at Akron, Colorado, in 1910.[9] When the measurements were completed in 1917, transpiration data were summarized for nearly all types of farm crops grown in the West, together with similar data for some types of native vegetation.[61] Measurements of transpiration by farm crops also were made at Newell, South Dakota, and Mandan, North Dakota, by Dillman, during 1912 to 1922.[16] Measurements of transpiration by a few crop plants and a number of Arizona range plants were made at the Desert Grassland Station, about 30 miles south of Tucson, by McGinnies and Arnold during 1932 to 1936.[46]

Results of transpiration measurements on plants growing in containers usually have been reported as transpiration ratios. Transpiration ratios determined for potted plants may not accurately represent actual consumptions of moisture under field conditions. However, they are valuable and should be considered. Probably plants growing under natural conditions use water more economically than plants growing in containers.

Veihmeyer measured transpiration by prune trees growing in containers at Mountain View, California, and reported the data in pounds of water in 1927.[72] More recently, investigators in southern California have determined quantities of water consumed by fruit trees from analyses of soil samples taken periodically after irrigation.[80] Mulches were maintained on the soil surfaces and losses of moisture computed from sampling below the mulches were assumed to represent transpiration. Although mulches are effective in reducing soil evaporation, the computed data may include small amounts of evaporation and may be slightly higher than actual transpiration.

Transpiration Ratios. Transpiration ratios are ratios of weights of water consumed by plants during the growing season to weights of dry matter produced. In some measurements of transpiration by trees, transpiration ratios have been calculated on the basis of total dry leaf matter produced instead of total dry matter.

Most investigators of water consumption by crops have computed transpiration ratios on the basis of total dry matter, exclusive of roots, except for root crops. Some have made supplemental computations on the basis of grain produced, for corn, cereals, beans, and similar crops; on the basis of tubers, for potato crops; and on the basis of roots, for sugar beet crops.

For use in irrigation studies, transpiration ratios should be computed on the basis of products harvested. Equivalent yields per acre also should be given, whenever feasible, so that weights of water consumed can be converted into depths over the crop-producing areas.

In early reports on transpiration investigations, the term water requirement often was used instead of transpiration ratio. However, the latter term is preferable inasmuch as irrigation engineers use the term water requirement to mean the total depth of water needed for normal crop production under field conditions, including soil evaporation, percolation, and other unavoidable losses.

Althcugh growing plants contain relatively large proportions of water, usually from 65 to 90 per cent, actual quantities of water present at the time of harvesting are negligible in comparison with the total quantities consumed during growth. Therefore, total quantities consumed may be considered as total transpiration.

Transpiration by Farm Crops. Table 5 shows transpiration ratios for farm crops as determined at Akron, Colorado, during 1911 to 1917.[61] Numbers of varieties tested, ranges in transpiration ratios, and mean ratios for the different crops are shown. Ratios were calculated on the basis of total dry matter, grain, seed, roots, or tubers, according to the nature of the crop. Inasmuch as several varieties were tested during different years, under varying weather conditions, the transpiration data were weighted in order to obtain ratios that would show variations in quantities of water consumed by specific crops growing under similar weather conditions.

The ratios in Table 5 show wide variations in transpiration for different crops, also considerable ranges in transpiration for different

TABLE 5

TRANSPIRATION RATIOS FOR CROPS AS DETERMINED AT
AKRON, COLORADO [61]

Crop	Varieties tested, no.	Transpiration ratio * Range	Mean
Grains:			
Proso	2	531–603	567
Millet	3	863–1,117	959
Buckwheat	1	. . . .	969
Sorgo	3	863–1,804	1,237
Grain sorghum	4	750–1,050	868
Barley	4	1,128–1,464	1,241
Corn	2	821–1,998	1,405
Oats	4	1,379–1,915	1,627
Wheat, emmer	1	. . . .	1,167
Wheat, durum	6	1,365–1,622	1,475
Wheat, common	11	1,244–3,398	1,872
Wheat, hybrids	2	1,995–2,163	2,079
Rye	1	. . . .	2,142
Flax	6	2,010–5,162	3,252
Legumes:			
Clover	2	636–759	698 †
Clover, sweet	1	. . . .	731 †
Vetch	5	562–899	708 †
Alfalfa	10	626–920	844 †
Cowpeas	1	. . . .	1,632
Beans	2	1,583–1,815	1,699
Beans, soy	1	. . . .	1,974
Chickpeas	1	. . . .	1,685
Peas, Canadian field	1	. . . .	2,153
Lupinus albus	1	. . . .	4,734
Grasses:			
Sudan grass	1	. . . .	380 †
Wheat grass	1	. . . .	678 †
Brome grass	1	. . . .	977 †
Miscellaneous:			
Cotton	1	. . . .	568 †
Sugar beets	1	. . . .	629
Potatoes	2	1,325–2,877	2,101
Cabbage	1	. . . .	518 †
Rape	1	. . . .	714 †
Watermelons	1	. . . .	1,102
Cantaloupes	1	. . . .	1,754
Turnips	1	. . . .	1,471
Cucumbers	1	. . . .	1,549

* Weighted values in pounds of water per pound of crop product.
† Based on total dry matter.

varieties of the same crop. Ratios for grains, given in pounds of water per pound of grain, vary from 567 for proso to 3,252 for flax. Ratios for eleven varieties of common wheat vary from 1,244 to 3,398. Ratios for four legumes, based on total dry matter, vary from 698 for clover to 844 for alfalfa.

Table 6 shows yearly variations in transpiration ratios for some crops as determined at Akron, also weighted mean ratios for the dif-

TABLE 6

YEARLY TRANSPIRATION RATIOS FOR CROPS AS DETERMINED
AT AKRON, COLORADO [61]

Crop and variety	1911	1912	1913	1914	1915	1916	1917	Mean *
Millet, Kursk	287	187	286	295	202	367	284	274
Sorgo, Minnesota Amber	...	239	298	284	203	296	272	274
Corn, Northwestern Dent	368	280	399	368	253	495	346	361
Barley, Hannchen	527	443	...	501	404	664	522	523
Wheat, Kubanka	468	394	496	418	405	636	471	491
Cotton, Triumph	...	488	657	574	443	612	522	568
Potatoes, Irish Cobbler	448	...	659	...	329	630	...	499
Oats, Swedish Select	615	423	617	599	448	876	635	604
Rye, Vern	724	496	...	622	469	800	625	634
Cowpeas	...	...	571	659	413	767	481	569
Alfalfa, Grimm	...	657	834	898	695	1,047	822	851

* Weighted values, all based on dry matter produced.

ferent crops. All ratios in Table 6 were calculated on the basis of dry matter produced. The variations from year to year were due primarily to changes in weather. For some crops, transpiration ratios during 1916 were about twice as great as during 1912. Transpiration ratios for some crops determined in southern Arizona were higher than the ratios determined at Akron.[46]

Studies of transpiration rates at Akron during 1914 and 1915 showed that for the 10 days of maximum moisture consumption the daily transpiration was 12 to 16 times the dry weight of the crop for small grains; 6 to 9 times the dry weight for millet, corn, and sorghum; and 36 to 56 times the dry weight for alfalfa. Alfalfa crops doubled their transpiration rates every 8 days during periods between cuttings.[12]

Transpiration by Native Plants. Table 7 shows mean transpiration ratios for some weeds and native plants as determined at Akron. All ratios were calculated on the basis of total dry matter. The ratios vary from 260 pounds for tumbleweeds to 1,131 pounds for Franseria.

TABLE 7

TRANSPIRATION RATIOS FOR WEEDS AND NATIVE PLANTS
AS DETERMINED AT AKRON, COLORADO [61]

Weeds or native plants	Transpiration ratio *	Weeds or native plants	Transpiration ratio *
Weeds:		Native weeds (continued):	
Tumbleweed	260	Mountain sage	654
Pigweed	305	Verbena	702
Russian thistle	314	Fetid marigold	847
Lamb's quarters	658	Native plants:	
Polygonum	678	Buffalo grass	296
Native weeds:		Buffalo and grama grass	338
Purslane	281	Clammyweed	483
Cocklebur	415	Iva	534
Nightshade	487	Western ragweed	912
Buffalo bur	536	Western wheat grass	1,035
Gumweed	585	Franseria	1,131
Sunflower	623		

* Weighted values in pounds of water per pound of dry matter.

Sunflowers transpired 623 pounds of water per pound of dry matter. Buffalo grass transpired 296 pounds. Buffalo grass mixed with grama grass transpired 338 pounds. Western wheat grass transpired 1,035 pounds, about 100 pounds less than Franseria.

In southern Arizona, mean transpiration ratios varied from 522 to 588 pounds of water per pound of dry matter for six desert grassland plants; from 478 to 705 pounds for three plains grassland plants; and from 472 to 706 pounds for three southern tall grass plants. Ratios varied from 464 to 897 pounds for six winter annuals, and from 331 to 581 pounds for four summer annuals.[46]

Transpiration ratios for native trees and shrubs in southern Arizona were considerably higher than for grasses and annuals, except for foothill paloverde which consumed 772 pounds of water per pound of dry matter. Other trees and shrubs, including jojobe, velvet mesquite, mormon tea, burroweed, and catclaw, transpired from 1,708 to 2,404 pounds of water per pound of dry matter. Catclaw consumed the most water.

Transpiration by Fruit Trees. Table 8 shows seasonal and annual transpiration by fruit trees in southern California, as observed during different periods between 1927 and 1938.[80] The data were determined from soil samples taken periodically at different depths below mulches.

Table 8

TRANSPIRATION BY FRUIT TREES IN SOUTHERN CALIFORNIA
AS DETERMINED FROM SOIL SAMPLES [80]

Fruit trees	Location	Soil type	Growing season, inclusive	Transpiration, in.	
				Seasonal	Annual
Citrus, clean cultivated	Escondido	Sandy loam	Apr.–Oct. 15	13.4	....
Citrus, clean cultivated	Fallbrook	Sandy loam	Apr.–Oct. 15	9.2	....
Citrus, clean cultivated	Vista	Sandy loam	Apr.–Oct. 15	6.3	....
Citrus, 12–14 years old	Orange County	Sandy loam	Apr.–Oct.	10.7	....
Citrus, mature	Orange County	Sandy loam	Apr.–Oct.	15.5	....
Citrus, mature	Orange County	Sandy loam	Apr.–Nov.	16.4	21.6
Citrus, mature	Riverside and San Bernardino counties	....	Apr.–Oct.	20.7	....
Citrus, mature	Azuza	Fine sandy loam	Apr.–Oct.	16.7	23.5
Citrus, with cover crops	San Fernando Valley	Loam	Apr.–Oct.	25.8	35.0
Citrus, clean cultivated	San Fernando Valley	Loam	Apr.–Oct.	17.1	23.3
Avocados	Vista	Sandy loam	Apr.–Oct. 15	9.2 *	....
Walnuts, mature	Orange County	Sandy loam	Apr.–Oct.	25.0	....
Peaches, 12 years old	Ontario	Sand	Apr.–Oct.	27.3	27.5
Date palms	Coachella Valley	Very fine sandy loam	Jan.–Dec.	72.4	72.4
Seedless grapes, mature	Coachella Valley	Fine sand	Apr.–Oct.	39.0	43.6

* Water supply deficient.

Consequently, they may include small amounts of soil evaporation. An item for Thompson seedless grapes is given at the bottom of the table. Citrus trees were mostly oranges, but included some lemons and a few grapefruit.

Depths of seasonal transpiration by citrus fruits shown in Table 8 vary from 6.3 inches for clean cultivated trees at Vista to 25.8 inches for trees with cover crops in the San Fernando Valley. Depths of annual transpiration vary from 21.6 inches in Orange County to 35.0 inches in the San Fernando Valley. Clean cultivated citrus in the San Fernando Valley transpired 17.1 inches from April to October, and 6.2 inches from November to March.

Avocados at Vista, inadequately supplied with water, transpired 9.2 inches from April 1 to October 15. Mature walnut trees in Orange County transpired 25.0 inches from April to October. Peach trees at Ontario, 12 years old, transpired 27.3 inches from April to October, and only 0.2 inch from November to March.

In the Coachella Valley, seedless grapes transpired 39.0 inches from April to October, and 4.6 inches from November to March. Date palms, which use water throughout the year, transpired 72.4 inches from January to December. This was about 86 per cent of the mean annual evaporation at a water surface as observed at a ground pan at Indio. Figure 4 shows monthly transpiration by date palms as determined by Pillsbury, also mean monthly temperatures, plotted from data reported by Young.[80]

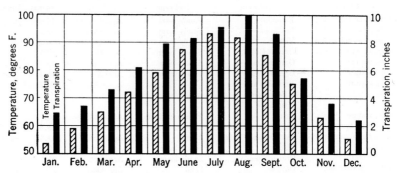

FIGURE 4. Monthly transpiration by date palms and mean monthly temperatures, Coachella Valley, California. (Plotted from data in Young's report.[80])

Transpiration by Forest Trees. Transpiration by forest trees, functions of moisture within the tree structures, and general relations between water and tree growth have been studied intensively. Raber reviewed such studies in 1937.[55] However, only a few laboratory measurements of transpiration ratios have been reported. Holch measured seasonal transpiration of some deciduous seedlings in different environments and reported losses as grams per square centimeter of total leaf area.[26]

Seasonal transpiration ratios for some Rocky Mountain conifers were determined by Bates in 1917 and 1920.[3] The determinations were made on nursery seedlings, 5 or 6 years old, transplanted to small containers which were sealed to prevent soil evaporation. Pearson made similar measurements for a few conifers in 1919 and 1920.[52] Average seasonal transpiration ratios determined by Bates and Pearson are shown in Table 9. They vary from 295 pounds of water per pound of dry weight accretion for Siberian larch to 958 pounds for limber pine.

Comprehensive investigations of transpiration by forest trees were made for the Austrian Forest Service, by Höhnel, during 1878 to 1880. Abstracts of the data, with discussions, were published by Horton in 1923.[29] The measurements were made on potted seedlings, 5 to 6 years old. Transpiration ratios were computed on the basis

TABLE 9

SEASONAL TRANSPIRATION RATIOS FOR SOME WESTERN CONIFERS [3,52,53]

Tree	Tests by Pearson			Tests by Bates		
	Number of seedlings	Age of seedlings, yr.	Trans-piration ratio *	Number of seedlings		Trans-piration ratio *
				1917	1920	
Limber pine	. .	. .	. . .	1	1	958
Lodgepole pine	. .	. .	. . .	2	6	786
Yellow pine ·	9	2–3	396	2	8	768
Bristlecone pine	6	5	440	2	2	743
Douglas fir	6	4	381	2	3	634
Englemann spruce	. .	. .	. . .	2	9	456
Blue spruce	6	4	359	. .	. .	. . .
Scotch pine	. .	. .	. . .	. .	2	436
Siberian larch	. .	. .	. . .	. .	2	295

* Pounds of water per pound of dry weight accretion.

of total dry-leaf matter. Data obtained during the 12 months from March 1879 to February 1880 are shown in Table 10. Nearly all the transpiration took place during May to October. The average transpiration ratio for all trees for November to April was 27.2 pounds of water per pound of dry-leaf matter, only about 3.6 per cent of the average for the 12 months.

Calculations of average forest transpiration from transpiration ratios constitute only approximate estimates. Horton computed yearly transpiration by fully stocked stands of 30-year trees as 5.22 inches for Douglas fir, 5.86 inches for white pine, 9.70 inches for hickory, 15.04 inches for red spruce, and 16.6 inches for beech. His computations for 60-year trees gave depths 38 to 54 per cent higher, except for hickory trees which showed only slight increases with age.

Rowe, from researches at North Fork, California, estimated an average annual transpiration of 3.81 inches by undisturbed woodland chaparral, where the annual precipitation is about 35 inches.[58] Hoover, from similar studies in western North Carolina, estimated an annual transpiration of 19 inches by a hardwood forest with an understory of dense shrubs, where the annual precipitation is about

TABLE 10

TRANSPIRATION RATIOS FOR TREES DETERMINED BY HÖHNEL, MARCH 1879 TO FEBRUARY 1880 [29]

Tree	Scientific name	Transpiration ratio *
Ash	Fraxinus excelsior	981
White birch	Betula alba	849
Beech	Fagus sylvatica	1,043
Hornbeam	Carpinus betulus	787
Field elm	Ulmus campestris	738
Stiel oak	Quercus pedunculus	454
Trauben oak	Quercus sessilifolia	790
Zerr oak	Quercus cerris	669
Black alder	Alnus glutinosa	840
Gray alder	Alnus incana	678 .
Sycamore maple	Acer platanoides	520
Mountain maple	Acer pseudoplat	635
Field maple	Acer campestria	1,281
Linden	Tilia grandifolia	1,038
Aspen	Populus tremula	873
Service berry	Sorbus tormin	1,748
Larch	Larix europea	1,165
Spruce	Abies excelsa	242
Fir	Abies pectinata	96
Scotch white pine	Pinus silvestris	110
Black Austrian pine	Pinus larico	123

* Pounds of water per pound of dry-leaf matter.

62 inches.[78] Kittredge estimated that the annual transpiration by forests usually varies between 5 and 15 inches but may be as much as 35 inches for dense stands of large trees on the best sites and may approach zero as the vegetation becomes smaller and sparser.[36]

EVAPO-TRANSPIRATION

Evapo-transpiration is the total quantity of water consumed by evaporation and transpiration. It is sometimes referred to as evaporation, total evaporation, land evaporation, water losses, total losses, fly-off, or consumptive use.

For a small area of native vegetation, devoid of ponds or streams, evapo-transpiration for the growing season represents interception, soil evaporation, and transpiration, plus such evaporation as may take place from water held on the ground at times of precipitation. For a small cropped area in an irrigated region, evapo-transpiration represents interception, soil evaporation, and transpiration by crop plants and accompanying weed growths, plus such evaporation as may take place from water surfaces during delivery of irrigation supplies. For a large area including different types of surfaces, evapo-transpiration represents interception, evaporation from soil and water surfaces, and transpiration by all kinds of plant growth.

When evapo-transpiration is determined for the winter season or for annual periods in regions subject to snowfall, it includes evaporation from snow surfaces and intercepted snowfall.

The term consumptive use is commonly used in considerations of irrigation hydrology in western United States. When determined for farm areas, it is designated farm consumptive use. When determined for relatively large areas, it is designated project consumptive use or valley consumptive use. The term is also used in discussing data obtained by tank, lysimeter, and plot measurements. However, it seems better to use evapo-transpiration for such data and to use consumptive use for the larger areas. When evapo-transpiration consumptions are determined for entire drainage basins, they usually are referred to as natural water losses, total evaporation, or simply evaporation.

Water consumptions that are not utilized in crop production, such as interception, evaporation from water and bare land surfaces, and evapo-transpiration on areas of native vegetation, are sometimes referred to as nonbeneficial consumptive uses.

In 1944, Thornthwaite proposed a distinction between actual evapo-transpiration and potential evapo-transpiration. He defined the latter as the water loss that would take place if the soil contained sufficient moisture for plant growth at all times. In order to evaluate potential evapo-transpiration for a particular irrigated area it would be necessary to specify the types of crops. Different crops require different quantities of water for normal growth. Some crops use more water than they need when more is available. Alfalfa, growing on fertile soil in warm climates, can use as much as 10 feet annually, whereas many crops use less, even when amply supplied with moisture.

Available data on consumptive use in irrigated regions show actual water consumptions. When determined on areas where adequate quantities of water are supplied, they are substantially the same as potential evapo-transpiration for the crops grown. Evapo-transpiration data are commonly given in acre-inches per acre, acre-feet per acre, or simply as inches or feet of depth over the areas considered.

Another term used in studies of water consumption is streamflow depletion. Streamflow depletion is the annual quantity of water that enters a valley, or flows to a land area, minus the annual quantity that leaves the valley, or flows off the land area. It usually is less than consumptive use. It may be expressed as an average rate of flow or converted to depth over the area considered.

Evapo-Transpiration Measurements. Measurements of evapo-transpiration have been made for various crop plants and native plants growing in tanks or lysimeters. Determinations for different crops and different types of native vegetation, growing separately or together, have been made on field plots, sections along streams, irrigated farms, irrigation projects, portions of river valleys, and entire drainage basins.

In general, methods of evaluating evapo-transpiration involve determinations of inflow, outflow, and changes in quantities of moisture stored underground. In tank tests, water is supplied as needed to maintain normal plant growth, or to maintain water tables at definite depths. In lysimeter tests, percolation is measured and deducted from quantities of water supplied by irrigation or precipitation. In plot tests, water supplied by irrigation or precipitation is measured and portions consumed by plants determined from analyses of soil samples. Plot tests are practicable only when water tables are too deep to be reached by downward movements of moisture following irrigation or rainfall.

For relatively large areas, determinations of evapo-transpiration are based on measurements of precipitation, streamflow, irrigation deliveries, drainage outflows, changes in elevation of water tables, and differences in amounts of water stored in the soil. The method of determining consumptive use by subtracting outflow from inflow plus precipitation, with proper corrections for changes in underground storage, is commonly known as the inflow-outflow method.

For entire drainage basins, determinations of evapo-transpiration are usually made for the water year and are assumed to equal total precipitation minus total runoff. Such determinations should be reasonably accurate when geological structures are such as to prevent deep losses of water and when moisture contents of the soils are essentially the same at the beginning and ending of the water year. Probably the most uncertain element involved in determining evapo-transpiration on any large area is the correction to be made for changes in underground storage.

In irrigated regions where summer rainfall is negligible and the water table is so high that plants can secure moisture from the capillary fringe, evapo-transpiration may be determined from measurements of irrigation water and seasonal fluctuations in the water table. In order for such determinations to be reliable, no underground inflow or outflow should take place. Harding determined consumptive use in this manner during his investigations of groundwater in the San Joaquin Valley, California.[22] Briefly, the method consisted in plotting irrigation deliveries for several years against water table fluctuations, drawing a curve through the plotted points, and considering consumptive use to be represented by the point where the curve showed no change in the elevation of the water table.[23]

White studied daily fluctuations of the water table during his investigations in the Escalante Valley, Utah.[74] He derived the following formula for computing daily consumptive use:

$$q = y(24r \pm s)$$

where q = depth of water, in inches, withdrawn by evaporation and transpiration during a 24-hour period.

y = specific yield of the soil where the daily fluctuation in water table takes place.

r = hourly rate of rise of the water table from midnight to 4 A.M., in inches.

s = net rise or fall of the water table during the 24-hour period, in inches.

Quantities r and s can be determined from records of automatic water-level gages installed in wells at different locations throughout the area under consideration. The quantity y, specific yield, must be determined by special tests. Specific yield is defined as the depth of water that enters the soil or drains out of the soil as the water table rises or falls, expressed as a percentage of the depth of soil alternately saturated or drained. It is a measure of the volume of pore space alternately filled or emptied. Daily consumptions for the period of plant growth can be totaled to obtain seasonal consumptive use.

Early estimates of consumptive use on large areas may not be comparable because of differences in methods of evaluation. Sometimes depths of consumptive use were computed for net cropped areas. Other times they were computed for gross acreages, including seeped areas and other uncropped lands. Sometimes they were assumed to equal streamflow depletion. Methods of evaluation should always be carefully examined before drawing conclusions from early estimates of consumptive use.

Water Consumption by Native Plants. Water consumption by native plants constitutes a loss of moisture that otherwise could be used in producing crops. Many measurements of water used by native plants have been made in western United States. Table 11 shows

TABLE 11

EVAPO-TRANSPIRATION DATA FOR WESTERN NATIVE PLANTS
AS DETERMINED BY TANK MEASUREMENTS

Plants	Location	Period of record	Depth to water table, in.	Evapo-transpiration, ft.	Ref. no.
Bermuda grass	San Bernardino, Calif.	Yearly, May–April	24 and 36	2.85 and 2.35	81
Mixed meadow grass	Burns, Ore.	Growing season	0	1.34	21
Sugar grass	Burns, Ore.	Growing season	0	1.60	21
Meadow grass	Parma, Colo.	June–November 1936	3.8–10.0	2.54	48
Sedge grass	Fort Collins, Colo.	May–October 1930	6–18	3.85–5.02	51
Sedge	Isleta, N. Mex.	June 1936–May 1937	+3	6.41	81
Salt grass	Isleta, N. Mex.	June 1936–May 1937	8	2.63	81
Salt grass	Milford, Utah	May–October	21–41	1.36	74
Greasewood	Milford, Utah	May–October	15–30	2.10	74
Sunflowers	Fort Collins, Colo.	July–October 1931	12 and 18	3.28 and 4.26	51
Rushes	Fort Collins, Colo.	May–September 1932	1	6.42	51
Wire rush	Santa Ana, Calif.	August 1930–July 1931	24	6.58	81
Willow	Isleta, N. Mex.	June 1936–May 1937	13	2.54	81
Willow	Sacramento-San Joaquin delta	Calendar year	..	2.88	45
Willow	Santa Ana, Calif.	May 1930–April 1931 *	24	4.39	81
Cattail	Mesilla Valley, N. Mex.†	January–December 1937	+2	10.07	81
Cattail	Fort Collins, Colo.	May–September 1932	1	6.42	51
Cattail	Clarksburg, Calif.	January–December 1930	0	16.52	81
Cattail	King Island, Calif.†	January–December 1932	+12	7.50	81
Tule	Los Griegos, N. Mex.	Water year, October–September	0	5.39	31
Tule	Mud Lake, Idaho	June 13–Sept. 23, 1921	0	4.28	65
Tule	Victorville, Calif.†	Calendar year	0	6.54	81
Tule	King Island, Calif.†	January–December 1932	+12	8.64	81
Tule	Santa Ana, Calif.	Water year, May–April	0	13.35	81

* For 11 months, January omitted.
† Tank in swamp.

evapo-transpiration data for some western types of native vegetation as determined by tank measurements.

Cattails and tules consume large amounts of water. Some tank measurements in exposed locations, not included in Table 11, showed tule consumptions as high as 3.6 inches per day, with average consumptions as high as 1.5 inches per day during periods as long as 6 weeks. Young and Blaney concluded that tules growing in swamps use about 40 per cent as much water as tules growing in exposed tanks.[81]

Figure 5 shows some data on evapo-transpiration for salt grass, for different depths to groundwater. Numbers used to identify the curves also identify sources of information as listed later. Plotted points represent consumptive uses for 6-month periods at Garnett, Colorado, and for 12-month periods at other locations. Differences in evapo-transpiration for the same depth to groundwater are due to differences in soil and weather conditions.

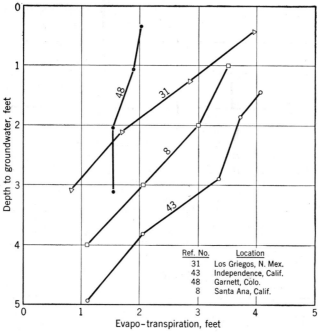

Ref. No.	Location
31	Los Griegos, N. Mex.
43	Independence, Calif.
48	Garnett, Colo.
8	Santa Ana, Calif.

FIGURE 5. Tank data on evapo-transpiration for salt grass, for different depths to groundwater.

Evapo-transpiration on areas of native brush, where the water table is too low to permit absorption of moisture from groundwater, depends largely on the depth and frequency of precipitation. Measurements at field plots in southern California showed that seasonal rainfalls of less than 19 inches usually were consumed by brush covers consisting of chamisal, wild olive, scrub oak, sage brush, cactus, and yucca.[7] In regions of higher precipitation, native vegetation includes brush and trees that require more moisture, so that evapo-transpiration losses are higher. In the Coweeta Experimental Forest, North Carolina, deciduous trees and brush consume about 34 inches of water.[78]

Soil sampling on field plots in southern California showed that native grasses and weeds consumed from 12.6 to 15.5 inches of rainfall.[81] They probably would have consumed more moisture if more had been available.

Table 12 gives evapo-transpiration data for some western weeds as determined by tank measurements. Measurements for redroot and

TABLE 12

EVAPO-TRANSPIRATION DATA FOR SOME WESTERN WEEDS
AS DETERMINED BY TANK MEASUREMENTS [51,67,81]

Weed	Period of record	Depth to water table, in.	Yield per acre, tons, air dried	Evapo-transpira-tion, ft.
Cocklebur	Apr. 13–Nov. 8, 1932	18–42	4.98– 8.16	4.61– 7.24
Nettle	Apr. 6–Dec. 30, 1932	. . . .	1.88– 2.55	4.00– 5.15
Smartweed	Apr. 12–Oct. 6, 1932	18–42	18.01–23.62	8.49–10.65
Prickly lettuce	Apr. 20–Sept. 28, 1932	18–42	4.95–12.88	3.60– 8.31
Kelp	Nov. 16, 1932–Nov. 10, 1933	16–36	3.14– 5.18	4.24– 8.82
Lamb's quarters	May 11–Sept. 20, 1933	30	4.52– 7.15	3.84– 4.57
Nut grass	June 3–Nov. 8, 1933	18 and 24	2.29– 5.19	3.60– 4.16
Curly dock	Feb. 13–Nov. 10, 1933	18 and 24	13.70 and 13.75	8.36 and 7.92
Goldenrod	May 31–Nov. 10, 1933	30	5.62 and 8.88	5.75 and 8.04
Redroot (pigweed)	May 3–Sept. 27, 1932	18	. . . .	2.64
Russian thistle	May 3–Sept. 27, 1932	12 and 18	. . . .	1.91 and 2.17

Russian thistles were made at Fort Collins, Colorado, and were reported by Parshall.[51] Other measurements were made at King Island, California, and were reported by Stout.[67] In most tests, the water table was maintained at a definite depth below the soil surface. In general, the higher water consumptions are for the higher water tables. Consumptions measured at King Island vary from 3.60 feet for prickly lettuce and nut grass to 10.65 feet for smartweed. The relatively high values shown in Table 12 emphasize the need for rigid weed control in regions where water supplies are limited.

Water Consumption along Streams. Appreciable amounts of water are consumed by evaporation and transpiration along stream channels, where water tables are relatively close to the ground surfaces. Measurements on about 13 acres of moist land along Temescal Creek, near Corona, southern California, in 1929, showed a total evapo-transpiration loss of 12.9 inches during a 30-day period from April 28 to May 27.[7] This was about three times the evaporation at a Class A pan. Vegetation along the creek included willows, tules, and other moist-land plants.

Similar investigations were made in two sections of Coldwater Canyon, near San Bernardino, California, in 1931 and 1932.[8] The lower section included 2.36 acres, and the upper section, 5.89 acres. Elevations vary from about 2,300 to 2,500 feet in the lower section, and from 2,500 to 3,100 feet in the upper section. Vegetation included alder, sycamore, bay, willow, and maple, with a few oak, mountain mahogany, cedar, spruce, and cottonwood; also vines, berries, ferns, and other types of underbrush.

During 1932, evapo-transpiration losses in Coldwater Canyon, for the 6 months from May to October, amounted to 5.33 feet in the lower section, and 4.17 feet in the upper section. The maximum daily loss was 0.61 inch in the lower section on September 8, 1932. Losses of streamflow caused by evapo-transpiration along stream channels are mentioned briefly in Chapter 7.

The Geological Survey investigated water uses by bottom-land vegetation in Safford Valley, Arizona, during 1943 and 1944. The report by Gatewood and others, made in 1950, showed that 12-month consumptions in acre-feet per acre, for growth densities of 100 per cent, were 7.2 for salt cedar, 4.7 for baccharis, 6.0 for cottonwood, and 3.3 for mesquite.[20]

Water Consumption by Crops. Amounts of water consumed by crops vary in different sections of the country, in accordance with differences in soil evaporation and transpiration. They also vary for different crops produced on similar soils in the same locality. Crops with long growing seasons consume more moisture than crops with short growing seasons. Crops supplied with excessive depths of irrigation water consume more moisture than similar crops supplied with limited depths.

Table 13 shows monthly, seasonal, and annual depths of evapo-transpiration for some crops in the Sacramento-San Joaquin delta, as determined by tank measurements.[45] The tanks were filled with peat or sedimentary soils, characteristic of the delta lands, and water tables were maintained at depths comparable with surrounding field conditions. The tests were described in a state bulletin.[64]

Maximum depths of monthly evapo-transpiration in the delta region amount to 0.85 foot for corn and only slightly less for grain and hay. Depths of seasonal evapo-transpiration vary from 1.20

TABLE 13

EVAPO-TRANSPIRATION DATA FOR CROPS IN THE
SACRAMENTO-SAN JOAQUIN DELTA [45,64]

(Depths in feet)

Month	Alfalfa	Asparagus	Beans	Beets	Celery	Corn	Fruit	Grain and hay	Onions	Potatoes
January	(0.06)	0.05	(0.06)	(0.06)	(0.04)	(0.04)	(0.04)	(0.04)	(0.04)	(0.06)
February	(0.08)	0.05	(0.08)	(0.08)	(0.04)	(0.04)	(0.04)	(0.04)	(0.04)	(0.08)
March	0.10	0.05	(0.08)	(0.08)	(0.04)	(0.04)	(0.04)	0.07	0.08	(0.08)
April	0.30	0.05	(0.16)	0.13	(0.08)	(0.08)	0.18	0.60	0.13	(0.16)
May	0.40	0.08	(0.20)	0.32	(0.10)	(0.10)	0.32	0.83	0.27	0.15
June	0.50	0.14	0.14	0.51	0.10	0.24	0.50	0.20	0.49	0.38
July	0.65	0.40	0.24	0.61 *	0.10	0.85	0.57	(0.14)	0.43	0.52
August	0.55	0.68	0.58	0.53 *	0.20	0.84 *	0.40	(0.23)	0.20	0.30
September	0.50	0.55	0.37	0.20 *	0.25	0.40 *	0.23	(0.21)	(0.16)	0.15
October	0.20	0.42	(0.09)	(0.13)	0.30	0.10	0.07	(0.14)	(0.13)	(0.09)
November	(0.10)	0.12	(0.07)	(0.10)	0.20	(0.10)	(0.07)	(0.07)	(0.10)	(0.07)
December	(0.07)	0.10	(0.05)	(0.07)	0.05	(0.07)	(0.05)	(0.05)	(0.07)	(0.05)
Growing season	3.20	2.69	1.33	2.30	1.20	2.43	2.27	1.70	1.60	1.50
Year	3.51	2.69	2.12	2.82	1.50	2.90	2.51	2.62	2.14	2.09

* Including additional use of water by weeds.
Figures in parentheses show estimated losses by soil evaporation and weed transpiration.

feet for celery to 3.20 feet for alfalfa. Annual depths of evapo-transpiration, including soil evaporation and weed transpiration during the winter, vary from 1.50 feet for celery to 3.51 feet for alfalfa. Annual depths of evapo-transpiration on pasture and truck lands, not included in the table, were estimated at 2.16 and 2.61 feet, respectively.

Subsequent measurements on plots near Firebaugh, California, together with other investigations, indicate that seasonal depths of evapo-transpiration for cotton crops in the San Joaquin Valley average about 2.50 to 2.83 feet.[80]

Plot tests and tank measurements in the Rio Grande Valley showed seasonal evapo-transpiration for crops as follows: [48]

Cotton, State College, New Mexico, 2.21 to 2.63 feet, May to October.

Alfalfa, Albuquerque, New Mexico, 2.53 feet, July to October.
Potatoes, San Luis Valley. Colorado, 1.41 feet, June to September.
Wheat, San Luis Valley, Colorado, 1.07 feet, June to August.

Figure 6 shows seasonal evapo-transpiration for some crops grown on fertile soils in Idaho, Utah, and Alberta, as determined from plot measurements by Lewis, Widstoe and Harris, and Snelson. Percola-

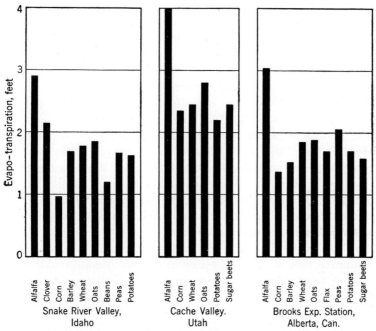

FIGURE 6.   Seasonal evapo-transpiration for farm crops in Idaho, Utah, and Canada.
(See references 23 and 63.)

tion was not measured. Soil conditions, as reported, indicate that percolation was negligible on the plots in Utah and Alberta. Small amounts of percolation may have occurred on the plots in Idaho. Depths shown on the diagrams probably represent farm consumptive uses. Israelsen and Winsor's tests in the Sevier Valley, Utah, indicated a farm consumptive use of 3.1 feet for sugar beets, 2.6 feet for potatoes, and 3.4 feet for alfalfa.[23]

Lysimeter tests in Oregon, reported by Hastings and Dean, showed that evapo-transpiration for alfalfa may be unusually high when large quantities of water are available.[25]   Average seasonal evapo-transpiration at five lysimeters supplied with 5.04 feet of water varied

from 3.02 to 4.69 feet. Evapo-transpiration at two lysimeters supplied
with 9.73 feet of water amounted to 8.90 and 8.96 feet. The two
lysimeters supplied with excessive depths produced yields approximately twice as great as those supplied with nominal depths.

Project Consumptive Use. Project consumptive use varies with
location, elevation, soil conditions, weather conditions, length of
growing season, crops produced, and quantities of water available for
irrigation. At high elevations, where growing seasons are short and
only special crops can be grown, seasonal consumptions may be only
about 1 acre-foot per acre. At low elevations in warm climates, where
crops can be grown throughout the year, annual consumptive uses
may be 4 to 5 acre-feet per acre. Where rice crops are grown, seasonal
consumptive uses may be higher than 5 acre-feet per acre.

Seasonal consumptive uses compiled by the Duty of Water Committee, American Society of Civil Engineers, showed depths of 1.9 feet
on the Nampa Meridian Drainage Districts, southwestern Idaho, and
2.6 feet on the Twin Falls Project, south central Idaho.[23] Annual
consumptive uses compiled by the Bureau of Reclamation showed
2.2 feet on the West Tule Lake area of the Klamath Project, northern
California; 2.0 feet on the Garland Division of the Shoshone Project,
northern Wyoming; and 2.0 feet on the Greenfields Division of the
Sun River Project, northern Montana.[44]

Harding, on the basis of water table fluctuations, estimated annual
consumptive uses of 1.7 to 2.0 feet in the San Joaquin Valley, California.[22] Burkholder reported annual consumptive uses of from 4.2
to 5.5 feet on the Barahona Project, Dominican Republic, where sugar
cane was the sole crop.[44]

The consumptive use of water is high on rice projects, where evaporation losses are increased by continuous flooding. Tibbetts reported
a seasonal use of 5.67 feet in the Colusa Basin, California, where rice
is grown during April to September.[70] The highest monthly use
occurred in July and amounted to about 1.3 feet. Water surface
evaporation during the growing season amounted to 4.14 feet, leaving
1.53 to be accounted for by rice transpiration.

Valley Consumptive Use. Valley consumptive use varies with the
same conditions as project consumptive use. When determined on
a seasonal basis, it varies from about 1.0 foot in high mountain
meadows, where the growing season is only 2 or 3 months, to 4.0 feet
or more in low warm valleys, where crops and native plants can grow
throughout the year. When determined on an annual basis, it varies
from about 1.5 to more than 4.0 feet.

Valley consumptive use often is lower than project consumptive use in the same region, because valley areas include greater proportions of uncropped land where moisture supplies are lower than those delivered to irrigated fields. Lowry and Johnson attempted to allow for this by using an equivalent valley area on which rates of moisture consumption by native vegetation would be the same as on irrigated land.[44]

Table 14 shows selected data on annual consumptive use in some irrigated valleys, compiled from various sources as indicated. Al-

TABLE 14

ANNUAL CONSUMPTIVE USE OF WATER
IN SOME IRRIGATED VALLEYS

State	Valley	Area, 1,000 acres	Average elevation, ft.	Mean annual temperature, °F.	Length of growing season, days	Average consumptive use, ft.	Ref. no.
California	Sacramento-San Joaquin delta	489	20	60	Variable	2.6	45
California	San Jacinto	90	. . . . .	62	214	2.25	59
California	San Gabriel	103	. . . . .	62	210	1.9	59
Colorado	North Park	120	8,200	38	60	1.8	23
Colorado	San Luis, southwest area	400	7,700	42	90	1.71	48
Colorado	Cache la Poudre	220	5,000	48	135	2.4	23
Colorado	South Platte	229	4,100	48	145	2.3	23
Colorado	Uncompahgre	138	5,500	49	145	2.24	44
Idaho	Boise, part of Boise Project	49	2,500	50	155	2.2	23
New Mexico	Rio Grande, Isleta-Belen	21	4,900	56	240	2.73	48
New Mexico-Texas	Rio Grande, Mesilla Valley	109	3,900	61	270	2.87	15
New Mexico	Pecos near Carlsbad	38	3,100	63	240	2.94	44
Texas	Lower Rio Grande	325 *	. . . . .	. .	365	3.8	44
Utah	Sevier	65	5,200	48	110	2.0	23
Wyoming	New Fork, Green River	25	7,400	35	90	1.53	44
Wyoming	Little Laramie	28	7,300	40	95	2.1	23
Wyoming-Nebraska	North Platte	462	4,100	48	180	2.0	44

* Cropped area.

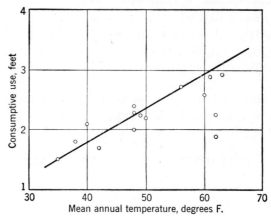

FIGURE 7. Annual consumptive uses and mean annual temperatures in some irri
gated valleys.

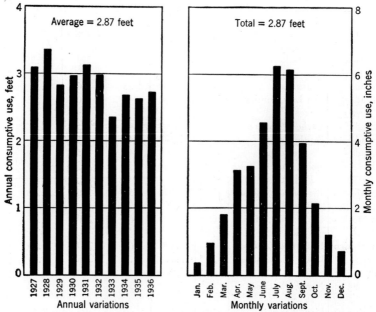

FIGURE 8. Annual and monthly variations in consumptive use, Mesilla Valley,
New Mexico and Texas. (Plotted from data in reference 15.)

though some data are indefinite, most acreages, except for the Lower Rio Grande Valley, probably are either gross areas or equivalent areas, rather than irrigated areas. The consumptive use in the Lower Rio Grande Valley probably would be lower if determined for the gross area. Consumptive uses in some of the other valleys might be higher if determined for irrigated areas. In the Mesilla Valley, the annual consumptive use on the basis of the irrigated acreage would be 4.24 feet instead of 2.87 feet.

Although the data in Table 14 are somewhat erratic, depths of annual consumptive use increase with increasing mean annual temperatures, as shown in Figure 7. According to the straight line, which was purposely drawn somewhat high, the depths increase from about 1.8 feet for a mean temperature of 40 degrees to about 3.2 feet for a mean temperature of 65 degrees. Some points below the line may represent valleys where limited quantities of water were available for irrigation.

In the Mesilla Valley, Rio Grande Project, annual depths of consumptive use for the 10 years reported by Debler varied from 2.35 to 3.36 feet.[15] Mean monthly depths of consumptive use varied from 0.03 foot in January to 0.52 foot in July. Figure 8 shows variations in annual consumptive use from year to year, also variations in mean monthly consumptive use throughout the year.

Estimates of Consumptive Use. Estimates of consumptive use may be needed in considering water supplies for new irrigation projects. Estimates also may be needed in studying water uses on existing projects where depths of moisture consumption cannot be determined by inflow-outflow methods or from water table fluctuations as previously discussed.

For existing projects, estimates of consumptive use often are made by the integration method. Briefly, the integration method consists in adding total quantities of water consumed on different areas in the project and dividing by the total area. To apply this method, data must be available regarding total areas, acreages used in producing different crops, areas of native vegetation, and areas of water and bare land surfaces. Rates of evaporation and evapo-transpiration on the different areas also must be known. When rates of moisture consumption for different surfaces have been determined by tank or plot measurements, estimates by the integration method are fairly reliable.

Table 15 shows two integration estimates of consumptive use in the Mesilla Valley during 1936. They were made by the Bureau of Agricultural Engineering during studies of the Upper Rio Grande Valley.[48]

TABLE 15

INTEGRATION ESTIMATES OF CONSUMPTIVE USE IN MESILLA VALLEY
DURING 1936 [48]

Land classification	Area, acres	Consumptive use, estimate 1		Consumptive use, estimate 2	
		Unit use, ft.	Total use, acre-ft.	Unit use, ft.	Total use, acre-ft.
Irrigated crops:					
Alfalfa and clover	17,077	4.1	70,016	4.0	68,308
Cotton	54,513	2.5	136,282	2.5	136,282
Native hay and pasture	216	2.5	540	2.3	497
Miscellaneous crops	11,117	2.2	24,457	2.0	22,234
Total irrigated area	82,923	2.79 *	231,295	2.74 *	227,321
Native vegetation:					
Grass	2,733	2.5	6,833	2.3	6,286
Brush	6,933	2.8	19,412	2.5	17,332
Trees, bosque	3,532	4.8	16,954	5.0	17,660
Total native vegetation	13,198	3.27 *	43,199	3.13 *	41,278
Miscellaneous:					
Temporarily uncropped	5,569	1.0	5,569	1.5	8,354
Towns	1,523	2.0	3,046	2.0	3,046
Water surfaces	4,081	4.5	18,364	4.5	18,364
Bare land, roads, etc.	3,124	0.7	2,187	0.7	2,187
Total miscellaneous	14,297	2.04 *	29,166	2.23 *	31,951
Total valley land	110,418	2.75 *	303,660	2.72 *	300,550

* Total consumption divided by total area.

They illustrate the elements of the integration method. Although
slightly different depths of evapo-transpiration were used for some
areas, average depths of consumptive use shown by the two estimates
are practically the same, namely, 2.75 and 2.72 feet. The results agree
with the depth determined by the inflow-outflow method (see Figure 8).

The integration method may be used in estimating consumptive
use on a proposed project when only one or two particular crops are
to be grown, so that areas are fairly definite. When diversified crops
are to be grown, and areas for the different crops are uncertain, estimates by the integration method are likewise uncertain.

Estimates of consumptive use on new irrigation projects usually
can be made from studies of data already determined on similar

projects, where soils, crops, water supplies, growing seasons, and weather conditions are comparable. The data in Table 14 and Figure 7 may be useful in such studies. Depths of consumptive use are not always the same for equal mean annual temperatures, because of temperature differences during the growing season. Depths consumed for the same mean annual temperature also may differ because of differences in available water supplies. On irrigation projects amply supplied with water, producing similar crops, depths of consumptive use generally vary approximately as mean annual temperatures.

Computations of Consumptive Use. Methods of computing consumptive use from weather records have been proposed. Hedke found that consumptive use varied with the amount of heat available for plant growth. He evaluated available heat for each crop by computing degree days above the germinating or minimum growing temperature and summating values for the growing season.[23]

Lowry and Johnson used a procedure somewhat similar to Hedke's. They found that annual consumptive use varied approximately as the total number of effective heat units during the growing season.[44] Effective heat units were really degree days. They were determined by summating values of maximum daily temperature minus 32 degrees during the growing season. Although their data showed a relation between annual consumptive use and total effective heat units, the relation was not much if any more definite or consistent than the relation between annual consumptive use and mean annual temperature.

In 1942, Blaney and Morin proposed that evaporation and evapotranspiration be computed from weather records, using an empirical formula containing factors for temperature, relative humidity, and daytime hours.[6] Later, Blaney and Criddle proposed a method for transferring consumptive use data from one drainage basin to another, based on mean monthly temperatures, monthly percentages of annual daytime hours, and an empirical coefficient evaluated from actual determinations of consumptive use.[5] The method may be represented by the equation:

$$U = KF$$

where U = consumptive use, in inches, for any period.

K = an empirical coefficient determined from observed data.

F = the summation of mean monthly temperatures times monthly percentages of annual daytime hours for the period considered.

322 Land Evaporation and Transpiration

Computations of K from observed data, for full water supplies and for normal growing seasons, gave values as follows: alfalfa, 0.85; grass, hay, and pasture, 0.75; corn, small grains, and beans, 0.75; deciduous orchards, 0.65; and native vegetation, 0.80 to 1.35, depending on density and types of growth. Corresponding coefficients for annual consumptive use by native vegetation varied from 0.65 to 1.10.

Drainage Basin Consumptions. Annual consumptions of water in drainage basins vary with surface topography, soil characteristics, types of vegetation, and weather conditions, particularly temperature and precipitation. Yearly variations in evapo-transpiration in a particular drainage basin are caused principally by differences in temperature, depths of precipitation, and seasonal distribution of rainfall.

In arid regions, annual depths of water consumed in drainage basins are relatively low, because available quantities of moisture are not sufficient to maintain high rates of evaporation and transpiration. In headwater areas of some large basins and on irrigated lands amply supplied with water, depths consumed may be relatively high. On lands adjoining irrigated areas, depths of rainfall are too low to maintain appreciable soil evaporation or transpiration. Therefore, average depths of evapo-transpiration for the entire basins are greatly reduced. In basins where no runoff takes place, annual water losses equal annual precipitations.

Data on annual consumptions of moisture in some drainage basins of central and eastern United States are given in Table 3, Chapter 7. Data for many basins in the eastern half of the country were reported by Williams and others in 1940.[75] Their studies showed an increase in consumption with mean annual temperature, varying from about 1.6 feet for 40 degrees to about 3.1 feet for 65 degrees. These values are only slightly lower than those shown by the line in Figure 7.

REFERENCES

1. Adams, Frank, Paul A. Ewing, and Martin R. Huberty, *Hydrologic Aspects of Burning Brush and Woodland-Grass Ranges in California*, Calif. Dept. Natural Resources, Div. of Forestry, 1947.
2. Anderson, Henry W., "The Effect of Freezing on Soil Moisture and on Evaporation from a Bare Soil," *Trans. Am. Geop. Union,* December 1946, pp. 863–870.
3. Bates, C. G., "Physiological Requirements of Rocky Mountain Trees," *Jour. Agr. Res.,* Apr. 14, 1923, pp. 97–164.
4. Bates, C. G., and A. J. Henry, "Forest and Stream-Flow Experiment at Wagon Wheel Gap, Colo.," *U.S. Weather Bur. Monthly Weather Rev. Suppl.* 30, 1928.

5. Blaney, Harry F., and Wayne D. Criddle, *Consumptive Use of Water in the Irrigated Areas of the Upper Colorado River Basin (Provisional)*, U.S. Dept. Agr. Soil Cons. Ser., 1949.

6. Blaney, Harry F., and Karl V. Morin, "Evaporation and Consumptive Use of Water Empirical Formulas," *Trans. Am. Geop. Union,* 1942, Part I, pp. 76–83.

7. Blaney, Harry F., C. A. Taylor, and A. A. Young, "Rainfall Penetration and Consumptive Use of Water in Santa Ana River Valley and Coastal Plain," *Calif. Dept. Pub. Works Bull.* 33, 1930.

8. Blaney, Harry F., Harold C. Troxell, and others, "Water Losses under Natural Conditions from Wet Areas in Southern California," *Calif. Dept. Pub. Works Bull.* 44, 1933.

9. Briggs, Lyman J., and H. L. Shantz, "The Water Requirement of Plants. I.—Investigations in the Great Plains in 1910 and 1911," *U.S. Dept. Agr. Bull.* 284, 1913.

10. ——— "The Water Requirement of Plants. II.—A Review of the Literature," *U.S. Dept. Agr. Bull.* 285, 1913.

11. ——— "Relative Water Requirement of Plants," *Jour. Agr. Res.,* Oct. 15, 1914. pp. 1–64.

12. ——— "Daily Transpiration during the Normal Growth Period and Its Correlation with the Weather," *Jour. Agr. Res.,* Oct. 23, 1916, pp. 155–212.

13. Browning, G. M., and others, "Investigations in Erosion Control and the Reclamation of Eroded Land at the Missouri Valley Loess Conservation Experiment Station, Clarinda, Iowa, 1931–42," *U.S. Dept. Agr. Tech. Bull.* 959, 1948.

14. Clark, O. R., "Interception of Rainfall by Prairie Grasses, Weeds, and Certain Crop Plants," *Ecol. Monog.,* April 1940, pp. 243–277.

15. Debler, E. B., "Valley Consumptive Use," *Trans. Am. Geop. Union,* 1937, Part II, pp. 532–536.

16. Dillman, A. C., "The Water Requirement of Certain Crop Plants and Weeds in the Northern Great Plains," *Jour. Agr. Res.,* Feb. 15, 1931, pp. 187–238.

17. Feustel, I. C., and H. G. Byers, "The Comparative Moisture-Absorbing and Moisture-Retaining Capacities of Peat and Soil Mixtures," *U.S. Dept. Agr. Tech. Bull.* 532, 1936.

18. Forest Service, "A National Plan for American Forestry," *Sen. Doc.* 12, 73rd Cong., 1st Sess., Vol. 1, 1933.

19. Fortier, Samuel, and S. H. Beckett, "Evaporation from Irrigated Soils," *U.S. Dept. Agr. Exp. Stas. Bull.* 248, 1912.

20. Gatewood, J. S., and others, "Use of Water by Bottom-Land Vegetation in Lower Safford Valley, Arizona," *U.S. Geol. Sur. Water-Supply Paper* 1103, 1950.

21. Hammatt, W. C., "Determination of the Duty of Water by Analytical Experiment," *Trans. Am. Soc. C. E.,* Vol. 83, 1919–1920, pp. 200–276.

22. Harding, S. T., "Ground Water Resources of the Southern San Joaquin Valley," *Calif. Dept. Pub. Works Bull.* 11, 1927.

23. Harding, S. T., and others, "Consumptive Use of Water in Irrigation, Progress Report of the Duty of Water Committee of the Irrigation Division," *Trans. Am. Soc. C. E.,* Vol. 94, 1930, pp. 1349–1399.

24. Harris, F. S., and J. S. Robinson, "Factors Affecting the Evaporation of Moisture from the Soil," *Jour. Agr. Res.,* Dec. 4, 1916, pp. 439–461.

25. Hastings, S. H., and H. K. Dean, "Percolation and Water Requirement Studies with Alfalfa by Means of Lysimeters in Oregon," *Ore. Agr. Exp. Sta. Bull.* 404, 1942.

26. Holch, A. E., "Development of Roots and Shoots of Certain Deciduous Tree Seedlings in Different Forest Sites," *Ecol.*, April 1931, pp. 259–298.

27. Hoover, M. D., "Effect of Removal of Forest Vegetation upon Water-Yields," *Trans. Am. Geop. Union*, 1944, Part VI, pp. 969–977.

28. Horton, Robert E., "Rainfall Interception," *U.S. Weather Bur. Monthly Weather Rev.*, September 1919, pp. 603–623.

29. ——— "Transpiration by Forest Trees," *U.S. Weather Bur. Monthly Weather Rev.*, November 1923, pp. 571–581.

30. Houk, Ivan E., "Rainfall and Runoff in the Miami Valley," *Miami Conservancy Dist. Tech. Rep.* Part VIII, Dayton, Ohio, 1921.

31. ——— "Evaporation from Soils," *Trans. Am. Soc. C. E.*, Vol. 94, 1930, pp. 982–995.

32. Hoyt, W. G., and others, "Studies of Relations of Rainfall and Run-Off in the United States," *U.S. Geol. Sur. Water-Supply Paper* 772, 1936.

33. Johnson, W. M., "The Interception of Rain and Snow by a Forest of Young Ponderosa-Pine," *Trans. Am. Geop. Union*, 1942, Part II, pp. 566–570.

34. Jones, J. H., and others, "San Joaquin River Basin," *Calif. Dept. Pub. Works Bull.* 29, 1931.

35. Kiesselbach, T. A., "Transpiration as a Factor in Crop Production," *Nebr. Agr. Exp. Sta. Res. Bull.* 6, 1916.

36. Kittredge, Joseph, Jr., "Natural Vegetation as a Factor in the Losses and Yields of Water," *Jour. Forestry*, November 1937, pp. 1011–1015.

37. ——— "The Magnitude and Regional Distribution of Water Losses Influenced by Vegetation," *Jour. Forestry*, August 1938, pp. 775–778.

38. Kittredge, J., H. J. Loughead, and A. Mazurak, "Interception and Stemflow in a Pine Plantation," *Jour. Forestry*, June 1941, pp. 505–522.

39. Kittredge, J., and others, "Report of Committee on Transpiration and Evaporation, 1940–41," *Trans. Am. Geop. Union*, 1941, Part III, pp. 906–915.

40. Langbein, W. B., "Monthly Evapo-Transpiration Losses from Natural Drainage Basins," *Trans. Am. Geop. Union*, 1942, Part II, pp. 604–614.

41. Lee, Charles H., "An Intensive Study of the Water Resources of a Part of Owens Valley, California," *U.S. Geol. Sur. Water-Supply Paper* 294, 1912.

42. ——— "Total Evaporation for Sierra Nevada Watersheds by the Method of Precipitation and Runoff Differences," *Trans. Am. Geop. Union*, 1941, Part I, pp. 50–71.

43. ——— "Transpiration and Total Evaporation," Chapter VIII in Meinzer's *Hydrology*, 1942, pp. 259–330 (see reference 23 in Chapter 1).

44. Lowry, Robert L., Jr., and Arthur F. Johnson, "Consumptive Use of Water for Agriculture," *Trans. Am. Soc. C. E.*, No. 107, 1942, pp. 1243–1302.

45. Matthew, Raymond, "Variation and Control of Salinity in Sacramento-San Joaquin Delta and Upper San Francisco Bay," *Calif. Dept. Pub. Works Bull.* 27, 1931.

46. McGinnies, W. G., and Joseph F. Arnold, "Relative Water Requirement of Arizona Range Plants," *Ariz. Agr. Exp. Sta. Tech. Bull.* 80, 1939.

47. Musgrave, G. W., and R. A. Norton, "Soil and Water Conservation Investigations at the Soil Conservation Experiment Station, Missouri Valley Loess

Region, Clarinda, Iowa, Progress Report 1931–35," *U.S. Dept. Agr. Tech. Bull.* 558, 1937.

48. National Resources Committee, *Regional Planning, Part VI, The Rio Grande Joint Investigation in the Upper Rio Grande Basin in Colorado, New Mexico, and Texas, 1936–1937,* Vol. I, Washington, 1938.

49. National Resources Planning Board, *The Pecos River Joint Investigation, Reports of the Participating Agencies,* Washington, 1942.

50. Parshall, Ralph L., "Experiments to Determine Rate of Evaporation from Saturated Soils and River-Bed Sands," *Trans. Am. Soc. C. E.,* Vol. 94, 1930, pp. 961–999.

51. ――― "Laboratory Measurement of Evapo-Transpiration Losses," *Jour. Forestry,* November 1937, pp. 1033–1040.

52. Pearson, G. A., "Studies in Transpiration of Coniferous Tree Seedlings," *Ecol.,* October 1924, pp. 340–347.

53. ――― "Forest Types in the Southwest as Determined by Climate and Soil," *U.S. Dept. Agr. Tech. Bull.* 247, 1931.

54. Post, William S., "Santa Ana Investigation, Flood Control and Conservation," *Calif. Dept. Pub. Works Bull.* 19, 1928.

55. Raber, Oran, "Water Utilization by Trees, with Special Reference to the Economic Forest Species of the North Temperate Zone," *U.S. Dept. Agr. Misc. Pub.* 257, 1937.

56. Rafter, George W., "The Relation of Rainfall to Run-Off," *U.S. Geol. Sur. Water-Supply Paper* 80, 1903.

57. Ridgaway, C. B., "Experiments in Evaporation," *Wyo. Agr. Exp. Sta. Bull.* 52, 1902.

58. Rowe, P. B., "Some Factors of the Hydrology of the Sierra Nevada Foothills," *Trans. Am. Geop. Union,* 1941, Part I, pp. 90–101.

59. Rule, Rhodes E., "Use of Water," *Trans. Am. Soc. C. E.,* No. 107, 1942, pp. 1268–1275.

60. Scofield, Carl S., "The Water Requirement of Alfalfa," *U.S. Dept. Agr. Cir.* 735, 1945.

61. Shantz, H. L., and Lydia N. Piemeisel, "The Water Requirement of Plants at Akron, Colo.," *Jour. Agr. Res.,* June 15, 1927, pp. 1093–1190.

62. Sleight, R. B., "Evaporation from the Surfaces of Water and River-Bed Materials," *Jour. Agr. Res.,* July 30, 1917, pp. 209–261.

63. Snelson, W. H., "Irrigation Practice and Water Requirements for Crops in Alberta," *Can. Int. Dept., Irr. Ser. Bull.* 7, 1930.

64. Stafford, Harlowe M., "Report of Sacramento-San Joaquin Water Supervisor for the Period 1924–1928," *Calif. Dept. Pub. Works Bull.* 23, 1930.

65. Stearns, Harold T., and others, "Geology and Water Resources of the Mud Lake Region, Idaho, Including the Island Park Area," *U.S. Geol. Sur. Water-Supply Paper* 818, 1939.

66. Stoltenberg, N. L., and T. V. Wilson, "Interception Storage of Rainfall by Corn Plants," *Trans. Am. Geop. Union,* June 1950, pp. 443–448.

67. Stout, O. V. P., "Discussion of Transpiration and Evaporation Losses from Areas of Native Vegetation," *Trans. Am. Geop. Union,* 1934, Part II, pp. 559–563.

68. Thornthwaite, C. W., "The Moisture-Factor in Climate," *Trans. Am. Geop. Union,* February 1946, pp. 41–48.

69. Thornthwaite, C. W., "An Approach Toward a Rational Classification of Climate," *The Geog. Rev.*, Vol. 38, No. 1, 1948, pp. 55–94.

70. Tibbetts, Fred H., "Return Water from Irrigation," *Trans. Am. Soc. C. E.*, Vol. 94, 1930, pp. 341–344.

71. Troxell, Harold C., and Harlowe M. Stafford, "Natural Water Losses in Mountain Drainage Areas of Southern California," *Trans. Am. Geop. Union*, October 1949, pp. 752–758.

72. Veihmeyer, F. J., "Some Factors Affecting the Irrigation Requirements of Deciduous Orchards," *Hilgardia*, January 1927, pp. 125–291.

73. ——— "Evaporation from Soils and Transpiration," *Trans. Am. Geop. Union*, 1938, Part II, pp. 612–619.

74. White, Walter N., "A Method of Estimating Ground-Water Supplies Based on Discharge by Plants and Evaporation from Soil, Results of Investigations in Escalante Valley, Utah," *U.S. Geol. Sur. Water-Supply Paper* 659–A, 1932.

75. Williams, G. R., and others, "Natural Water Loss in Selected Drainage Basins," *U.S. Geol. Sur. Water-Supply Paper* 846, 1940.

76. Wilm, H. G., and C. H. Niederhof," Interception of Rainfall by Mature Lodgepole-Pine," *Trans. Am. Geop. Union*, 1941, Part III, pp. 660–665.

77. Wilm, H. G., and others, "Report of the Committee on Transpiration and Evaporation, 1943–1944," *Trans. Am. Geop. Union*, 1944, Part V, pp. 683–693.

78. ——— "Report of the Committee on Evaporation and Transpiration, 1946–1947," *Trans. Am. Geop. Union*, April 1948, pp. 258–262.

79. ——— "Report of Committee on Evaporation and Transpiration, 1947–1948," *Trans. Am. Geop. Union*, February 1949, pp. 131–133.

80. Young, Arthur A., "Irrigation Requirements of California Crops," *Calif. Dept. Pub. Works Bull.* 51, 1945.

81. Young, Arthur A., and Harry F. Blaney, "Use of Water by Native Vegetation," *Calif. Dept. Pub. Works Bull.* 50, 1942.

82. Zon, Raphael, "Forests and Water in the Light of Scientific Investigation," *Final Rep. Natl. Waterways Comm.*, Forest Service reprint, 1927.

Chapter 11

IRRIGATION AND WATER REQUIREMENTS

Irrigation requirements are the quantities of irrigation water that must be delivered to arid and semiarid lands in order to insure profitable crop production. Water requirements are the quantities of water nee led for crop growth.

Water requirements may be supplied entirely by precipitation, as in humid regions; by precipitation and irrigation, as in many semiarid regions; or entirely by irrigation, as in arid regions. When moisture for crop growth is supplied entirely by irrigation, irrigation requirements are the same as water requirements. In considering agricultural uses of water, both irrigation requirements and water requirements are sometimes referred to as crop requirements.

Precipitations that can be utilized in crop growth are principally those that occur during the spring and summer months. In some localities, heavy precipitations occurring late in the winter may provide enough soil-moisture storage to permit some delay in beginning spring irrigations. However, in most regions where spring and summer rainfalls are negligible, irrigation must supply practically all the water needed to produce crops. When spring and summer rainfalls supply some water for crop growth, irrigation requirements equal water requirements minus soil moisture that becomes available for evapo-transpiration as a result of precipitation. When spring and summer rainfalls are great enough to supply crop requirements throughout the growing season, no irrigation is needed.

Seasonal consumptive uses by crops, as discussed in the preceding chapter, are depths of water consumed by evapo-transpiration during crop growth, including water used by accompanying weed growths. Inasmuch as some surface runoff and percolation may occur during rainfall, or may be unavoidable during irrigation, such losses of water must be included in water requirements. Therefore, total quantities of water needed to produce crops equal seasonal consumptive uses plus such surface runoff and percolation as may be unavoidable.

Total quantities of irrigation water needed to produce crops equal seasonal consumptive uses, plus surface runoff and percolation, minus soil moisture that becomes available for evapo-transpiration as a result of precipitation preceding and during the growing season.

Total amounts of irrigation water that must be obtained at the sources of supply equal irrigation requirements plus such losses and wastes of water as may be unavoidable in bringing water supplies to the irrigated fields. Losses and waste of water in transit from sources of supply to the irrigated fields are commonly called conveyance losses and waste.

The following pages discuss irrigation requirements of relatively large areas, past uses of water on existing irrigation projects, some records of past diversions at sources of supply, and a few of the more important results obtained during investigations of crop requirements in different parts of western United States and Canada. Some data assembled by government agencies are given in tabular form and shown on diagrams. Losses and waste of irrigation water, in both transit and delivery, are taken up in the next chapter.

Terminology. During early irrigation in the West, the term duty of water was commonly used to express the relation between irrigation water and area irrigated. Duty was often given as the area irrigated per unit of flow for a particular time, or as the rate of flow per acre for a particular time. Other times it was given as the amount of water applied in acre-inches or acre-feet per acre. It was variously designated gross duty, head-gate duty, lateral duty, farm duty, or net duty, depending on the place of measurement. Gross duty was the same as head-gate duty, and net duty the same as farm duty. In discussing water used by particular crops, it was sometimes referred to as crop duty.

Since about 1920, the term irrigation requirement has come into general use in lieu of duty of water. The original term may still be used in legal procedures, because of its early use in laws relating to water rights. However, irrigation requirement is the term now commonly used by engineers.

Both irrigation requirements and water requirements are given in acre-inches or acre-feet per acre, or simply as inches or feet of depth on the irrigated area. Sometimes amounts of irrigation water that need to be obtained at sources of supply are called gross irrigation requirements, and amounts that need to be delivered to the fields, net irrigation requirements. In such cases, differences between the two amounts represent losses and waste in transit. Water requirements are usually defined as the amounts of water, regardless of source, needed for normal crop growth.

In the following discussions, the term water requirement is used in the sense just stated, but the qualifications gross and net are omitted in referring to needs for irrigation water. The term irrigation requirement is used to mean the quantity of irrigation water that should be delivered to the fields. Total quantities that should be diverted are referred to as diversion requirements. In discussing past practices on existing projects, quantities delivered to fields are called water uses, and quantities diverted, diversions.

The designation irrigation efficiency, often used in discussing irrigation operations on farm or field units, is the percentage of the irrigation delivery that enters the root zone, does not percolate beyond reach of the plant roots, and thus becomes available for use in crop growth. It may be referred to as farm irrigation efficiency or field irrigation efficiency, depending on the place of measurement.

IRRIGATION REQUIREMENTS

Irrigation requirements must be carefully considered in planning new irrigation developments, also in considering the production of new or different crops on existing projects. Irrigation requirements, like consumptive uses, vary for different types of crops. They also vary for different land, soil, and weather conditions and for different cultural practices. In estimating irrigation requirements for new projects, past experiences in the same general locality should be carefully studied, including all conditions and procedures that affect the use of water.

Quantities of water that have been used on existing projects do not necessarily represent irrigation requirements. On some projects, ample water supplies have not been obtainable, so that seasonal deliveries have been smaller than irrigation requirements. On such projects, successful agriculture has been maintained largely through the production of special crops, the maintenance of high soil fertility, and the application of water with high irrigation efficiencies. On other projects, water supplies have been more than ample, irrigation efficiencies have been relatively low, and quantities of water delivered to the lands have been greater than irrigation requirements.

When water supplies for irrigating small areas are obtained locally, irrigation requirements are about the same as the quantities that must be diverted or pumped at the sources of supply, since losses and waste in transit are relatively small. When supplies are brought to large projects through long conveyance and distribution systems, irrigation requirements are considerably lower than the quantities that must be obtained at the sources, because of the large losses and waste in transit.

Factors Affecting Irrigation Requirements. Factors that affect irrigation requirements on large irrigation projects include nearly all conditions involved in irrigation agriculture. Many factors are interrelated. For instance, irrigation requirements on particular soils are largely determined by types of crops. Types of crops that can be grown successfully are largely determined by weather characteristics. Crops that can be raised profitably are largely determined by labor costs, value of crop products, and general market conditions.

Certain factors that affect irrigation requirements either directly or indirectly, are beyond the control of man. Other factors are subject to some control. Weather influences can be modified temporarily, at times, by suitable protective measures; but general climatic conditions are beyond control. Some factors can be controlled, either wholly or partially, by irrigation farmers, by project supervisors, or by proper cooperation between users of water and representatives of the organizations that supply the water.

In some irrigated regions, limitations on uses of water are imposed by economic considerations. In many irrigated sections of the country, limitations on uses are imposed by community, corporate, or state regulations.

Some factors that affect irrigation requirements are discussed in preceding chapters. Others are discussed in subsequent chapters. The following paragraphs outline briefly the various items that should be considered in studying needs for irrigation water and the feasibility of securing supplies sufficient to meet the irrigation requirements on a large irrigation project:

1. Climate, particularly precipitation, temperature, relative humidity, sunlight, and wind. Altitude affects irrigation requirements primarily through its effects on weather conditions, especially night temperatures and lengths of growing seasons.

2. Obtainable water supplies, cost of water, existing regulations controlling the use of water, past uses of water on similar projects,

quality of water supplies, and damages to lands that may result from excessive applications of water.

3. Crops that can be grown, feasibility of raising diversified crops, quantities of water needed by particular crops, available test data on crop requirements, probable crop yields, and possible financial returns.

4. Soil conditions, particularly surface topography, composition, presence of organic matter, salt contents, texture, permeability, soil profiles, depths of root zones, elevation of the water table, existing natural drainage, and feasibility of future drainage improvements.

5. Farm procedures, particularly leveling and grading operations, design of delivery systems, methods of irrigation, time, frequency, and depth of irrigations, skill of the irrigator, possible irrigation efficiencies, labor costs, cultural practices, possible maintenance of soil fertility, and length of time the lands have been utilized in crop production.

Any or all of the above-listed factors may be important in particular studies. Probably climatic factors warrant first consideration.

Climatic Influences on Irrigation Requirements. Climatic influences on irrigation requirements, as listed above, include effects of precipitation, temperature, relative humidity, sunlight, and wind. Low relative humidities, long periods of sunlight, and high wind velocities mean increased evapo-transpiration and increased irrigation requirements. However, the more important climatic influences are precipitation and temperature.

Rainfall, if occurring in sufficient depths and at proper intervals throughout the growing season, eliminates the need for irrigation and thus reduces irrigation requirements to zero. In semiarid regions, rainfall may be sufficient for crop growth in some years and deficient in others. Thus, irrigation requirements vary from zero to amounts needed to make up deficiencies in precipitation.

Depths of rainfall during single showers, in order to supply appreciable quantities of moisture to the root zones, should be greater than about 0.5 inch but should not be intense enough to cause excessive surface runoff or serious soil erosion. Therefore, studies of precipitation records should include considerations of daily rainfalls as well as monthly totals. They should also include considerations of winter and early spring precipitation. Winter and early spring rainfalls, or the spring melting of accumulated winter snowfalls, may replenish soil-moisture storage to such an extent as to supply crop needs during the early part of the growing season.

Temperatures affect rates of crop growth, rates of evapo-transpiration, total quantities of moisture consumed during the growing season, and total irrigation requirements. Temperatures determine the length of the growing season. The length of the growing season, in turn, largely determines the types of crops that can be raised when sufficient supplies of irrigation water can be secured. Types of crops, in turn, affect irrigation requirements. Thus, the circle of interrelated factors continues.

Types of Crops. Types of crops raised on large irrigation projects usually include diversified products. Where growing seasons are relatively short, forage crops, some cereals, and a few cool-season vegetables are about the only types that can be produced profitably. Where growing seasons are longer, more diversified types of farm crops can be grown. When ample supplies of water are available, some acreages can be utilized in producing crops that consume large amounts of water. Forage crops, because of their growth characteristics, usually can be raised during either long or short growing seasons.

Where water is plentiful and growing seasons extend throughout the year, large acreages may be utilized in producing crops that consume large quantities of water. In such regions, some acreages often are used in producing more than one crop annually.

From the viewpoint of irrigation requirements, the production of diversified crops is desirable when feasible. Some crops need more water than others during the early part of the growing season. Other crops need more water later. Some need appreciable amounts of water throughout the production period. When different crops are grown, irrigation requirements are more nearly uniform throughout the growing season. Furthermore, diversification facilitates rotation of crops which is an important factor in maintaining soil fertility. During normal crop production, irrigation requirements are lower for fertile soils than for soils deficient in plant nutrients.

In some irrigated regions where ample supplies of water can be obtained at reasonable costs, types of crops that can be produced profitably may be determined by local needs, labor costs, and marketing conditions. Where stock raising is a major industry, large acreages of forage crops may be desirable. Where project lands are close to city markets, large acreages of truck products may be profitable.

Other Influences on Irrigation Requirements. Soil conditions, particularly permeability, have important influences on irrigation requirements, inasmuch as they affect losses and waste. Highly permeable soils, such as some sandy types, are difficult to irrigate without losses by percolation. Impermeable soils, such as heavy clay types, are difficult to irrigate without waste by surface runoff. Both percolation and surface waste increase irrigation requirements. Losses and waste can be reduced to some extent by proper planning and control of irrigation procedures.

Cultural practices affect evapo-transpiration consumptions, soil fertility, and irrigation requirements. Beneficial effects of crop rotations have been mentioned. Cultivation and mulching, which tend to reduce soil evaporation, as discussed in the preceding chapter, also tend to reduce irrigation requirements.

In general, lands that have been farmed for several years produce satisfactory crop yields with much less water than new lands. On new lands, irrigation requirements during the first 2 or 3 years may be 50 per cent higher than normal requirements on well-established projects. Later, as soils become adjusted to crop production, irrigation requirements decrease and gradually approach normal values.

Methods of regulating water uses and assessing costs of water have some effects on irrigation requirements. When farmers are required to pay for water on the basis of quantities used, they can reduce their costs by applying water with high irrigation efficiencies. High irrigation efficiencies mean lower irrigation requirements.

Economic Irrigation Requirements. In general, economic irrigation requirements, from the viewpoint of national welfare, are lower than the depths of water commonly applied to irrigated lands in the past. Many additional acreages could be developed if water supplies could be used more economically. Still further extensions in irrigated areas could be made if all unused streamflows could be stored, delivered to the lands as actually needed, and applied with high irrigation efficiencies.

Data on irrigation requirements in western United States were studied exhaustively and reported in a series of government bulletins, prepared by Fortier and Young.[23] The reports include tables of estimated monthly and seasonal economic requirements for nearly a hundred geographic divisions. Depths of irrigation water needed for profitable crop production are approximately the same in each division. In preparing the tables the authors assumed that additional storage would be provided in the future, water supplies would be more efficiently regulated, lands would be better prepared for irrigation, water would be applied with higher efficiencies, waste would be

TABLE 1

ECONOMIC WATER REQUIREMENTS IN THE GREAT BASIN [19]

Div. no.	Division description	State	Irrigation season, inclusive	Total depth, ft.
1	Bear River basin	Idaho and Utah	May–Oct.	2.0
2	Utah Lake and Great Salt Lake valleys *	Utah	May–Oct.	2.2
3	Sevier River basin	Utah	May–Oct.	2.1
4	Irrigable lands, southwest Utah	Utah	Apr.–Oct.	1.8
5	Irrigable lands, southern Nevada	Nevada	Apr.–Oct.	1.7
6	Antelope Valley and Mohave River areas	California and Nevada	Mar.–Oct.	1.8
7	Mono, Owens, and Inyo-Kern valleys	California	Mar.–Oct.	2.1
8	Walker River basin	California and Nevada	Apr.–Oct.	2.0
9	Truckee and Carson river basins	California and Nevada	May–Oct.	2.1
10	Humboldt, Quinn, and White river basins	Nevada	May–Sept.	2.0
11	Honey Lake basin	California and Nevada	Apr.–Sept.	1.7
12	Malheur Lake, Harney Lake, and other basins	Oregon	Apr.–Sept.	1.5

* South of Weber River basin.

TABLE 2

ECONOMIC IRRIGATION REQUIREMENTS IN THE MISSOURI AND ARKANSAS RIVER BASINS [20]

Div. no.	Division description	State	Irrigation season, inclusive	Total depth, ft.
1	Northeast Montana	Montana	May–Aug.	1.40
2	North central Montana	Montana	May–Aug.	1.50
3	Central Montana	Montana	May–Aug.	1.70
4	Upper Missouri River basin	Montana	May–Aug.	1.60
5	Upper Yellowstone River basin	Montana	May–Aug.	1.90
6	Southeast Montana	Montana	May–Sept.	1.95
7	Big Horn River basin	Wyoming	May–Sept.	1.65
8	Yellowstone and Missouri river basins	Wyoming	May–Sept.	1.70
9	Upper Platte River basin	Wyoming	May–Sept.	1.60
10	Northeast Colorado	Colorado	Apr.–Sept.	2.05
11	North central Colorado	Colorado	Apr.–Sept.	2.20
12	South central Colorado	Colorado	Apr.–Sept.	2.10
13	Southeast Colorado	Colorado	Apr.–Oct.	2.30
14	West Kansas	Kansas	Apr.–Oct.	1.75
15	Central Nebraska	Nebraska	Apr.–Oct.	1.25
16	West Nebraska	Nebraska	Apr.–Oct.	2.00
17	Western South Dakota	South Dakota	May–Sept.	1.50
18	Western North Dakota	North Dakota	May–Sept.	1.35

TABLE 3

ECONOMIC IRRIGATION REQUIREMENTS IN THE SOUTHWEST [21]

Div. no.	Division description	State	Irrigation season, inclusive	Total depth, ft.
1	Imperial Valley	California	Jan.–Dec.	3.10
2	South Nevada	Nevada	Jan.–Dec.	2.90
3	Southwest Arizona	Arizona	Jan.–Dec.	3.00
4	Northwest Arizona	Arizona	Mar.–Oct.	2.30
5	Navajo country	Arizona	Mar.–Oct.	2.30
6	Southeast Arizona	Arizona	Feb.–Nov.	2.60
7	San Juan basin	New Mexico	Apr.–Sept.	2.20
8	West New Mexico	New Mexico	Apr.–Oct.	1.70
9	Rio Grande basin	New Mexico	Jan.–Dec.	2.60
10	Pecos River basin	New Mexico	Jan.–Dec.	2.40
11	Northeast New Mexico	New Mexico	Feb.–Nov.	1.60
12	Central Rio Grande basin	Texas	Jan.–Nov.	2.40
13	Pecos River basin	Texas	Jan.–Nov.	2.25
14	West central Texas	Texas	Jan.–Dec.	1.60
15	Lower Rio Grande basin	Texas	Jan.–Dec.	1.75
16	Upper Nueces and Colorado river basins	Texas	Jan.–Dec.	1.30
17	Upper Brazos and Red river basins	Texas	Jan.–Dec.	1.10
18	Eastern Panhandle	Texas	Mar.–Oct.	1.35
19	Western Panhandle	Texas	Mar.–Oct.	1.65
20	Panhandle	Oklahoma	Apr.–Oct.	1.25
21	West Oklahoma	Oklahoma	Apr.–Oct.	1.00
22	San Luis basin	Colorado	May–Sept.	1.80
23	San Juan basin	Colorado	Apr.–Sept.	1.90
24	Yampa and White river basins	Colorado	May–Aug.	1.35
25	Upper Colorado River basin	Colorado	Apr.–Sept.	1.70
26	Virgin River basin	Utah	Feb.–Nov.	2.25
27	San Juan basin	Utah	Apr.–Sept.	2.10
28	Green River basin	Utah	Apr.–Oct.	2.00
29	Uintah basin	Utah	Apr.–Sept.	1.75
30	Green River basin	Wyoming	May–Aug.	1.60

largely prevented, and some percolation would be recovered by pumping. They also assumed that in each division types of crops produced in the future would be the same as those produced in the past.

Tables 1 to 5 show economic seasonal requirements in the different divisions as given by Fortier and Young. Monthly requirements are not shown, but lengths of irrigation seasons are given. Table 1 shows water requirements in the Great Basin, where spring and summer rainfalls are usually negligible and irrigation requirements are about the same as water requirements. Tables 2 to 5 show irrigation re-

TABLE 4

ECONOMIC IRRIGATION REQUIREMENTS IN THE COLUMBIA RIVER
BASIN [22]

Div. no.	Division description	State	Irrigation season, inclusive	Total depth, ft.
1	Snake River Valley	Idaho	Apr.–Oct.	2.5
2	Upper Snake River Valley	Idaho	Apr.–Sept.	2.3
3	Jackson Lake and Upper Snake basin	Idaho and Wyoming	May–Sept.	1.7
4	Southwest Idaho and north Nevada	Idaho and Nevada	Apr.–Sept.	1.9
5	Salmon River basin	Idaho	May–Aug.	2.0
6	North Idaho	Idaho	May–Sept.	1.5
7	Bitterroot and Missoula river basins	Montana	Apr.–Nov.	2.1
8	Flathead Lake and River basins	Montana	Apr.–Sept.	1.8
9	Owyhee and Malheur river basins	Oregon	Apr.–Sept.	2.4
10	Northeast Oregon	Oregon	Apr.–Sept.	2.0
11	Umatilla, John Day, Deschutes, and Hood basins	Oregon	Apr.–Oct.	2.5
12	Central Oregon	Oregon	May–Aug.	2.4
13	Yakima and Wenatchee river basins	Washington	Apr.–Nov.	2.6
14	Southeast Washington	Washington	Apr.–Oct.	2.1
15	Northeast Washington	Washington	Apr.–Oct.	2.2
16	Okanogan River basin	Washington	Apr.–Nov.	2.3
17	Lower Columbia River basin	Washington	May–Sept.	1.3
18	Willamette River basin	Oregon	May–Sept.	1.2
19	Puget Sound region *	Washington	May–Sept.	1.4

* Not in the Columbia River basin.

quirements in the Missouri and Arkansas river basins, the Southwest, the Columbia River basin, and Pacific slope basins.

Variations in seasonal irrigation requirements as shown in Tables 1 to 5 may be summarized as follows:

The Great Basin	1.5 –2.2 feet
Missouri and Arkansas river basins	1.25–2.30 feet
The Southwest	1.00–3.10 feet
The Columbia River basin	1.2 –2.6 feet
Pacific Slope basins	0.85–2.30 feet

Crops grown in the different divisions vary widely but usually include diversified products. In some high mountain basins, crops are limited to native grasses, alfalfa, a few cereals, and certain vegetables. At lower elevations, crops include most small grains, corn, potatoes, sugar beets, sorghums, fruits, melons, and canning vegetables, as well as alfalfa, clover, timothy, and mixed grasses. In some regions, large

TABLE 5

ECONOMIC IRRIGATION REQUIREMENTS IN PACIFIC SLOPE BASINS [23]

Div. no.	Division description	State	Irrigation season, inclusive	Total depth, ft.
1	Umpqua, Coquill, and lower Rogue basins	Oregon	Apr.–Sept.	0.85
2	Upper Rogue River basin	Oregon	Mar.–Sept.	1.50
3	Klamath Lake and River basins	Oregon and California	Apr.–Sept.	2.00
4	Northwest California	California	Apr.–Oct.	1.40
5	Pit River basin	California	Apr.–Sept.	1.60
6	Feather, Yuba, and American river basins	California	Mar.–Nov.	1.50
7	Sacramento Valley	California	Mar.–Oct.	2.10
8	Sacramento-San Joaquin delta	California	May–Sept.	2.00
9	San Francisco Bay basin	California	Mar.–Nov.	1.50
10	Salinas River basin	California	Mar.–Oct.	1.70
11	Santa Maria, Santa Inez, and Santa Clara basins	California	Jan.–Dec.	1.60
12	San Joaquin Valley	California	Feb.–Oct.	2.30
13	West slope of Sierras	California	Feb.–Nov.	1.70
14	East slope of Coast Range	California	Feb.–Oct.	1.80
15	Antelope and Victor valleys	California	Mar.–Oct.	1.90
16	Los Angeles, San Gabriel, and Santa Ana basins	California	Jan.–Dec.	1.70
17	Upper Santa Ana River Valley	California	Jan.–Dec.	1.80
18	San Diego County	California	Jan.–Dec.	1.40

acreages are used in producing forage crops. Truck crops are grown extensively in some divisions.

In southern Arizona and California, citrus fruits, dates, avocados, grapes, and nuts are grown extensively. In parts of the Columbia basin, large areas are used in producing potatoes and deciduous fruits. Cotton is grown in parts of Texas, New Mexico, Arizona, and California. Rice is raised in some sections of Texas and California.

The seasonal requirements listed in Tables 1 to 5 are really ideal requirements. Actual uses of water often are higher where water is plentiful, and sometimes lower where water supplies are limited. The tabulated depths are useful in showing minimum quantities of irrigation water that should be secured whenever possible. If such quantities cannot be secured, irrigation may be profitable with slightly smaller quantities. Some districts in California have operated with seasonal supplies lower than the economic requirements shown in Table 5.[4]

Where growing seasons are long and lands are utilized in raising crops that consume large quantities of water, economic irrigation requirements may be considerably greater than the depths shown in the tables.   In the Coachella Valley, southeastern California, where crops can be grown throughout the year, average depths of application have exceeded 4 feet for cotton and grapes, 5 feet for mixed crops, and 8 feet for alfalfa, citrus fruits, and dates (see Table 13).

Farm Irrigation Requirements.   From the viewpoint of the farmer, the economic irrigation requirement often is higher than the depth tabulated for his locality.   He is interested in securing maximum returns at minimum cost, without impairing the productivity of his land. When ample water is available at reasonable rates, he produces crops that can be marketed at the greatest profit.   When labor is costly, it may be cheaper to use more water than to apply water with a high efficiency.   When his fields are adequately drained and sufficient water can be obtained, he is justified in using depths that result in maximum profits.

Depths of water that result in maximum profits may be lower than depths that produce maximum yields.   For some crops, yields approaching maximum values increase slowly with increases in irrigation water, so that costs of obtaining and applying additional water may be greater than the market value of the increased yields.

The farmer's choice of crop practices depends largely on his irrigable acreage, the amount of water needed, and the extent to which he is entitled to water.   His procedures usually are limited by either available land or available water.   When he has more land than he can irrigate properly with his water supply, he may find it more profitable to produce certain crops on large acreages with small depths of water than to produce other crops on smaller areas with greater depths of water.

Powers and Lewis, in their Oregon studies, concluded that the best measure of economic duty from the viewpoint of the farmer may be the maximum net profit per acre of land or the maximum net profit per acre-foot of water, depending on his particular limitations of irrigable acreage and available water.[45]   They found that in the Willamette Valley, where rainfall furnishes some moisture for crop growth, economic irrigation requirements are about 1.0 foot for annual crops and 1.5 to 2.0 feet for meadows, with an average requirement of about 1.5 feet.   This is about 0.3 foot more than the value given in Table 4.

Uses of Irrigation Water.   Data on past uses of irrigation water on existing projects are useful in studying needs for water on contemplated developments.   Past uses of water as previously mentioned, may differ from actual irrigation requirements.   However, studies of such uses, together with considerations of climatic, soil, and crop conditions, constitute valuable guides in estimating water needs on new lands where conditions are similar.

Depths of monthly and seasonal deliveries of irrigation water on existing projects are commonly measured. Such measurements furnish data needed in distributing available supplies and assessing

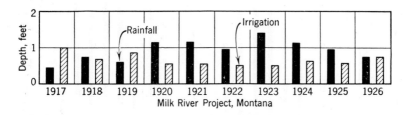

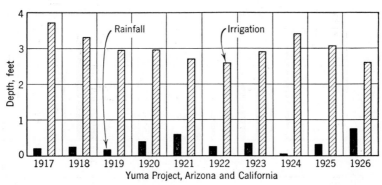

FIGURE 1.   Seasonal rainfall and irrigation deliveries on two federal projects, 1917 to 1926.[15]

charges for water. They also furnish data needed by state officials in the adjudication and administration of water resources.

A detailed compilation of data regarding water uses on Bureau of Reclamation projects was prepared by Debler.[15]   Considerations of water uses on federal projects are especially valuable, inasmuch as the projects are widely distributed throughout the western states, include different soil types, and involve many variations in climate, crop production, irrigation procedures, and agricultural practices. The data reported include records for from 8 to 16 years at 24 projects, together with general summaries, mostly for the 10-year period from 1917 to 1926.

Figure 1 shows depths of seasonal rainfall and seasonal irrigation deliveries on the Milk River Project, northern Montana, and the

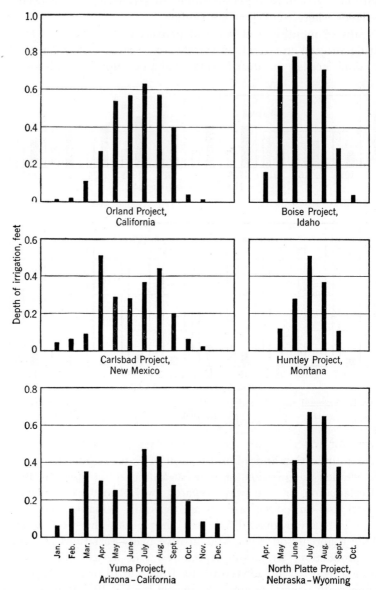

FIGURE 2.   Average monthly irrigations on some federal projects, 1917 to 1926.[15]

Yuma Project, southwestern Arizona and southeastern California. These two projects are widely separated, are located in different climates, and represent different types of irrigation agriculture. Figure 2 shows average monthly deliveries of irrigation water at six projects located in different parts of the West.

TABLE 6

GENERAL DATA FOR FEDERAL IRRIGATION PROJECTS [15]

Project	State	Main soil type	Average elevation, ft.	Mean growing season temp., °F.	Crops grown, per cent of area *			
					Forage †	Small grain	Furrow crops	Trees
Belle Fourche	South Dakota	Heavy	2,800	65	62	22	16	..
Boise	Idaho	Light	2,500	62	53	31	13	3
Carlsbad	New Mexico	Medium	3,100	66	33	4	63	..
Grand Valley	Colorado	Heavy	4,700	65	36	24	33	7
Huntley	Montana	Heavy	3,000	64	42	34	24	..
King Hill	Idaho	Very light	2,750	64	75	7	11	6
Klamath	Oregon-California	Medium	4,100	60	77	21	2	..
Lower Yellowstone	Montana	Heavy	1,900	64	45	33	22	..
Milk River	Montana	Heavy	2,200	58	73	22	5	..
Minidoka, S. Side Pumping	Idaho	Medium	4,200	59	50	28	22	..
Newlands	Nevada	Medium	4,000	59	85	11	4	..
North Platte	Nebraska-Wyoming	Medium	4,100	66	36	26	38	..
Okanogan	Washington	Light	1,000	63	9	..	3	88
Orland	California	Light	250	70	53	5	19	23
Rio Grande	New Mexico-Texas	Medium	3,700	66	37	8	53	2
Shoshone, Frannie Division	Wyoming	Heavy	4,150	60	72	17	11	..
Shoshone, Garland Division	Wyoming	Medium	4,400	59	59	28	13	..
Sun River, Fort Shaw Division	Montana	Heavy	3,700	58	75	20	5	..
Sun River, Greenfields Division	Montana	Medium	3,700	57	23	75	2	..
Umatilla	Oregon	Light	470	60	85	1	6	8
Uncompahgre	Colorado	Medium	5,500	61	47	25	25	3
Yakima, Sunnyside Division	Washington	Medium	800	63	57	7	21	15
Yakima, Tieton Division	Washington	Light	1,500	62	44	12	11	33
Yuma	Arizona-California	Medium	120	72	39	3	58	..

* During 10-year period from 1917 to 1926.
† Alfalfa, hay, and pasture.

Table 6 shows general data for the federal projects, including locations, soil types, average elevations, mean temperatures during the growing season, and percentages of acreages used in producing different crops.

Table 7 shows average irrigation and rainfall conditions on the federal projects, including irrigated areas, lengths of irrigation seasons,

TABLE 7

AVERAGE IRRIGATION AND RAINFALL CONDITIONS
ON FEDERAL PROJECTS [15]

Project *	Irrigated area, 1,000 acres	Irrigation season, inclusive	Seasonal farm deliveries, ft.	Precipitation, ft.		Deliveries plus growing season rainfall, ft.
				Before growing season	During growing season	
Belle Fourche	45	May–Sept.	1.22	0.48	0.86	2.08
Boise	146	Apr.–Oct.	3.60	.43	.38	3.98
Carlsbad	23	Jan.–Nov.	2.36	.06	.86	3.22
Grand Valley	10	Apr.–Nov.	3.61	.27	.48	4.09
Huntley	19	May–Sept.	1.39	.37	.63	2.02
King Hill	6	Apr.–Nov.	7.01	.41	.35	7.36
Klamath	43	Apr.–Sept.	1.43	.68	.18	1.61
Lower Yellowstone	18	May–Sept.	1.34	.33	.71	2.05
Milk River	17	Apr.–Oct.	0.65	.18	.91	1.56
Minidoka, S. Side Pumping	45	Apr.–Oct.	2.54	.32	.53	3.07
Newlands	39	Mar.–Nov.	2.88	.15	.25	3.13
North Platte	108	May–Sept.	2.23	.47	.81	3.04
Okanogan	5	May–Sept.	2.60	.51	.42	3.02
Orland	15	Jan.–Nov.	3.17	1.02	.37	3.55
Rio Grande	97	Feb.–Dec.	2.89	.06	.60	3.49
Shoshone, Frannie Division	8	Apr.–Oct.	2.19	.11	.39	2.58
Shoshone, Garland Division	32	Apr.–Nov.	2.38	.09	.33	2.71
Sun River, Fort Shaw Division	8	May–Oct.	1.54	.23	.60	2.14
Sun River, Greenfields Division	10	May–Oct.	1.28	.28	.65	1.93
Umatilla	11	Mar.–Nov.	5.02	.40	.35	5.37
Uncompahgre	61	Apr.–Oct.	5.76	.26	.55	6.31
Yakima, Sunnyside Division	92	Mar.–Oct.	3.29	.27	.21	3.50
Yakima, Tieton Division	28	Apr.–Sept.	2.51	.44	.16	2.67
Yuma	52	Jan.–Dec.	3.01	.33	.33	3.34

* Data are mostly for 10-year period from 1917 to 1926.

seasonal farm deliveries, precipitation preceding the growing season, precipitation during the growing season, and deliveries plus growing season rainfall. On some projects, precipitation prior to seeding supplies some moisture for crop growth. Owing to under-measurement, actual deliveries of water may have been from 0 to 10 per cent greater than the tabulated values.

The data in Table 7 show that average seasonal deliveries of irrigation water on the federal projects varied from 0.65 foot on the Milk River Project, northern Montana, to 7.01 feet on the King Hill Project, southern Idaho. Heavy soils predominate on the Milk River Project, and very light soils on the King Hill Project. Crops grown on the two projects are about the same. Except for the King Hill, Umatilla, and Uncompahgre projects, where considerable water probably was lost by waste and percolation, average seasonal deliveries varied from 0.65 to 3.61 feet.

On the Okanogan Project, Washington, where deciduous fruits constitute the principal crops, the seasonal delivery or irrigation water averaged 2.60 feet. On the Yuma Project, where crops are grown throughout the year, annual deliveries averaged 3.01 feet.

In general, depths of water needed to produce crops on a particular project vary from year to year, in accordance with differences in weather conditions, soil fertility, and cultural practices. In arid regions, where all the water must be supplied by irrigation, depths of water that should be delivered vary similarly. However, actual depths delivered may differ from those that should be delivered, owing to differences in available supplies.

In semiarid regions, where rainfall supplies some moisture for crop growth, irrigation requirements from year to year are more variable than water requirements, because of pronounced differences in depths of rainfall. In such regions, irrigation deliveries may be more variable than irrigation requirements, inasmuch as the farmers may wait in vain for rainfall rather than incur the expense of obtaining and applying irrigation water when needed.

Project Diversions. Average seasonal diversions at sources of water supply for the federal projects are shown in Figure 3. They vary from 1.44 feet on the Milk River Project, where some moisture was supplied by precipitation, to 13.21 feet on the King Hill Project, where considerable water was lost by percolation.

The Milk River Project was the only project able to produce satisfactory crops with average diversions less than 2 feet. Average diversions between 2 and 3 feet were made on the Belle Fourche and Klamath projects, also on the Greenfields Division of the Sun River Project. These projects are located in climates where growing seasons are relatively short and precipitation supplies some moisture for crop growth.

Average diversions exceeding 10 feet were made on the Grand Valley, Umatilla, and Yuma projects, as well as on the King Hill

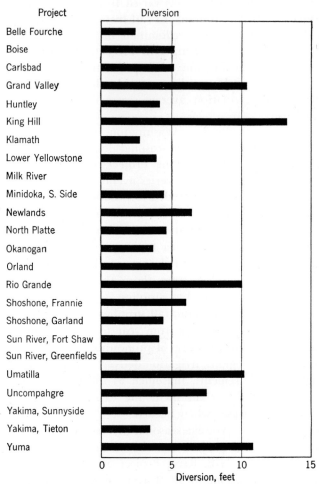

Figure 3. Average seasonal diversions on federal irrigation projects.[15]

Project. On the Yuma Project, excess diversions were made to maintain nonsilting velocities in the main canal and thus reduce the frequency of sluicing operations, also to supply water needed for the operation of a power plant. Excess quantities were subsequently returned to the river, where they became available for rediversion to downstream lands.

CROP REQUIREMENTS

Quantities of irrigation water needed to produce crops on an existing project during a particular year, under the same weather conditions, vary with the type of crop. Local variations in soils, fertility, irrigation procedures, and cultural practices have some modifying effects on crop requirements. However, for similar soil and weather conditions, the principal cause of differences in amounts of water needed is the type of crop.

Total depths of water needed by different crops equal consumptive uses plus such depths of surface runoff and percolation as may be unavoidable during precipitation or irrigation. Total depths of irrigation water needed equal consumptive use, plus surface runoff and percolation, minus soil moisture that becomes available for evapotranspiration as a result of precipitation.

Water requirements and irrigation requirements, like consumptive uses, vary for the same crop grown on the same soil during different years, owing to differences in weather conditions. They also vary for the same crop grown on different soils under the same weather conditions.

Crops commonly require more water when grown on light sandy soils than when grown on heavy clay soils, because more water percolates to depths below the root zones. For this reason, rice crops, which require continuous flooding during the growing season, usually are produced on clay or adobe soils. Most crops require less water when grown on soils of high fertility. Many crops have an optimum water requirement, that is, a certain seasonal depth that results in maximum yield. Seasonal water requirements of forage crops, such as alfalfa, that may be grown continuously and cut several times during prolonged periods of suitable temperature, increase with the length of the growing season.

In general, crops that require relatively large quantities of water include alfalfa, Rhodes grass, clover, mixed grasses, pastures, rice, sugar cane, and dates. Crops that require medium quantities include cotton, sugar beets, potatoes, vegetables, common cereals, and many fruits. Crops that require relatively small quantities include some vegetables and certain field crops such as millet, milo, feterita, and buckwheat. Millet and certain vegetables, produced in cool climates during short growing seasons, may need less than a foot of water. Alfalfa, rice, and dates, produced in hot dry climates during long growing seasons, may need more than 8 feet.

Investigations of Crop Requirements. Investigations of irrigation and water requirements of different crops produced in the western parts of the United States and Canada have been conducted more or less continuously for many years. Valuable records of uses of water in producing different crops under different conditions also have been assembled by irrigation engineers, irrigation districts, and other irrigation organizations. The more comprehensive studies of crop requirements usually have been carried on cooperatively by federal and state agencies, and reports on the studies usually have been published in federal and state bulletins.

Fortier and Young, in their previously mentioned reports on irrigation requirements, reviewed the available data on crop requirements up to the time of their compilations. Since that time, reports on some additional investigations have been published. Many of the older sources of information, as well as most of the more recent bulletins, are listed at the end of the chapter. Pertinent data abstracted from certain bulletins, as specifically noted later, are presented and discussed on the following pages. Frequent references are made to Young's excellent report on irrigation requirements of California crops, published in 1945.[51]

Investigations of crop requirements are commonly conducted on small field tracts or farm plots. Areas selected for use in such investigations should be located where irrigation deliveries can be accurately measured and where no additional moisture for crop growth can be supplied, either by seepage from adjacent areas or by capillary movements from underlying water tables. Irrigation water should be supplied in different amounts and at different times, as needed, and crop yields should be determined at the time of harvesting, so that results obtained by applying irrigation water in different amounts and at different times can be properly evaluated and compared.

Depths of rainfall preceding and during the growing season should be measured and recorded in all investigations of crop requirements. In regions where rainfall is negligible, determinations of irrigation requirements may be sufficient. In regions where precipitation sometimes furnishes considerable quantities of moisture for crop growth, total water requirements should be determined.

When total water requirements are determined, measurements of soil moisture stored in the root zones should be made at the beginning and end of the growing season, so that actual depths of precipitation utilized in crop growth can be computed. Additional measurements of available soil moisture throughout the growing season are useful in determining how much irrigation water should be supplied and when it should be supplied. They are also useful in studying plant responses following irrigations.

Many of the earlier investigations of crop requirements were made primarily for the purpose of determining desirable irrigation procedures to be followed in producing different crops. In general, they sought to determine proper depths of single irrigations, suitable frequencies of irrigation, and total seasonal depths of irrigation water that should be supplied in order to secure most profitable yields. In some cases, measurements were continued for several years on the same plots, on which different crops were raised in rotation, in order to determine effects of differences in soil fertility resulting from the production of different crops during preceding seasons.

Effects of Soil Fertility. When irrigation is begun in arid regions, the soils usually contain ample supplies of mineral nutrients but are deficient in organic matter. Therefore, water requirements may be relatively high and crop yields relatively low until suitable soil conditions can be established by applications of manure, plowing under of cover crops, production of different crops in rotation, and other beneficial practices.

Table 8 shows some comparisons of water uses and crop yields on soils of different fertility in Idaho.[19] The tests were made on small

TABLE 8

COMPARISONS OF WATER USES AND CROP YIELDS ON SOILS
OF DIFFERENT FERTILITY IN IDAHO [19]

Crop	Location	Year	Water applied, ft.	Yield, bu. per acre	Soil conditions
Wheat	Filer	1911	0.64	63.2	Alfalfa sod, manured.
Wheat	Buhl	1911	2.15	38.0	First crop after clearing.
Wheat	Buhl	1910	1.44	67.2	Clay loam, manured.
Wheat	Gooding	1910	1.84	26.3	Raw sagebrush clay loam.
Wheat	Kimberley	1912	1.16	82.9	Alfalfa sod, manured.
Wheat	Buhl	1912	1.21	24.1	Fourth year of grain on raw soil.
Wheat	Boise	1912	1.04	54.5	Two years from clover sod.
Wheat	Meridian	1912	2.47	31.2	Cropped 10 years without fertilizer.
Oats	Oakley	1911	0.64	76.5	Alfalfa sod.
Oats	Twin Falls	1911	2.26	68.9	Third crop from sagebrush, unfertilized.
Oats	Boise	1911	1.08	73.0	Two years from clover sod.
Oats	Richfield	1911	1.89	50.8	Two years from sagebrush.
Oats	Gooding	1912	2.04	106.3	Manured.
Oats	Gooding	1913	2.7	66.0	Fourth crop from brush, unfertilized.
Barley	Gooding	1912	1.52	90.0	First year from alfalfa sod.
Barley	Gooding	1913	2.75	32.8	Fourth crop from brush, unfertilized.

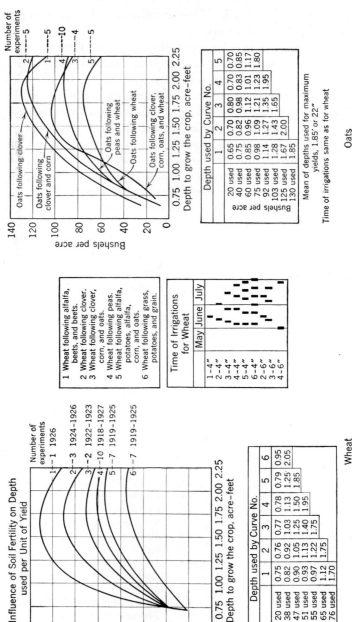

FIGURE 4. Water requirements and crop yields for wheat and oats, soils of different fertility, Alberta. (After Snelson.)

plots of less than an acre to more than 13 acres. Although they were made years ago, they are still excellent examples of the effects of soil fertility. The last two items for Gooding show that 1.52 feet of water on alfalfa sod produced 90 bushels of barley per acre, whereas nearly twice as much water on a new soil produced only about one-third as much.

Figure 4 shows water requirements and crop yields for wheat and oats on soils of different fertility as determined by Snelson at the Brooks Experiment Station, Alberta, Canada.[49] Crops produced on the same plots during preceding seasons are noted on the diagrams. Maximum yields of wheat were produced by 1.70 feet of water on plots of high fertility, where alfalfa, beets, and beets had been grown during three preceding seasons. On plots of low fertility, where grass, potatoes, and grain had been grown previously, 2.05 feet of water produced yields only half as great.

Maximum yields of oats were produced by 1.85 feet of water on plots of high fertility, where clover had been grown previously. On plots of low fertility, where wheat had been grown previously, 1.80 feet of water produced yields only a little more than half as great. Investigations of sugar beets at Brooks showed that 1.50 feet of water produced 18.0 tons per acre on soils of high fertility, and only 10.5 tons per acre on soils of low fertility.

Depths of water used in producing crops at Brooks were determined by adding irrigation deliveries to growing-season rainfall and correcting for differences in soil-moisture storage to a depth of 6 feet, as observed at times of seeding and harvesting. The soil was described as a silt loam, containing very fine sand, approximately uniform to depths of 12 or 14 feet.

Optimum Crop Requirements. Optimum water requirements of different crops are the seasonal depths of water that result in maximum yields, where the depths include soil moisture supplied by precipitation as well as water delivered by irrigation. Optimum irrigation requirements are the seasonal depths of irrigation water, exclusive of rainfall, that result in maximum yields. Optimum water and irrigation requirements, like most hydrological factors involved in irrigation agriculture, vary widely for different crops produced in different localities. Considerable differences in requirements may be caused by differences in soil texture or soil fertility.

For the smaller amounts of irrigation, yields of many crops increase at comparatively rapid rates with increasing depths of water. For some crops, produced on certain soils, optimum requirements

are fairly well defined. For other crops, yields increase slowly as
depths of water approach optimum requirements, then decrease slowly
as the depths are increased beyond optimum requirements. Yields of
a few crops, such as alfalfa, sometimes continue to increase with in-

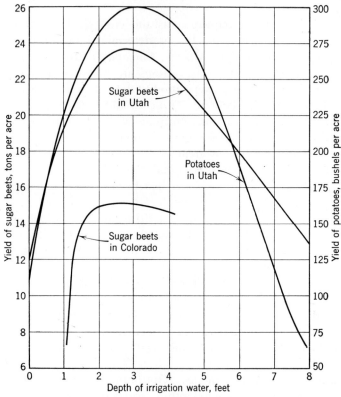

FIGURE 5.   Water-yield relations for potatoes and sugar beets. (After Harris [27]
and Hemphill.[31])

creasing depths of water, so that no optimum requirements are
apparent.

The curves in Figure 4 show water-yield relations for wheat and
oats at the Brooks Experiment Station. The summits of the curves
identify the depths of optimum water requirements. All curves for
wheat show gradually increasing depths of optimum requirements
with decreasing conditions of soil fertility. Curves 1, 2, and 4, for
oats, show similar relations, but curves 3 and 5 show different variations with fertility.

Figure 5 shows water-yield relations for sugar beets and potatoes in the Cache Valley, Utah, also for sugar beets in the Cache la Poudre Valley, northern Colorado. The diagrams show yields for different seasonal depths of irrigation water, without allowances for precipitation. However, corrections for precipitation probably would not change the general relations. The Utah tests, reported by Harris, were conducted on a deep uniform loam at the Greenville Experimental Farm near Logan.[27] The Colorado tests, reported by Hemp-

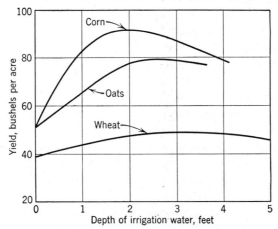

FIGURE 6.   Water-yield relations for corn, oats, and wheat, Cache Valley, Utah.
(After Harris.)

hill, were conducted on sandy loams that probably are more permeable than the Utah soil.[31]

The curves for sugar beets and potatoes in Utah show well-defined optimum irrigation requirements. For depths of water greater than optimum, the curve for potatoes falls more rapidly than the curve for sugar beets. The curve for sugar beets in Colorado shows rapidly increasing yields with increasing depths of water up to about 1.5 feet, then gradually diminishing rates of increase up to a depth of about 2.5 feet, then slowly decreasing yields with further increases in irrigation water. Differences in the curves for sugar beets in Utah and Colorado may be largely due to differences in soils.

Figure 6 shows water-yield relations for corn, oats, and wheat in the Cache Valley, Utah.[27] Optimum irrigation requirements are fairly well defined for corn, but not so well defined for oats and wheat, particularly wheat. A curve for wheat in Idaho, reported by Bark, showed a fairly well-defined optimum irrigation requirement of 1.7

feet, which is considerably lower than the value shown by the Utah curve. The Idaho tests were conducted at the Gooding Experiment Station, where the soil is a rather impervious, medium clay loam averaging 6 to 8 feet in depth.[5]

Pittman and Stewart, in reviewing 28 years of irrigation experiments near Logan, concluded that the use of more than 20 or 25 inches of irrigation water resulted in little or no increased yields; that the use of more than 30 inches usually reduced the yields of all crops except alfalfa; and that alfalfa yields continued to increase with increasing depths of irrigation water up to 60 inches or more.[43] Crops investigated included wheat, oats, barley, corn, potatoes, sugar beets, and alfalfa.

Investigations of cotton and grain sorghum on moderately well-drained loams in eastern Texas, reported by McDowell, showed optimum water requirements of about 2.50 feet for cotton and 3.25 feet for sorghum.[39] Average depths of rainfall during the growing season were 13.60 inches for cotton and 15.82 inches for sorghum. On loam soils in the Salt River Valley, Arizona, where the annual rainfall is about 7 inches, maximum yields of grain sorghum were produced with about 1.5 feet of irrigation water, a requirement considerably lower than in eastern Texas.[38]

Studies of cotton production in the San Joaquin Valley, California, where summer rainfall is negligible, showed water requirements about the same as in eastern Texas.[3] In the Mesilla Valley, New Mexico, where the growing season rainfall averages about 6 inches, good yields of cotton were produced with 1.5 to 2.0 feet of irrigation water, and only slightly better yields with 3.4 feet.[12]

Profitable Water Uses. Depths of water that produce most profitable yields may be lower than optimum water requirements, especially for crops whose yields increase slowly as applied depths approach optimum values. For such crops, costs of buying and delivering additional water beyond certain limits, in order to obtain maximum yields, may be greater than the market value of the resulting increases in yields. Points at which further irrigations become unprofitable depend on local labor and water costs, prices obtainable for crop products, and shapes of water-yield curves.

In studies of irrigation on silt loam at Corvallis, Oregon, where rainfall supplies about half the moisture needed for crop growth, Powers and Lewis found that most profitable returns were obtained from total seasonal depths of about 11.4 inches for beets, 11.5 inches for corn ensilage, 10.4 inches for potatoes, 18.1 inches for red clover, and 20.9 inches for alfalfa.[45] They concluded that for good farming methods and maximum net profits water requirements in the Willamette Valley were about as follows:

Alfalfa hay and red clover	5 inches per ton
Grain	10 inches per 25 bushels
Potatoes	5 inches per 100 bushels
White beans	8.2 inches per 10 bushels
Beets	6.9 inches per 10 tons
Corn ensilage	1.1 inches per ton

Scotts Bluff Investigations. Table 9 shows depths of water used in raising some field crops at the Scotts Bluff Field Station, western

TABLE 9

DEPTHS OF WATER USED IN RAISING SOME FIELD CROPS
IN WESTERN NEBRASKA [48]

(Rainfall plus irrigation in feet)

Crop produced	1941	1942	1943	1944	Mean for period
Oats, alone	1.48	....	....	....	1.48
Oats, with alfalfa	3.61	....	....	....	3.61
Barley	....	2.12	1.26	1.43	1.60
Wheat	1.81	....	....	....	1.81
Corn	1.69	2.20	1.23	1.48	1.65
Potatoes	2.56	2.12	2.04	2.09	2.20
Sugar beets	2.62	2.50	2.27	2.30	2.42
Beans	....	2.10	1.80	1.79	1.90
Alfalfa	4.89	3.62	4.05	3.60	4.04
Sweetclover	....	....	1.89	3.61	2.75
Sweetclover pasture	2.92	....	2.98	3.27	3.06
Alfalfa and clover pasture	....	3.27	....	....	3.27
Alfalfa pasture	4.22	....	....	....	4.22
Rainfall, April–September, inclusive	1.04	1.16	0.58	0.72	0.87

Nebraska, during 1941 to 1946, as reported by Scofield and Howe.[48] The investigations were made on ¼-acre plots, where rotation tests had been carried on since 1912. They were made to determine how much irrigation water is needed, in addition to rainfall, in order to insure satisfactory crop production. No serious water shortages occurred during the 4 years. The investigations were conducted by an experienced irrigator, whose aim was to deliver water to all plots as needed rather than to deliver definite amounts to different plots.

The soil at the Scotts Bluff Station is a well-drained, very fine sandy loam, which can retain about 0.28 foot of available moisture per foot of depth. Some percolation may have taken place during some of the tests. Losses by surface waste and excessive seepage from field ditches were measured and deducted in determining deliveries of irrigation water. Tabulated depths represent seasonal irrigation deliveries, plus seasonal rainfall, plus total precipitation from the time of the preceding harvest to the beginning of the growing season, without deductions for losses by runoff, percolation, or land evaporation during the fall and winter months.

The growing season in western Nebraska includes the months of April to September. Depths of growing-season rainfall at Scotts Bluff are shown at the bottom of Table 9. Annual precipitation during the 4 years varied from 9.98 inches in 1943 to 16.97 inches in 1942.

Average depths of water used in producing crops at the Scotts Bluff Station during 1941 to 1944 varied from 1.48 feet for oats to 4.04 feet for alfalfa and 4.22 feet for alfalfa pasture. Barley used 1.60 feet; corn, 1.65 feet; and wheat, 1.81 feet. Potatoes used 2.20 feet, and sugar beets, 2.42 feet. Depths used by the same crop during different years varied from 1.23 to 2.20 feet for corn, and from 3.60 to 4.89 feet for alfalfa. Other variations are apparent in the table.

Crop yields during 1941 to 1944 varied considerably for the same crops, probably due largely to differences in fertility. Average yields were about normal. Some tests showed no apparent correlation between water input and yield, some showed a fair correlation, and some a good correlation. Depths of water for all crops would be a little lower if adjustments were made for losses during the fall and winter.

Variations in Crop Requirements. Variations in crop requirements due to differences in weather conditions, soil texture, soil fertility, irrigation practices, and cultural procedures have been mentioned on the preceding pages. For particular crops grown on similar soils, differences in water requirements in different regions probably are caused mainly by differences in weather conditions. Evapo-transpiration consumptions are greater in warm dry climates than in cooler, more humid climates. For forage crops, such as alfalfa, that may be cut several times during long growing seasons, seasonal water requirements increase as the length of the growing season increases.

Consequently, variations in water requirements with regional locations are commonly more pronounced for forage crops than for crops
that are harvested only once a year.

TABLE 10

VARIATIONS IN WATER REQUIREMENTS OF DIFFERENT CROPS
PRODUCED IN THE MISSOURI AND ARKANSAS RIVER BASINS [20]

Crop	No. of tests	Range in water require-ments, ft.	Crop	No. of tests	Range in water require-ments, ft.
Forage, including			Apples	4	2.10–2.60
alfalfa	648	1.94–2.62	Beans	4	1.30–1.60
Barley	335	1.33–1.82	Buckwheat	3	1.05–1.30
Oats	409	1.35–1.81	Cantaloupes	10	1.50–2.30
Wheat	542	1.36–1.80	Peas	168	1.36–1.94
Corn	70	1.23–1.83	Potatoes	350	1.38–1.70
Kafir corn	15	1.43–1.57	Sugar beets	128	1.60–2.50
Flax	50	1.47–1.85	Sunflowers	16	1.20–1.40
Millet	14	0.81–0.94	Tomatoes	6	2.10–2.80
Milo maize	27	1.09–1.70	Cucumbers	7	1.73–3.75
Sorghum	26	1.06–1.47			

Table 10 shows variations in average water requirements for the
more common crops produced on irrigated areas in the Missouri and
Arkansas river basins, as summarized by Fortier.[20] Table 11 shows

TABLE 11

VARIATIONS IN WATER REQUIREMENTS OF DIFFERENT FARM CROPS
PRODUCED IN THE SOUTHWEST [21]

Crop	No. of tests	Range in water require-ments, ft.	Crop	No. of tests	Range in water require-ments, ft.
Alfalfa	369	3.47–5.08	Emmer	6	1.19–1.87
Rhodes grass	12	3.49–4.43	Feterita	8	0.97–1.10
Sudan grass	25	2.88–3.16	Millet	5	0.91–1.09
Barley	3	1.24–1.83	Milo	35	0.96–1.67
Oats	2	1.90–2.09	Sorghum	34	1.69–2.08
Wheat	46	1.46–2.24	Cotton	103	2.35–3.51
Corn	42	1.44–1.99	Potatoes	12	1.59–2.04
Kafir	16	1.32–1.54	Soybeans	36	1.66–2.81
Flax	3	1.23–1.59	Sugar beets	5	1.77–2.72
Broomcorn	9	0.97–1.15	Sugar cane *	41	3.48–4.56

* Not commonly produced in the Southwest.

similar data for various farm crops produced on irrigated areas in the Southwest, as given by Fortier and Young.[21] Both tables are based on the results of comprehensive investigations conducted in several localities. The number of tests considered for each crop is shown in the second column of each tabulation. Detailed test data are given in the original publications.

Sugar cane, the last item in Table 11, is not ordinarily produced in the irrigated sections of the West. Tests of the water requirements of sugar cane were made in Texas and Arizona; but no data for sugar cane production are given in the 1940 census report on irrigation in the United States.

Tables 10 and 11 show that average water requirements for alfalfa vary from about 1.9 to 2.6 feet in the Missouri and Arkansas river basins, and from about 3.5 to 5.1 feet in the Southwest. Water requirements for potatoes and sugar beets are from 0.2 to 0.3 foot higher in the Southwest than in the Missouri and Arkansas river basins. Water requirements for the more common cereals vary from about 1.2 to 1.8 feet in the Missouri and Arkansas river basins and from about 1.2 to 2.2 feet in the Southwest. In general, profitable grain crops cannot be produced with less than about 12 inches of water, whether supplied by irrigation, rainfall, or both.

Pasture Requirements. Pasture lands require about the same quantities of water as alfalfa and other forage crops. Most pasture grasses derive their moisture supplies principally from the upper 1 to 2 feet of soil. Consequently, they generally need lighter and more frequent irrigations than most farm crops. Alfalfa, sweetclover, Ladino clover, and various mixed grasses are commonly used for pastures. Inasmuch as the grasses grow continuously during periods of suitable temperature and moisture supply, seasonal irrigation and water requirements increase with increasing lengths of growing season.

In western Nebraska, where the growing season extends from April to September, water used by pasture lands, including rainfall, amounted to 3.06 feet for sweetclover, 4.22 feet for alfalfa, and 3.27 feet for mixed alfalfa and clover (see Table 9). At Corvallis, Oregon, an average depth of 4.02 feet of irrigation water per season was delivered to Ladino clover pastures during the 4-year period from 1930 to 1933.[17] In Tulare County, California, seasonal deliveries of irrigation water to 23 pastures on loam and sandy soils, during 1940, varied from 3.25 to 12.0 feet, averaging 6.33 feet.[51]

Vegetable Requirements. In general, most vegetable crops require less water than the more common field crops. Some truck crops, such as sweet potatoes and watermelons, that are raised commercially in regions where growing seasons are relatively long and warm, require greater depths of water than many farm crops. In certain sections of the Southwest, where cool-season vegetables are grown during the winter months, after other crops are harvested, total annual requirements may be considerably higher than in most farming regions.

Because of their wide variations in temperature and water requirements, some types of vegetables can be grown for home use in all regions where irrigation agriculture is practiced. Truck crops are produced principally in regions easily accessible to city markets and in warm climates where fresh vegetables can be grown during the winter months, to supply demands from colder sections of the country.

Table 12 gives ranges in average seasonal water requirements for some vegetable crops in the Southwest, compiled from test data as-

TABLE 12

SEASONAL WATER REQUIREMENTS OF VEGETABLE CROPS
IN THE SOUTHWEST [21]

Crop	No. of tests	Range in water requirements, ft.	Crop	No. of tests	Range in water requirements, ft.
Beans, snap	9	0.83–1.44	Onions	4	0.73–1.52
Beets, table	28	0.87–1.37	Peas	8	1.21–1.56
Cabbage	21	0.94–1.49	Melons	3	2.48–3.40
Carrots	6	1.27–1.60	Spinach	12	0.80–1.07
Cauliflower	6	1.43–1.77	Sweet potatoes	3	1.77–2.25
Lettuce	49	0.72–1.35	Tomatoes	17	0.95–1.42

sembled by Fortier and Young.[21] The data show that several vegetables can be grown in some parts of the Southwest with seasonal depths of less than a foot. Other vegetables require more than a foot, particularly sweet potatoes and melons.

In the Missouri and Arkansas river basins, cantaloupes used from 1.5 to 2.3 feet, and cucumbers from 1.7 to 3.7 feet (see Table 10). In the Mesilla Valley, New Mexico, most satisfactory yields of White Grano onions were produced with 2.5 feet of irrigation water.[14] In the Salt River Valley, Arizona, highest yields of head lettuce were produced with from 1.3 to 1.5 feet of irrigation water,[47] and highest yields of cantaloupes with about 3.0 feet of water.[38]

Measurements made in Los Angeles County, California, in 1940, showed that depths of irrigation water applied in producing tomatoes on different soils varied from 1.07 to 1.97 feet, averaging 1.50 feet. In the San Fernando Valley, measurements during 1930 to 1937, when the mean yearly rainfall was 1.33 feet, showed average seasonal deliveries of 1.04 feet for beans and 1.92 feet for asparagus. In the Sacramento and San Joaquin valleys, seasonal deliveries during 1935 to 1942 averaged 1.20 feet for asparagus and 2.00 feet for beans and beets.[51]

Seasonal deliveries of irrigation water for miscellaneous truck crops averaged 1.37 feet in the San Fernando Valley and 2.00 feet in the Sacramento and San Joaquin valleys. In the Coachello Valley, southeastern California, where rainfall is negligible, annual depths of water applied in producing miscellaneous truck crops during 1936 to 1939 averaged 5.00 feet (see Table 13).

TABLE 13

AVERAGE DEPTHS OF IRRIGATION WATER APPLIED TO CROPS
COACHELLA VALLEY, SOUTHEASTERN CALIFORNIA [41]

(Depths in inches)

Month	Alfalfa	Cotton	Truck crops	Grapes	Mixed crops	Citrus	Dates	Dates under 4 yr.
January	2.3	0.0	3.0	1.0	2.6	2.3	3.9	0.5
February	5.8	0.0	4.0	5.2	3.9	4.1	5.2	1.2
March	7.5	3.3	4.5	4.7	5.3	5.7	7.6	3.8
April	9.1	3.4	7.1	5.4	7.3	8.2	10.3	6.3
May	11.7	1.5	9.4	8.3	8.7	11.3	12.0	5.5
June	11.1	4.0	6.8	7.3	7.6	12.8	13.1	5.4
July	13.6	10.8	3.0	5.9	6.4	15.2	14.6	5.9
August	9.9	13.9	1.3	6.4	5.5	15.4	13.4	5.6
September	10.3	13.6	5.5	4.5	7.6	11.0	12.2	6.0
October	6.3	5.7	5.7	0.9	6.1	7.5	6.4	3.6
November	6.2	0.0	5.3	0.6	4.8	4.3	4.0	2.3
December	2.5	0.0	4.4	0.6	2.5	1.6	2.7	0.8
Total, in.	96.3	56.2	60.0	50.8	68.3	99.4	105.4	47.0
Total, ft.	8.02	4.68	5.00	4.23	5.69	8.28	8.78	3.92

Coachella Valley Water Uses. Table 13 shows average monthly and annual depths of water applied to different crops in the Coachella Valley during 1936 to 1939, as reported by Pillsbury.[41] Inasmuch as the mean annual rainfall in the valley is only about 3 inches, irrigation requirements are essentially the same as water requirements. Water supplies for irrigation were obtained from underground sources, largely by pumping. Soils are alluvial deposits, varying from coarse materials to fine sands and fine clay loams. Some percolation probably takes place in most irrigated sections of the valley. Because of the warm climate, crops can be grown throughout the year.

Crops grown in the Coachella Valley include alfalfa, cotton, grapes, citrus fruits, dates, truck vegetables, and a few miscellaneous products. Grapes are mostly the Thompson seedless variety. Citrus fruits are largely grapefruit, with some tangerines. In many orchards, cover crops are grown between the trees during the winter months.

The more common truck crops raised in the Coachella Valley include tomatoes, beans, peas, summer squash, Italian squash, corn, peppers, carrots, okra, lettuce, spring onions, and sweet potatoes. Sweet potatoes and okra are grown during the summer months, but other vegetables are usually grown during the cooler seasons of the year. Frequently, more than one crop can be raised on the same field during the same year.

The data in Table 13 show that maximum monthly applications of irrigation water varied from 6.3 inches for young dates to 15.4 inches for citrus trees. Annual applications varied from 3.92 feet for young dates to 8.78 feet for mature dates. Citrus orchards received 8.28 feet annually, and alfalfa crops 8.02 feet. Grape vineyards received 4.23 feet, and cotton crops 4.68 feet. Areas devoted to cotton production required no irrigation water during November to February. Other crops required some water during all months of the year. Deliveries of irrigation water to some orchards during the winter months probably were increased to supply moisture for cover crops.

Although climatic conditions in the Coachella Valley are unusually favorable for high rates of transpiration and evaporation, the total annual deliveries for most crops probably were somewhat greater than actual irrigation requirements.

Fruit Requirements. In general, fruit crops, except dates, require about the same quantities of water as the more common field crops. Where temperatures and lengths of growing seasons are suitable, both citrus and deciduous fruits, including berries, grapes, and nuts, can be produced profitably with about 1.5 to 4.0 feet of water, including rainfall. Where other conditions are similar, citrus trees probably need a little more water than deciduous trees, because they retain their leaves during the winter. However, differences in soil texture, climate, and cultural practices often obscure effects of differences in winter transpiration. Probably differences in winter transpiration by mature citrus and deciduous trees, growing under similar conditions, seldom exceed about 6 inches.

Dates are the only fruits grown in the irrigated sections of the United States that require unusually large amounts of water. Dates can be produced profitably only in regions of long growing seasons, prolonged high temperatures during the summer, and low relative humidities during the ripening season.

Unusually large amounts of water were delivered to vineyards and citrus orchards in the Coachella Valley, as shown in Table 13, but profitable grape and citrus crops are produced in many parts of the Southwest with normal depths of water. In some parts of California where winter rainfall wets the root zones thoroughly, grapes are produced with but little, if any, irrigation.

TABLE 14

DEPTHS OF IRRIGATION WATER APPLIED TO FRUIT CROPS
WESTERN UNITED STATES

Fruit crop	Location of measurements	Soil type	Growing season, inclusive	Seasonal irrigation, ft.	Annual rainfall, ft.	Ref. no.
Apples *	Canon City, Colo.	Light to heavy loam	Apr.–Sept.	1.28	0.63 †	20
Apples	Snake Valley, Idaho	Fine sandy loam	Apr.–Sept.	1.79	0.42 †	22
Apricots	Hemet, Calif.	Sandy loam	Apr.–Nov.	2.53	1.10	51
Avocados	Vista, Calif.	Sandy loam	Apr.–Oct.	1.54	1.77	51
Berries	Sacramento Valley, Calif.	Not given	Mar.–Oct.	2.80	....	51
Citrus fruit	San Jacinto Valley, Calif.	Sandy loam	Apr.–Oct.	2.66	1.18	51
Dates	Coachella Valley, Calif.	Alluvial	Jan.–Dec.	8.78	0.26	41
Deciduous fruit	Beaumont, Calif.	Not given	Apr.–Nov.	1.52	1.58	51
Deciduous fruit ‡	Wenatchee, Wash.	Sandy loam	Apr.–Oct.	1.61	0.83	22
Figs	San Fernando Valley, Calif.	Not given	Feb.–Dec.	1.07	1.33	51
Grapes	San Fernando Valley, Calif.	Not given	Feb.–Dec.	0.50	1.33	51
Grapes	Sacramento Valley, Calif.	Not given	Mar.–Oct.	2.10	....	51
Grapefruit	Rialto, Calif.	Sandy loam	Apr.–Oct.	1.92	1.32	42
Lemons	San Diego County, Calif.	Sandy loam	Apr. 1–Oct. 15	1.30	1.39	51
Olives	San Fernando Valley, Calif.	Not given	Feb.–Dec.	0.91	1.33	51
Oranges	Riverside, Calif.	Loam	Apr.–Oct.	1.80	0.93	42
Peaches	Ontario, Calif.	Sand	Apr.–Oct.	2.58	....	51
Pears	Antelope Valley, Calif.	Not given	Mar.–Oct.	1.43	0.50	51
Pears	Medford, Ore.	Heavy	Apr.–Sept.	1.50	1.39	37
Small fruits §	Corvallis, Ore.	Sandy loam and loam	Apr.–Aug.	1.5–2.0	0.42 †	10
Walnuts	Orange County, Calif.	Sandy loam	Apr.–Oct.	1.61	1.29	51
Walnuts	Hemet, Calif.	Sandy loam	Apr.–Oct.	2.90	1.27	51

* Clean cultivated.
† Seasonal rainfall.
‡ Mostly apples, some cherry, peach, pear, and plum trees; clean cultivated.
§ Loganberries, blackberries, raspberries, and strawberries.

Table 14 gives average seasonal depths of irrigation water applied to different fruit crops on some areas in western United States. Pertinent data regarding locations, soil types, growing seasons, and annual depths of rainfall are shown. Many additional records of irrigation deliveries for fruit crops are given in the original publications. The apple orchards at Canon City, Colorado, and the deciduous orchards at Wenatchee, Washington, were clean cultivated. A few additional orchards represented in the table may have been clean cultivated, but most California orchards probably included some winter vegetation, either from fall seedings or growth of native plants.

Except for dates, depths of seasonal irrigation shown in Table 14 do not exceed 2.9 feet. In California, 2.66 feet were applied to citrus fruits on sandy loam soils in the San Jacinto Valley, 2.58 feet to peaches on sand near Ontario, 2.53 feet to apricots on sandy loam near Hemet, and 2.10 feet to grapes on certain areas in the Sacramento Valley. In the San Fernando Valley, grapes received only 0.50 foot, olives received 0.91 foot, and figs 1.07 feet. Greater depths of water are used in some locations where ample supplies are available.

Walnut trees near Hemet received an average of 2.90 feet of irrigation water during 1935 to 1938, but trees in Orange County received an average of only 1.60 feet during the 10-year period from 1929 to 1938. Almonds, not listed in the table, probably need less water than walnuts.

Young trees use less water than mature trees. In the Coachella Valley, dates under 4 years required about 45 per cent as much water as mature trees (see Table 13). Near Delhi, California, peach trees were supplied with 1.34 feet of water when 3 years old, and 1.81 feet when 6 years old.[32] They produced some fruit during the fourth year.

Summary of Crop Requirements. Although moisture requirements of different crops grown in different regions and on different soils vary widely, as discussed on the preceding pages, it may be pertinent to summarize briefly the ranges in depth of water needed by the more common crops. Except in certain unusually warm and arid interior locations, such as the Coachella and Imperial valleys, water requirements for profitable production, including rainfall, are about as follows:

Alfalfa and other forage crops, including pastures	1.0 to 6.0 feet or more
Potatoes, sugar beets, and cotton	1.5 to 3.5 feet
Cereals, except rice	1.0 to 2.5 feet
Rice	4.5 to 9.5 feet
Deciduous fruits	2.0 to 3.5 feet
Small fruits and grapes	1.5 to 3.0 feet

Citrus fruits, with and without cover

crops	2.0 to 4.0 feet
Walnuts and almonds	2.0 to 3.5 feet
Vegetables, garden and truck products	1.0 to 4.0 feet

Seasonal depths of irrigation water required for profitable production equal the above depths minus such quantities of soil moisture as may become available as a result of precipitation.

Mature date palms, a specialized crop grown commercially only in the warm and arid interior valleys of the Southwest, probably require from 6 to 10 feet of water annually. However, irrigation deliveries greater than 10 feet are sometimes supplied to dates in the Coachella Valley.

REFERENCES

1. Adams, Frank, "Rice Irrigation Measurements and Experiments in Sacramento Valley, 1914–1919," *Calif. Agr. Exp. Sta. Bull.* 325, 1920.
2. Adams, Frank, and others, "Investigations of Economical Duty of Water for Alfalfa in Sacramento Valley, California, 1910–1915," *Calif. Dept. Eng. Bull.* 3, 1917.
3. Adams, Frank, F. J. Veihmeyer, and Lloyd N. Brown, "Cotton Irrigation Investigations in San Joaquin Valley, California, 1926 to 1935," *Calif. Agr. Exp. Sta. Bull.* 668, 1942.
4. Bailey, Paul, "Irrigation Requirements of California Lands," *Calif. Dept. Pub. Works Bull.* 6, 1923.
5. Bark, Don H., "Experiments on the Economical Use of Irrigation Water in Idaho," *U.S. Dept. Agr. Bull.* 339, 1916.
6. Bartel, A. T., and Charles Hobart, "Irrigation Experiments with Wheat," *Ariz. Agr. Exp. Sta. Bull.* 151, 1935.
7. Batchelor, L. D., O. L. Braucher, and E. F. Serr, "Walnut Production in California," *Calif. Agr. Exp. Sta. Cir.* 364, 1945.
8. Beckett, S. H., and Carroll F. Dunshee, "Water Requirements of Cotton on Sandy Loam Soils in Southern San Joaquin Valley," *Calif. Agr. Exp. Sta. Bull.* 537, 1932.
9. Bloodgood, Dean W., and Albert S. Curry, "Net Requirements of Crops for Irrigation Water in the Mesilla Valley, New Mexico," *N. Mex. Agr. Exp. Sta. Bull.* 149, 1925.
10. Brown, W. S., "Influences of Irrigation upon Important Small Fruits," *Ore. Agr. Exp. Sta. Bull.* 347, 1936.
11. Clyde, Harry S., Willard Gardner, and Orson W. Israelsen, "The Economical Use of Irrigation Water Based on Tests," *Eng. News-Rec.*, Oct. 4, 1923, pp. 548–552.
12. Curry, A. S., "Results of Irrigation Treatments on Acala Cotton Grown in the Mesilla Valley, New Mexico," *N. Mex. Agr. Exp. Sta. Bull.* 220, 1934.
13. ——— "Irrigation Experiments with the Early Grano Onion," *N. Mex. Agr. Exp. Sta. Bull.* 245, 1937.

14. Curry, A. S., "Effect of Irrigation Practices on the Growth and Yield of White Grano Onions," *N. Mex. Agr. Exp. Sta. Bull.* 281, 1941.

15. Debler, E. B., "Use of Water on Federal Irrigation Projects," *Trans. Am. Soc. C. E.*, Vol. 94, 1930, pp. 1195–1241.

16. Dunshee, Carroll F., "Rice Experiments in Sacramento Valley, 1922–1927," *Calif. Agr. Exp. Sta. Bull.* 454, 1928.

17. Ewalt, H. P., and I. R. Jones, "The Value of Irrigated Pastures for Dairy Cattle," *Ore. Agr. Exp. Sta. Bull.* 366, 1939.

18. Fife, Arthur, "Duty-of-Water Investigations on Coal Creek, Utah," *Utah Agr. Exp. Sta. Bull.* 181, 1922.

19. Fortier, Samuel, "Irrigation Requirements of the Arable Lands of the Great Basin," *U.S. Dept. Agr. Bull.* 1340, 1925.

20. ―――― "Irrigation Requirements of the Arid and Semiarid Lands of the Missouri and Arkansas River Basins," *U.S. Dept. Agr. Tech. Bull.* 36, 1928.

21. Fortier, Samuel, and Arthur A. Young, "Irrigation Requirements of the Arid and Semiarid Lands of the Southwest," *U.S. Dept. Agr. Tech. Bull.* 185, 1930.

22. ―――― "Irrigation Requirements of the Arid and Semiarid Lands of the Columbia River Basin," *U.S. Dept. Agr. Tech. Bull.* 200, 1930.

23. ―――― "Irrigation Requirements of the Arid and Semiarid Lands of the Pacific Slope Basins," *U.S. Dept. Agr. Tech. Bull.* 379, 1933.

24. Fortier, Samuel, and others, "Irrigation Practices in Growing Alfalfa," *U.S. Dept. Agr. Farmers' Bull.* 1630, 1940.

25. Gustafson, E. N., "Irrigation of Rice in the United States," *Civ. Eng.*, July 1937, pp. 501–503.

26. Hamilton, J. G., and others, "Irrigated Pastures for Forage Production and Soil Conservation," *U.S. Dept. Agr. Farmers' Bull.* 1973, 1945.

27. Harris, F. S., "The Duty of Water in Cache Valley, Utah," *Utah Agr. Exp. Sta. Bull.* 173, 1920.

28. Harris, Karl, and R. S. Hawkins, "Irrigation Requirements of Cotton on Clay Loam Soils in the Salt River Valley," *Ariz. Agr. Exp. Sta. Bull.* 181, 1942.

29. Hastings, Stephen H., "Irrigation and Related Cultural Practices with Cotton in the Salt River Valley of Arizona," *U.S. Dept. Agr. Cir.* 200, 1932.

30. Hawthorn, Leslie R., "Cultural Experiments with Yellow Bermuda Onions under Irrigation," *Tex. Agr. Exp. Sta. Bull.* 561, 1938.

31. Hemphill, Robert G., "Irrigation in Northern Colorado," *U.S. Dept. Agr. Bull.* 1026, 1922.

32. Hendrickson, A. H., and F. J. Veihmeyer, "Irrigation Experiments with Peaches in California," *Calif. Agr. Exp. Sta. Bull.* 479, 1929.

33. ―――― "Irrigation Experiments with Prunes," *Calif. Agr. Exp. Sta. Bull.* 573, 1934.

34. ―――― "Irrigation Experiments with Pears and Apples," *Calif. Agr. Exp. Sta. Bull.* 667, 1942.

35. Israelsen, Orson W., and Luther M. Winsor, "The Net Duty of Water in Sevier Valley," *Utah Agr. Exp. Sta. Bull.* 182, 1922.

36. Knight, C. S., and George Hardman, "Irrigation of Field Crops in Nevada," *Nev. Agr. Exp. Sta. Bull.* 96, 1919.

37. Lewis, M. R., R. A. Work, and W. W. Aldrich, "Studies of the Irrigation of Pear Orchards on Heavy Soil near Medford, Oreg.," *U.S. Dept. Agr. Tech. Bull.* 432, 1934.

38. Marr, James C., "The Use and Duty of Water in the Salt River Valley," *Ariz. Agr. Exp. Sta. Bull.* 120, 1927.
39. McDowell, C. H., "Irrigation Requirements of Cotton and Grain Sorghum in the Wichita Valley of Texas," *Tex. Agr. Exp. Sta. Bull.* 543, 1937.
40. Nixon, Roy W., and Dewey C. Moore, "Date Growing in the United States," *U.S. Dept. Agr. Leaflet* 170, 1939.
41. Pillsbury, Arthur F., "Observations on Use of Irrigation Water in Coachella Valley, California," *Calif. Agr. Exp. Sta. Bull.* 649, 1941.
42. Pillsbury, Arthur F., O. C. Compton, and W. E. Picker, "Irrigation-Water Requirements of Citrus in the South Coastal Basin of California," *Calif. Agr. Exp. Sta. Bull.* 686, 1944.
43. Pittman, D. W., and George Stewart, "Twenty-Eight Years of Irrigation Experiments near Logan, Utah, 1902–29, Inclusive," *Utah Agr. Exp. Sta. Bull.* 219, 1930.
44. Powers, W. L., "Twenty-Five Years of Supplemental Irrigation Investigations in Willamette Valley," *Ore. Agr. Exp. Sta. Bull.* 302, 1932.
45. Powers, W. L., and M. R. Lewis, "Irrigation Requirement of Arable Oregon Soils," *Ore. Agr. Exp. Sta. Bull.* 394, 1941.
46. Schuster, C. E., and others, "Preliminary Report on Effect of Irrigation on Major Berry Crops in the Willamette Valley," *Ore. Agr. Exp. Sta. Bull.* 277, 1931.
47. Schwalen, H. C., and M. F. Wharton, "Lettuce Irrigation Studies," *Ariz. Agr. Exp. Sta. Bull.* 133, 1930.
48. Scofield, Carl S., and Orlando W. Howe, "Water Input Used for Field Crops at the United States Scotts Bluff (Nebr.) Field Station, 1941–44," *U.S. Dept. Agr. Cir.* 777, 1948.
49. Snelson, W. H., "Irrigation Practice and Water Requirements for Crops in Alberta," *Can. Int. Dept., Irr. Ser. Bull.* 7, 1930.
50. Taylor, C. A., "Irrigation Problems in Citrus Orchards," *U.S. Dept. Agr. Farmers' Bull.* 1876, 1941.
51. Young, Arthur A., "Irrigation Requirements of California Crops," *Calif. Dept. Pub. Works Bull.* 51, 1945.

Chapter 12

LOSSES AND WASTE OF
IRRIGATION WATER

Losses and waste of irrigation water occur in three ways: (1) in conveyance and distribution systems while water is in transit from points of diversion to the farms; (2) in farm ditches or conduits while farmers are using water; and (3) in furrows, corrugations, or flooded basins while irrigators are delivering water to field units.

Reductions in flow from points of diversion to places of use constitute conveyance losses and waste. Water lost or wasted in furrows, corrugations, or flooded basins during deliveries of water constitute irrigation losses and waste.

Conveyance losses and waste from points of diversion to farm head gates depend on the design and construction of the conveyance and distribution systems and on the efficiencies of the project representatives who operate and maintain the systems. Conveyance losses and waste in farm ditches or conduits depend on the design and construction of the farm distribution systems and on the efficiencies of the farmers in taking their water supplies. Irrigation losses and waste during delivery depend on slopes of ground surfaces, soil conditions, subdivision of farms into field units, preparation of field surfaces, methods of irrigating, and skill of the irrigators.

Amounts of water lost and wasted in both transit and delivery usually are high during the early life of a project. Later, as canals become seasoned, lands become adjusted to irrigation, and efforts are made to conserve water, amounts lost and wasted gradually decrease. This is especially true in regions where water supplies are limited and costly, and values of crop products are high. In such regions, considerable expenditures are justified in order to improve conveyance and irrigation efficiencies. However, losses and waste can never be completely eliminated, even with the most costly installations and the most efficient methods of water control.

On irrigation projects producing common types of farm crops, quantities of water actually used in crop growth seldom amount to more than about one-third the total seasonal diversions. In other words, combined conveyance and irrigation efficiencies seldom are higher than about 33 per cent. On most large projects, over-all efficiencies probably vary between about 20 and 35 per cent.

Inasmuch as some losses and waste of irrigation water must always be expected, such losses and waste should be carefully studied in planning new projects, in considering extensions of existing projects, and in operating project systems after conveyance and distribution works are completed.

The following pages discuss elements involved in losses and waste of irrigation water during both transit and delivery, some pertinent data determined on irrigated farms and large irrigation projects, and irrigation efficiencies which are dependent on losses and waste. A general summary of irrigation water, including some items discussed in preceding chapters, is given at the end of the chapter.

IRRIGATION LOSSES AND WASTE

Irrigation losses and waste include evaporation, surface runoff, and percolation. Evaporation and percolation constitute losses. Surface runoff constitutes waste. Although some runoff and percolation may be recovered and subsequently used on lower lands, the farmer should keep losses and waste as low as possible, so that large proportions of the water will be retained in the root zones for crop use.

Losses in farm ditches, although really conveyance losses, may be considered under irrigation losses and waste, inasmuch as the farm ditches are operated by the farmers. When irrigation efficiencies are determined from measurements at farm head gates, losses in farm ditches reduce calculated efficiencies.

When irrigation water is delivered to a field through furrows or by flooding, a small part of the water evaporates during and immediately following delivery, a part runs off the lower end of the field as waste, and the remainder infiltrates into the soil. Some water that enters the soil may move to depths below the root zone. This is percolation. The rest of the infiltration is held in the root zone as capillary moisture. This is the part that becomes available for evapo-transpiration during intervals between irrigations. It is the part that should be kept as high as possible.

When delivery of irrigation water is discontinued, surface runoff and infiltration decrease rapidly and cease as soon as the furrows or field surfaces become drained. Evaporation and percolation may continue at gradually decreasing rates for several days.

Evaporation Losses. Evaporation losses take place from water and moist soil surfaces during irrigation, and from moist soil surfaces during periods following irrigation. They occur at comparatively high rates during and immediately following irrigation, while ground surfaces are wet, but decrease rapidly as the topsoil dries and as moisture in the upper part of the root zone becomes depleted by evaporation and evapo-transpiration.

Evaporation losses during irrigation by flooding are greater than during irrigation through furrows. When water is applied to fields on a hot summer day, rates of evaporation from water and wet soil surfaces may be higher than rates observed in standard measuring pans. This is because of the shallow depths of water and the increased temperatures attained as the water moves over the heated soil surfaces.

When water is applied by sprinkling, additional evaporation losses may be experienced. The small droplets of water lose some volume by evaporation while in the air. Furthermore, some droplets may be intercepted by plant foliage and evaporated without reaching the ground.

After irrigation water is shut off, evaporation losses continue at decreasing rates until the surface soil dries to depths of 6 or 8 inches, or until capillary movements of soil moisture are reduced by mulching or cultivation. Evaporation losses during deliveries of water are not generally of major proportions, owing to the short periods of time consumed in applying the water; but total evaporation losses during irrigation and during the first 2 or 3 days following irrigation may be appreciable.

In warm arid regions, rates of evaporation from flooded fields, irrigated before crops are seeded or before plants become well developed, may be as high as 0.5 inch per day. In such regions, total evaporation losses per irrigation, from the time delivery of water is begun until the topsoil becomes relatively dry, may be from 0.5 to 1.5 inches. In cooler regions, total evaporation losses per irrigation, for similar periods, are lower. On particular projects, such losses vary throughout the growing season, in accordance with weather and crop conditions. Except in unusually warm and arid regions, evaporation losses during irrigation and during the first 2 or 3 days following irrigation probably vary from about 0.3 to 1.0 inch. Some engineers assume an average loss of 0.5 inch per irrigation.

Evaporation losses during irrigation can be reduced by terminating the delivery of water as soon as practicable, or by applying water during the night instead of during the day. Evaporation losses following irrigation can be reduced by mulching or cultivating as soon as possible.[11] However, evaporation losses can never be entirely prevented. In some regions, evaporation losses may be beneficial, because of their cooling effect on the soil. In hot dry climates, frequent irrigations sometimes are made in order to reduce soil temperatures as well as to supply water needed by crops.

In field investigations, reductions in moisture content of the root zone by evaporation during intervals between irrigations can hardly be separated from transpiration, particularly after the crop plants attain considerable growth. Therefore, the two methods of moisture depletion are usually considered together as evapo-transpiration or consumptive use (see Chapter 10).

Surface Runoff. Surface runoff during irrigation may be due to inadequately prepared field surfaces, poorly designed delivery systems, use of excessive heads, application of too much water, or lack of attention during delivery of water. Surface runoff constitutes a waste that can be greatly reduced, often completely eliminated, by proper irrigation procedures. When unavoidable, it often can be recovered and used on adjoining lands at lower elevations.

The control of surface waste is more difficult on tight soils than on pervious soils. Surface runoff is more likely to occur on fields with steep slopes than on fields with flat slopes. Waste is seldom serious on flat lands with pervious soils, but it may be of undesirable proportions on sloping lands or on lands with impervious topsoils. Poorly prepared field surfaces require greater depths of flooding in order to cover high spots. Consequently they may be difficult to irrigate without some surface runoff.

Surface runoff can be measured in drainage ditches at the lower ends of the fields. In Idaho field tests, Bark observed surface runoff varying from 0 to about 31 per cent of the water applied to gravelly soils, and from 0 to about 83 per cent of the water applied to clay loam soils. Average percentages wasted on gravelly soils were 1.8 for alfalfa and 2.3 for grain. Average percentages wasted on clay loams were 19.1 for alfalfa and 25.3 for grain.[2]

Table 1 shows ranges in average surface runoff during the irrigation of some field crops in Utah, expressed as percentages of seasonal

TABLE 1

SURFACE RUNOFF DURING IRRIGATION OF SOME FIELD
CROPS IN UTAH

(Percentages of depths applied)

Crop	Coal Creek Valley, Utah, 1917–1919	Sevier Valley, Utah, 1915–1920		
		Shallow irrigations	Medium irrigations	Heavy irrigations
Alfalfa	13–16	6–28	6–24	11–25
Grain	6–21	....	.....	.....
Potatoes	12–25	1–17	9–28	12–28
Sugar beets	.....	3–26	17–33	20–35

depths applied. The Coal Creek data were reported by Fife,[8] and the Sevier Valley data by Israelsen and Winsor.[15] The Sevier Valley tests showed that percentages of runoff usually increased with increased depths of irrigation water.

On relatively flat areas, farmers can prevent surface runoff by building dikes of suitable height around the lower edges of the fields. If they have lower lands to irrigate, they can excavate ditches to collect runoff from the upper fields and convey the water to the lower lands. Sometimes runoff from one farm can be used on adjoining farms. However, if the farmer is paying for water on a quantity basis, he will want to use all his diversions on his own lands. One of the best methods of reducing surface waste is to assess charges on a quantity basis and to increase the rates when excessive amounts are diverted.

Average percentages of water wasted by surface runoff on large irrigation projects are lower than those wasted on some single farms. Bark concluded that, for normal conditions in Idaho, average deliveries from 7.5 to 12.5 per cent greater than actual crop requirements would be sufficient to allow for surface waste.[2] In a detailed investigation of irrigation practices in the Cache la Poudre Valley, northern Colorado, Hemphill found that the average surface runoff was only about 6 per cent of the total depth applied.[13]

Inasmuch as large proportions of the surface runoff from single farms can be recovered and used on lower lands, allowances of 10 per cent for surface waste probably are adequate in considering needs for water on large irrigation projects.

Percolation Losses. Percolation following irrigation continues until the moisture content of the wetted soil is reduced to field capacity. If the depth of the wetted soil exceeds the depth of the root zone, some percolation loss takes place. Infiltrated water that percolates to depths below the plant roots, unlike surface runoff, is not visible. Therefore, percolation may not always receive adequate consideration.

Percolation losses depend on depths of water applied to the fields, distances the water must travel in reaching the lower ends of the fields, ground slopes, soil texture throughout the root zones, and various additional factors, as discussed in Chapter 5.

Soil conditions constitute an important influence on percolation. Percolation losses seldom occur in irrigating clay or adobe soils. On such soils, the principal problem is to secure sufficient infiltration rather than to prevent deep percolation. On loose sandy soils or shallow loams underlaid by porous materials, percolation losses may be of undesirable proportions if irrigation procedures are not carefully planned and properly conducted. The high deliveries required on the King Hill Project, southern Idaho, because of pervious soils, are mentioned in the preceding chapter.

From the viewpoint of water conservation, percolation losses may not be objectionable when they can be recovered by pumping and used on other areas, or when they occur on well-drained lands where they move back to the streams as return flow. They are objectionable on poorly drained lands because they raise groundwater levels. If the water table rises too high, plant roots may be rotted, salts may accumulate in the topsoils, and low lands may become seeped until they can no longer be cultivated. Excessive percolation during early irrigation in the West caused the development of large areas of alkali and water-logged lands.

From the viewpoint of the farmer, percolation losses generally are objectionable. On soils containing high percentages of undesirable salts, some deep percolation may be needed to flush concentrated soil solutions beyond the plant roots. However, large amounts of percolation are undesirable, not only because they result in losses of water and may result in rising water tables but also because they leach out mineral nutrients and thus reduce supplies of plant food.

Accurate measurements of percolation losses in irrigated fields are not practicable. Approximate estimates can be made from moisture analyses of soil samples taken periodically at different depths. In special investigations which include lysimeter installations, direct measurements of percolation are possible. Except on unusually porous soils, seasonal percolation losses probably vary between 0 and about 1.5 acre-feet per acre.

Lysimeter Measurements of Percolation. Lysimeter measurements of percolation probably do not accurately represent percolation losses under field conditions. Nevertheless, data obtained at lysimeters are valuable in that they illustrate the variations in percolation that may occur through different soils, with different crop surfaces, when supplied with variable amounts of irrigation water.

Table 2 shows seasonal percolations through some soils at Umatilla, Oregon, from 1915 to 1931, as determined during lysimeter investiga-

TABLE 2

SEASONAL PERCOLATION AT UMATILLA, OREGON, AS DETERMINED
BY LYSIMETER MEASUREMENTS [12]

Year	Inches of water applied to lysimeter no.		Percolation, in per cent of water applied as observed at lysimeter no.							
	1 to 6	7 and 8	1	2	3	4	5	6	7	8
1915	38.66	......	64	48	35	34	..	..	..	..
6	50.36	......	76	41	12	12	..	..	..	..
7	53.57	42.00	74	41	31	21	12	24	0	0
8	61.67	61.67	62	48	15	12	10	23	0	0
9	60.33	60.33	62	46	14	9	6	18	0	0
1920	57.19	57.19	74	45	17	12	11	30	0	0
1	61.38	61.38	67	41	12	9	2	25	0	0
2	61.02	113.02	65	42	13	9	1	17	0	0
3	72.64	141.64	82	43	12	13	5	25	13	16
4	68.00	134.00	78	32	18	9	4	18	2	7
1925	57.43	88.93	70	54	35	38	25	45	21	13
6	61.12	121.12	72	22	1	6	0	4	0	0
7	59.67	122.67	73	44	12	16	3	30	14	13
8	61.24	121.24	67	38	4	3	0	5	4	0
9	51.74	102.74	65	33	23	25	31	39	22	19
1930	54.50	108.50	70	63	9	8	3	14	5	8
1	57.63	114.63	73	33	5	5	2	11	7	7
Means:										
1915–1921	54.74	56.51	68	44	19	16	8	24	0	0
1922–1931	60.50	116.85	72	40	13	13	7	21	9	8
1922–1931 *	.....	......	43.56	24.20	7.86	7.86	4.24	12.70	10.52	9.35
Crops	.....	......	None	Soy-beans and vetch	Alfalfa on lysimeters 3 to 8					
Soils	.....	......	Sandy	Sandy	Sandy	Sandy	Fine sandy	†	Very fine sandy loam	Silt loam

* Percolation in inches.
† Intermediate between 4 and 5.

tions reported by Hastings and Dean.[12] Seasonal amounts of percolation are given as percentages of total water applied, including seasonal rainfall. Depths of water applied are given in inches. Average
depths of seasonal percolation from 1922 to 1931, in inches, also notes
on crops and soils, are shown in the lower part of the tabulation.
Alfalfa was reseeded on lysimeter 3 in the spring of 1917, and on
lysimeters 3 to 8 in 1921 and 1925. Manure was applied to the soil
in lysimeter 4 during all years between 1915 and 1921, except 1918.

The Oregon lysimeters were built with oil-mixed concrete. They
were 3.3 feet square, inside, by 6 feet deep, with drains and percolation
measuring installations at the bottoms. Soil was taken from field
sites, in 6-inch increments of depth down to 6 feet, and placed in the
lysimeters in the same position as in the field.

The data in Table 2 show that average seasonal applications of
60.50 inches of water to sandy soils during 1922 to 1931 caused average percolation losses of 43.56 inches at the uncropped lysimeter,
24.20 inches at lysimeter 2 where soybeans were grown in the summer
and hairy vetch in the winter, and 7.86 inches at lysimeters 3 and 4
where alfalfa crops were grown. At lysimeter 5, where alfalfa was
grown on a fine sandy soil, the percolation for the same application
of water was 4.24 inches. The percolation of 12.70 inches at lysimeter 6, also growing alfalfa, seems to be somewhat high, since the soil
was described as being intermediate between the sandy and fine sandy
types.

Comparisons of results obtained at lysimeters 7 and 8 with those
obtained at lysimeters 3 to 6, all growing alfalfa, are particularly
pertinent. Average percolation losses through the fine-textured soils
in lysimeters 7 and 8 were only slightly greater than those through
the sandy soils in lysimeters 3 to 6, although depths of water applied
were nearly twice as great. In fact, no percolation losses occurred at
lysimeters 7 and 8 during 1917 to 1921, when depths of water input
varied from 42.00 to 61.67 inches, during 1922 when the water input
was 113.02 inches, or during 1926 when the water input was 121.12
inches.

Reducing Percolation Losses. Percolation losses in pervious soils
may be reduced by providing properly planned systems of field
ditches, applying water in relatively shallow depths, and carefully controlling irrigation deliveries. Ditches should be laid out so that water
can be released to the land at different locations, as needed, and can
reach all parts of the irrigation units without flowing long distances.

The aim should be to apply only such amounts of water as can be retained in the root zones.

Sometimes percolation losses can be reduced by working organic matter into the soil to improve structural conditions, adding chemicals that deflocculate the soil particles, or irrigating with silty water. Such methods also add fertilizing elements to the soil. Care must be exercised to prevent excessive deflocculation, also to prevent too great an accumulation of silt at the soil surface. The continued use of silty water on some lands resulted in the formation of tight surface coatings that reduced infiltration too much and caused difficulties in tillage.

Percolation rates in sandy soils can be greatly reduced by relatively small additions of silt, when the silt particles can be thoroughly mixed with the sand. McGeorge found that 10 per cent of Colorado River silt added to sandy soils on the Yuma Mesa, southwestern Arizona, reduced percolation rates as much as 75 per cent.[18] The silt also decreased rates of capillary moisture movements, decreased the size of the pore spaces, and increased the total volume of pore spaces, so that greater amounts of moisture could be held in the soil. The silt improved fertility by increasing available quantities of potash and phosphate.

In sandy soils deficient in organic matter, some improvements in structure and moisture properties probably can be attained by adding considerable proportions of peat or other organic materials. Changes in infiltration rates that may be caused by applications of certain fertilizers are mentioned briefly in Chapter 5.

Losses in Farm Ditches. Losses of water in farm ditches occur principally by seepage. Some evaporation takes place at the water surfaces and some transpiration by native vegetation takes place along the banks, but evapo-transpiration consumptions are small in comparison with the amounts of water that seep through the bed and banks of the ditches.

Losses of water per unit length of farm ditches depend primarily on the permeability of the earth materials through which the ditches are excavated. They may be affected to some extent by weeds along the channels, gopher infestations, and depths of flow. Rates of infiltration when water is turned into dry ditches are higher than after the perimeters become saturated. In regions of high groundwater, seepage losses may be affected by elevations of the water tables.

In the Scotts Bluff investigations reported by Scofield and Howe, ditch losses sometimes were as high as 4 per cent per 100 feet of ditch

length. Average losses during the first 3 hours after water was turned
into dry ditches were about 1 per cent per 100 feet. Materials
through which the ditches were located were sandy loams.[25]

In the Idaho investigations reported by Bark, measurements in a
large number of ditches carrying less than 5 second-feet of water,
excavated through soils of different texture, showed losses varying
from about 2 to 58 per cent of the discharge per mile of length.[2]

In general, losses in farm ditches probably vary from about 5 to 50
per cent of the discharge per mile of length. Total quantities of
water lost depend on the length of the ditches. For small farms, located close to supply canals, total losses in farm ditches are relatively
small. For large farms, where water must flow long distances before
being delivered to the fields, total amounts of water lost in the ditches
may be of considerable proportions. Losses in large canals and
laterals are discussed in subsequent sections.

Transpiration losses along farm ditches can be prevented by keeping
the channels free from vegetation. Seepage losses can be greatly reduced by lining the beds and banks with good concrete or other impervious materials. All losses can be reduced to negligible proportions
by installing underground pipe distribution systems, as sometimes is
done in fruit-growing regions where water supplies are limited and
costly.

Irrigation Efficiencies. Irrigation efficiencies, as defined in the preceding chapter, are percentages of the irrigation deliveries that are
retained in the root zones where they are available for use in crop
growth. In other words, they represent proportions of the deliveries
remaining in the upper soil layers after all losses and waste of water
are deducted. Irrigation efficiencies sometimes are referred to as
water-application efficiencies.

When water is scarce and crop products are unusually valuable, as
in some irrigated sections of the Southwest, relatively high irrigation
efficiencies may be obtained. In such sections, large expenditures are
justified in order to conserve water. In farming regions where crop
returns do not warrant large expenditures in order to reduce losses
and waste, irrigation water is applied with lower efficiencies than
otherwise would be possible. This is especially true in regions where
large supplies of water are available.

An average irrigation efficiency of about 80 per cent during 3 years
of tests was reported by Pillsbury for some date plots in the Coachella
Valley, southeastern California.[22] However, he emphasized that such
efficiencies might not be obtained in actual practice without excessive

labor and investment costs. Considerably lower efficiencies were reported for furrow-irrigations in some citrus orchards in southern California. Measurements for oranges and lemons growing on gravelly loam soils showed efficiencies varying from 21 to 74 per cent, averaging 44 per cent.[23]

Tests for different crops produced on different soils in the Pecos River valley, New Mexico, reported by Blaney and his associates in 1942,[21] showed the following irrigation efficiencies:

Fort Sumner area
    Orchards on sandy loam and fine sand   67–70 per cent
    Corn on silt loams   32–46 per cent
Carlsbad-Malaga area
    Cotton on fine sand and fine sandy loam   22–76 per cent
    Alfalfa on silt loam   34–47 per cent
    Alfalfa on fine sandy loam and fine sand   26–65 per cent

Irrigation efficiencies for cotton on sandy loam soils at the United States Cotton Field Station, Shafter, California, during 1927 to 1930, were reported by Beckett and Dunshee in 1932.[3] Measurements on field plots, 16 by 90 feet in size, irrigated by different flooding treatments, showed average efficiencies during the growing season varying from 69.4 to 75.5 per cent for the different treatments, with a general average of 72.8 per cent for all treatments during the four growing seasons.

Irrigation efficiencies for field crops in Utah were reported by Israelsen and his associates in 1944.[16] Investigations were made on 11 farms in Utah County and 6 farms in Salt Lake County. Cropped areas on the different farms varied from about 13 to 68 acres. Crops included alfalfa, grain, pasture, orchard fruit, berries, beets, potatoes, and several types of vegetables. Soils varied from gravelly and sandy loams to clay loams and clays. Depths of root zones varied from 2 to 5 feet.

The Utah measurements showed some high efficiencies, but most values were lower than 60 per cent. In Utah County, average farm efficiencies varied from 24 to 51 per cent, averaging 40 per cent. In Salt Lake County, average farm efficiencies varied from 18 to 58 per cent, averaging 35 per cent. In some fields, efficiencies during single irrigations were lower than 10 per cent. The tests usually showed higher efficiencies for deep-rooted crops than for shallow-rooted crops, but some exceptions were noted. In general, low efficiencies were due to applications of too much water per irrigation, uneven distribution of water over the field surfaces, irrigating when the soil was too moist, or combinations of such conditions.

The curves in Figure 1, plotted from similar diagrams in Israelsen's report, show variations of irrigation efficiencies with depths per irrigation. Points shown on the original diagrams are omitted. The curves show that for the crops and soils in Utah, depths of application greater than about 5 inches resulted in irrigation efficiencies lower than about 50 per cent.

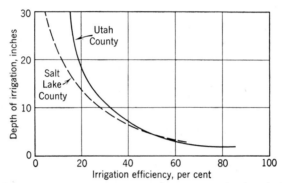

FIGURE 1.   Irrigation efficiencies for different depths per irrigation, in Utah.   (After Israelsen and others.[16])

Probably 50 per cent is about as high an average efficiency as ordinarily can be obtained in irrigating common types of farm, orchard, and vegetable crops. Average irrigation efficiencies on large projects probably vary between about 30 and 50 per cent.

CONVEYANCE LOSSES AND WASTE

Conveyance losses and waste include (1) evaporation from canal surfaces; (2) evapo-transpiration by native vegetation on canal banks; (3) seepage through the bed and banks of the channels; and (4) such waste as may occur naturally or inadvertently, or may be necessary in operating the conveyance and distribution system. Amounts of water lost by leakage at canal structures are considered as elements of waste.

Evaporation losses, which fortunately are small, cannot be recovered. Evapo-transpiration losses, although not recoverable, can be greatly reduced by removing vegetation from canal banks. Seepage losses, which often are of considerable proportions, can be recovered by pumping or drainage. When not recovered, some portions of the seepage losses find their way back to stream channels as return flow. Other portions build up seeped areas where subsequent seepage losses are evaporated or transpired by native vegetation. Under special geological and groundwater conditions, seepage losses sometimes percolate into adjoining drainage basins.

Amounts of water wasted at canal structures, or at the downstream ends of canals, usually return to stream channels as surface runoff through natural or artificial drainage courses. Such amounts, together with seepage losses that reach stream channels, can be rediverted at downstream locations and used to supply irrigable acreages at lower elevations. Exceptions may occur when seepage waters percolate through alkali soils and attain salt concentrations too high for irrigation use.

From the general viewpoint of water conservation, large conveyance losses and waste are not especially objectionable when the water can be recovered and used beneficially at other locations. From the viewpoint of a particular project, large losses and waste generally are objectionable, even when ample water supplies are available. Continued waste at some control works may impair the operation and safety of the structures. At poorly drained locations, seepage from canals may impair the stability of the banks as well as damage adjoining lands by producing seeped areas. Seepage losses may raise water tables along the canals until costly drainage improvements are necessary for continued cultivation.

The following pages present brief discussions of conveyance losses and waste on irrigation projects, particularly seepage losses, which are of major importance. Some summarized data on observed canal losses and waste are included.

Evaporation from Canal Surfaces. Losses of water by evaporation from canal surfaces depend on areas of the water surfaces and prevailing rates of evaporation. They seldom amount to appreciable quantities of water, even on midsummer days in hot arid climates. Possible magnitudes of such losses may be estimated on the basis of evaporation rates observed at local evaporation stations.

An evaporation rate of 0.5 inch per day, which is about as high as may be experienced during warm summer weather in most irrigated regions, would cause a loss of about 2 acre-feet per day in a canal 20 feet wide at the water surface and 20 miles long. This would be equivalent to a continuous flow of 1 second-foot, a flow that ordinarily would be less than 1 per cent of the discharge in a canal of such width.

Evaporation losses from canal surfaces, expressed as percentages of canal flow, may be a little higher than 1 per cent in wide canals carrying shallow depths of water, but usually are negligible in comparison with other items of losses and waste, particularly seepage. They can be ignored in most studies of water supply for irrigation projects.

Evapo-Transpiration at Canal Banks. Quantities of water lost from canals by evapo-transpiration at canal banks depend principally on the nature of the bank materials and the extent to which weeds and other types of native vegetation are allowed to grow along the banks. When growths are unrestricted, evapo-transpiration may take place at relatively high rates, expressed as inches per day. When vegetation is removed and bank materials are favorable for capillary movements of moisture, soil evaporation may take place at relatively rapid rates from moistened areas along the edges of the water surfaces.

Because of the limited areas involved, total quantities of water lost by evapo-transpiration at canal banks seldom are serious. They may amount to small percentages of the canal flow when vegetation is allowed to grow along the edges of shallow canals. However, if too high, they can be greatly reduced by removing the vegetation and lining the bank slopes. Such losses, like evaporation at canal surfaces, usually can be ignored in water-supply studies.

Evapo-transpiration consumptions by native vegetation on low areas along the outer edges of canal banks are supplied by seepage through the bed and banks of the canals. Therefore they are included in canal seepage. They may amount to considerable quantities of water (see Chapter 10).

Seepage Losses. Seepage losses through the beds and banks of canals and laterals take place principally in unlined channels excavated through earth materials. Some seepage losses occur in lined channels, but when the linings have been properly constructed and maintained the losses are small in comparison with those that occur in unlined channels. In canals where linings have deteriorated and disintegrated, so that the concrete is porous, cracked, and open at the joints, seepage losses may be as high as in unlined canals.

Most water supplies delivered to irrigated farms in the West are conveyed through unlined channels. According to the sixteenth census of irrigation in the United States, the total length of all irrigation canals and laterals in 1940 was approximately 127,500 miles, of which only 3.67 per cent were lined. Probably many of the canal linings were ineffective in preventing seepage losses.

Seepage losses in canals and laterals may be expressed in three ways: (1) as quantities of flow in second-feet lost per mile of canal length; (2) as percentages of total canal flow lost per mile of canal; or (3) as average quantities of water in cubic feet lost through each square foot of wetted area per 24 hours. The second and third methods are commonly used in discussions of seepage. The percentage of flow lost per mile shows the general efficiency of the canal as regards seepage. However, the second-feet lost per mile, or the cubic feet lost per square foot per 24 hours, probably are more useful, especially when seepage losses are measured and compared in different sections of a particular canal.

In general, total seepage losses in conveyance on large irrigation projects, where only small percentages of the canal lengths are lined, vary from about 15 to 45 per cent of the total diversions. On small irrigation projects where large percentages of the canal lengths are effectively lined, total seepage losses may vary from about 5 to 15 per cent of the diversions. Ordinarily, expenditures involved in reducing seepage losses to values as low as 5 per cent are economically justified only in regions where water supplies are insufficient and crop products are unusually valuable.

Where crop returns do not justify the installation of costly linings, seepage losses may be reduced by running silty water through the canals. This method is often used to tighten the channel materials when the canals are first put into operation. Runs of silty water should be discontinued as soon as thin impermeable coatings are formed along the wetted perimeters; otherwise the deposits may increase in thickness until canal capacities are impaired.

When operation of the All-American Canal, southeastern California, was begun in September 1940, seepage losses in two sections, based on input, were about 2.1 and 2.5 per cent per mile. During the first 9 months of operation, these losses were reduced, largely by silting, to about 0.2 and 0.5 per cent per mile, corresponding to total losses of 4 and 18 per cent in the total lengths of the two sections. Figure 2 shows variations in discharge and seepage losses in the two sections during the early months of operation, plotted from a similar diagram prepared by Foster.[10]

The All-American Canal is an unusually large canal, designed for an input capacity of 15,155 second-feet. Sections where the seepage measurements were made are from 130 to 160 feet wide. The more permeable portions were lined with compacted clay materials. During 1941, about 540 tons of suspended silt were carried into the canal daily. About 92 per cent of the silt particles were smaller than 0.05 millimeter, and about 50 per cent smaller than 0.005 millimeter.

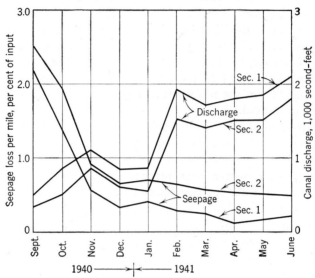

FIGURE 2.   Variations in discharge and seepage loss, All-American Canal.   (After Foster.)

Factors Affecting Seepage.   Factors that affect seepage in unlined canals and laterals are principally those that affect movements of soil moisture (see Chapter 5).   Water infiltrates into the beds and banks of the channels and moves through the open pores and passageways in the earth materials in accordance with hydrostatic pressures, gravity forces, and capillary tensions.

At locations along water surfaces in canals, some water is drawn into the smaller pore spaces in the bank materials and moved outward and upward by capillarity.   At locations below the water surfaces, water is moved outward and downward through the pore spaces in the bank materials by capillarity and gravity, and downward through the pore spaces in the beds and banks, principally by gravity. Probably the greater portions of the seepage losses in unlined channels take place through the larger pore spaces and passageways, the water percolating downward, owing to gravity, until it finally reaches the underlying water table.

Downward movements of water through canal beds and through the lower portions of the banks are aided by hydrostatic pressures in the canals. Thus, rates of seepage and total seepage losses usually are somewhat greater when the canals are carrying water at full capacity. Seepage losses expressed as percentages of canal flow usually are greater when the canals are only partly filled, inasmuch as canal flows increase with depth more rapidly than rates of seepage.

Rates of seepage loss in unlined canals and laterals are also affected by elevations of the water table in the soil formations through which the channels are excavated. When the water table is above the bed of the channel, percolation through the bed and lower portions of the banks is greatly retarded. When the water table is above the flow line, groundwater moves through the wetted perimeter into the canal sections, thus causing seepage gains instead of seepage losses.

Seepage losses are affected to some extent by water temperatures and accompanying changes in viscosity. However, considerations of data obtained by measurements usually show that temperature effects are obscured by other influences or by unavoidable inaccuracies in observed data.

Seepage losses in canals vary from place to place along the channels, principally with the permeabilities of the bed and bank materials. Losses commonly occur at maximum rates when water is turned into dry channels, then decrease slowly as the bed and banks become saturated to increasing distances from the wetted perimeters. Seepage losses in new unlined canals usually are higher than in old canals. Canal perimeters gradually become seasoned and tightened by continued use, particularly when canal flows carry silt particles that settle out and seal the openings in the bed and bank materials.

Determining Seepage Losses. Seepage losses in existing canals may be determined by two methods: (1) by measurements of inflow and outflow in selected lengths of the canal, preferably as long as possible; and (2) by measurements of the drop in water surface in sections of the canal where all inflow and outflow can be shut off, so as to form pools of still water.

Most measurements of canal seepage have been made by the first method. The second method, which can be used in either short or long sections, was recently discussed by Rohwer and Stout.[24] It is believed to be more accurate than the first method and therefore preferable when canal and operating conditions are suitable. Seepage losses determined by both methods should be corrected for precipitation and evaporation, especially when rates of seepage are relatively low. Leaks at canal structures within the measuring sections should be plugged or carefully measured. Whenever possible, seepage measurements should be made in canal lengths where no inflows or diversions take place.

Determinations of seepage by inflow and outflow methods are more reliable when made during uniform stages of flow. Measurements made while depths of water are increasing or decreasing require corrections for changes in canal storage. Furthermore, they involve uncertainties due to variations in bank storage, which are difficult to evaluate. Discharge measurements are commonly made with current meters. Sometimes weirs for measuring flows can be installed in the smaller canal sections.

Estimates of maximum rates of seepage that may occur at different locations along the route of a proposed canal may be based on measurements of the drop in water surface in pits excavated along the route. The pits should be excavated to the proposed bottom elevations of the canal, filled with water, and measurements of water surface elevations continued until rates of seepage become constant. Observed rates of seepage probably will be higher than those that will be experienced when the canal is first operated. Water is free to percolate laterally in all directions through the walls of the pits, whereas lateral movements of water through the banks of the canal are restricted to one direction.

Laboratory and Experimental Tests. Laboratory and experimental tests of seepage may be useful in comparing permeabilities of different materials along the route of a proposed canal, but seldom are they suitable for estimating canal seepage. Such tests usually are made on artificially packed specimens which do not accurately represent soil conditions in the field. Furthermore, the tests determine coefficients of permeability for saturated soils. Such coefficients can be utilized only when data on hydraulic gradients are available. Along the bed and banks of a canal, depths of saturation and hydraulic gradients through the permeable materials are both too variable and indeterminate to warrant computations of seepage on the basis of coefficients of permeability.

Certain types of permeameters and seepage-measuring equipment for use in canals have been developed and used in some seepage investigations. Israelsen and Reeve, in their Utah investigations, tested constant-head permeameters, variable-head permeameters, and a seepage meter developed at the United States Regional Salinity Laboratory, Riverside, California.[14] Permeameters were useful in measuring permeabilities of materials in place along the canal sections. The variable-head permeameter was particularly suitable for measurements where the soils were relatively tight. The seepage meter, designed to measure actual seepage through bed materials while a canal is carrying water, did not give results that could be correlated with inflow-outflow measurements. Further tests and developments of design details may produce a seepage meter that will be valuable in measurements of canal losses.

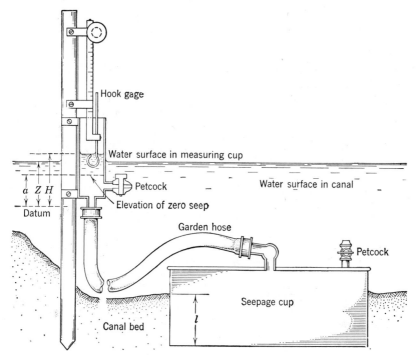

FIGURE 3. General design and installation of a seepage-cup permeameter. (After Rohwer and Stout.)

A seepage-cup permeameter, designed for use in canals carrying water, was tested at several locations in the investigations reported by Rohwer and Stout.[24] Figure 3, taken from their report, shows the general design and method of installing the instrument. Observations are reduced to seepage losses by equations based on Darcy's law or by graphical methods. The authors discussed the design and use of the instrument in detail and concluded that, although the results of the measurements were not conclusive, the method has some merit. Figure 4, also taken from Rohwer and Stout's report, shows the design of the seepage meter developed at the Riverside Salinity Laboratory.

Permeameters and seepage meters, when perfected for use in canals carrying water, will be useful in measuring permeabilities and seepage

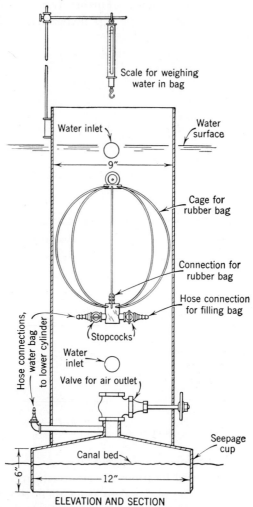

ELEVATION AND SECTION

FIGURE 4.   General design of seepage meter developed at Riverside Salinity Laboratory.   (After Rohwer and Stout.)

losses at different stations along a canal, under actual conditions of operation. They probably will not replace seepage measurements by methods 1 and 2 discussed above. The inflow-outflow and pool-drop methods of measurement can be used to obtain integrated data on

seepage losses through comparatively long sections of canal. Such
data ordinarily are more valuable than determinations at particular
stations.

Data on Canal Seepage. Measurements of canal seepage in irrigation channels of different size, excavated through all types of earth
formations, have been made intermittently for many years. In 1914,
Fortier reported observational data for about 1,500 miles of separate
canal sections in western United States, carrying discharges from less
than 1 to nearly 3,200 second-feet.[9] In 1916, Bark reported data for
118 measurements on canals in Idaho, the most of which probably
were included in Fortier's tabulations.[2] Additional, more limited data
for particular projects have been published in various reports on early
irrigation investigations.

The early measurements, probably all made by the inflow-outflow
method, showed seepage losses per mile varying from less than 1 to
more than 60 per cent of the flow. Quantities of water lost per square
foot of wetted area per day varied from practically zero to more than
6 cubic feet. A canal in Idaho, carrying 3,192 second-feet, lost 6.32
cubic feet per square foot per day through a wetted perimeter of clay
loam overlying a creviced lava rock formation.

In 1922, the United States Department of Agriculture, in cooperation with the California Agricultural Experiment Station and other
agencies, began a comprehensive investigation of seepage losses in
irrigation channels. Results of the investigations were reported by
Rohwer and Stout in 1948.[24] The report includes detailed data for
tests conducted in many canals of different size, excavated through
various soil formations. Some canal sections were unlined, some in
clay had been puddled, and some were lined with concrete or other
materials. Some measurements were made by the pool-drop method,
others by the inflow-outflow method.

Table 3 shows summarized data for some canal sections where
seepage losses through different materials and different linings were
measured by the pool-drop method. The East Contra Costa and
Fresno canals are in California, the others in Colorado. Ranges in
rates of seepage in cubic feet per square foot of wetted area per day
are given in the last column. Ranges in mean depth are given in
the preceding column, and additional pertinent data are listed in
other columns.

For concrete-lined channels, the data in Table 3 show seepage rates
varying from a few hundredths of a cubic foot to more than 3 cubic
feet per square foot per day. For unlined channels, seepage rates

TABLE 3

CANAL SEEPAGE THROUGH DIFFERENT MATERIALS AND LININGS
DETERMINED BY POOL–DROP METHODS [24]

Canal and location	Channel material or lining	No. of tests	Length of pool, ft.	Mean depth, ft.	Rate of seepage cu ft.*
East Contra Costa, basin 2	Concrete	5	7,076	3.16–5.46	0.030– 0.059
East Contra Costa, basin 5	Concrete	5	3,255	2.45–4.10	0.042– 0.223
East Contra Costa, lateral 3, south	Clay, untreated	21	1,418	1.19–2.68	0.838– 1.325
East Contra Costa, lateral 5, south	Clay, puddled	6	1,620	0.94–1.78	5.68 – 8.98
East Contra Costa, lateral 2, north	Clay, untreated	17	1,327	0.57–2.86	2.18 – 5.13
East Contra Costa, lateral 6, north	Heavy clay, puddled	16	1,291	0.93–2.49	0.069– 0.292
East Contra Costa, lateral 3, north	Fine sand, new	24	323	7.11–14.6	3.78 –27.20
East Contra Costa, lateral 6, south	Clay, concrete lined	17	850	0.54–2.56	0.86 – 3.11
Fresno Irrigation District, Houghton lateral	Sandy loam, untreated	6	9,150	1.40–1.83	0.157– 0.281
Pumping plant lateral, Gilcrest, Colo.	Sand, untreated	13	211	0.99–1.75	13.20 –20.31
N–S Farm lateral, Fort Collins, Colo.	Earth, untreated	7	355	0.86–1.34	5.61 – 7.34
E–W Farm lateral, Fort Collins, Colo.	2-in. concrete lining	3	218	0.65–0.98	0.231– 0.374
N–S Farm lateral, Fort Collins, Colo.	2-in. oil lining	6	136	0.68–0.88	1.41 – 2.00
N–S Farm lateral, Fort Collins, Colo.	3-in. bentonite	6	63	0.37–0.61	1.71 – 2.25

* Per square foot of wetted area per day.

varied from a few hundredths of a cubic foot in some clay sections to more than 27 cubic feet in a new channel excavated through fine sand. In general, rates of seepage in particular pools decreased as pool surfaces dropped and hydrostatic heads on the wetted materials decreased.

Table 4 shows summarized data for some unlined canals in California where seepage losses through different materials were measured by the inflow-outflow method. Average rates of seepage are given in the last column, and general data in other columns.

The data in Table 4 show rates of seepage per square foot per day varying from less than 0.10 cubic foot to more than 8 cubic feet. Some measurements, not listed in the table, showed seepage gains instead of losses. Measurements in two sandy loam channels on the Orland Project showed average seepage losses of 5.06 and 8.24 cubic feet per square foot per day. Measurements in a loam and gravelly loam channel in the Anderson-Cottonwood Irrigation District showed an average seepage loss of 0.10 cubic feet per square foot per day.

Considerations of all available data on seepage in unlined canals, including early observations as well as the more recent measurements, fail to reveal any definite correlation between rates of seepage and types of channel materials. Elevations of water tables along the canals

TABLE 4

CANAL SEEPAGE IN SOME UNLINED CHANNELS DETERMINED
BY INFLOW–OUTFLOW METHODS [24]

Irrigation district or project	Canal	Channel material	No. of tests	Average discharge, sec.-ft.	Average rate of seepage, cu. ft.*
Alta	Main	Fine sandy loam and adobe	4	115	1.65
Alta	Main	Fine sandy loam	2	111	2.07
Alta	Main	Adobe	8	96–105	1.08–3.04
Alta	Main	Loam and adobe	6	101–108	0.09–1.38
Imperial	West side main	Sand and clay	7	276–277	0.07–0.14
Imperial	Fillaree lateral	Sand and silty clay	3	6	0.42
Imperial	Fillaree lateral	Silty clay	2	6	0.87
Merced	Yosemite LeGrand	Loam and adobe	19	26–98	0.33–0.56
Anderson-Cottonwood	Main	Gravelly loam	5	137	0.50
Anderson-Cottonwood	Main	Loam and gravelly loam	6	70	0.10
Anderson-Cottonwood	Lateral 9	Gravelly loam	2	8	5.31
Orland	Laterals 8 and 101	Sandy loam	4	8–14	5.06–8.24
Fresno	Briggs ditch	Loam and sandy loam	9	30–34	0.20–3.33
Turlock	Highline	Loam, sandy loam, clay loam	2	137	0.24
Turlock	Lateral 17-B	Sand and sandy loam	9	15–18	1.58–3.38
Sutter-Butte	Main	Loam	5	178–209	0.86–1.14
Sutter-Butte	Green lateral	Clay adobe	6	6	0.60

* Per square foot of wetted area per day.

may account for some of the differences in seepage rates through similar materials. However, the lack of correlation probably is due largely to two reasons: (1) the sealing effect of silt particles deposited by canal flows, and (2) influences on percolation imposed by soil strata of different permeabilities, located along the channels.

In view of the lack of correlation between observed rates of seepage and types of materials, engineers needing seepage data for existing canals should secure such information by actual measurements, using either the pool-drop or the inflow-outflow method.

TABLE 5

CONVEYANCE LOSSES AND WASTE ON BUREAU OF
RECLAMATION PROJECTS [5]

Project	State	Length of canals and laterals, miles		Seasonal diversions, ft.	Losses and waste, per cent of diversions	
		Total	Lined or enclosed		Canal losses	Waste
Belle Fourche	South Dakota	547	58	2.35	33	15
Boise	Idaho	1,004	37	5.15	28	2
Carlsbad	New Mexico	45	11	5.11	48	6
Grand Valley	Colorado	180	7	10.31	43	22
Huntley	Montana	232	. .	4.09	36	30
King Hill *	Idaho	96	43	12.56	34	15
Klamath	Oregon-California	240	2	2.75	39	9
Lower Yellowstone	Montana	202	. .	3.83	44	21
Milk River	Montana	275	. .	1.44	36	19
Minidoka, S. Side Pumping	Idaho	275	. .	4.38	39	3
Newlands	Nevada	319	. .	6.40	41	14
North Platte	Nebraska-Wyoming	1,154	. .	4.55	43	8
Okanogan	Washington	68	39	3.66	29	0.4
Orland	California	135	89	4.95	27	9
Rio Grande	New Mexico-Texas	485	10	9.96	32	39
Shoshone, Frannie Division	Wyoming	166	. .	5.92	42	21
Shoshone, Garland Division	Wyoming	279	4	4.33	38	7
Sun River, Fort Shaw Division	Montana	99	. .	4.05	36	26
Sun River, Greenfields Division	Montana	190	. . .	2.72	31	22
Umatilla	Oregon	173	157	10.04	32	18
Uncompahgre	Colorado	470	11	7.48	13	10
Yakima, Sunnyside Division	Washington	602	125	4.70	23	7
Yakima, Tieton Division	Washington	335	86	3.39	24	2
Yuma	Arizona-California	336	. .	10.75	14	58

* Data for 1921–1925.

Seepage estimates for use in planning canal sections or determining needs for lining installations on particular canals may be based on pit measurements along the canal locations, as discussed under a preceding heading. For the general design of canal sections on a proposed irrigation project, total seepage losses usually are assumed to equal a percentage of the diversions. The determination of the proper percentage is based on considerations of actual losses observed in existing projects where irrigable areas, soil formations, and other pertinent conditions are comparable.

Canal Losses on Irrigation Projects. Total canal losses have been measured or estimated on many irrigation projects. They probably include evaporation as well as seepage, but, inasmuch as evaporation losses generally are negligible, they may be considered as primarily seepage. Total losses are commonly given as percentages of total diversions.

In 1923, Bailey published detailed tabulations of data for irrigation projects in California and certain adjoining regions, one column showing losses in conveyance.[1] The losses varied from negligible quantities on some small areas to a maximum of 76 per cent of the diversions on one project. Most values were between 5 and 60 per cent of the diversions. The data were assembled from various sources, and some items may include appreciable quantities of waste.

In 1930, Debler presented summarized data on canal losses and waste for Bureau of Reclamation projects. The summaries were mostly for the years 1917 to 1926, when water supplies usually were adequate.[5] Since the Bureau's projects are located in practically all parts of the West, the data are particularly pertinent. Average seasonal canal losses are shown in the next to the last column of Table 5. Total lengths of canals and laterals, lengths of lined or enclosed conduits, and average seasonal diversions are shown in preceding columns. Predominating soil types and other data are shown in Table 6 and 7 of Chapter 11. Total yearly losses in conveyance on the Newlands Project, Nevada, and the Lower Yellowstone Project, Montana, are shown in the lower parts of Figure 5.

The data in Table 5 show average seasonal canal losses varying from 13 per cent of the diversions on the Uncompahgre Project, Colorado, to 48 per cent of the diversions on the Carlsbad Project, New Mexico. Seasonal canal losses on most projects during the period represented by the table did not vary greatly from year to year, as shown by the diagrams in the lower part of Figure 5. The tabulated canal losses do not include losses in canals used to fill project reservoirs. On practically all projects, seepage waters return to the streams and become available for rediversion to downstream lands.

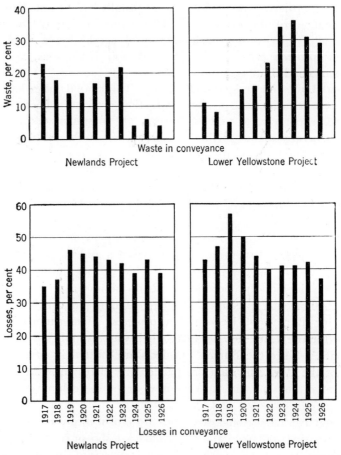

FIGURE 5. Conveyance losses and waste on two reclamation projects.[5]

Waste during Conveyance. Waste of irrigation water during conveyance includes leakage at canal structures, excess water returned to the streams at the lower ends of the projects, and discharges at spillways or wasteways along the canals. Except for small amounts of leakage at some isolated structures, most items of waste return to the streams through natural or artificial channels and thus become available for use on downstream lands.

Discharges at spillways occur principally at times of sudden accidental interruptions in use, or at times of intense local rainfall when large quantities of surface runoff reach the canal sections and raise the water surfaces to higher than normal levels. They seldom amount to large proportions of the seasonal diversions. Discharges at some wasteways may be required for short periods each day, in order to sluice out accumulated silt deposits. They may amount to as much as 5 per cent of the diversions. Quantities of water used to sluice silt deposits from main canal headgates, at points of diversion, usually are not included in either diversions or waste. Leakage at canal structures seldom amounts to appreciable proportions of the diversions.

Excess flows may be carried through the canals to facilitate service, maintain nonsilting velocities, operate power plants as at Yuma, or for other reasons. They may amount to relatively large proportions of the seasonal diversions when ample supplies are available, but often can be reduced if necessary to conserve water.

Average seasonal amounts of waste on federal irrigation projects are shown in the last column of Table 5. Yearly amounts wasted on the Newlands and Lower Yellowstone projects are shown in the upper portions of Figure 5. The small quantities wasted on the Newlands Project during 1924 to 1926, as compared with those wasted during earlier years, illustrate the reductions that can be made when water supplies are limited.

The data in Table 5 show that average seasonal quantities of waste on the federal projects varied from less than 1 per cent of the diversions on the Okanogan Project, Washington, to 58 per cent of the diversions on the Yuma Project, Arizona and California, where excess diversions were made to supply water for power development. Probably most of the higher percentages of waste could have been reduced if water supplies had been limited.

In general, waste of water on large irrigation projects, when ample supplies are available, may vary from about 5 to 30 per cent of the diversions. When water supplies are limited, waste on most large projects usually can be reduced to amounts varying between 1 and 10 per cent of the diversions.

SUMMARY OF IRRIGATION WATER

The preceding conclusions regarding losses and waste of irrigation water during delivery and conveyance, together with a few items discussed in preceding chapters, may be briefly summarized as follows:

During Delivery

Average field evaporation before topsoil dries	0.5 inch per irrigation
Surface waste, allowance for large projects	10 per cent of diversions
Seasonal percolation losses, except on porous soils	0–1.5 acre-feet per acre
Losses of flow in farm ditches	5–50 per cent per mile
Deliveries to farms (see Chapter 11)	1–7 acre-feet per acre
Consumptive use, diversified crops (see Chapter 10)	1–3.5 acre-feet per acre
Irrigation efficiencies, common farm crops	20–50 per cent
Irrigation efficiencies, fruit and special crops	35–70 per cent
Average irrigation efficiencies on large projects	30–50 per cent

During Conveyance

Evaporation from canal surfaces	Negligible
Evapo-transpiration at canal banks	Negligible
Canal seepage, large projects, mostly unlined canals	15–45 per cent of diversions
Seepage losses, most canals lined	5–15 per cent of diversions
Waste on large projects, ample water supplies	5–30 per cent of diversions
Waste on large projects, limited water supplies	1–10 per cent of diversions
Over-all efficiencies, large projects	20–35 per cent
Diversions for large projects (see Chapter 11)	2–10 acre-feet per acre

Most of the above items show estimated ranges in quantities rather than particular values. Conditions affecting the diversion, conveyance, and use of irrigation water are so variable that definite recommendations cannot be made for general use. Definite recommendations for particular projects can be made only after careful considerations of local soil, climatic, hydrological, and agricultural conditions.

REFERENCES

1. Bailey, Paul, "Irrigation Requirements of California Lands," *Calif. Dept. Pub. Works Bull.* 6, 1923.
2. Bark, Don H., "Experiments on the Economical Use of Irrigation Water in Idaho," *U.S. Dept. Agr. Bull.* 339, 1916.
3. Beckett, S. H., and Carroll F. Dunshee, "Water Requirements of Cotton on Sandy Loam Soils in Southern San Joaquin Valley," *Calif. Agr. Exp. Sta. Bull.* 537, 1932.
4. Blaney, H. F., Harold C. Troxell, and others, "Water Losses under Natural Conditions from Wet Areas in Southern California," *Calif. Dept. Pub. Works Bull.* 44, 1933.
5. Debler, E. B., "Use of Water on Federal Irrigation Projects," *Trans. Am. Soc. C. E.*, Vol. 94, 1930, pp. 1195–1241.

6. Debler, E. B., "Duty of Water in Terms of Canal Capacity," *Civ. Eng.*, September 1932, pp. 546–548.

7. ——— "Conveyance Losses in Irrigation Canals," *Civ. Eng.*, October 1941, pp. 584–585.

8. Fife, Arthur, "Duty-of-Water Investigations on Coal Creek, Utah," *Utah Agr. Exp. Sta. Bull.* 181, 1922.

9. Fortier, Samuel, "Concrete Lining as Applied to Irrigation Canals," *U.S. Dept. Agr. Bull.* 126, 1914.

10. Foster, L. J., "Placing the All-American Canal in Operation," *Civ. Eng.*, October 1941, pp. 580–583.

11. Harris, F. S., and H. H. Yao, "Effectiveness of Mulches in Preserving Soil Moisture," *Jour. Agr. Res.*, Mar. 3, 1923, pp. 727–742.

12. Hastings, S. H., and H. K. Dean, "Percolation and Water Requirement Studies with Alfalfa by Means of Lysimeters in Oregon," *Ore. Agr. Exp. Sta. Bull.* 404, 1942.

13. Hemphill, Robert G., "Irrigation in Northern Colorado," *U.S. Dept. Agr. Bull.* 1026, 1922.

14. Israelsen, Orson W., and Ronald C. Reeve, "Canal Lining Experiments in the Delta Area, Utah," *Utah Agr. Exp. Sta. Tech. Bull.* 313, 1944.

15. Israelsen, Orson W., and Luther M. Winsor, "The Net Duty of Water in Sevier Valley," *Utah Agr. Exp. Sta. Bull.* 182, 1922.

16. Israelsen, Orson W., and others, "Water-Application Efficiencies in Irrigation," *Utah Agr. Exp. Sta. Bull.* 311, 1944.

17. Marr, James C., "The Use and Duty of Water in the Salt River Valley," *Ariz. Agr. Exp. Sta. Bull.* 120, 1927.

18. McGeorge, W. T., "Influence of Colorado River Silt on Some Properties of Yuma Mesa Sandy Soil," *Ariz. Agr. Exp. Sta. Tech. Bull.* 91, 1941.

19. Means, Thomas H., "Drainage of Irrigated Lands, Report of the Committee of the Irrigation Division," *Trans. Am. Soc. C. E.*, Vol. 94, 1930, pp. 1425–1449.

20. Moritz, E. A., "Conveyance Losses of Water on U.S. Reclamation Service Irrigation Projects," *Recl. Rec.*, April 1921, pp. 180–182.

21. National Resources Planning Board, *The Pecos River Joint Investigation, Reports of the Participating Agencies*, Washington, 1942.

22. Pillsbury, Arthur F., "Observations on Use of Irrigation Water in Coachella Valley, California," *Calif. Agr. Exp. Sta. Bull.* 649, 1941.

23. Pillsbury, Arthur F., O. C. Compton, and W. E. Picker, "Irrigation-Water Requirements of Citrus in the South Coastal Basin of California," *Calif. Agr. Exp. Sta. Bull.* 686, 1944.

24. Rohwer, Carl, and Oscar Van Pelt Stout, "Seepage Losses from Irrigation Channels," *Colo. Agr. Exp. Sta. Tech. Bull.* 38, 1948.

25. Scofield, Carl S., and Orlando W. Howe, "Water Input Used for Field Crops at the United States Scotts Bluff (Nebr.) Field Station, 1941–44," *U.S. Dept. Agr. Cir.* 777, 1948.

26. Smith, G. E. P., "Use and Waste of Irrigation Water," *Ariz. Agr. Exp. Sta. Bull.* 101, 1925.

27. Young, Arthur A., and Harry F. Blaney, "Use of Water by Native Vegetation," *Calif. Dept. Pub. Works Bull.* 50, 1942.

Chapter 13

IRRIGATION WATER SUPPLIES

Adequate supplies of water are essential for the successful development and continued operation of irrigation projects. No project can be justified financially if sufficient amounts of water cannot be secured for the production of profitable crop yields. Furthermore, the water must be obtainable when needed. Streamflows during the non-irrigation season cannot be utilized. Winter and early spring runoff must be stored in reservoirs until required for crop growth. For full utilization of water resources, quantities of water not needed during years of high runoff must be stored in large holdover reservoirs for use during years of low runoff.

During early periods of irrigation in western United States, water supplies did not constitute serious problems. Irrigated areas were relatively small, and ample supplies were diverted from natural flows in creeks and rivers. As irrigated areas were expanded, natural flows became fully appropriated and problems of securing additional water became more and more important.

Continually increasing demands for irrigation water led to the construction of storage reservoirs, development of pumping projects, use of return flows, and rediversion of water recovered by drainage. Later, as needs for additional water became more urgent, projects were designed to import water from adjacent drainage basins and to replenish underground supplies by spreading flood waters over porous formations to increase infiltration.

Today, readily available supplies of irrigation water in most parts of the West are largely utilized. Natural flows are fully appropriated, and all easily developed storage projects have been constructed. Some projects, over-expanded during wet years, need additional supplies for dry years. In many valleys, pumping from subsurface storage is utilizing all available groundwater. Water tables have been lowered to minimum levels for profitable pumping, and further extensions of the irrigated areas are not feasible. Only a few new irrigation enterprises of appreciable size are being developed at the present time. These are mostly federal projects.

Further expansions in irrigation and increases in regional prosperity which accompany such expansions are now feasible in most western states only through more efficient use of water on existing projects, building additional large and costly reservoirs, or expensive importations of water from remote drainage basins. In some regions, limited expansions still may be feasible through the spreading of flood flows over permeable surface soils, to increase underground storage.

Excess water supplies still are available in the Columbia River and certain other streams of the Northwest. In time, the unprecedented costs involved in constructing aqueducts to convey water long distances from such streams to lands badly in need of water may become justified.

Some agencies are now investigating the feasibility of artificially producing rainfall from overhead cloud formations in order to augment water supplies. However, such methods may not be generally beneficial, even if found possible. If all the moisture in the atmosphere above an irrigation project were suddenly precipitated, the rainfall would not exceed about 2 or 3 inches. In order to secure greater depths, moist air would have to be blown in from adjacent areas. Thus, the artificial production of heavy rainfalls on a particular area probably would mean a decrease in natural rainfall on other areas.

Current researches regarding the practicability of purifying salt water and conveying the purified water to irrigable lands, if successful, will prove a boon to many arid areas not too far inland. Unlimited supplies of water are available in the Pacific Ocean. If these supplies can be tapped, purified, and conveyed inland at reasonable costs, further expansions of irrigated acreages in coastal regions will be possible. Problems involved in developing economical methods of purifying and conveying sea water should not be unsurmountable. They probably will be worked out some time in the future.

The following pages discuss various matters pertaining to irrigation water supplies, particularly problems that must be solved by engineers. Some of the more important problems, such as storage, return flow, and pumping from groundwater, are treated at considerable length. Others, such as water rights, are treated briefly. Water rights often constitute serious problems, but detailed discussions of water rights logically belong in chapters on legal and administrative matters. Qualities of irrigation water are discussed in the next chapter.

Sources of Water Supply. The basic source of water supply for irrigation is precipitation. This is true whether the water is secured from surface supplies or from underground storage. For the production of streamflow which can be diverted, stored, or pumped for irrigation, heavy winter and spring precipitations on upstream drainage areas, or on adjoining watersheds from which water can be imported, are especially valuable.

In western United States, the spring melting of accumulated snow covers at high elevations constitutes the most satisfactory source of water for diversion from natural flow, storage to supply late season demands, or pumping from surface supplies during the irrigation season. In some regions, flood flows caused by heavy rainfalls are impounded in reservoirs for irrigation use as needed, but storm runoff is not so dependable as snow runoff. In other regions, water supplies are obtained from springs, flowing artesian wells, or pumping from underground storage.

In general, water supplies for irrigation are obtained by one or more of the following methods

1. Diversion from regulated or unregulated streamflow.
2. Direct release from storage reservoirs to canals.
3. Rediversion of return flows from irrigated lands.
4. Recovery of excess irrigation water by drainage.
5. Pumping from lakes, rivers, canals, and other surface waters.
6. Importation of water from other drainage basins.
7. Purchase of water from municipal water-supply systems.
8. Diversion of flows from municipal sewage systems.
9. Diversion of effluents from sewage treatment plants.
10. Pumping from free groundwater storage.
11. Pumping from artesian aquifers.
12. Appropriation of discharges from flowing artesian wells and natural springs.

When irrigation water supplies are obtained from more than one source, the source furnishing the principal supply is commonly designated the primary source, and the sources furnishing the additional supplies, the supplemental sources. Reservoirs built to store winter runoff and flood flows usually constitute supplemental sources. Pumping projects may constitute either primary or supplemental sources. Importation projects generally constitute supplemental sources but may constitute primary sources.

Table 1, compiled from the sixteenth census report on irrigation, shows areas under irrigation in western United States in 1939, segre-

TABLE 1

IRRIGATION AREAS IN WESTERN UNITED STATES—DIFFERENT
SOURCES OF WATER SUPPLY—SIXTEENTH CENSUS REPORT

(Thousands of acres)

Primary sources of supply	Irrigated areas			Areas works could supply, 1940	Number of enterprises, 1940
	1939	Change since 1929, per cent	Per cent of total		
Streams, gravity	13,064	0.6	62.2	16,811	25,726
Streams, pumped	1,725	0.7	8.2	2,761	5,915
Streams, gravity and pumped	1,266	390.6	6.0	1,796	344
Wells, pumped	2,508	22.2	11.9	3,622	38,715
Wells, flowing	41	−14.4	0.2	50	1,398
Wells, pumped and flowing	21	24.0	0.1	25	163
Lakes, gravity	26	−55.8	0.1	45	149
Lakes, pumped	46	−41.1	0.2	70	354
Springs	210	−3.2	1.0	253	3,432
Springs and streams	230	.....	1.1	287	995
Stored storm water	21	−45.9	0.1	33	434
City water	11	555.2	...	14	184
Sewage	5	49.1	...	6	53
Streams, gravity; wells, pumped	1,252	7.6	6.0	1,534	580
Streams, gravity; wells, flowing	72	236.1	0.3	82	111
Streams, pumped; wells, pumped	173	.....	0.8	225	437
Waste water, seepage, or drainage	66	.....	0.3	113	770
Other, mixed, and not reported	267	−70.2	1.3	326	742
Total	21,004	7.4	100.0	28,055	80,502

gated for different primary sources of supply. The data include areas in Arkansas and Louisiana as well as in the seventeen western states. Areas that received additional water from supplemental sources are not shown separately but are included in the totals for the primary sources. Total irrigated areas are given in the second column. Changes during the preceding decade, percentages of total irrigated area, and other related data are given in subsequent columns. The item for stored storm water applies primarily to small farm reservoirs. Areas supplied by large storage projects are included in the first item.

The data in Table 1 show that 21 million acres were irrigated in 1939. This was 7.4 per cent greater than the total irrigated in 1929.

Gravity flows from streams supplied 62.2 per cent of the total in 1939, pumping from wells supplied 11.9 per cent of the total, and pumping from streams supplied 8.2 per cent. Combined gravity flows and pumping from streams supplied 6.0 per cent of the total. Combined gravity flows from streams and pumping from wells supplied another 6.0 per cent. Areas supplied from other sources were relatively small.

Classification of Water Supplies. Water supplies for irrigation are usually considered in two general classes depending on the source of the water: (1) surface supplies, or water obtained from surface sources; and (2) subsurface supplies, or water obtained from subsurface sources. Sometimes the supplies are designated according to methods of obtaining the water. For instance, they may be called diversion supplies, gravity supplies, pumped supplies, storage supplies, or importation supplies. Other designations may be used in referring to irrigation water supplies, but most terms are self-explanatory.

Surface supplies include water diverted from streams, released from lakes or reservoirs, pumped from lakes, reservoirs, rivers, and canals, or obtained from other surface sources. Excess irrigation waters that reach stream channels as surface drainage, as flow through drainage ditches, or as percolating return flow from irrigated lands become available for rediversion and therefore are usually considered as surface supplies.

Subsurface supplies include water pumped or otherwise obtained directly from underground sources. They include groundwater pumped from wells driven into porous formations below the water table, water appropriated from flowing artesian wells and natural springs, and water pumped from artesian aquifers where pressures are not high enough to raise water to the ground surface. Water supplies obtained from artesian aquifers are commonly referred to as artesian supplies but may be referred to as confined groundwater supplies.

Groundwater is defined as water in the zone of saturation; that is, as water held in formations below the water table. It is designated free or unconfined groundwater when directly connected with the water table, or confined groundwater when held under hydrostatic pressures beneath an impermeable formation, as in an artesian aquifer.

Prior to about 1939, groundwater was sometimes referred to as phreatic water. In 1939, Meinzer proposed that the term phreatic water be restricted to mean free or unconfined groundwater in the zone of saturation. He also proposed the term piestic water to mean confined groundwater, and the term plerotic water to mean groundwater in general, whether confined or unconfined.[45]

Water-Supply Studies. Water-supply studies constitute one of the first and most important procedures required in determining the feasibility of a proposed irrigation project. All possible sources and methods of obtaining water must be carefully considered, analyzed, and evaluated before proceeding with a new development.

In conducting water-supply studies, three basic requirements should be kept in mind: (1) the water supply should be adequate for the irrigable areas included in the project; (2) the supply should be dependable from year to year; and (3) the quality of the water should be suitable for irrigation without impairing crop growth, qualities of crop products, or properties of the soils on which crops are grown.

Amounts of water needed to produce crops and diversions that may be necessary in order to insure the arrival of such amounts at the irrigated fields are discussed in preceding chapters.

For surface supplies, possibilities of fulfilling the first two requirements depend primarily on precipitation and runoff conditions in upstream drainage areas, amounts of natural flow, if any, remaining unappropriated, and the feasibility of building reservoirs to impound such flows as may remain unappropriated. Consequently, water-supply studies for projects to be supplied from surface sources require analyses of precipitation and runoff records, considerations of existing water rights, determinations of the nature and quantities of streamflow that may be available for the project, investigations of storage possibilities, estimates of total capacities needed in reservoirs, and detailed studies of other related problems.

When ample supplies of water cannot be obtained from upstream drainage areas, possibilities of obtaining supplemental supplies by importation from other drainage basins or by pumping from underground storage must be investigated.

For projects to be supplied with water from subsurface sources, possibilities of fulfilling the first two requirements depend primarily on existing amounts of underground storage, elevations of water tables, the extent to which subsurface supplies already are being utilized, rates at which water can be withdrawn from underground storage, annual rates of recharge, and increases in annual recharge that may be secured by spreading unused surface flows to increase infiltration.

Proper considerations of factors enumerated in the preceding paragraph require intensive subsurface investigations. Some conditions that require investigation include the geologic nature of the subsurface formations, their capacities for holding water, rates at which water can percolate through the materials, pumping heads, and amounts of water already being pumped. Necessary investigations also include analyses of the precipitation and runoff conditions that produce annual recharge and thus determine the quantities of water that can be withdrawn from the underground reservoir.

The possibility of fulfilling the third basic requirement, for either surface or subsurface supplies, depends primarily on (1) the chemical nature of the earth formations through which the water percolates before reaching stream channels, flowing wells, or pumping plants; and (2) the amount of dilution the water may attain during passage from the source of supply to the irrigated lands. In general, canal flows diverted from surface runoff or released from storage in surface reservoirs usually have qualities suitable for irrigation (see Chapter 14).

Water Rights. Information regarding rights to use surface waters can be obtained from state officials. Irrigation states have enacted laws controlling rights to divert streamflow for beneficial uses, also laws providing for the administration and adjudication of water rights. Furthermore, courts have handed down many decisions pertaining to water rights.

In most western states, laws and court decisions have been fairly well developed as regards surface water supplies, but not as regards subsurface supplies. A model groundwater law was passed by the New Mexico Legislature in 1931. Texas and Arizona recently enacted special laws pertaining to groundwater. However, in many irrigation states, laws and judicial opinions governing rights to use subsurface waters still are in the course of development.

The subject of water rights is too comprehensive and involved to be treated adequately in this chapter. For the most part, the more satisfactory laws accept priority of use as a basis, rather than the riparian doctrine set forth in the common law of England and generally followed in eastern United States. Colorado took the lead in recognizing the inadequacy of the riparian doctrine as applied to western water problems and passing more appropriate water laws based on priority of use.

In developing new irrigation projects or absorbing existing projects, purchases of prior water rights may be necessary. For some projects, such purchases may add appreciable items of cost. For other projects, they may be negligible. The 1940 census report showed that total irrigation investments included about 26 million dollars for water rights. This was about 2.5 per cent of the total investments. Methods of evaluating water rights were discussed by Field in 1930.[16]

SURFACE WATER SUPPLIES

Surface water supplies constitute the principal source of water for irrigation. The sixteenth census report shows that 85 per cent of the water delivered to irrigated farms in western United States in 1939 was obtained from surface sources.

Most large irrigation projects use water from surface sources, secured either through gravity diversions and gravity conveyance systems or by pumping at large, centrally located plants and delivery through gravity systems. Gravity diversions supply the greater proportions of the irrigated lands, but many large areas are supplied by pumping from rivers and canals.

When the Columbia Basin Project is completed in central Washington, water pumped from the reservoir above Grand Coulee Dam will furnish a primary supply for about a million acres of new land. This is one of the few new irrigation projects of large size now in the process of development. Grand Coulee Dam, located on the Columbia River, was completed in 1941; but the irrigation works, including additional dams and reservoirs as well as numerous smaller irrigation structures, are yet to be completed. The project is being built by the Bureau of Reclamation.

During recent years, many areas located downstream from large irrigation projects have been irrigated with drainage recoveries and return flows from upstream areas where excess amounts of water were delivered to the fields. Some relatively small areas are irrigated with flows obtained from municipal water supply and sewage systems. Small areas also are irrigated with water diverted or pumped from lakes (see Table 1).

Stream Supplies. Surface waters obtained from streams supplied more than 16 million acres of irrigated land in 1939. The first three items in Table 1 show that 76.4 per cent of the 21 million acres irrigated in 1939 were supplied with water diverted or pumped from streams. Additional areas of 1.5 million acres, about 7 per cent of the total, were supplied partly from streams and partly from wells.

Table 2, compiled from census data, shows irrigated areas in the western states, also in Arkansas and Louisiana, supplied by gravity diversions and pumping from streams during 1939. Total areas exceeded 1 million acres in Colorado, California, Idaho, Montana, Wyoming, and Utah. During the 10-year period preceding 1939, total areas irrigated from stream supplies decreased slightly in Colo-

TABLE 2

IRRIGATED AREAS SUPPLIED BY STREAMS AND TOTAL
RESERVOIR CAPACITIES—1940 CENSUS

| | Areas supplied by streams, 1,000 acres | | | | Reservoir |
State	Total	Gravity diversions	Pumped supplies	Gravity and pumped	capacity, 1,000 acre-ft.*
Arizona	120	71	1	48	4,861
Arkansas	7	.....	7	...	32
California	2,463	1,742	471	251	3,582
Colorado	3,039	3,010	5	24	2,072
Idaho	2,098	1,629	294	175	3,795
Kansas	49	41	8	...	33
Louisiana	250	.....	247	2	34
Montana	1,657	1,476	36	146	1,301
Nebraska	511	488	10	13	2,306
Nevada	582	578	1	3	696
New Mexico	418	344	4	70	3,281
North Dakota	21	19	2	...	4
Oklahoma	3	2	1	...	1
Oregon	963	786	45	132	2,212
South Dakota	57	20	2	35	210
Texas	729	191	526	12	1,405
Utah	1,072	907	13	151	3,418
Washington	565	329	44	192	1,166
Wyoming	1,450	1,431	8	12	3,380
Total	16,055	13,064	1,725	1,266	33,787

* Not including multiple-purpose reservoirs.

rado, but increased in the other 5 states. Total areas irrigated from streams in all 19 states increased 1.1 million acres during the preceding 10 years. All areas are given to the nearest 1,000 acres.

Surface waters, particularly flood flows, now being wasted because of insufficient storage facilities probably will supply large proportions of the additional lands that may be developed in the future. In 1934, the Water Planning Committee, National Resources Board, estimated that with the ultimate possible development of about 50 million acres of irrigable lands about 85 per cent of the total would be supplied by surface waters and about 90 million acre-feet of additional reservoir capacities would be needed.[50]

For many years, water supplies that can be diverted or pumped from streams have been gradually increasing along downstream sections of some western rivers, owing to return flows and drainage recoveries. These items are discussed under subsequent headings. Detailed data on streamflow in all parts of the country, including some measurements of return flow and drainage recovery, are published annually in the water-supply papers of the United States Geological Survey.

Storage Supplies. Storage supplies for irrigation include waters held in natural lakes and surface reservoirs. Reservoirs storing water for irrigation vary from small farm ponds holding less than an acre-foot of storm runoff to large main-stream reservoirs holding several million acre-feet of streamflow.

The 1940 census report shows 7,709 irrigation reservoirs in western United States, with a total storage capacity of 33.8 million acre-feet, not including multiple-purpose reservoirs. Total storage capacities in the different states are shown in the last column of Table 2. Ponds or tanks holding less than 0.5 acre-foot are not included in the totals. Probably all storage projects included in the census compilations were built primarily to impound water for irrigation, although secondary purposes, such as power development, often are served at the larger reservoirs.

Table 3 lists some large reservoirs built for irrigation in the western states. Capacities and areas are shown in the last two columns. All but two of the reservoirs were built by the Bureau of Reclamation. Some were enlargements of natural lakes.

Since about 1935, large storage capacities for irrigation have been provided through the construction of multiple-purpose reservoirs, where portions of the capacities are reserved for different uses. Such uses, in addition to irrigation, may include domestic water supply, flood control, silt control, stream regulation, navigation, recreation, and hydroelectric power development. Examples of multiple-purpose projects include Hoover, Grand Coulee, Shasta, and Marshall Ford dams, all built by the Bureau of Reclamation.

Hoover Dam, completed on Colorado River near Las Vegas, Nevada, in 1936, is the most noteworthy example of a multiple-purpose project. Lake Mead, the storage reservoir formed by the dam, has a capacity of 30.5 million acre-feet, of which 18 million acre-feet are allotted to irrigation and domestic water supply. Since the total capacity is equivalent to about 2 years of normal runoff, the reservoir provides effective stream regulation for all purposes.

Most future irrigation developments will require holdover storage of flood flows now being wasted. The Water Planning Committee estimated that, for the fullest possible use of irrigation water, about

TABLE 3

SOME LARGE RESERVOIRS BUILT FOR IRRIGATION

Reservoir	State	Stream	Year com- pleted	Capacity, 1,000 acre-ft.	Area, 1,000 acres
Elephant Butte	New Mexico	Rio Grande	1916	2,638	40.0
American Falls	Idaho	Snake	1927	1,704	56.1
Roosevelt	Arizona	Salt	1911	1,420	18.3
Coolidge	Arizona	Gila	1928	1,200	22.0
Owyhee	Oregon	Owyhee	1932	1,120	13.0
Pathfinder	Wyoming	North Platte	1922	1,070	22.7
Seminoe	Wyoming	North Platte	1939	1,020	18.4
Jackson Lake	Wyoming	Snake	1919	847	25.5
Lake Tahoe	California- Nevada	Truckee	1915	732	120.0
Clear Lake	California	Lost	1910	538	26.5
Cle Elum	Washington	Cle Elum	1933	529	4.9
Upper Klamath Lake	Oregon	Klamath	1921	525	91.0
Friant	California	San Joaquin	1942	521	4.9
Big Wichita	Texas	Big Wichita	1923	500	22.8
Anderson Ranch	Idaho	South Fork of Boise	1948	500	4.0
Shoshone	Wyoming	Shoshone	1910	457	6.6

175 million acre-feet of storage capacity would be needed. Probably the greater part of the additional storage capacity will have to be secured through the construction of multiple-purpose projects by federal agencies.

In contrast with the gigantic multiple-purpose projects are the small farm reservoirs built to store water for stock use and for irrigating gardens, orchards, and fields at times when other supplies cannot be secured. Several thousand small farm reservoirs have been built throughout the West. During drought periods, they often save at least some of the farmer's crops as well as his livestock.

Farm reservoirs are usually built in small drainage courses or in nearby offchannel depressions, where expensive spillway constructions are not required. Sometimes they are built by excavating low areas and using excavated materials in constructing necessary embankments. Dams across natural channels are commonly built of earth, but may be built as rock fills, timber cribs, or concrete structures. Small ponds are sometimes kept full by pumping from wells.

Storage Capacities. In considering storage capacities for a new irrigation project, reservoirs large enough to hold excess runoff during wet years, for use during dry years, should be contemplated whenever feasible. Whether such capacities can be developed depends on available reservoir sites and probable costs of construction. Whether such capacities can be utilized, if developed, depends on quantities of run-off available for storage. Some large reservoirs built in the past have been filled only at intervals of several years, if at all, because of insufficient streamflow.

When large holdover reservoirs are not feasible, smaller reservoirs may be built to equalize seasonal flow. In such reservoirs, spring

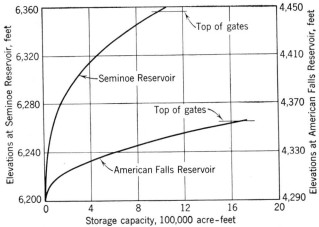

FIGURE 1.   Capacity curves for Seminoe and American Falls reservoirs.

flows are impounded, temporarily, for subsequent release as needed during the later weeks of the irrigation season.

Storage capacities increase rapidly with rising reservoir stages in slightly rolling regions where relatively small depths of water cover large areas, but much more gradually in mountainous regions where areas subject to flooding are limited. Figure 1 shows capacity curves for Seminoe Reservoir on the North Platte River, Wyoming, and American Falls Reservoir on the Snake River, Idaho. The former is located in a mountain canyon, the latter in rolling country.

In determining capacities needed at storage reservoirs, allowances should be made for probable losses of water by evaporation and seepage, also for probable losses of capacity by silting. Evaporation losses may be estimated on the basis of records maintained at local evaporation stations, or by other methods discussed in Chapter 9. Losses of water by seepage and losses of capacity by silting are more difficult to evaluate.

When geologic formations surrounding a reservoir are so tight that stored water cannot percolate to outlets at downstream locations or in adjoining drainage basins, amounts of water that enter the banks constitute bank storage. They increase as reservoir stages rise, then drain back into the reservoir as water levels are drawn down. Therefore, they constitute increases in effective storage capacity rather than seepage losses. Such effects on storage capacity may reach appreciable magnitudes in deep reservoirs, where shore lines are long and banks include considerable depths of permeable materials.

Reservoir Seepage. Losses of reservoir water by seepage depend on (1) permeabilities of earth and rock materials throughout the surrounding geological formations, including the bed of the reservoir; (2) elevations of water tables already present in the surrounding formations; and (3) hydrostatic heads produced by stored water.

When a reservoir is constructed in a deep valley where water tables in surrounding formations are higher than reservoir stages, no seepage losses can take place. When a reservoir is constructed in a valley where water tables in surrounding formations are lower than reservoir stages, seepage losses depend on rates at which water can percolate through the surrounding formations under the increased hydraulic gradients. Many small irrigation reservoirs are included in the latter classification.

Seepage losses usually percolate back to the stream channels below the reservoirs, but under special geological and topographical conditions may percolate to outlets in adjacent drainage basins. Naturally, seepage losses are more objectionable when they percolate into streams from which they cannot be recovered for project use. High seepage losses, although objectionable, may not prevent efficient reservoir operations. Some small reservoirs in the lower South Platte Valley, Colorado, are used to equalize streamflows, although annual losses are sometimes as great as total capacities.

Seepage losses at shallow reservoirs in irrigated valleys where permeable materials predominate may be relatively large when storage is begun, then decrease as the bed and banks become covered with silt and as water tables rise in surrounding formations. The Deer Flat Reservoir, Boise Project, Idaho, now known as Lake Lowell, may be cited as an example. It has a capacity of 177 thousand acre-feet, and a mean depth of 18 feet when full. When storage began in 1909, nearly all the stored water was lost by seepage. During succeeding years, annual seepage losses decreased and became approximately stable in 1916. Figure 2, plotted from Bureau of Reclamation records, shows annual seepage losses during 1909 to 1921.

During recent years, seepage from canals and irrigated lands east and southeast of Lake Lowell has increased until annual quantities entering the reservoir during low stages now exceed annual quantities lost during high stages. According to Clinton of the Boise Office, records from 1931 to 1949 show annual gains in storage in all years except 1938 and 1940.

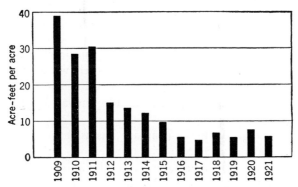

FIGURE 2. Seepage losses at Deer Flat Reservoir, Boise Project, Idaho.

At large holdover reservoirs, considerable quantities of initial storage may be consumed in saturating surrounding formations, even when water cannot escape permanently. At Lake Mead, annual losses, including evaporation, amounted to 32.8 acre-feet per acre of reservoir area during the first year of storage, then decreased to 8.8 acre-feet per acre during the fourth year. Since that time, losses can be accounted for by evaporation which varies between 6 and 7 feet a year.

Seepage losses at reservoirs have varied from negligible quantities to amounts that required discontinuance of storage operations. Most data reported have been for projects where losses were excessive and therefore required thorough investigation. At some abandoned reservoirs, losses were due to leakage through large fissures or open passageways in underlying rock strata rather than to percolation through permeable materials.

Probably the greatest rate of seepage loss through permeable materials thus far reported was at the Cedar Reservoir, a municipal storage project near Seattle, Washington. At Cedar Reservoir, a long morainal deposit extended from one end of a concrete dam 217 feet high. The dam was completed in 1914 and, when reservoir stages were allowed to approach maximum levels in 1918, average rates of seepage were about 500 second-feet. During the night of December 23, 1918, a large portion of the morainal material sloughed out, requiring the abandonment of the project.[34]

Storage projects where large leakages occurred through fissures, cracks, holes, or other openings in foundation and abutment rocks include McMillan and Hondo reservoirs in New Mexico, Tumalo Reservoir, Oregon, Jerome Reservoir, Idaho, and others. Serious losses of water by leakage may be anticipated where underlying and surrounding formations consist of gypsum, limestone, or other soluble rocks, or where they include badly fissured volcanic rocks such as basalt.[2]

Whether a proposed reservoir site, if developed, will or will not be subject to serious seepage or leakage of stored water is primarily a geological problem. No large reservoir should be constructed without thorough geological investigations and approval by a competent engineering geologist.

Reservoir Silting. In many drainage basins throughout the West, silting may rapidly reduce capacities of reservoirs built to store water for irrigation. Some of the smaller reservoirs built during the earlier periods of irrigation have already lost nearly all their usable capacities by silting. A few have been replaced by new storage projects.

Rates of reservoir silting depend on geological, topographical, and hydrological conditions throughout the drainage areas above the reservoir sites. Vegetal covers, surface soils, rainfall intensities, runoff conditions, streamflow characteristics, geological formations along river channels, and other related conditions all exert important influences on quantities of material that may be eroded from watershed surfaces and transported through drainage courses to reservoir sites.

In the arid regions of the Southwest, rates of silting are accelerated by the sparsity of vegetation, the erodible nature of the surface soils, and the intense rates of rainfall that often are experienced on local areas even though annual depths of precipitation are relatively low.

In 1943, Brown reported rates of silting at 63 reservoirs built for public or industrial water supplies in various parts of the United States. Annual rates of silting varied from 0.05 to 6.0 per cent of total storage capacities. On the basis of silt conditions at 151 projects, he estimated that 21 per cent of the nation's water supply reservoirs would have a useful life of less than 50 years, 25 per cent would last between 50 and 100 years, and 54 per cent would supply present requirements for 100 years or longer. He also estimated that rates of storage depletion by silting at irrigation reservoirs would be similar, if not somewhat faster, than at reservoirs constructed for public or industrial water supplies.[3]

Table 4, compiled from data reported by Stevens in 1936, shows silting conditions at 17 western reservoirs where quantities of accumu-

TABLE 4

SILTING OF RESERVOIRS IN WESTERN UNITED STATES
DETERMINED BY SURVEYS [63]

				Period	Silt deposited		
Reservoir	Stream and location	Drainage area, sq. miles	Original capacity, 1,000 acre-ft.	meas-ured, yr.	Total, acre-ft.	Per cent of ca-pacity	An-nual rate, acre-ft.
Elephant Butte	Rio Grande, N. Mex.	30,000	2,640	8.7	178,000	6.7	20,500
Roosevelt	Salt, Ariz.	5,670	1,370	20.0	101,000	7.4	5,050
McMillan	Pecos, N. Mex.	......	90.0	39	50,000	55.5	1,280
Guernsey	North Platte, Wyo.	16,200	72.0	5.9	8,400	11.0	1,430
Lake Worth	West Fork, Trinity, Tex.	1,870	47.2	13	13,900	29.6	1,060
Cucharas	Cucharas, Colo.	......	43.0	22	7,850	18.3	357
Sweetwater	Sweetwater, Calif.	181	36.3	39	6,170	17.0	158
Lake Austin, new	Colorado, Tex.	38,200	32.0	13	30,600	95.6	2,350
Lake Chabot	San Leander, Calif.	42	17.0	48	3,700	21.7	77
White Rock	White Rock, Tex.	114	16.9	5	680	4.0	136
Boysen	Bighorn, Wyo.	7,740	16.0	13	13,000	80.0	1,000
Zuni	Zuni, N. Mex.	650	14.8	26.2	11,300	76.5	432
Gibraltar	Santa Ynez, Calif.	220	14.6	11	2,100	14.4	190
Furnish	Umatilla, Ore.	1,200	5.50	22	4,500	82.0	204
Lake Penick	Clear Fork, Brazos, Tex.	2,250	3.09	7	965	32.2	138
LaGrange	Tuolumne, Calif.	1,500	2.33	36	1,940	83.0	54
Buckhorn	Buckhorn, Colo.	130	1.19	18	565	47.5	31

lated silt deposits were determined by surveys.[63] Similar tables giving data for some additional reservoirs were presented by Eakin and Brown in 1939,[13] and by Hall in 1940.[20]

At 5 reservoirs listed in Table 4, more than 75 per cent of the original capacities had been filled with silt up to the times of the last surveys. At Boysen Reservoir, Wyoming, where 80 per cent of the capacity had been filled up to 1924, a new and larger reservoir is now in the course of construction.

At McMillan Reservoir, New Mexico, the average rate of silting was about 1,930 acre-feet per year prior to 1915. After 1915, a dense growth of tamarisk, salt cedar, developed at the upper end of the reservoir. This caused spreading of the river flow and deposition of large proportions of the silt loads before the flows entered the reservoir. Consequently, average rates of reservoir silting were reduced to about 350 acre-feet per year during 1915 to 1925, and to about 215 acre-feet per year during 1925 to 1932.

When silt-laden streams enter bodies of stored water, they deposit the greater portions of their loads in delta formations at the upstream ends of the reservoirs. As the flows decrease in velocity, suspended materials are deposited progressively in order of size. All sand grains and the heavier silt particles soon come to rest on the reservoir bed. Some unusually fine silt particles may move slowly through the stored water or along the bottom of the original channel until they finally reach the downstream end of the reservoir.

Relatively low diversion dams can be designed so that silt loads during flood periods can be passed through the structures, and so that silt deposits accumulated during other periods can be sluiced out periodically. However, such methods are not practicable for large storage reservoirs. Thus far, no feasible method of removing silt deposits from storage reservoirs has been developed. At some locations, the inflowing silt probably could be stopped just above the reservoir by developing dense growths of vegetation, as at Lake McMillan, but the advisability of resorting to such methods is questionable. Such methods not only prevent utilization of the lands but also cause large losses of water by evapo-transpiration.

Past remedies for losses of storage capacity by silting have consisted of building new reservoirs. Obviously, such remedies cannot be continued indefinitely. Ultimately, all available storage sites will be developed and other remedies must be found. The erosion-control program now being promoted by the Soil Conservation Service should postpone the time when other remedies become essential, but it will not permanently eliminate the need for solving the silt problem.

Return Flow. In general, the return flow from an irrigation project is the portion of the diverted water that finds its way back to the stream channel. Some of the returning water, often called visible return flow, reaches the channel as surface runoff through natural or artificial drainage courses. The remainder, often called invisible return flow, reaches the stream as percolation through the bed and banks of the channel. Irrigation waters draining into stream channels from areas supplied by pumping also constitute return flows.

Unused irrigation waters usually return to the streams from which they were diverted. Exceptions occur when diverted flows are conveyed to irrigable lands in other drainage basins. Under special conditions of subsurface formations and water tables, some invisible return flow may percolate beyond the boundaries of the watershed and reach streams in adjoining drainage basins.

Return flow from irrigation is sometimes defined as percolating water not retained in the root zone that ultimately reaches a natural stream. However, it seems better to use the definition given above. By the above definition, return flow includes surface runoff during irrigation, drainage from canal seepage, leakage at canal structures, wasteway discharges during conveyance, and discharges at the lower ends of the canals, as well as drainage from excess percolation during irrigation.

Portions of return flow that reach stream channels through drainage ditches often are referred to as drainage recovery or drainage return. On some projects where extensive drainage improvements have been constructed, visible return flows may be largely drainage recovery.

Portions of diverted supplies that subsequently reach stream channels as return flow depend on amounts of water diverted, conveyance and irrigation efficiencies, texture of surface soils, subsurface soil formations, drainage facilities, and periods of years the lands have been irrigated. Return flows during the irrigation season, unless containing objectionable salt concentrations that cannot be remedied by mixing with other waters, generally can be rediverted to supply additional project lands at lower levels. Return flows during the nonirrigation season can be impounded in reservoirs for use during the subsequent irrigation season. When they cannot be utilized by the project where they originate, they become available for diversion to irrigable lands farther downstream.

During early years of irrigation in the West, excessive amounts of water usually were diverted and conveyed to the fields. Large portions of the excess deliveries percolated to groundwater storage, gradually raising the water tables. In a few years, water tables reached levels high enough to cause percolation toward natural drainage courses, thus beginning return flow.

Subsequent raising of water tables increased return flow, caused the development of salt troubles, and produced seeped areas where large amounts of water were lost through evaporation and transpiration by nonuseful vegetation. Drainage systems were then constructed to reclaim seeped areas and prevent further damages to project lands. These improvements recovered large percentages of the water previously lost by evapo-transpiration and thus produced further increases in return flow.

In general, the return flow from a new irrigation project develops and gradually increases about as described above. Eventually, when complete and effective drainage has been provided, a stage is reached where no further increase in return flow can be expected unless additional water supplies can be secured and new lands developed. This stage has been reached on many of the older projects. Ultimately, it probably will be reached on all projects.

In many western valleys, gradual increases in return flow during past years have made possible gradual development of new irrigated areas that otherwise could not be supplied with water. In some valleys, prior water rights for downstream lands can now be supplied by return flow, thus leaving more water available for storage and diversion in the upper parts of the drainage basins.

Investigations of Return Flow. Investigations of return flow were begun in the Cache la Poudre Valley, northern Colorado, about 1885. Since that time, measurements of return flow have been made on nearly all the more important rivers in the irrigation states. Comprehensive data may be consulted in reports, bulletins, and water-supply papers issued by state and federal agencies, many of which are listed at the end of the chapter.

In 1934, the United States Department of Agriculture published a bulletin on the ownership of return waters, prepared by Hutchins.[24] This bulletin discussed physical aspects of return flow in several large river valleys as well as legal and administrative matters.

In the South Platte Valley, northeastern Colorado, where several large irrigation projects were developed during 1883 to 1885, annual return flows increased from about 375 thousand acre-feet in 1891 to about 1 million acre-feet in 1926. These increases occurred along the main stream from Waterton, where the river emerges from the mountains, to Julesburg, near the Colorado-Nebraska line. A little more than a million acres were under irrigation along this section of the river in 1926.[40]

Figure 3, plotted from records in the State Engineer's office, shows how rates of return flow increased along the South Platte River from 1891 to 1926.[23] Flows were measured during the fall months, when return waters were reaching the channel at relatively high rates. Apparently, stable conditions of return flow for water supplies then available were reached about 1916. In general, subsequent measurements did not show greatly different return flows. At some locations, 1926 return flows were a little lower than in 1916, and 1930 return flows a little higher. The total increase in flow along the main stream in 1930 amounted to about 1,485 second-feet.

Figure 4 shows the monthly distribution of annual return flow in the South Platte River as determined by detailed investigations dur-

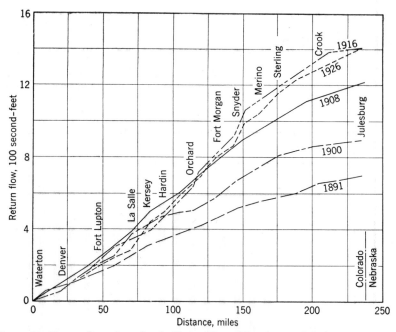

FIGURE 3. Return flow along South Platte River, Waterton to Julesburg, Colorado.

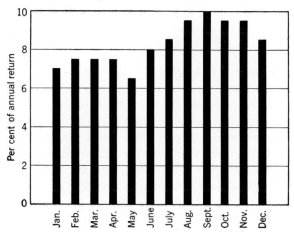

FIGURE 4. Monthly distribution of annual return flow, Lower South Platte River, Colorado.

ing 1919 and 1920.[39] Monthly return flows varied from 6.5 per cent of the annual in May to 10 per cent of the annual in September.

In 1922, Parshall estimated that return flow to the South Platte River in the 143 miles between Kersey and Julesburg averaged 5.25 second-feet per mile, also that about 1 second-foot was returned for each 275 acres of irrigated land. He further estimated that about 20 per cent of the return flow originated as seepage from small equalizing reservoirs near the river.[52]

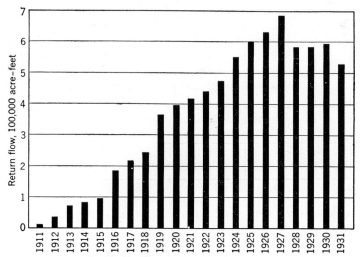

FIGURE 5.   Visible return flow, North Platte River from Wyoming-Nebraska state line to Bridgeport, Nebraska.

Follansbee estimated that irrigation return flows to the North Platte River in the 231 miles between Whalen Dam, Wyoming, and North Platte, Nebraska, amounted to about 1.26 million acre-feet during the water year ending September 30, 1931. About 43 per cent of the total was invisible return flow.[18] The total return flow amounted to about 2.5 acre-feet per acre from the 502 thousand acres irrigated. Similar data for water years 1932 to 1934, reported by Le Fever, showed about the same conditions, except that invisible return flows during 1933 and 1934 made up a little more than 50 per cent of the totals.[31] River discharges during the irrigation seasons of 1931 to 1934 were below normal.

Figure 5 shows visible return flows to the North Platte River between the Wyoming-Nebraska line and Bridgeport, Nebraska, during 1911 to 1931, as reported by Willis [72] and as given in the biennial reports of the Nebraska Department of Roads and Irrigation. Apparently, stable conditions were reached about 1926. During 1927, visible return flows were nearly 700 thousand acre-feet, but after that year they did not exceed about 600 thousand acre-feet. Many drainage ditches were excavated prior to 1926, and visible return flows during the later years shown in Figure 5 probably were largely drainage recovery.

Measurements in California during 1924 to 1929 showed that average annual return flows from irrigated lands, expressed as percentages of annual gross diversions, could be estimated at 42.5 per cent in the Sacramento Valley, 35 per cent in the San Joaquin Valley, 15 per cent in the delta uplands, and 14 per cent in the Mokelumne Valley.[36] For the Sacramento Valley, return flows during the irrigation season from April to October were estimated at 65 per cent of the annual return for general crops, and at 75 per cent of the annual return for all crops including rice.[68] Rice crops usually return practically all their unused water during the irrigation season.

Conclusions Regarding Return Flow. Some general conclusions regarding return flow from irrigation projects appear to be justified on the basis of such investigations as have been made thus far. The principal conclusions may be briefly stated as follows:

1. Return flow from a new project may begin within a relatively short time after the beginning of irrigation, possibly as early as the second or third year, depending on the original elevation of the water table and the depths of water applied to the fields.

2. On large, new projects developed in arid regions not previously irrigated, stable conditions of return flow may not be reached until 20 or 30 years following the beginning of irrigation.

3. On large, well-established irrigation projects, amply supplied with water, annual return flows may vary from about one-third to two-thirds of annual diversions.

4. Annual return flows on well-established projects may vary from less than 1 to more than 3 acre-feet per acre of irrigated land, depending on soil conditions, diversions, and conveyance and irrigation efficiencies.

5. On projects provided with complete and efficient drainage systems, visible return flows may be almost entirely drainage recovery.

6. Invisible return flows may be one-half or more of annual return flows, depending on the extent to which artificial drainage has been provided.

7. Maximum rates of return flow occur during the summer and fall months, following the periods of irrigation, and minimum rates during the winter and spring months, preceding the periods of irrigation.

8. Monthly return flows throughout the year may vary from about 5 to 12 per cent of annual returns, but variations may be somewhat greater when return flows are largely drainage recovery.

9. On projects producing common types of farm crops, from 50 to 65 per cent of annual return flows reach the streams during the irrigation season and become available for rediversion to other lands.

10. On lands producing rice crops exclusively, nearly all excess waters return to the streams during the irrigation season.

11. Return flows from irrigation projects constitute a valuable source of water supply for additional arable lands that otherwise could not be utilized in crop production.

Drainage Recovery. The amount of water that can be recovered by draining an irrigation project depends on soil formations, losses and waste during conveyance, and excess depths delivered to the irrigated fields. The actual value of the water recovered seldom, if ever, justifies costly drainage improvements requiring long and intricate ditch systems. However, when such improvements are necessary in order to reclaim seeped areas and prevent further damages to project lands, the water recovered constitutes a net gain in supplies available for use on other areas.

In the Middle Rio Grande Conservancy District, central New Mexico, the drainage return from about 59 thousand acres of irrigated land during 1936 amounted to 2.92 acre-feet per acre. This was 28 per cent of gross diversions. In the different divisions of the district, drainage returns varied from 0.94 acre-feet per irrigated acre in the Cochiti Division to 4.77 acre-feet per irrigated acre in the Socorro Division where some seepage from the river may have reached the drainage ditches.[51]

In the Albuquerque and Belen divisions of the Middle Rio Grande District, monthly drainage recoveries during 1936 varied from 5.1 per cent of the yearly total in February to 10.9 per cent of the yearly total in June.

In the Mesilla Division of the Rio Grande Project, just above El Paso, Texas, the annual drainage return from about 73 thousand acres of irrigated land averaged 2.63 acre-feet per irrigated acre during 1930 to 1936. Table 5 shows annual drainage returns in the three

TABLE 5

DRAINAGE RETURNS ON RIO GRANDE PROJECT, 1930–1936 [51]

(Thousands of acre-feet)

Year	Rincon division		Mesilla division		El Paso division		Project total	
	Amount	Per cent of diversion	Amount	Per cent of diversion	Amount	Per cent of diversion	Amount	Per cent of diversion
1930	31.9	49.5	183.8	43.4	132.5	49.4	348.2	46.0
1931	36.7	57.3	196.5	47.9	131.2	55.4	364.4	51.2
1932	39.2	53.0	194.4	44.2	138.0	56.4	371.6	49.0
1933	41.0	59.1	205.4	49.4	137.2	56.4	383.6	52.6
1934	40.9	49.5	217.8	51.1	132.8	50.1	391.5	50.5
1935	26.8	52.3	167.1	56.0	109.5	55.1	303.4	55.3
1936	28.5	45.3	185.2	50.2	112.9	47.6	326.6	48.8
Mean	35.0	52.2	192.9	48.5	127.7	52.7	355.6	50.3

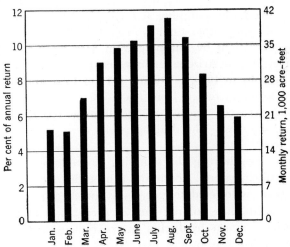

FIGURE 6. Monthly distribution of annual drainage return, Rio Grande Project, 1930–1935.[51]

divisions of the Rio Grande Project, also totals for the project, for the 7 years reported. Figure 6 shows average monthly distributions of drainage returns for the entire project. This project is one of the older irrigation enterprises developed by the Bureau of Reclamation. The irrigation season is from about February to December.

In the San Luis Valley, southern Colorado, annual drainage recoveries measured prior to 1922 averaged 1.2 acre-feet per acre from 5,700 acres in the Carmel Drainage District, and about 1.0 acre-feet per acre from 25,000 acres in the Rio Grande Drainage District. Monthly drainage returns varied from 3 to 16 per cent of the annual. Maximum monthly returns occurred during June or July, and minimum monthly returns during January and February.[39]

Drainage Recovery by Pumping. On some projects, adequate drainage can be secured by pumping from deep wells located near irrigation canals, and the pumped water discharged into the canals to augment project supplies. Such methods may be feasible where underground formations are sufficiently porous, extend to considerable depths, and are continuous through large areas, so that percolating waters can be drawn from long distances.

Similar methods of drainage recovery can be used on small local areas where porous formations are not so deep or extensive, but the drainage of a large project by pumping under such conditions requires the installation of many small plants at carefully selected locations. Drainage recoveries by pumping at small plants are usually made by farmers individually rather than as project enterprises.

Drainage operations by pumping from deep wells were begun on the Salt River Project, Arizona, many years ago.[35] They were discussed briefly by Murphy in 1930.[49] During 1919 to 1926, annual quantities of pumped water increased from about 56 thousand to more than 251 thousand acre-feet. Nearly all the drainage recoveries were used as irrigation supplies. The drainage wells were driven to depths of 150 to 300 feet.

For project use, drainage by pumping has certain advantages over drainage by ditch systems. Pumping can be discontinued as soon as the water table is lowered to safe levels and the need for pumped water has passed, thus holding further percolation in underground storage. With drainage by ditches, percolation from irrigation water applied late in the season, also percolation from rainfall during the winter and early spring, may maintain ditch flows when they cannot be diverted for use on project lands. Furthermore, large amounts of water can be pumped from the groundwater reservoir during dry years,

when surface supplies are limited, and the underground storage replenished by percolation during subsequent wet years, when surface
supplies are more than adequate for crop requirements.

Drainage waters recovered by pumping and used in irrigation are
really subsurface supplies and logically should be discussed under that
heading. They are taken up here because of their relation to the
general subject of drainage recovery and return flow.

Importation of Water. The importation of irrigation water from
other drainage basins having excess supplies was begun in western
United States about the beginning of the present century. Since that
time, many importation projects have been built in the various irrigation states.

Probably the first importation projects consisted of relatively short,
inexpensive ditches that collected runoff from high areas near watershed divides, such as those constructed in the mountains of Colorado.
The Skyline Ditch, northern Colorado, began diverting runoff from
the headwaters of Laramie River into the Cache la Poudre Valley in
1899. Early transmountain diversions in Colorado, where water supplies are deficient in the eastern half of the state and more plentiful
in the western half, were described by Follansbee in 1930.[17] Later,
as demands for water increased, more expensive projects were built,
including collection conduits, reservoirs, tunnels, and other engineering works.

Two early tunnel projects, built by the Bureau of Reclamation, are
the Gunnison Tunnel in western Colorado and the Strawberry Tunnel
in eastern Utah.[12] The Gunnison Tunnel, completed in 1910, diverts
water from the Gunnison River into the adjoining Uncompahgre
Valley. The Strawberry Tunnel, completed in 1912, diverts water
from Strawberry Reservoir, on the headwaters of Strawberry River,
into the Spanish Fork Valley, for irrigating lands south of Provo.

Large and costly importation developments now being made by
the Bureau of Reclamation include the Colorado-Big Thompson
Project, northern Colorado, the Columbia Basin Project, central Washington, and the Delta Cross Channel, a unit of the Central Valley
Project, California. The Delta Cross Channel, which extends about
50 miles from the Sacramento River to the San Joaquin Valley, will
facilitate flushing of salt water from the delta waterways as well as
supplying water to the intakes of the Contra Costa Canal and the
San Joaquin Pumping System.

Most importation projects in the West are now planned to provide
water for multiple uses, including irrigation. Provisions for the devel-

opment of hydroelectric power often constitute important elements of the projects. The larger projects are usually built by municipalities or agencies of the federal government. City water departments, which must supply water for domestic and industrial uses, regardless of cost, have built many large importation projects. They generally supply some water for irrigating orchard fruits and truck products.

The Colorado River Aqueduct, built by the Metropolitan Water District of Southern California, constitutes the most noteworthy importation project completed during recent years.[71] It was designed to carry about 1,500 second-feet of water from the Colorado River at Parker Dam to Los Angeles and other municipalities in that section of southern California. Importation of water was begun in November 1939. Parker Dam is located about 18 miles upstream from Parker, Arizona.

Use of City Water. Most water departments of western cities furnish water for the irrigation of some suburban lands. The sixteenth census showed that city water constituted primary sources of supply for nearly 11 thousand acres of suburban lands irrigated in 1939. These areas included projects where receipts from irrigation water were segregated and comprised substantial amounts. Areas irrigated with city water were greatly expanded during the 10-year period preceding the sixteenth census. The total area irrigated with city water in 1939 was about 6.5 times the total area irrigated from such sources in 1929.

City water as a source of irrigation supply is of considerable importance locally, inasmuch as crops grown on suburban lands usually include vegetables, berries, fruits, and other valuable products. However, the total area of suburban lands irrigated with city water is very small in comparison with the total area of farm lands irrigated with water from other sources. In 1939, the total area irrigated with city water was only about 0.05 per cent of the total area irrigated in the western states.

Use of Sewage. Sewage discharges may constitute sources of water supply for irrigating relatively small areas near municipalities. Some farmers in suburban areas use sewage as supplemental water supplies during the irrigation season. A few suburban farmers depend entirely on sewage for their irrigation water. The sixteenth census showed that sewage constituted a primary source of supply for about 5,000 acres, only about half of the area supplied by city water.

Sewage discharges may be diverted to the lands as raw sewage, direct from outfall lines, or as effluents from sewage treatment plants. Many of the larger cities in western United States have built sewage treatment plants and deliver effluents for irrigation use on nearby lands. Some cities maintain municipal irrigation farms in connection with their sewage disposal plants. Fresno, California, and San Antonio, Texas, may be cited as examples.

In general, coarse-textured sandy soils are more suitable for sewage irrigation than fine-textured silt and clay soils. Structures of sandy soils may be improved by the screening out of fine sediments in sewage flows, whereas permeabilities of silt and clay soils may be decreased by the deposition of such sediments at the soil surfaces. Inasmuch as sewage discharges contain some fertilizing elements, crop yields under sewage irrigation often are higher than under irrigation with normal streamflows.

In considering the use of sewage as irrigation water, possibilities of contaminating crop products and polluting groundwater supplies must be investigated. Such dangers are greater for raw sewage than for effluents from treatment plants. Vegetable products that are normally consumed without cooking are especially susceptible to contamination. Most western states have established regulations governing the use of sewage in irrigation. They exercise control of sewage irrigation projects through their public health boards or departments.

Sewage irrigation in some form probably is about as old as irrigation agriculture. Two of the earlier water-supply papers published by the United States Geological Survey, prepared by Rafter, were devoted to sewage irrigation in the United States and certain foreign countries.[54] In 1939, sewage irrigation in the western states was described in a Department of Agriculture bulletin prepared by Hutchins.[25]

Where sewage flows or sewage effluents are delivered to natural stream channels, the flows automatically become available for diversion to downstream irrigation projects. Sewage discharges are really return flows from domestic and industrial uses. In some cities, they may amount to two-thirds or more of the water delivered to consumers. In Denver, Colorado, combined discharges of all sanitary sewers during 1927 to 1947 averaged 71 per cent of the total water consumption. Thus, sewage flows from large cities may constitute important additions to the quantities of water available for irrigation, even though they may not be diverted directly to irrigation projects.

SUBSURFACE WATER SUPPLIES

Subsurface water supplies utilized in irrigation are obtained by pumping from groundwater storage in porous formations below the

Irrigation Water Supplies

water table, pumping from artesian aquifers, or appropriating discharges from flowing artesian wells or large natural springs.

Most irrigated lands supplied with water from subsurface sources are located where valuable fruit and truck crops are grown. Along coastal regions in southern California, large acreages of citrus fruits are irrigated with subsurface waters. Irrigated areas supplied with subsurface waters in western United States comprise only about one-seventh the total irrigated area. However, Meinzer estimated that irrigation waters obtained from wells have a total value about one-fourth as great as irrigation waters obtained from surface sources.[44]

Table 6, compiled from the sixteenth census data, shows irrigated areas in the western states, also in Arkansas and Louisiana, that received their entire water supplies from wells and springs during 1939.

TABLE 6

IRRIGATED AREAS SUPPLIED BY WELLS AND SPRINGS
DURING 1939—SIXTEENTH CENSUS REPORT

(Thousands of acres)

		Areas supplied by wells			
State	Total	Pumped wells	Flowing wells	Pumped and flowing wells	Areas supplied by springs
Arizona	146.5	144.2	1.9	0.4	3.1
Arkansas	149.9	149.9	...	...	....
California	1,519.3	1,511.8	1.6	5.9	28.5
Colorado	63.5	56.8	6.3	0.5	12.8
Idaho	8.4	5.9	2.1	0.4	20.8
Kansas	45.1	45.0	...	0.1	0.3
Louisiana	136.8	135.2	1.4	0.2	....
Montana	1.5	0.8	0.7	...	10.2
Nebraska	81.0	80.7	0.4	...	2.1
Nevada	3.4	0.6	2.6	0.2	54.9
New Mexico	98.8	75.6	11.5	11.7	3.1
North Dakota	...	...	...	...	....
Oklahoma	0.8	0.8	...	...	....
Oregon	8.3	8.2	0.2	...	15.3
South Dakota	0.7	0.1	0.6	...	0.7
Texas	266.9	262.8	2.9	1.1	9.7
Utah	15.9	8.9	6.7	0.3	35.9
Washington	20.0	17.9	2.1	...	5.8
Wyoming	3.5	3.0	0.5	...	7.0
Total	2,570.4	2,508.1	41.5	20.8	210.4

Some additional areas received partial supplies from subsurface sources. The data show that most areas supplied from wells obtained their water by pumping. Only 2.4 per cent of the total area obtained water from flowing wells or from pumped and flowing wells. The area supplied by springs was about 8.2 per cent of the total area supplied by wells.

Irrigation enterprises that utilize water from subsurface sources are usually developed and operated by individual farmers or by a few adjacent landowners working together. Pumping plants or collection works, also areas irrigated per enterprise, are generally small in comparison with those involved in irrigating lands with surface waters.

Subsurface supplies constitute the principal source of water for irrigation in humid states, where large cooperative diversions of surface waters seldom are feasible. Pumping from wells to irrigate rice fields is common practice in Arkansas. Discharges from flowing wells are utilized in irrigating vegetables and citrus fruits in some sections of Florida.

Subsurface waters used in irrigating lands in humid regions are supplemental supplies. They are developed to furnish the additional water needed for normal crop growth during times of deficient rainfall. In humid regions, rainfall constitutes the primary source of water supply and all irrigation supplies are supplemental.

As previously mentioned, subsurface waters used in irrigation are logically considered in two classifications: (1) free or unconfined groundwater, held in porous formations below the water table; and (2) confined groundwater, held in artesian aquifers where overlying impermeable strata prevent direct connections with water in the upper portions of the zone of saturation. Natural springs may be maintained by flows coming from bodies of free groundwater or by discharges through leaks in formations that confine artesian aquifers.

Data on Subsurface Waters. Data on subsurface waters and the conditions under which they exist are available in reports on water-supply investigations conducted by municipal, state, and federal agencies. Early investigations of subsurface waters were confined principally to localities where problems of water supply were urgent. Later, as needs for groundwater data became more general, systematic observations of water tables in underground reservoirs and hydrostatic pressures in artesian aquifers were begun in other parts of the country.

Early measurements of underground waters were usually made at existing or abandoned wells. Then special observation wells were installed. These were equipped with automatic recording gages or with instruments suitable for periodic measurements of water data. During 1946, measurements were made at about 7,000 observation wells, located throughout the United States and Hawaii.

In 1935, the United States Geological Survey began publishing data on elevations of water tables in reservoirs of free groundwater and hydrostatic pressures in bodies of confined groundwater. From 1935 to 1939, records for the entire country were published annually in a special water-supply paper. Beginning with 1940, annual records have been published in six parts as follows:

Part 1—Northeastern States
Part 2—Southeastern States
Part 3—North-central States
Part 4—South-central States
Part 5—Northwestern States
Part 6—Southwestern States and Hawaii

The Geological Survey also has published many special water-supply papers on technical problems involved in studies of subsurface waters (see references at end of chapter, also Chapter 5).

Free Groundwater Supplies. Free groundwater supplies often are utilized for irrigation in regions where porous formations below the water table constitute large underground reservoirs. When water tables are high enough to permit economic pumping operations, large areas can be supplied from such sources. Valley lands where alluvial fills include deep deposits of open sands and gravels are especially suitable for irrigation with water pumped from subsurface sources. In fact, the presence of open sand and gravel formations usually is necessary in order to permit pumping at rates high enough for effective irrigation operations.

Primary water supplies for irrigating large acreages are obtained from groundwater storage in many western states, particularly Texas, New Mexico, Arizona, and California. Probably all irrigation states include some areas where water supplies are obtained exclusively from underground storage. Many additional areas obtain water from subsurface storage for supplemental use during dry periods, when surface supplies are not sufficient to satisfy crop requirements. In some regions adjoining large irrigation projects, return flows caused by excessive deliveries of surface supplies are recovered by pumping and used on additional irrigable lands, as previously mentioned.

Probably the most important problem involved in irrigating lands with water pumped from underground storage is the danger of over-development. Water tables can be drawn down to some extent during dry years if permitted to rise during subsequent wet years. However, average annual withdrawals during a few consecutive years should not exceed average annual recharges. When annual withdrawals continuously exceed annual recharges, water tables soon fall to undesirable levels, pumping heads and pumping costs increase to prohibitive amounts, and farming operations on some lands have to be discontinued.

Irrigated regions where excessive withdrawals from groundwater storage have been made in the past include the High Plains area south of Amarillo, Texas, the Mimbres Valley in southwestern New Mexico, the West Basin near Los Angeles, California, and various additional areas, principally in the southwestern states. In some areas, average annual withdrawals have been several times as great as average annual recharges.

In New Mexico, the groundwater law passed in 1931 now permits state control of irrigation developments where water supplies are obtained from underground sources. Similar laws, more recently enacted in a few states and being considered for enactment in other states, should ultimately permit adequate control of groundwater supplies throughout the West.

Another groundwater problem that has developed in certain coastal basins is contamination by salt water. In some basins of southern California, water tables have been drawn down to elevations so far below sea level that sea water is gradually percolating into the underground reservoirs. This problem, too, should be effectively solved by adequate state control of subsurface waters.

When pumping from subsurface sources is protected against depletion of supplies by overexpansion, irrigation with groundwater has some advantages over irrigation with surface water supplied by large irrigation districts. For instance, the farmer can install his own pumping plant and operate it as required, at his own convenience. Thus, he can irrigate his crops when water is needed, without waiting for his turn at ditch deliveries as may be necessary when a large district supplies water by the rotation system. Furthermore, he may be able to obtain water at a more convenient location than would be possible at a main supply ditch. Pumped water is more desirable than surface water in that it does not carry weed seeds.

The principal disadvantages of irrigating with groundwater are (1) the dangers of groundwater depletion where future developments on adjoining lands are uncontrolled by state officials, and (2) the costs involved in installing, maintaining, and operating adequate pumping plants.

Pumping from Groundwater. Pumping from groundwater to irrigate farm lands commonly requires larger wells and pumps than those used in pumping domestic supplies and stock water. For irrigating fields, continuous discharges of 300 to 1,000 gallons per minute are desirable, depending on acreages irrigated and types of surface soils. Sandy soils require the larger flows.

A continuous flow of 300 gallons per minute for 10 hours will supply a 2-inch irrigation to about 3.3 acres. Therefore, greater discharges or more than one well often are needed for large farms. Where water tables are relatively close to the ground surface, batteries of two or more wells sometimes are installed and connected to a central pump in order to obtain increased discharges with low drawdowns.

Continuous flows of less than 300 gallons per minute can be used in irrigating small gardens and orchards. Relatively low flows may be utilized when water can be stored in farm ponds or reservoirs and released as needed for supplemental supplies.

When water tables are close to the ground surface, pumps are usually installed in pits or open wells. Pumping plants should be located so that water can reach the fields through minimum lengths of discharge pipes or delivery ditches. Sometimes pumps can be installed in old sand or gravel pits, thus saving excavation costs. When water tables are deeper than about 25 feet, drilled wells generally are desirable. Methods of installing and developing wells for irrigation have been described in a government publication.[56]

Practically all types of pumps have been used in pumping irrigation water, including air-lift, plunger, screw, centrifugal, and deep-well turbine types. However, most of the newer plants have been equipped with horizontal or vertical centrifugal pumps, or with deep-well turbines. Horizontal centrifugal pumps can be installed in pits or open wells, where the water table is close to the ground surface and does not fluctuate greatly. Vertical centrifugal or deep-well turbine pumps are needed in the deeper wells. Deep-well turbine pumps have been used in wells 500 feet deep. Types of pumps and conditions under which they should be installed have been discussed in detail.[58]

Pumping plants may be operated by electrical equipment, natural gas, gasoline, oil, or other types of fuel. Electricity is preferable when available. In 1943, Rohwer reported on power requirements as follows: "Tests indicate that well-designed, efficient, modern pumping plants using the different types of fuel require about 35 cubic feet of natural gas, one-third of a gallon of gasoline, one-fourth of a gallon of distillate, one-seventh of a gallon of Diesel fuel, or 1.7 kilowatt-hours of electrical energy to lift 1 acre-foot 1 foot." [56]

In designing plants to pump water for irrigation, all conditions that affect plant operation and delivery of water to the fields must be considered. The essential requirement is the pumping of an adequate supply as economically as possible. Factors that often affect details of equipment and installation include permissible drawdown of the water table, losses of head in the well, necessity for discharging water through pipe lines, probable peak demands for water, feasibility of continuous pumping, available labor supplies, prevailing wages, available sources of power, power costs, and other local matters.

In regions where groundwater is being used for irrigation, required pumping installations may be planned largely on the basis of past experiences. In unirrigated regions, an experimental well should be installed and tested before proceeding with costly developments. Reliable calculations of probable well discharges cannot be made with formulas unless accurate data on all conditions of the water-bearing formations are at hand, including average permeability coefficients as well as depths. Such data seldom are obtainable for underground strata in undeveloped regions.

In regions where lands have not been irrigated, the presence of sand and gravel formations of depths and permeabilities suitable for pumping irrigation water may be indicated by eroded drainage courses, highway or railroad cuts, old gravel pits, or other excavations. The presence of high water tables, suitable for pumping, may be indicated by natural springs along valley floors or by certain types of native vegetation.

On low lands near stream channels, shallow depths to water tables are indicated by rushes, reeds, cattails, salt grass, willows, and similar types of marshy plants. On arid lands beyond the channels, depths suitable for pumping may be indicated by giant wild rice, pickleweed, arrow weed, rabbit brush, or luxuriant growths of alkali sacaton or big greasewood. Mesquite may grow where depths to groundwater vary from less than 10 to more than 50 feet.[41]

Conditions during Pumping. Typical conditions while pumping from free groundwater are illustrated in Figure 7. The static water table at the well is drawn down until hydraulic gradients extending outward in radial directions are sufficient to bring in percolating supplies as fast as the pump removes water from underground storage. When pumping operations are begun, the water table is drawn down rapidly in the immediate vicinity of the well. As pumping continues and storage close to the well becomes depleted, the drawdown gradually extends outward to distances where additional supplies are available.

The vertical distance the water table is lowered by pumping is referred to as the drawdown. A profile of the pumped water table along a vertical radial section through the well is known as a drawdown curve. The cone-shaped volume between the static water table and the

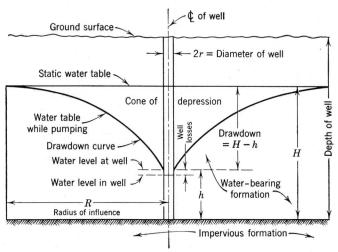

FIGURE 7. Typical conditions while pumping from free groundwater storage.

pumped water table is designated the cone of depression or the cone of influence. The area under the pumped water table, also under the cone of depression, is referred to as the area of influence. The radius of the area of influence is the radius of influence.

Rates at which water can percolate through formations in the zone of saturation depend on slopes of water tables and permeabilities of the materials. They are usually expressed as permeability or transmission coefficients (see Chapter 5). The amount of water a formation can yield per unit of volume when drained by gravity is commonly designated specific yield, but may be referred to as drainable voids, effective porosity, or noncapillary porosity. It is commonly given as a percentage by volume. It may be given as a fraction of a cubic foot per cubic foot.

Permeability coefficients and specific yields are the two most pertinent properties involved in technical studies of pumping groundwater for irrigation. Methods of determination and probable values are discussed later.

Figure 8, a partial reproduction of a diagram in a Geological Survey report prepared by Wenzel, shows drawdown curves measured after different intervals of pumping groundwater from sand and gravel beds near Grand Island, Nebraska.[69] The tests were made for

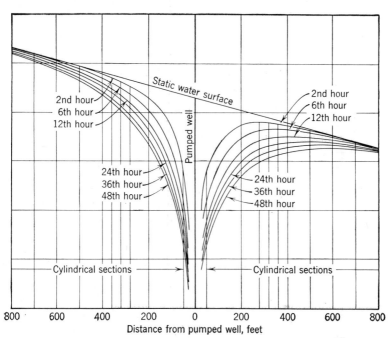

FIGURE 8. Drawdown curves while pumping from free groundwater at Grand Island, Nebraska. (After Wenzel.)

the purpose of determining permeability coefficients and specific yield. Pumping was maintained continuously for 48 hours, at an average rate of 540 gallons per minute. Drawdown measurements were made at more than 80 observation wells, some more than 1,000 feet from the pumped well.

The curves in Figure 8 illustrate the changes in drawdown that take place as pumping continues, the gradual increases in the cone of depression, and the uncertainties involved in evaluating the radius of influence, even when actual measurements of water levels are made. The observed data showed measurable drawdowns as far as 1,200 feet from the well, after 12 hours of pumping. How much farther they may have extended after 48 hours of pumping was not determined.

Theoretically, effects of continued pumping from an underground reservoir, receiving no inflow and experiencing no other outflow, would eventually extend to the limits of the reservoir.

In many irrigated valleys, subsurface reservoirs receive their principal recharges from precipitation during the winter and early spring months. In such regions, water tables rise during the dormant periods preceding the irrigation season, then are drawn down later, as water supplies are pumped for irrigation.

Discharge of Wells. Equations for computing the discharge of a well pumping from free groundwater storage are commonly given in substantially the following form:

$$Q = \frac{\pi P(H^2 - h^2)}{2.3 \log R/r} \tag{1}$$

where Q = discharge, in gallons per day.

P = Meinzer's permeability coefficient, in gallons per square foot per day, for a hydraulic slope of 100 per cent.

H = height of static water level above bottom of water-bearing formation, in feet (see Figure 7).

h = height of water level at well, above bottom of water-bearing formation, while pumping, in feet.

R = radius of influence, in feet.

r = radius of well, in feet.

The corresponding equation for the discharge of a well pumping confined groundwater from an artesian aquifer is

$$Q = \frac{2\pi Pt(H - h)}{2.3 \log R/r} \tag{2}$$

where t is the thickness of the aquifer in feet, $(H - h)$ is the drawdown of the piezometric surface in feet, and other quantities are the same as for equation 1. The piezometric surface at an artesian aquifer is the imaginary surface to which the confined water would rise if observation wells were drilled into the aquifer.

The only definite quantities in equations 1 and 2 are the factor π and the radius of the well. The height H and the thickness t may be known if subsurface geological investigations have been made in the locality where pumping is contemplated. Values of h may be assumed but are always uncertain unless based on previous pumping experiences in the same region. Values of P and R are difficult to predict in advance of pumping tests. In fact, the value of R at a particular well pumping free groundwater is difficult to evaluate even after pumping has been continued for some time, as previously mentioned.

The permeability coefficient can be determined fairly well in a laboratory, when sufficient samples of the water-bearing materials can be secured and can be tested in undisturbed conditions. However, more satisfactory information regarding permeability coefficients can be secured by pumping tests, as was done at Grand Island.

At Grand Island, the pumping tests showed an average permeability coefficient of 997 gallons per square foot per day, for a hydraulic gradient of 100 per cent. The average coefficient determined from laboratory tests of samples, weighted according to thickness of the different strata, was about 1,200 gallons per square foot per day, about 20 per cent higher than the value shown by the pumping tests.

In pumping free groundwater for irrigation, high permeability coefficients are especially desirable. Probably the more satisfactory underground reservoirs that are pumped for irrigation have permeability coefficients of at least 500 gallons per square foot per day. Many determinations of permeability coefficients in underground formations have been published.[70]

The Thiem formula for computing the permeability coefficient from a pumping test is

$$P = \frac{527.7q \log \dfrac{a_1}{a}}{m(s - s_1)} \tag{3}$$

where P = Meinzer's permeability coefficient.

q = the rate of pumping, in gallons per minute.

a and a_1, are distances of two observation wells from the pumped well, in feet.

s and s_1, are drawdowns at the two observation wells, in feet.

m for free groundwater reservoirs is the average vertical thickness of the saturated water-bearing material at the two observation wells, in feet.

m ror artesian aquifers is the vertical thickness of the water-bearing formation, in feet.[69]

All logarithmic factors in equations 1, 2, and 3 are to the base 10. Equations 1 and 2 are based on theoretical considerations of percolation as water moves through the underground formations toward the well. They do not include allowances for friction losses and velocity head as the water moves through the screened or perforated casing into the well and upward to the ground surface. Drawdowns that account for losses of head into and through the well occur at the well and are called well losses (see Figure 7). They usually are small in comparison with the drawdowns that cause percolation toward the well, but they may be large enough to affect details of well installation.

Obviously, when pumping tests are required in order to evaluate factors contained in discharge equations, the need for calculating discharges by equations disappears. Actual discharges can be measured during the pumping tests.

Probably the principal value of equations 1 and 2 is in studying differences in discharge that may result from drilling wells of different diameter or conducting pumping operations so as to produce different depths of drawdown. Such studies may supply information needed in determining desirable well sizes, proper types of pumps, and other features of plant design and operation.

Drawdown-Discharge Relations. Considerations of equation 1 show that, when drawdown conditions at a particular well are maintained constant, the discharge that may be pumped increases only slowly with increased diameter of well. Flows that may be pumped from a particular formation vary inversely with the logarithm of R/r. Assuming R to have a constant value of 1,000 feet, the increased discharges, compared with a 1-foot well, would be 10 per cent for a 2-foot well, 21 per cent for a 4-foot well, and 37 per cent for an 8-foot well.

For actual wells, the above-noted increases may be modified by well losses and details of installation, particularly the type and length of screened or perforated casing installed in the water-bearing formation.

In general, increases in drawdown increase discharges more rapidly than increases in well diameter. This is especially true in thick water-bearing formations. In thick formations, well discharges are practically proportional to drawdowns. In thin formations, increased drawdowns mean decreased depths of water-bearing formations through which water can percolate to the well; so that increases in discharge produced by increases in drawdown decrease as the total drawdown increases.

The ratio of the discharge of a well to the drawdown is known as the specific capacity. It is commonly expressed in gallons per minute per foot of drawdown. It is useful in studying the probable yield of a well under different methods of operation, also in comparing the probable yields of two or more wells. However, specific capacities of wells in the same water-bearing formation may differ considerably. Investigations of wells in the Roswell artesian aquifer, New Mexico, showed specific capacities varying from 7 to 10 gallons per minute per foot of head for 6-inch wells, from 13 to 22 gallons per minute for 8-inch wells, and from 50 to 73 gallons per minute for 10-inch wells.[15] The specific capacity of a particular well may also vary with discharge or with time, as discussed by Jacob.[27]

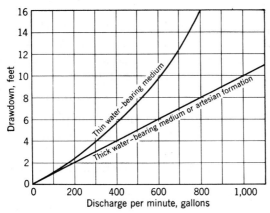

FIGURE 9. Typical drawdown-discharge curves for wells in different water-bearing formations. (After Rohwer.)

Figure 9 shows typical drawdown-discharge curves for wells in different water-bearing formations, taken from Rohwer's 1943 report on small irrigation pumping plants.[57] The curve for thick formations applies to artesian aquifers as well as to porous strata just below the water table. For artesian conditions, the drawdown scale in feet applies to the decline in piezometric surface at the location of the well.

In considering the feasibility of securing increased flows of water by pumping from deeper drawdowns, additional power requirements must be carefully analyzed and compared with costs of installing a larger well or more than one well. Power costs increase as drawdown increases. When increased flows are essential, pumping from a larger well or from a battery of wells, with a shallow drawdown, may be more economical than pumping the same flow from one small well, with a deep drawdown.

Pumping from a larger well or from a battery of wells may also be desirable in order to reduce well losses and percolation velocities.

In some valley fills, high percolation velocities may cause the movement of too much sediment into the well.

Specific Yield. The average specific yield of the earth materials that comprise a free groundwater reservoir varies with the size and gradation of the soil particles. Specific yields of soils may vary from less than 10 per cent for relatively tight clay and clay loams to as much as 40 per cent for porous sand and gravel deposits. In shallow valley fills of porous sand and gravel, where large flows can be pumped for irrigation, average specific yields probably vary between about 15 and 25 per cent.

Specific yields of water-bearing deposits can be determined by laboratory analyses of samples or by special field investigations. Meinzer discussed seven methods of determination in 1923 and again in 1932.[43] The seven methods are listed briefly as follows:

1. Saturation and drainage of samples in the laboratory.

2. Saturation and drainage of materials in place in the field.

3. Analyses of samples taken just above the capillary fringe after the water table has declined.

4. Pumping tests in which discharges and drawdowns are measured.

5. Field measurements of volumes saturated by definite quantities of water.

6. Laboratory measurements with a centrifuge.

7. Estimates of specific retention and specific yield based on laboratory determinations of porosity.

In 1946, Conkling reported that estimates of specific yield of debris cones in southern California could be based on measurements of cone slopes and distances from the mountains.[10] Field investigations and laboratory analyses of samples for conditions in the San Gabriel Valley showed that the methods supplied fairly reliable data. Possibly such methods may be found useful at other locations along mountain ranges.

Inasmuch as drainage of permeable materials by gravity takes place rapidly at first, then at gradually diminishing rates, most methods of measuring specific yield should be continued through considerable intervals of time in order to furnish accurate information. From the viewpoint of irrigation, pumping tests, when feasible, probably constitute the most satisfactory method of determination. When water tables are deep, costs of installing sufficient observation wells may be prohibitive. When groundwater is only 2 to 10 feet below the ground

surface, as at Grand Island, Nebraska, determinations of specific yield
by pumping probably are justified.

Table 7 shows values of specific yield for the sand and gravel deposits at Grand Island, as computed for different cylinders unwatered

TABLE 7

SPECIFIC YIELD OF SAND AND GRAVEL DEPOSITS AT GRAND ISLAND,
NEBRASKA, DETERMINED FROM PUMPING TESTS [69]

Radii of cylinders, ft.	Specific yield computed for different periods of pumping, hr.				
	0–6	0–12	0–24	0–36	0–48
50 and 280	9.8	12.8	16.7	18.7	20.0
50 and 320	9.2	11.9	16.0	18.2	19.8
50 and 360	9.2	12.0	16.3	18.5	19.9
50 and 400	9.1	11.9	16.3	18.5	19.9
50 and 500	9.3	11.8	16.4	18.5	19.9
50 and 600	9.0	11.4	15.9	18.6	20.0
50 and 700	8.7	11.1	15.9	18.8	20.8
50 and 800	8.8	11.1	15.7	18.4	20.5
50 and 900	...	11.2	15.5	18.2	20.3
Average	9.2	11.7	16.1	18.5	20.1

during different periods of pumping. Average values increased from
9.2 per cent for the first 6-hour period to 20.1 per cent for the full 48
hours of the test. They probably would have increased further if
pumping had been continued longer. Studies of rates of increase
during the different periods led to the conclusion that the true specific
yield was between 22 and 23 per cent.[69]

An inspection of the data in Table 7 shows that, for an accurate
evaluation of average specific yield from pumping data, continuance
of pumping through a relatively long period is more important than
calculations for a large number of cylinders. Values of specific yield
computed for the different cylinders are nearly the same for each period
of pumping.

For the Grand Island materials, the specific yield determined from
analyses of samples was about the same as the value computed from
the pumping data. Laboratory tests showed a porosity of 27.1 per
cent, a moisture equivalent of 2.6 per cent, by volume, and a specific
yield of 24.5 per cent. When the moisture equivalent is adjusted
to the probable specific retention of 5 per cent, the specific yield
becomes 22.1 per cent.

Where storage in a subsurface reservoir of known horizontal dimensions is being fully utilized by pumping operations throughout the area, the average specific yield can be computed from records of annual withdrawals and corresponding declines in water table elevations. However, values computed by such methods may be too low when appreciable quantities of water that cannot be measured are percolating out of the reservoir. In deep underground reservoirs, specific yields of the permeable beds probably decrease with increasing depths, owing to consolidation produced by overlying materials.

Storage Coefficient. The storage coefficient of an artesian aquifer is the amount of stored water that may be released from a vertical column of unit cross section, extending through the entire thickness of the aquifer, per unit drop in piezometric surface. It is commonly expressed in cubic feet per square foot of area per foot of drawdown. Its value depends primarily on the compressibility and thickness of the water-bearing formation. It probably increases directly as the thickness increases.[65]

For a free groundwater reservoir, the storage coefficient is the same as specific yield, when specific yield is expressed as a fraction of a cubic foot instead of a percentage by volume. In a free groundwater reservoir, the specific yield is dependent on the characteristics of the water-bearing materials and does not increase with thickness. In fact, it may decrease with thickness owing to compaction of the materials, as previously noted.

The storage coefficient of an artesian aquifer is usually much lower than the specific yield of an unconfined aquifer. The specific yield of an unconfined aquifer of sand and gravel, expressed as a fraction, often is about 0.20, but the storage coefficient of an artesian aquifer made up of permeable rock strata often is lower than 0.002. It may be lower than 0.0002. This shows that most artesian aquifers composed of rock formations must be of extensive dimensions and must carry water under relatively high pressures in order to permit large withdrawals.

Artesian Water Supplies. Discharges from flowing artesian wells or pumped from artesian aquifers are utilized in many parts of western United States. Where artesian aquifers underlie large areas and carry water at relatively high pressures, substantial amounts of water may be obtained from such sources. However, irrigated acreages should not be expanded beyond limits that can be adequately supplied with water.

Annual withdrawals from artesian aquifers should not continuously exceed annual recharges at intake areas. When annual withdrawals continuously exceed annual recharges, artesian pressures decrease, flowing wells soon cease discharging, and pumping from gradually increasing depths below the ground surface becomes necessary. In some irrigated regions that utilize artesian water, wells that originally discharged adequate supplies at ground levels now have to be pumped a hundred feet or more.

In the Pecos Valley near Roswell, New Mexico, where artesian water supplies are obtained from limestone formations several hundred feet below the ground surface, overexpansions of irrigated areas caused a pronounced reduction in the artesian area. When irrigation was begun about 1903, the artesian area included 663 square miles. In 1925, when about 60 thousand acres were under irrigation, the area of free flow included only 425 square miles. At that time, the annual draft on the artesian reservoir was about 200 thousand acre-feet. Since 1931, withdrawals of artesian water have been subject to state control.

When Fiedler and Nye investigated the Roswell artesian basin during 1925 to 1928, 85 wells were discharging from 1,000 to more than 3,000 gallons per minute. One well, drilled in 1926, produced a surface flow of about 6,000 gallons per minute. This was said to be the largest artesian well in the United States, probably the largest in the world at that time.[15]

Figure 10 shows a diagrammatic section along the Roswell aquifer, similar to the one prepared by Meinzer on the basis of the Geological Survey data.[44]

As a result of overdevelopments in the Pecos Valley, many artesian wells had to be abandoned, permitting water to escape into porous formations above the artesian aquifer. A subsequent program of plugging abandoned wells, carried on with state funds, was estimated to have produced an annual saving of about 56 thousand acre-feet of water.[38]

Many artesian aquifers utilized as sources of irrigation supplies are located closer to the ground surface than in the Roswell basin and carry water at considerably lower pressures. In some valleys, artesian aquifers may carry water under hydrostatic pressures of only a few pounds per square inch. In some areas, the aquifers may be partially connected with overlying bodies of groundwater.

Geologic formations that confine artesian aquifers often are referred to as aquicludes or aquifuges. Usually, the latter term is used when the rock is impervious, and the former when the rock is sufficiently porous to absorb water but not to transmit appreciable amounts. Artesian wells that require pumping sometimes are referred to as subartesian wells.

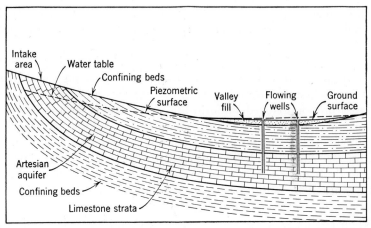

Figure 10.   Diagrammatic section along Roswell artesian aquifer. (After Meinzer.)

Artesian Pressures and Pumping.   In general, hydrostatic pressures in artesian aquifers depend on heights of intake areas above the artesian strata, heads consumed in moving water through the permeable materials, tightness of confining formations, and rates at which water supplies are discharged through pumped wells, flowing wells, or natural outlets.

Artesian pressures may be affected temporarily by earthquakes, by changes in barometric pressure, or by superimposed loads such as flood flows or passing trains.   At locations near the seashore, artesian pressures may be affected by tidal fluctuations.[30]

During pumping operations at an artesian well, hydrostatic pressures in the vicinity of the well are lowered in a manner similar to the drawdown of the water table when pumping from free groundwater storage.   However, the drawdown in pressure at an artesian well takes place more rapidly and extends in radial directions farther than the drawdown in the water table while pumping free groundwater.   Pressure reductions caused by pumping at an artesian well spread through the aquifer at rapid rates and may be registered at wells a mile or more away in only a few minutes.[32]

The zone in which pressures are reduced by pumping an artesian well is called the cone of pressure influence or pressure relief.   The area under the cone of influence is called the area of influence. The reduction in pressure, or the corresponding lowering of the piezometric surface, is called the drawdown.

At an artesian well, the discharge that may be obtained by pumping is proportional to the pressure drawdown in the aquifer materials surrounding the well. An additional drawdown in pressure occurs at the well, to account for well losses. Drawdown tests to determine the effective radius of an artesian well, also well losses, were discussed by Jacob in 1947.[27]

Bodies of confined water, permeable formations in which they are confined, and confining aquicludes or aquifuges are all more or less elastic. Therefore, reductions in hydrostatic pressures and accompanying compressions of aquifer materials caused by weights of overlying formations often result in the release of more water through wells than can be accounted for by percolation at intake areas. Water supplies initially obtained from artesian wells in the extensive Dakota sandstone formations are believed to have come principally from water released by compaction of the sandstone as hydrostatic pressure decreased.[37]

Water Available for Pumping. The total amount of water available for pumping from an underground basin, directly connected with the water table, depends on the dimensions of the basin, the depth the water table can be lowered, the average annual recharge of the basin, the average annual discharge through natural outlets, and the average specific yield of the materials that constitute the water-bearing formations.

The average annual withdrawal of groundwater that can be made by pumping without causing an excessive permanent lowering of the water table or the development of other objectionable conditions is called the safe yield of the basin.

Basin dimensions usually can be determined from topographic surveys and subsurface geological explorations. Geological investigations should reveal characteristics of soil profiles at typical locations, down to the lower limits of the permeable materials or to the lowest elevation of the water table that can be produced by economical pumping operations.

When pumping for irrigation is begun on valley lands, some permanent lowering of the water table often is desirable. When groundwater is too close to the ground surface, considerable losses of water take place by evaporation, evapo-transpiration, outflow through springs, and percolation beyond the limits of the underground reservoir. Lowering the water table sufficiently may salvage appreciable proportions of these losses and increase annual recharges. Evaporation and evapo-transpiration losses can be almost completely recovered. Probably pumping during a series of normal or dry years should lower the water table to levels where recharges during a subsequent series of wet years cannot raise groundwater to undesirable elevations.

The maximum depth the water table can be lowered in an underground reservoir depends on economic pumping lifts and objectionable conditions that may result from excessive pumping. Objectionable conditions that may develop pertain principally to qualities of water, but may include other items. If the water table is lowered to such a depth that all natural outflow is shut off, percolation from irrigation may soon produce undesirable concentrations of salts in the stored water. In coastal regions, excessive lowering of the water table may permit percolation of salt water into the underground reservoir, as previously mentioned. At certain places in California, excessive overdrafts on groundwater reservoirs have caused subsidence of ground surfaces as great as 5 to 7 feet.

After pumping operations at an underground basin have become stabilized at about the safe yield, further permanent lowering of the water table should not take place. Through a series of wet and dry years, the average annual lowering of the water table during the irrigation season should not exceed the average annual raising of the water table during the nonirrigation season.

Annual recharges, discussed more fully under the next heading, are difficult to evaluate accurately but can be estimated from intensive hydrological investigations. Such investigations should include measurements of groundwater levels as well as precipitation, runoff, evaporation, evapo-transpiration, infiltration, and percolation. They should be conducted throughout the tributary areas that supply surface or subsurface waters to the basin, as well as throughout the basin itself. Precipitation is the original source of all recharge, but percolation is the item that determines the amount of recharge. It is the item that raises the water table.

In regions where replenishment of groundwater supplies takes place principally during the nonirrigation season, measurements of rising water tables during the winter and spring furnish direct data on storage recharge.

In general, determinations of safe yield of subsurface reservoirs are not essential until irrigation operations on overlying lands have reached advanced stages of development. This is fortunate because accurate determinations for undeveloped basins seldom, if ever, are possible. Hydrological influences on underground storage, particularly percolation inflow from stream beds and adjoining lands, also percolation outflow and proportions of the outflow that may be recovered, cannot be evaluated until actual data become available.

Even when pumping has been maintained for several years, estimates of safe yield may be only approximate and may have to be revised as time progresses. For instance, estimates based on data obtained during a period of normal or dry years may have to be revised after a subsequent period of abnormally wet years. Methods of determining safe yields of underground reservoirs in southern California were discussed by Conkling and others in 1946.[10]

Natural Recharge. Natural recharge of underground reservoirs occurs by percolation. Percolation that produces recharge may come directly from precipitation, from runoff or streamflow produced by precipitation, or from bodies of surface or subsurface water that result from precipitation. General conditions that affect percolation are discussed in Chapter 5.

A surface area where recharge percolation originates is known as an intake area. A surface area that contributes water to an intake area, either as surface or subsurface flow, is known as a contributing area or catchment area. Intake areas for reservoirs of free groundwater usually are directly overhead or at upstream locations in the same drainage basins, not far distant from the reservoirs. Intake areas for deep artesian aquifers may be at upstream locations in the same or other drainage basins and may be hundreds of miles from the area of utilization.

Precipitation is the original source of percolation, but only a part of the precipitated moisture, often only a very small part, becomes percolation. The remainder is disposed of by runoff or evaporation, or held in the soil to maintain evaporation and transpiration. Some portions of the runoff may subsequently seep out of stream channels into adjoining formations and become percolation. Some portions of the initial percolation may subsequently drain into stream channels from adjoining formations and become groundwater runoff. Thus, evaluations of percolation that reach particular underground reservoirs and produce usable recharges constitute complex hydrological problems.

Percolation that becomes recharge at a particular underground reservoir may come directly from rainfall or melting snow, from surface waters that drain into the valley, from seepage at lakes or surface reservoirs, from seepage through the bed and banks of influent streams, from underflow beneath stream channels, from underflow through other subsurface locations, from return flow at irrigated lands, or from seepage along irrigation canals. The last item generally is small, but the others may be large. The last two items might be considered as forms of artificial recharge, except that they are incidental rather than intentional.

Precipitation, being the original source of percolation, whether direct or indirect, is the most important factor that affects recharge. In general, periods of high precipitation are periods of high recharge. Amounts of direct percolation produced by particular rainfalls vary with the intensity and duration of the rainfall and with the soil and vegetal conditions at the time of the rainfall. Rainfalls or melting snows on unfrozen soils during the winter and spring usually produce more direct percolation than rainfalls during the growing season. Frozen soils usually impede or prevent percolation.

In the humid eastern sections of the United States, also in the Pacific Northwest, most groundwater recharge probably takes place by direct percolation from local rainfall. In California, winter rainfalls cause substantial amounts of direct percolation and groundwater recharge. Percolation from local rainfall produces less recharge in semiarid regions, and practically none in arid regions. In arid valleys near mountain ranges, recharge of subsurface reservoirs takes place largely by percolation from influent streams and by underflow beneath the channels as the streams emerge from the mountains.

Underflow beneath stream channels may be obstructed by rock barriers, then resumed after the barriers are overtopped. Percolation from influent streams may be decreased by silting along the bed and banks, then increased, later, as floods scour out the accumulated silt deposits.

Amounts of water that percolate from influent streams depend on characteristics of channel materials and adjoining earth formations, areas submerged, periods of submergence, and elevations of surrounding water tables. Depths of channel flow and temperatures of the water may have small effects on percolation rates.

Detailed investigations of groundwater recharge by underflow and percolation from influent streams seldom are made because of costs involved. Results of intensive investigations along the San Gabriel River, southern California, were reported by Conkling in 1929. Measurements of percolation rates in San Gabriel Wash showed that the maximum rate occurred where the sand was most uniform and free from gravel.[9]

Artificial Recharge.   Artificial recharge of groundwater reservoirs by spreading unused streamflows has been practiced on debris cones in southern California since about the beginning of the present century.   Some spreading operations were conducted along the South Platte River near Denver, Colorado, as early as 1889.[47]   Spreading operations in western United States were discussed in detail in a government bulletin prepared by Mitchelson and Muckel.[48]   They also have been discussed in many articles published by scientific journals (see references at end of chapter).

Artificial methods of recharging groundwater by spreading surface flows over small areas or by admitting water through wells are practiced to some extent in eastern states and certain foreign countries, in connection with water-supply systems for municipal and industrial uses.   However, amounts of groundwater recharge obtained for such purposes usually are small in comparison with those obtained for use in irrigation.

In southern California, spreading works are constructed on porous areas along stream channels, usually just below the mountains and upstream from irrigated lands.   In general, spreading operations are conducted by flooding comparatively flat areas, admitting streamflows to large basins, or diverting flows into ditches or furrows.   Particular methods depend on local conditions.   The ditch and furrow method can be used on irregular sloping areas.   The flooding or basin methods can be used on smoother areas of more gradual slopes.   Sometimes increased percolation along natural channels can be obtained by scarifying the stream beds, as discussed by Freeman.[1]

Artificial recharge through wells has been tried but has some disadvantages.   Percolation areas are limited and may soon become clogged unless clear water can be diverted.   Recharge through pits, shafts, or wells may have advantages when clean water can be diverted and when the water must pass downward through intercepting layers of clay or other impermeable materials before reaching porous formations directly connected with the underground reservoir.   The use of wells supplied by drainage from a spreading area in Orange County, California, was described by Bradley in his discussion of Conkling's paper.[10]   Silt loads carried by incoming flows were removed by filtration through sandy soil on the spreading grounds before the water reached the wells.

Spreading operations by flooding, basin, or ditch and furrow methods usually are conducted after the principal flood discharges have passed or at other times when surface flows are not heavily laden with silt. Where the basin system is utilized, upper basins may be operated largely for desilting rather than for recharge. Recharge by spreading is greatly facilitated where surface reservoirs have been constructed at upstream locations, so that streamflows are regulated and practically free from silt.

Efficient diversion and control works are necessary for all types of spreading systems. Diversion weirs, intakes, ditches, dikes, drops, return drains, and other features must be adequate not only to control flows during spreading operations but also to prevent shifting of natural channels along routes followed by the main streams. Because of uncertainties in stream characteristics and spreading efficiencies, the use of temporary timber structures may be advisable during early stages of development. Periodic thorough inspections are essential at all systems.

No elaborate spreading system should be constructed without first securing detailed information regarding subsurface conditions. Data particularly pertinent include the nature, extent, and depth of porous materials, the possible presence of impermeable strata, and depths to the water table. Most spreading systems are built and operated by local irrigation, water supply, or water conservation districts.

Rates of Artificial Recharge. Rates of artificial recharge during spreading operations depend principally on conditions of surface soils and permeabilities of subsurface materials. Conditions of surface soils determine rates at which water can infiltrate into the soil. Permeabilities of subsurface materials determine rates at which water can percolate downward to the water table and laterally to storage in adjoining materials as the water table rises beneath the spreading area.

Field tests show that, as spreading operations continue, the water table under the spreading area rises in the shape of a mound or cone. When the apex of the mound reaches the saturated surface soil, the rate of percolation decreases. Subsequently, as the water table declines through the first few feet, the rate of percolation increases. Except when groundwater is relatively close to the ground surface, rates of recharge apparently are not affected by depths to the water table.[48]

Temperature conditions probably have some effects on rates of groundwater recharge during spreading. However, since temperature ranges during periods of spreading are small, such effects usually are negligible in comparison with other effects.

Rates of recharge generally are highest when spreading is begun, then decrease gradually as spreading operations are continued. The decreases may be due to deposition of silt carried by the water supply, or to puddling of fine soil particles where spreading areas have been disked, harrowed, or cultivated. In some tests with clear water, decreases in recharge rates were attributed in part to the growth of algae at the ground surface. Some tests with clear water showed higher and more uniform rates of recharge on undisturbed areas of native vegetation than on cultivated areas where vegetation had been removed.

In 1936, Freeman reported that on the Saticoy spreading unit, Santa Clara Water Conservation District, the native vegetation had been left undisturbed and no noticeable reduction in the rate of percolation at the beginning of the spreading season could be observed, although the basin had been used since 1929. No water carrying more than 20 cubic feet of silt per acre-foot was used in spreading at the Saticoy unit.[1]

Observed rates of percolation during spreading have been reported for several locations in southern California. Some were based on experimental measurements at test plots, others on measurements during actual spreading operations at established systems. In general, they vary from less than 1.0 to more than 10 second-feet per acre of wetted area, depending on local conditions.

In 1929, Post reported rates of percolation varying from 0.9 to 4.8 second-feet per acre of wetted area for different sand and gravel deposits examined during the Santa Ana investigations.[53] In 1934, Volk reported rates varying from 1.37 to 8.06 second-feet per wetted acre for locations below surface reservoirs built by the Los Angeles County Flood Control District. The reported values represented averages for a number of measurements.[67] In 1946, Laverty reported maximum and minimum rates for seven spreading grounds and three test areas where measurements were made by the Flood Control District.[29]

Table 8, compiled from Laverty's report, shows maximum and minimum rates of percolation, together with pertinent data on soils, methods of spreading, wetted areas, and depths to groundwater. Maximum rates were observed when spreading began, and minimum rates after extended runs. Water tables were close to the ground surface during some measurements, as indicated by the footnotes. Maximum rates varied from 1.5 to 7.5 second-feet per wetted acre. Minimum rates varied from 0.7 to 3.8 second-feet per wetted acre.

TABLE 8

RATES OF PERCOLATION DURING SPREADING OPERATIONS, LOS ANGELES COUNTY FLOOD CONTROL DISTRICT [29]

Spreading grounds	Type of soil	Type of spreading *	Wetted area, acres	Percolation rates, sec.-ft. per wetted acre † Max.	Min.	Range in depth to water table, ft.
San Antonio	Tujunga stony sand	B, D	137	4.5	1.5	100–270
Big Dalton	Hanford stony sandy loam	D	9	6.0	1.1	18–139
Little Dalton	Hanford stony sandy loam	B	2.0	5.4 ‡	...	18–139
Canyon basin	Hanford fine sand	D	62	1.6 ‡	...	1–160
San Gabriel coastal basin						
Upper area	Hanford sand	B	54	2.5 §	1.0 §	20–73
Lower area	Hanford sand	B	54	4.0	1.8	20–73
Rio Hondo coastal basin	Hanford fine sandy loam	B	150	2.0 §	0.9 §	12–72
Pacoima						
Silty flows	Hanford fine sandy loam	B, D	80	...	0.8	196–260
Cultivated area, clear water	Hanford fine sandy loam	B, D	80	...	1.9	196–260
San Gabriel Valley ‖						
San Gabriel Cone (upstream area)						
In old overflow channel						
Before blasting ¶	River wash	B	0.92	1.5	0.7	124–144
After blasting	River wash	B	0.81	4.0 ‡	...	124–144
Off-channel basins	River wash	B	12.75	5.0	3.8	124–44
San Gabriel Cone, brush land	Tujunga stony sand	O	1.07	2.4 ‡	...	55–90
South side of Rio Hondo						
Natural river bed (3 days)	Hanford sandy loam	B	0.51	3.8	2.7	45–49
Cultivated surface (9 days)	Hanford sandy loam	B	0.51	7.5	3.8	45–49

* B, basin; D, ditch; O, shallow overflow.
† Maximum are initial rates, minimum are after extended runs.
‡ Mean rate for area.
§ Apex of groundwater mound at level of basin beds.
‖ Santa Fe Diversion; temporary testing grounds.
¶ Maximum rate is mean for month with clear water; minimum is mean for month following silty flows.

For efficient economic recharge of groundwater reservoirs by spreading, average percolation rates during spreading periods should be as high as possible. Average rates of at least 1.0 second-foot per wetted acre probably are desirable, but some systems have been designed on the basis of 0.5 second-foot per acre of spreading ground. Average rates obtained during spreading periods probably depend on the size of the spreading area and the time spreading is continued after the groundwater mound reaches the saturated surface, as well as on the permeability of the underlying materials. Under favorable conditions, average rates greater than about 3 second-feet per wetted acre seldom are attained on large areas.

Irrigation from Springs. Natural springs located near arable lands may be used as water supplies for irrigation when they discharge appreciable flows during the irrigation season. Table 6 shows that during 1939 relatively large areas were irrigated from springs in several western states, particularly Nevada, Utah, California, and Idaho. In Nevada, Utah, and Idaho, areas supplied from springs were greater than total areas supplied from wells.

In 1927, Meinzer proposed an eight-group classification of springs based on average discharges.[42] The three larger groups were: first magnitude, springs discharging more than 100 second-feet; second magnitude, those discharging between 10 and 100 second-feet; and third magnitude, those discharging between 1 and 10 second-feet. For western United States, he reported 16 springs of first magnitude in Oregon, 15 in Idaho, 7 in California, 4 in Texas, and 3 in Montana. Probably many western springs that fall in the first three groups are utilized as irrigation water supplies.

Spring flows may originate in either free or confined groundwater reservoirs. At some locations near artesian basins, the flows apparently come through fissures or faults in formations overlying the artesian aquifers. Discharges of some large springs in the Pecos Valley, New Mexico, decreased materially or even ceased entirely as water supplies were withdrawn and hydrostatic pressures lowered in the Roswell artesian basin.

Where springs originate from unconfined groundwater in irrigated regions, flows may fluctuate in accordance with irrigation operations. Such conditions have been observed in the Snake River Valley, Idaho. Some springs near Jerome, Idaho, produce maximum flows during the fall months, at about the end of the irrigation season.

REFERENCES

1. American Geophysical Union, "Symposium on Contribution to Ground-Water Supplies," *Trans.*, 1936, Part II, pp. 456–480.
2. American Institute of Mining and Metallurgical Engineers, "Geology and Engineering for Dams and Reservoirs," a symposium, *Tech. Pub.* 215, 1929.
3. Brown, Carl B., "The Control of Reservoir Silting," *U.S. Dept. Agr. Misc. Pub.* 521, 1943.
4. Bryan, Kirk, "Geology of Reservoir and Dam Sites with a Report on the Owyhee Irrigation Project, Oregon," *U.S. Geol. Sur. Water-Supply Paper* 597–A, 1929.
5. Bunger, Mills E., "Return-Flow," *Trans. Am. Geop. Union,* 1937, Part II, pp. 527–532.

6. Carpenter, L. G., "Seepage and Return Waters," *Colo. Agr. Exp. Sta. Bull.* 180, 1916.

7. Code, W. E., "Ground Water Supply of Prospect Valley, Colorado," *Colo. Agr. Exp. Sta. Tech. Bull.* 34, 1945.

8. Cole, Donald B., "Transmountain Water Diversion in Colorado," *Colo. Mag.*, March 1948, pp. 49–65; also May 1948, pp. 118–135.

9. Conkling, Harold, "San Gabriel Investigation—Analysis and Conclusions," *Calif. Dept. Pub. Works,* Bull. 7, 1929.

10. —— "Utilization of Ground-Water Storage in Stream System Development," *Trans. Am. Soc. C. E.,* Vol. 111, 1946, pp. 275–354.

11. Debler, E. B., "Return Flow and Its Problems on Reclamation Projects," *New Recl. Era,* August 1927, pp. 124-125.

12. —— "Inter-Water-Shed Diversions by Tunnels on United States Reclamation Projects," *Trans. Am. Soc. C. E.,* Vol. 94, 1930, pp. 346–351.

13. Eakin, Henry M., "Silting of Reservoirs," *U.S. Dept. Agr. Tech. Bull.* 524, 1936, revised by Brown, 1939.

14. Enger, Kyle, David G. Thompson, and Raphael G. Kazmann, "Ground Water Supplies for Rice Irrigation in the Grand Prairie Region, Arkansas," *Ark. Agr. Exp. Sta. Bull.* 457, 1945.

15. Fiedler, A. G., and S. S. Nye, "Geology and Ground-Water Resources of the Roswell Artesian Basin, New Mexico," *U. S. Geol. Sur. Water-Supply Paper* 639, 1933.

16. Field, John E., "Evaluation of Water Rights," *Trans. Am. Soc. C. E.,* Vol. 94, 1930, pp. 247–294.

17. Follansbee, Robert, "Trans-Mountain Diversions in Colorado," *Trans. Am. Soc. C. E.,* Vol. 94, 1930, pp. 359–367.

18. —— "Increase in Flow of the North Platte River from Whalen Dam to North Platte," *Nebr. Dept. Pub. Works, 19th Bien. Rep.,* 1931–1932, pp. 300–310.

19. Gardner, Willard, T. R. Collier, and Doris Farr, "Groundwater, Part I, Fundamental Principles Governing Its Physical Control," *Utah Agr. Exp. Sta. Tech. Bull.* 252, 1934.

20. Hall, L. Standish, "Silting of Reservoirs," *Jour. Am. Water Works Assn.,* January 1940, pp. 25–42.

21. Harding, S. T., "Ground Water Resources of the Southern San Joaquin Valley," *Calif. Dept. Pub. Works Bull.* 11, 1927.

22. Hemphill, R. G., "Silting and Life of Southwestern Reservoirs," *Trans. Am. Soc. C. E.,* Vol. 95, 1931, pp. 1060–1074.

23. Hinderlider, M. C., *Twenty-Fifth Biennial Report of the State Engineer to the Governor of Colorado, for the Years 1929–1930,* Denver, Colorado, 1931.

24. Hutchins, Wells A., "Policies Governing the Ownership of Return Waters from Irrigation," *U.S. Dept. Agr. Tech. Bull.* 439, 1934.

25. —— "Sewage Irrigation as Practiced in the Western States," *U.S. Dept. Agr. Tech. Bull.* 675, 1939.

26. Israelsen, O. W., and W. W. McLaughlin, "Drainage of Land Overlying an Artesian Groundwater Reservoir," *Utah Agr. Exp. Sta. Bull.* 259, 1935.

27. Jacob, C. E., "Drawdown Test to Determine Effective Radius of Artesian Well," *Trans. Am. Soc. C. E.,* Vol. 112, 1947, pp. 1047–1070.

28. Lane, D. A., "Artificial Storing of Groundwater by Spreading," *Jour. Am. Water Works Assn.,* Vol. 28, 1936, pp. 1240–1251.

29. Laverty, Finley B., "Correlating Flood Control and Water Supply, Los Angeles Coastal Plain," *Trans. Am. Soc. C. E.,* Vol. 111, 1946, pp. 1127–1158.

30. Lee, Charles H., "The Interpretation of Water-Levels in Wells and Test-Holes," *Trans. Am. Geop. Union,* 1934, Part II, pp. 540–554.

31. Le Fever, F. F., "Increase in Flow of the North Platte and Platte Rivers from Whalen Dam, Wyoming, to Overton, Nebraska," *Nebr. Dept. Roads and Irr., 20th Bien. Rep.,* 1933–1934, pp. 333–355.

32. Leggette, R. M., and G. H. Taylor, "The Transmission of Pressure in Artesian Aquifers," *Trans. Am. Geop. Union,* 1934, Part II, pp. 409–413.

33. Livingston, Penn, "Underground Leakage from Artesian Wells in the Las Vegas Area, Nevada," *U.S. Geol. Sur. Water-Supply Paper* 849–D, 1941.

34. Mackin, J. Hoover, "A Geologic Interpretation of the Failure of the Cedar Reservoir, Washington," *Univ. Wash. Eng. Exp. Sta. Bull.* 107, 1941.

35. Marr, James C., "Drainage by Means of Pumping from Wells in Salt River Valley, Arizona," *U.S. Dept. Agr. Bull.* 1456, 1926.

36. Matthew, Raymond, "Variation and Control of Salinity in Sacramento-San Joaquin Delta and Upper San Francisco Bay," *Calif. Dept. Pub. Works Bull.* 27, 1931.

37. McGuinness, Charles L., "Recharge and Depletion of Ground-Water Supplies," *Trans. Am. Soc. C. E.,* Vol. 112, 1947, pp. 972–998.

38. McClure, Thomas M., "Plugging Old Artesian Wells to Stop Underground Water Loss," *Eng. News-Rec.,* Mar. 19, 1936, pp. 425–427.

39. Meeker, R. I., "Return-Flow Water from Irrigation Developments," *Eng. News-Rec.,* July 20, 1922, pp. 105–108.

40. ——— "Return Water from Irrigation," *Trans. Am. Soc. C. E.,* Vol. 94, 1930, pp. 338–341.

41. Meinzer, Oscar E., "Plants as Indicators of Ground Water," *U.S. Geol. Sur. Water-Supply Paper* 577, 1927.

42. ——— "Large Springs in the United States," *U.S. Geol. Sur. Water-Supply Paper* 557, 1927.

43. ——— "Outline of Methods for Estimating Ground-Water Supplies," *U.S. Geol. Sur. Water-Supply Paper* 638–C, 1932.

44. ——— "Ground Water in the United States, a Summary of Ground-Water Conditions and Resources, Utilization of Water from Wells and Springs, Methods of Scientific Investigation, and Literature Relating to the Subject," *U.S. Geol. Sur. Water-Supply Paper* 836–D, 1939.

45. ——— "Discussion of Question No. 2 of the International Commission on Subterranean Water: Definitions of the Different Kinds of Subterranean Water," *Trans. Am. Geop. Union,* 1939, Part IV, pp. 674–677.

46. ——— "General Principles of Artificial Ground-Water Recharge," *Econ. Geol.,* May 1946, pp. 191–201.

47. Mitchelson, A. T., "Conservation of Water through Recharge of the Underground Supply," *Civ. Eng.,* March 1939, pp. 163–165.

48. Mitchelson, A. T., and Dean C. Muckel, "Spreading Water for Storage Underground," *U.S. Dept. Agr. Tech. Bull.* 578, 1937.

49. Murphy, D. W., "Drainage Recovery from Irrigation," *Trans. Am. Soc. C. E.,* Vol. 94, 1930, pp. 333–337.

50. National Resources Board, *Report of the Water Planning Committee,* Washington, 1934.

51. National Resources Committee, *Regional Planning, Part VI, The Rio Grande Joint Investigation in the Upper Rio Grande Basin in Colorado, New Mexico, and Texas, 1936–1937*, Vol. I, Washington, 1938.

52. Parshall, Ralph L., "Return of Seepage Water to the Lower South Platte River in Colorado," *Colo. Agr. Exp. Sta. Bull.* 279, 1922.

53. Post, William S., "Santa Ana Investigation, Flood Control and Conservation," *Calif. Dept. Pub. Works Bull.* 19, 1928.

54. Rafter, George W., "Sewage Irrigation," *U.S. Geol. Sur. Water-Supply Paper* 3, 1897.

55. ——— "Sewage Irrigation, Part II," *U.S. Geol. Sur. Water-Supply Paper* 22, 1899.

56. Rohwer, Carl, "Putting Down and Developing Wells for Irrigation," *U.S. Dept. Agr. Cir.* 546, 1940.

57. ——— "Design and Operation of Small Irrigation Pumping Plants," *U.S. Dept. Agr. Cir.* 678, 1943.

58. Rohwer, Carl, and M. R. Lewis, "Small Irrigation Pumping Plants," *U.S. Dept. Agr. Farmers' Bull.* 1857, 1940.

59. Rudolph, William E., "Water Supply Problems of a Desert Region," *Trans. Am. Soc. C. E.*, Vol. 94, 1930, pp. 600–625.

60. Simpson, T. R., "Recovery of Return and Seepage Waters in California," *Eng. News-Rec.*, Nov. 6, 1924, pp. 751–754.

61. Sonderegger, A. L., "Water Supply from Rainfall on Valley Floors," *Trans. Am. Soc. C. E.*, Vol. 94, 1930, pp. 1242–1311.

62. Stafford, Harlowe M., "Report of Sacramento-San Joaquin Water Supervisor for the Period 1924–1928," *Calif. Dept. Pub. Works Bull.* 23, 1930.

63. Stevens, J. C., "The Silt Problem," *Trans. Am. Soc. C. E.*, No. 101, 1936, pp. 207–288.

64. ——— "Future of Lake Mead and Elephant Butte Reservoir," *Trans. Am. Soc. C. E.*, Vol. 111, 1946, pp. 1231–1342.

65. Theis, Charles V., "The Significance and Nature of the Cone of Depression in Ground-Water Bodies," *Econ. Geol.*, December 1938, pp. 889–902.

66. ——— "The Source of Water Derived from Wells," *Civ. Eng.*, May 1940, pp. 277–280.

67. Volk, K. Q., "Maintenance and Operating Problems of Water Spreading-Grounds, Southern California," *Trans. Am. Geop. Union*, 1934, Part II, pp. 527–530.

68. Waddell, T. B., "Sacramento River Basin," *Calif. Dept. Pub. Works Bull.* 26, 1931.

69. Wenzel, Leland K., "The Thiem Method for Determining Permeability of Water-Bearing Materials and Its Application to the Determination of Specific Yield," *U.S. Geol. Sur. Water-Supply Paper* 679–A, 1936.

70. ——— "Methods for Determining Permeability of Water-Bearing Materials with Special Reference to Discharging-Well Methods," *U.S. Geol. Sur. Water-Supply Paper* 887, 1942.

71. Weymouth, F. E., and others, "Colorado River Aqueduct Makes Rapid Progress," a symposium, *Civ. Eng.*, February 1935, pp. 72–86.

72. Willis, R. H., "Return Water, North Platte River, Nebraska," *Trans. Am. Soc. C. E.*, Vol. 94, 1930, pp. 328–332.

73. Witzig, Berard J., "Sedimentation in Reservoirs," *Trans. Am. Soc. C. E.*, No. 109, 1944, pp. 1047–1106.

Chapter 14

QUALITY OF IRRIGATION WATER

The quality of a water used in irrigation depends on the impurities carried by the water, either in solution or in suspension. Impurities carried in solution usually determine water quality, but in some regions impurities carried in suspension may have important effects on quality. Whether a water supply of a certain quality will be suitable for use on a particular project depends on local conditions of climate, soils, crops grown, and depths of water applied.

Impurities carried in suspension are filtered out when water supplies reach the irrigated fields. They may damage the physical properties of the topsoils and make cultivation more difficult. Impurities carried in solution may be precipitated in the root zones, or at the ground surface, as soil moisture is consumed or evaporated. They may damage crop growth as well as the physical properties of the soils. When present in excessive amounts, they may ultimately make the soils too saline for further crop production.

In general, the quality of a water delivered to arable lands on an irrigation project should be adequate for continued profitable agriculture, without adversely affecting crop growth, impairing the quality of the crop products, or damaging the soils on which crops are grown.

Studies of the quality of irrigation waters in western United States were begun during the latter part of the nineteenth century. Hilgard of the University of California was one of the pioneers in conducting investigations of water quality. Early studies were confined principally to particular waters that were known to carry objectionable concentrations of undesirable salts. Later, as irrigation became greatly expanded, natural streamflows became fully utilized, return flows became important sources of supply, and pumping from groundwater became widespread, studies of water quality became more extensive and more detailed.

Today, considerations of water quality constitute important parts in hydrological studies for new irrigation developments. Some special investigations have included chemical determinations of nearly all salts carried in solution, whether detrimental or beneficial and whether carried in heavy concentrations or only as minor constituents.

Most minor constituents except boron are of minor importance as regards successful irrigation agriculture. Investigations reported by Kelley and Brown in 1928 showed that relatively minute proportions of boron may cause injuries to plant growth.[20] In 1935, Scofield of the United States Department of Agriculture suggested quality classifications of irrigation water and permissible limits of boron, chlorides, sulphates, per cent sodium, and total dissolved solids.[30]

Inasmuch as considerations of water quality are commonly based on results of chemical analyses, the following pages pertain largely to chemical factors and interpretations of quality data for particular climates, soils, and crop productions. Some sample analyses of western irrigation waters are presented. Discussions of suspended silt loads and their effects on quality are included at the end of the chapter. Saline and alkali lands are taken up in the next chapter.

Impurities in Irrigation Waters. All water supplies used for irrigation contain impurities. In fact, all natural waters, even freshly fallen rains and melting snows, contain some impurities. Amounts of precipitated moisture, whether liquid or solid, contain foreign materials derived from the atmosphere as they fall to the ground.

Freshly fallen rains and snowmelt waters pick up soluble salts and silt particles as they move along ground surfaces to stream channels. They may pick up additional impurities as they flow down the stream channels to points of diversions. Portions of the rains and snowmelt waters that infiltrate into the soil in excess of field capacities pick up soluble compounds as they percolate through earth formations to outlets in stream channels or to storage in underground reservoirs.

Percolating waters, because of greater opportunities, commonly dissolve more salts from earth formations than surface waters. Surface waters, unless flowing over exposed beds of soluble materials, seldom attain high salt concentrations. Thus, streamflows during low-water periods, when discharges are maintained by groundwater runoff, contain higher concentrations of salts than streamflows during high-water periods, when discharges are maintained largely by surface runoff.

During the summer and fall months, salt concentrations in streams flowing through irrigated regions often increase as the water moves downstream, owing to accretions from heavily charged return flows where excess amounts of irrigation water were delivered to the fields.

Because of the more favorable opportunities for picking up soluble compounds, water supplies pumped from underground reservoirs generally contain greater concentrations of salts than water supplies released from upstream surface reservoirs where storage capacities were filled largely from surface runoff.

From the viewpoint of general conditions as discussed in the preceding paragraphs, proportions of salts in irrigation waters usually may be expected to be approximately as follows:

1. Greater in groundwater runoff than in surface runoff.
2. Greater in low streamflows than in high streamflows.
3. Greater at downstream locations than at upstream locations.
4. Greater in underground reservoirs than in surface reservoirs.

Dissolved constituents and total concentrations of salts in particular irrigation waters depend on the earth formations the waters pass over or through before reaching points of utilization. Inasmuch as earth formations vary widely in composition and solubility, analyses of particular waters may show exceptions to the above general statements.

Although most groundwaters obtain their impurities from soluble salts in the earth or rock strata through which they percolate, particular waters sometimes receive contributions from magmatic sources. Hot-water flows or water vapors coming from deep below the earth's surface, through faults or other outlets, contain various salt constituents that may be absorbed by percolating waters with which they come in contact.

In general, water supplies obtained by diversion of streamflows during periods of surface runoff or by release from upstream surface reservoirs have qualities suitable for irrigation. Water supplies obtained by diversion of streamflow during periods of low discharge, by rediversion of return flows, or by pumping from groundwater storage may or may not have qualities suitable for irrigation. When water supplies available for particular projects do not have qualities acceptable for irrigation, remedial measures are necessary in order to prevent damages to crops and soils during continued crop production.

Salt Constituents. The principal salt constituents of irrigation water are considered to exist in solution as electrolytes or dissociated ions. Some ions are basic and are called cations; others are acid and are called anions. When common table salt, sodium chloride, is dissolved by water, it supplies sodium ions as cations and chloride ions as anions.

When salts are dissolved by irrigation water, proportions of cations and anions brought into solution depend on combining weights of the salt constituents. The combining weight of a constituent is its atomic weight divided by its valence. Hydrogen, with a combining weight taken equal to unity, is used as a reference basis. When common salt is dissolved by water, it supplies ionic constituents in the proportions of 23 sodium cations to 35.5 chloride anions.

The principal salt constituents of a water that are pertinent from the viewpoint of irrigation include 4 basic ions and 5 acid ions. The basic ions are calcium, magnesium, sodium, and potassium. The acid ions are carbonate, bicarbonate, chloride, sulphate, and nitrate. These cations and anions, together with their chemical symbols and combining weights, are listed in Table 1.

TABLE 1

PRINCIPAL BASIC AND ACID IONS IN IRRIGATION WATER

Cations			Anions		
Constituent	Chemical symbol	Combining weight	Constituent	Chemical symbol	Combining weight
Calcium	Ca	20.0	Carbonate	CO_3	30.0
Magnesium	Mg	12.2	Bicarbonate	HCO_3	61.0
Sodium	Na	23.0	Chloride	Cl	35.5
Potassium	K	39.1	Sulphate	SO_4	48.0
			Nitrate	NO_3	62.0

Other constituents that may be present in an irrigation water include aluminum, boron, fluoride, iron, selenium, silicon or silica, and sulphide. Most irrigation waters contain only traces or relatively small proportions of these constituents, but exceptions may occur when supplies are obtained from special sources. Boron is the minor constituent that requires greatest consideration. It is discussed under a subsequent heading.

Irrigation waters may be acid or alkaline, depending on the hydrogen ion concentration. Acidities or alkalinities are represented by pH values as for soils (see Chapter 2).

Some major and minor constituents of irrigation water are utilized in plant growth and are desirable when present in proper amounts. Excessive concentrations of certain salts may be objectionable, or toxic, even when used to a limited extent as plant nutrients. Of the four principal cations, some proportions of calcium, magnesium, and potassium, either in the irrigation water or in the root zones where they can be dissolved by the irrigation water, are essential for normal plant development. Elements essential for proper growth of food plants are discussed in Chapter 3.

The principal salt constituents of irrigation water that may be injurious are chlorides, sulphates, and sodium. Chlorides are more objectionable than sulphates, and high sodium contents are most objectionable. Excess sodium contents may result in deflocculation and chemical changes that damage the permeability of the root zones as well as plant growth. Excess potassium contents may cause effects similar to those caused by sodium, but potassium concentrations usually are small. Carbonate contents usually are only very small proportions of the bicarbonate contents.

Laboratory investigations reported by Fireman and Magistad in 1945 showed that undesirable effects of sodium contents on soil permeability are more pronounced when irrigations with high sodium waters are followed by natural rainfalls or by irrigations with water containing low salt concentrations.[9]

Concentrations of Soil Solutions. Total concentrations of salts in soil solutions throughout the root zones of irrigated lands generally are heavier, sometimes much heavier, than concentrations in irrigation water supplies. In most irrigated regions, average concentrations of soil solutions are at least 3 times as high as average concentrations of the irrigation water. In some regions, they may be more than 10 times as high.

Concentrations of salts in soil solutions depend not only on the salinity of the irrigation water but also on quantities of salts dissolved from the soils, soil permeabilities and drainage, crop growth, depths of water applied during irrigations, climatic conditions, and amounts of leaching obtained from rainfall or by special irrigations during the nongrowing season.

At a particular irrigated field, supplied with water of a particular quality, the salinity of the soil solution varies throughout the growing season, principally with the amount of moisture held in the soil. Plant roots absorb large quantities of moisture but take up only such salts as can be utilized in growth. Evaporation of moisture at the ground surface leaves the salts in the soil solution or as precipitates on the ground. Thus the concentration of the soil solution gradually increases following an irrigation and attains a maximum value just before additional water is supplied.

In general, the concentration of the soil solution at times of field capacity is about twice as great as at times of soil saturation and about one-half as great as at times of plant wilting. Detailed analyses of soil solutions extracted from root zones throughout the irrigated sections of the Pecos River Valley were reported in 1942.[25]

Salt constituents of soil solutions may be harmful to plants in three ways: (1) they may include toxic amounts of some elements; (2) certain constituents present in large proportions may combine with less predominant constituents essential as plant nutrients, forming insoluble compounds and thus decreasing available supplies of plant food; and (3) osmotic pressures characteristic of salt solutions may be so high that plant roots experience difficulties in absorbing amounts of moisture needed for growth.

Certain constituents of soil solutions may cause reactions of base exchange that alter the physical properties of the soils. Calcium and magnesium constituents cause reactions that tend to improve permeability and tilth. Sodium constituents cause reactions that tend to impair permeability and tilth. Thus, irrigation waters containing appreciable concentrations of calcium and magnesium usually are desirable, whereas waters containing similar concentrations of sodium usually are objectionable, especially when equal concentrations of calcium and magnesium are absent.

Concentrations of particular minor constituents sometimes are higher in irrigation waters than in soil solutions. Such conditions may be observed when soils are deficient in soluble compounds of the particular constituents and are leached by winter rainfall. Boron may be cited as an example. Investigations on some lands in southern California, irrigated with waters containing from about 1 to 16 parts per million of boron, showed lower concentrations in the soil solutions than in the irrigation waters.

Table 2, abstracted from a report by Eaton and Wilcox, gives some data on boron concentrations observed on different soils in San Benito County apricot and prune orchards. On most soils, concentrations in soil solutions below 6-inch depths were lower than in the irrigation water. Data observed on some lands irrigated with Los Angeles aqueduct water, containing about 0.6 part per million of boron, showed concentrations more than 50 per cent higher in the soil solutions than in the irrigation water.[8]

TABLE 2

CONCENTRATIONS OF BORON IN IRRIGATION WATER AND SOIL
SOLUTIONS, SAN BENITO COUNTY, CALIFORNIA [8]

Soil types	Per cent saturation, 6 to 36-in. depths	Years of use of irrigation water	Boron in irrigation water, p.p.m.*	Boron in soil solution, p.p.m. at depths in. of		
				0 to 6	6 to 36	36 to 72
Montezuma loam	57.3	9	12.5	7.94	2.63	1.33
Conejo gravelly loam	45.4	10+	4–16	4.63	8.31	6.85
Conejo loam	52.2	3	5.10	5.08	3.67	0.91
Yolo silt loam	33.0	17	4.39	2.83	2.53	2.63
Yolo silt loam	45.5	17	0.65	1.26	0.93	0.67
Rincon loam	48.1	5	1.35	1.01	1.01	0.71
Conejo loam	52.2	11	0.11	0.87	1.03	2.08
Montezuma loam	39.1	Unirrigated	....	0.62	0.48	0.55

* Parts per million.

Analyses of Irrigation Waters. Analyses of irrigation waters should determine total salt concentrations, total amounts of the principal cations and anions held in solution, boron contents of the water, and pH values of acidity or alkalinity. Determinations of iron, selenium, and silica contents are sometimes made. Determinations of other minor constituents generally can be omitted, except in analyzing special waters that are believed to contain more than normal concentrations. Sometimes determinations of certain minor constituents of groundwaters are useful in tracing the sources of the water.

In reporting results of chemical analyses, potassium contents, because of their relatively small concentrations, often are included with sodium contents. Carbonate contents, which seldom are appreciable, are commonly included with bicarbonate concentrations. Carbonate and bicarbonate constituents are sometimes designated total alkalinity.

Total salt concentrations can be obtained by three methods: (1) by measuring the specific electrical conductance or electrical conductivity of the water; (2) by adding total cations or anions, usually anions, as determined by the separate analyses of the different constituents; and (3) by weighing residues obtained by evaporating filtered samples of the water to dryness. Results are usually given as parts per million, by weight, or as tons of dissolved solids per acre-foot of water.

Values of specific electrical conductance of water samples are computed from measured values of electrical resistance. Ohms of resistance between immersed platinum electrodes are measured with a

Wheatstone bridge. Values of specific conductance, designated K, are reciprocals of observed resistances. They are reported for a temperature of 25 degrees C. Since actual values are only small decimals, they are commonly given as K times 10^5. In some recent reports, they are given as K times 10^6. Equivalent total concentrations in parts per million are approximately 7 times specific conductances reported as K times 10^5.

Since 1 acre-foot of water weighs 2.72 million pounds, total concentrations in parts per million multiplied by the factor 0.00136 equal total dissolved solids in tons per acre-foot. Considerations of total dissolved solids in tons per acre-foot are convenient in studies of salt balance on irrigated lands supplied with saline waters.

Concentrations of boron and such additional minor constituents as may be determined by an analysis of water quality are given in parts per million. Concentrations of the principal basic and acid constituents were given as parts per million in many early analyses but are now given as milligram equivalents per liter or equivalents per million. The last two designations are numerically the same when the specific gravity of the water is unity. For most waters that can be used in irrigation, differences in specific gravity are too small to require corrections.

The milligram equivalent of a salt constituent is the number of milligrams represented by its combining weight. Parts per million divided by combining weights equal milligram equivalents per million. Where analytical results are reported as equivalents per million or milligram equivalents per liter, they must be multiplied by their respective combining weights before summating to obtain total cations or total anions in parts per million.

In saline solutions, the total number of cation equivalents must equal the total number of anion equivalents. Therefore, either total can be used as an index of total concentration. The total number of cation equivalents or anion equivalents, per million, multiplied by 10 is approximately equal to the specific electrical conductance expressed as K times 10^5.

Hardness, the calcium carbonate equivalent of the calcium and magnesium contents, is not ordinarily included in reports on quality of irrigation water. Water supplies for irrigation, unlike those for domestic or industrial uses, should be hard rather than soft.

Methods of analyzing irrigation waters need not be so elaborate or precise as those used in research investigations or in determining qualities of water for domestic consumption. Procedures that have been found convenient, suitable, and sufficiently reliable for irrigation considerations are described in a government bulletin by Wilcox.[37]

Sodium and Chloride Percentages. Sodium and chloride percentages of irrigation waters are calculated from results of chemical analyses. They are useful in comparing different waters and in considering qualities of water supplies that may be made available for use on particular projects. The sodium percentage, which is the more pertinent of the two, is a valuable index of quality and is now in general use.

The sodium percentage is the ratio of the total sodium cations, or the total sodium plus potassium cations, to the total cations held in solution, multiplied by 100. In other words, it is the percentage of the total cations that may cause undesirable reactions of base exchange when the irrigation water infiltrates into the root zone. It may be expressed by the following equation:

$$\text{Sodium percentage} = \frac{(Na + K)100}{Ca + Mg + Na + K}$$

Inasmuch as reactions of base exchange produced by calcium and magnesium usually are beneficial whereas reactions produced by sodium are harmful, high values of sodium percentage mean poor qualities of water. In general, waters with sodium percentages lower than 60 are suitable for irrigation. The advisability of using a particular water supply becomes increasingly doubtful as the sodium percentage increases above 60.

The chloride percentage is the ratio of the total chloride anions, or the total chloride plus nitrate anions, to the total anions held in solution, multiplied by 100. It may be expressed by the following equation:

$$\text{Chloride percentage} = \frac{(Cl + NO_3)100}{CO_3 + HCO_3 + SO_4 + Cl + NO_3}$$

In calculating sodium and chloride percentages, cations and anions are expressed in milligram equivalents per liter or equivalents per million.

Chloride percentages were considered during investigations of subsoil waters in Nevada, reported in 1936.[34] They also were considered during investigations of the quality of water in the upper Rio Grande Basin, reported in 1938.[23] In the latter report, Scofield pointed out the meaning of the sodium percentage, then added:

The significance of the value, percent chloride, is less directly agricultural. It is probably true that with equal concentrations of total dissolved solids the water having the higher chloride percentage would be the less desirable because the chloride constituent is regarded as more toxic than the sulphate or bicarbonate. Probably the chief value of reporting the chloride percentage is that together with the percent sodium it indicates the general character of the water involved or the degree of relationship between waters from different sources.

Values of the chloride percentage for Rio Grande waters below San Marcial, New Mexico, are being reported in bulletins issued by the International Boundary and Water Commission, United States and Mexico.[18] When not given in reports on water quality, they can be easily computed from the constituent data, as indicated by the above equation.

Boron Concentrations. Concentrations of boron in irrigation water generally are injurious to crop growth when greater than about 2 parts per million. Smaller concentrations are injurious to some unusually sensitive crops. Concentrations of 1 to 2 parts per million may damage fruits and walnuts. Concentrations less than 0.4 part per million seldom harm crop plants.[7]

Inasmuch as minute proportions of boron are needed for crop growth, small amounts in the irrigation water may be beneficial on soils deficient in soluble boron compounds. Most soils contain sufficient amounts of boron, but some lands have been found to need boron fertilizers. Boron contents of soils and their effects on crop plants are mentioned briefly in Chapter 3. Their effects on plants were discussed in detail by Eaton in 1944,[6] also by Woodbridge in 1950.[38]

In general, citrus fruits, deciduous fruits, walnuts, and pecans are sensitive to boron. Most cereals, olives, cotton, and a few vegetables are semitolerant. Alfalfa, beets, and most vegetables are tolerant. Table 3 shows relative tolerances of crop plants to boron, determined on sand cultures, as originally reported by Eaton in 1935 and slightly revised in 1941.[7] The plants are tabulated in three groups and are listed according to increasing tolerances in each group.

Fortunately, most surface waters do not carry large proportions of boron. Some streams in California carry undesirable concentrations, but many streams in the irrigated regions of the West carry only traces or relatively minute concentrations. Analyses in regions where boron contents are troublesome often show higher concentrations in ground-

TABLE 3

RELATIVE TOLERANCES OF CROP PLANTS TO BORON AS DETERMINED
ON SAND CULTURES[7]

Sensitive	Semitolerant	Tolerant
Lemons	Lima beans	Carrots
Grapefruit	Sweet potatoes	Lettuce
Avocados	Bell peppers	Cabbage
Oranges	Tomatoes	Turnips
Thornless blackberries	Pumpkins	Onions
Apricots	Zinnias	Broad beans
Plums	Oats	Gladiolus
Prunes	Milo	Alfalfa
Peaches	Corn	Garden beets
Cherries	Wheat	Mangel
Persimmons	Barley	Sugar beets
Kadota figs	Olives	Palms
Grapes	Ragged Robin roses	Asparagus
Apples	Radishes	Athel (Tamarix
Pears	Sweet peas	aphylla)
American elm	Pima cotton	
Navy beans	Acala cotton	
Persian (English)	Sunflowers (native)	
walnuts	Canadian field peas	
Black walnuts		
Pecans		

waters than in surface streams. Excessive concentrations in ground-waters, especially waters obtained from deep wells, have caused serious damages to citrus fruits in the lower Rio Grande Valley, Texas. Amounts of boron held in soil moisture are mentioned briefly in the preceding discussions of soil solutions.

Qualities Suitable for Irrigation. Qualities of water suitable for irrigation depend principally on total salt concentrations, sodium percentages, and contents of boron, chlorides, and sulphates. Whether a water of a certain quality can be used on a particular project depends on local conditions of climate, soils, crops produced, and amounts of irrigation water or winter rainfall available for leaching concentrated soil solutions from the root zones.

Because of variable conditions of use, definite limits of quality applicable to all irrigated regions cannot be established. Several authorities have proposed classifications of water and permissible limits of the above-noted factors for use in determining qualities suitable for irrigation. In general, the various proposals do not differ widely.

Table 4 shows five quality classifications and limiting factors suggested by Scofield in 1935, for use in connection with considerations

TABLE 4

CLASSES OF IRRIGATION WATER AND PERMISSIBLE LIMITS
OF CONSTITUENTS [30]

	Total dissolved solids		So-dium, per cent	Boron, p.p.m.			Concentration, mg. equiv. per l.	
Class of water	Electrical conduct-ance, $K \times 10^5$, 25° C.	P.p.m.		Fruit trees	Vines and cereals	Vege-tables	Chlo-rides Cl	Sul-phates SO₄
1. Excellent, less than	25	175	20	0.33	0.67	1.0	4	4
2. Good	25–75	175–525	20–40	0.33–0.67	0.67–1.33	1.0–2.0	4–7	4–7
3. Permissible	75–200	525–1,400	40–60	0.67–1.00	1.33–2.00	2.0–3.0	7–12	7–12
4. Doubtful	200–300	1,400–2,100	60–80	1.00–1.25	2.00–2.50	3.0–3.75	12–20	12–20
5. Unsuitable, more than	300	2,100	80	1.25	2.50	3.75	20	20

of local conditions.[30]   He stated that a water should be judged unsuitable when total salinity, boron content, and sodium percentage rate class 3 or higher, or when any two or more characteristics rate class 4.   The five classes, as listed, vary from class 1, excellent, to class 5, unsuitable.

The limiting concentrations for chloride and sulphate constituents given in Table 4 are the same for each class of water.   Inasmuch as chlorides are more objectionable than sulphates, some writers have proposed slightly lower permissible limits for chlorides than for sulphates.[7]

Figure 1 shows a quality diagram based on total salinity and sodium percentages, proposed by Wilcox in 1948.[37]   The diagram shows five classes of water, namely, excellent to good, good to permissible, permissible to doubtful, doubtful to unsuitable, and unsuitable.   The permissible limits of the different classes are similar to those given in Table 4.   The scale of electrical conductivity at the top of the diagram is given as K times 10^6 instead of K times 10^5.   A scale of total concentration in equivalents per million is shown at the bottom of the diagram.   In using the diagram to determine the quality of a particular irrigation water, separate consideration should be given to contents of boron, chlorides, and sulphates.

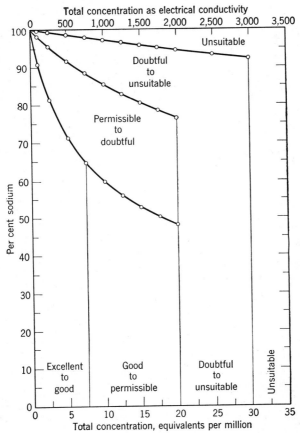

FIGURE 1. Diagram for determining quality of irrigation water. (After Wilcox.)

Some Analyses of Irrigation Water. Table 5 shows results of some chemical analyses of low or nominal flows in seven rivers of southwestern United States, as reported by the Geological Survey for the water year ending September 30, 1945.[27] Analyses of samples from two locations are given for the Pecos and Colorado rivers. Many analyses of samples taken at other times, also at other locations and on other rivers, are given in the original publication. Some minor constituents that were analyzed are not shown in Table 5, since they are not important from the viewpoint of irrigation.

Except for the Pecos River, all flows represented in Table 5 would be suitable for irrigation. The flow of the Pecos at the upper station would be of doubtful quality as regards total salinity. The flow at the lower station would be unsuitable, inasmuch as it contained exces-

TABLE 5

CHEMICAL ANALYSES OF SOME SURFACE WATERS
IN SOUTHWESTERN UNITED STATES [27]

Items of analyses	Red River near Dennison, Tex.	Rio Grande at Acacia, N. Mex.	Pecos River Near Acme, N. Mex.	Pecos River Near Orla, Tex.	Colorado River Near Glenwood Springs, Colo.	Colorado River Near Grand Canyon, Ariz.	Green River at Green River, Utah	San Juan River near Bluff, Utah	Gila River near Solomonsville, Ariz.
Date of sample	Nov. 1–10	July 21–31	Aug. 22–26	Sept. 11–20	Feb. 1–10	Feb. 20–28	Jan. 11–20	Mar. 1–10	June 1–10
Discharge, sec.-ft.	221	333	176	220	670	7,252	1,897	768	112
Electrical conductance *	166	68.2	280	828	86.2	158	113	120	109
Total salts, tons per acre-ft.	1.33	0.61	2.87	7.74	0.69	1.46	1.00	1.12	0.88
Sodium per cent	50	37	31	51	45	44	36	28	59
Borate, p.p.m.	0.2	0.3	.....	1.0	0.2	0.3	.....	0.8	0.2
pH	8.2	7.8	7.8	.....	8.3	7.7	.....	7.6	8.1
Cations, equiv. per million:									
Calcium	5.69	3.24	16.67	28.75	3.19	5.59	4.29	5.94	3.09
Magnesium	2.30	1.07	6.25	16.04	1.32	3.87	3.37	3.54	1.23
Sodium	8.21	2.65	10.34	47.25	3.83	7.70	4.40	3.76	6.32
Potassium	0.28	0.16	†	0.74	0.11	0.20	†	†	†
Total cations	16.48	7.12	33.26	92.78	8.45	17.36	12.06	13.24	10.64
Anions, equiv. per million:									
Bicarbonate	2.72	3.16	2.08	1.86	2.33	3.98	3.64	3.51	3.62
Sulphate	4.68	3.08	21.24	39.77	2.42	9.04	6.91	8.95	1.06
Chloride	9.03	0.82	9.87	51.05	3.78	4.26	1.47	0.71	5.87
Nitrate	0.03	0.02	0.07	0.05	0.01	0.11	0.04	0.05	0.02
Total anions	16.46	7.08	33.26	92.73	8.54	17.39	12.06	13.22	10.57

* $K \times 10^5$ at 25° C.
† Included with sodium.

sive concentrations of sulphates and chlorides as well as excessive total salinity. Salinity conditions at all stations were more concentrated during low discharges than during high discharges.

Figure 2, plotted from Geological Survey data, shows total salinity and discharge relations for the Colorado River near Glenwood Springs, Colorado, during January to August 1945. River flows at Glenwood Springs are maintained principally by snow runoff. Similar curves for other types of runoff, also for other streams, would differ in detail but would show decreasing salinities with increasing discharges.

Figure 3 shows principal constituents of groundwaters in the Angostura Irrigation Project, southwestern South Dakota, as reported by

Swenson in 1949.[21] Total salinities, not shown separately, varied from 246 to 3,260 parts per million. Inasmuch as the analyses were made on samples taken prior to the beginning of irrigation, the qualities may be modified by percolation of excess deliveries after agricultural operations become well established. Except when affected by major changes in hydrological conditions, groundwaters from particular sources are more uniform in quality than surface waters.

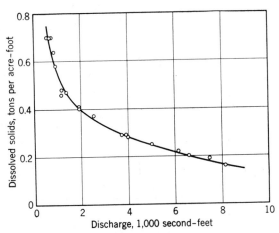

FIGURE 2. Total salinity and discharge relations, Colorado River near Glenwood Springs, Colorado.[27]

Table 6 shows salinities of drainage recoveries in the El Paso Division of the Rio Grande Irrigation Project, also salinities of river flows at the ends of the division, as compiled during the joint investigations of the upper Rio Grande basin.[23] Total salinities are given as values of electrical conductance and tons of dissolved solids per acre-foot. Contents of the various constituents are shown as percentages of total concentration. Mean annual discharges and annual salt loads are given in the original publication. Data are averages for the years from 1930 to 1936.

The data in Table 6 show how drainage recoveries from irrigated lands may become too saline for further irrigation use. Most drainage flows above Fabens are of doubtful or unsuitable quality when judged on the basis of electrical conductance. Practically all drainage flows in the Island and Tornillo districts are too heavily charged with salts to be satisfactory for irrigation.

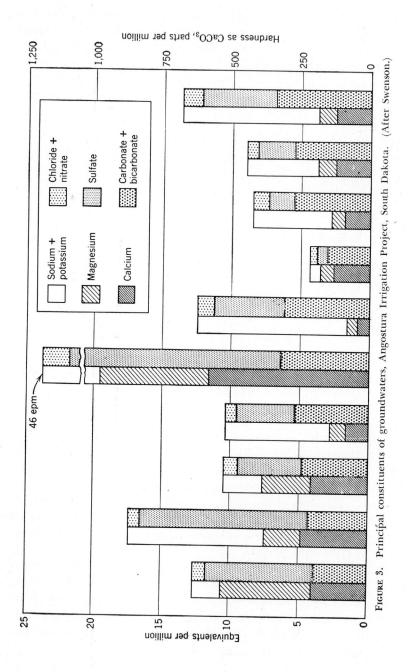

FIGURE 3. Principal constituents of groundwaters, Angostura Irrigation Project, South Dakota. (After Swenson.)

TABLE 6

SALINITIES OF DRAINAGE RECOVERIES, EL PASO DIVISION,
RIO GRANDE IRRIGATION PROJECT, 1930–1936 [23]

| | Mean concentrations | | Constituent, per cent | | | | | |
River or drain	Electrical conductance *	Tons per acreft.	Ca	Mg	Na	HCO$_3$	SO$_4$	Cl
Rio Grande at El Paso	127	1.22	35	12	53	26	43	31
Drains above Fabens:								
Playa	234	2.11	31	13	56	20	29	51
Franklin	300	2.68	29	13	58	17	28	55
Middle	353	3.10	30	10	60	14	29	57
River	419	3.83	32	10	58	13	27	60
Quadrilla	180	1.62	28	11	61	23	42	35
Mesa	351	3.21	27	10	63	16	36	48
Fabens, intercepting	289	2.64	36	13	51	17	34	49
Net total	...	3.15	..	..	..	..	..	..
Island and Tornillo drains:								
Fabens	299	2.50	36	12	52	16	30	54
Island	720	6.21	31	8	61	7	17	76
Border	945	8.25	27	7	66	5	19	76
Alamo	409	3.60	30	11	59	12	30	58
Tornillo	517	4.59	32	9	59	9	22	69
Net total	...	4.59	..	..	..	..	..	..
El Paso Division total	...	3.72	..	..	..	..	..	..
Rio Grande at Fort Quitman	296	2.75	26	11	63	12	29	59

* $K \times 10^5$ at 25° C.

Salt Balance. The salt balance of an irrigated area is commonly defined as the difference between the total dissolved solids brought to the land annually by the irrigation water and the total solids carried away annually by the drainage water. When the input of salts is less than the output, the salt balance is favorable. When the input is greater than the output, the salt balance is unfavorable.

When the salt input is definitely less than the salt output, undesirable salts probably do not accumulate in the root zones. When the salt input is definitely greater than the salt output, undesirable salts probably do accumulate in the root zones. Conditions within the root zones determine the suitability of the soils for irrigation agriculture.

Field measurements of discharge and chemical analyses of samples for both irrigation and drainage waters supply data for calculating approximate values of salt balance for lands under consideration. They do not supply data needed for accurate determinations of salt balance within the root zones. Some dissolved salts brought to the fields may percolate to depths below the root zones before being precipitated. Likewise some salts carried away in the drainage water may have been dissolved from soils below the root zones.

In 1940, Scofield reported results of salt-balance analyses for irrigated lands in the Mesilla and El Paso valleys, two divisions of the Rio Grande Irrigation Project, New Mexico and Texas; also for the Yuma Valley, Yuma Irrigation Project, southwestern Arizona. He also reported results of salt-balance tests conducted at the Rubidoux Laboratory, Riverside, California.[33]

Table 7 shows summarized salt-balance data reported for the Mesilla, El Paso, and Yuma valleys. A favorable salt balance was indicated

TABLE 7

ANALYSES OF SALT BALANCE IN SOME IRRIGATED VALLEYS [33]

Condition	Mesilla Valley 1931–1937	El Paso Valley 1931–1937	Yuma Valley 1938
Salinity of irrigation water, tons per acre-ft.	0.805	1.226	0.956
Salinity of drainage water, tons per acre-ft.	1.226	2.666	1.993
Salt balance, output minus input, tons	8,708 *	−146,282 †	−134,637 †
Output of constituents, per cent of input	101.5	75.9	45.8
Calcium	86.5	59.3	32.4
Magnesium	88.1	66.1	45.1
Sodium and potassium	120.3	91.0	67.6
Bicarbonate and carbonate	85.7	35.1	44.5
Sulphate	89.1	52.3	26.6
Chloride	155.8	145.3	116.1
Nitrate	103.0	34.8	11.4
Irrigated area, acres	80,000	60,000	40,000

* Favorable salt balance.
† Unfavorable balance.

for the Mesilla Valley, and unfavorable balances for the El Paso and Yuma valleys. Annual outputs of chlorides exceeded annual inputs in all three valleys. In the Mesilla Valley, the output of sodium and potassium was about 20 per cent higher than the input, and the output of nitrate about 3 per cent higher than the input. With these exceptions, outputs of all constituents were less than inputs in all three valleys.

The tests at the Rubidoux Laboratory were made with alfalfa growing in galvanized-iron cans, 15 inches in diameter and 20 inches deep. Measured amounts of saline irrigation water, containing an average salt concentration of 1.35 tons per acre-foot, were applied to the alfalfa as needed. Amounts of percolate were measured and analyzed, and crops produced were dried and weighed. The tests showed the following results:

1. It was necessary to use 22.5 per cent of the input for leaching in order to prevent accumulation of salts in the root zones.
2. The alfalfa and soil absorbed 13.7 per cent of the salts in the irrigation water.
3. The water evaporated and transpired weighed 772 times as much as the dried alfalfa crops produced.

The results of the Rubidoux tests supply valuable information for particular conditions of climate, soil, and crop growth. They cannot be applied directly to other crops and other conditions of crop production, or to large irrigated areas where many or all controlling factors may be different.

Contaminations of Quality. Contaminations of quality of irrigation water may be caused by repeated use of return flows or drainage recoveries, by wastes from various industrial operations, by seepage of sea water into underground reservoirs in coastal regions, or by other special conditions. Effluents from sewage treatment plants or discharges of raw sewage from municipal systems seldom contain excessive concentrations of dissolved solids, except when the sewers serve as drains for industrial wastes.

Industrial wastes that may impair qualities of water for domestic use include discharges from tanneries, packing plants, woolen mills, oil wells, oil refineries, laundries, chemical works, breweries, and other industrial activities.[12] Many of these may impair qualities desirable for irrigation. Drainage from packing houses where fruits are washed with borax may contain excessive concentrations of boron. Drainage from water-softening plants may contain undesirable amounts of sodium.

Except in thickly populated metropolitan districts, contaminations of irrigation water are most likely to be caused by repeated use of return flows and drainage recoveries.

Improvements of Quality. Major improvements in quality of irrigation water seldom are practicable. Minor improvements that may facilitate continued successful agriculture sometimes can be made by certain procedures.

Qualities of salt-laden return flows and drainage recoveries can be improved by mixing with waters of lower salinity when waters of lower salinity are available. On some projects, it may be possible to convey drainage recoveries of high salt concentration to pondage on low lands, where the water can be evaporated and the salts precipitated, thus avoiding contamination of river flows. Sometimes small tributary flows carrying excessive loads of dissolved solids can be diverted and disposed of in a similar manner.

In some river valleys, it may be possible to secure surface supplies of better quality by constructing new diversion works at upstream locations, where streamflows carry smaller loads of dissolved solids.

When reservoirs are constructed to impound runoff for irrigation, water supplies of better quality automatically become available. During storage operations, low streamflows of high salinity become mixed with high streamflows of low salinity. The mixing may not be 100 per cent effective inasmuch as low flows, heavily charged with salts, tend to descend into the lower portions of the reservoir, because of slightly higher densities. Nevertheless, some mixing takes place, and water supplies drawn from the lower levels are of better quality than the low water flows that passed down the river prior to the beginning of storage.

Although the above discussed procedures, when feasible, may supply some relief, irrigation farmers in most regions where serious salt troubles are experienced must leach their soils thoroughly, adopt special cultural practices, or raise salt-tolerant crops as discussed in the next chapter. Possible methods of reducing salt troubles in the Pecos River Valley were discussed in the report of the National Resources Planning Board.[24]

In metropolitan districts, objectionable industrial wastes should not be discharged into municipal sewage systems. They can be treated to remove excessive concentrations of undesirable constituents, or they can be conveyed to disposal areas where they cannot contaminate irrigation water supplies. Along coastal regions, objectionable industrial wastes sometimes can be conveyed directly to the ocean.

Infiltration of sea water into underground reservoirs utilized as sources of irrigation water supply can be avoided by keeping water tables high enough to prevent percolation from the ocean. This requires supervision of pumping operations by regional or state officials.

Effects of Silt. In some irrigated regions, fine silt and clay particles carried in suspension affect qualities of irrigation water. Silt effects on quality are usually detrimental but may be beneficial, depending on the quantity of silt transported, the time the silty flow continues, and the texture of the soil to which the water is applied.

Occasional deliveries of silty water may be beneficial on coarse sandy soils, inasmuch as they tend to improve the physical properties of the root zones as well as to add some fertilizing elements. Effects of Colorado River silt on sandy Yuma Mesa soils, determined by McGeorge, have been mentioned in Chapter 5. Additions of river silt not only reduced rates of soil-moisture movements but also added substantial amounts of available potassium, calcium, and phosphate.

Deliveries of silty water to tight soils are objectionable, since they tend to make the surface soils still more impermeable and difficult to cultivate. Thin impermeable coatings deposited by silty water during the early part of the irrigation season may prevent sprouting or kill young seedlings. Similar coatings deposited during hot weather may hold water on the field surfaces until plants become scalded.

Continuous deliveries of silty water are undesirable, inasmuch as they increase costs of maintaining farm ditches and keeping field surfaces in proper shape for irrigation. Silt may be deposited in the ditches at such rates as to require removal several times during the irrigation season. When silty water is delivered to a field, the silt is deposited principally at locations near the point of delivery, thus building up ground surfaces until releveling of the field becomes necessary. As irrigation with silty water continues, magnitudes and costs of releveling operations increase. Eventually, silt deposits may have to be completely removed from the irrigated area.

Suspended silt particles carried in long natural streams usually are finer at downstream locations, because of the increased length of travel and the greater opportunity for reduction to minimum sizes.

Fortier and Blaney's investigations in Imperial Valley, southeastern California, where water is obtained from the Colorado River, showed that most silt particles carried in the irrigation canals were fine enough to pass a 300-mesh sieve, also that as much as 90 per cent of the silt carried in the smaller laterals might reach the irrigated fields. They estimated that annual deliveries of 3 acre-feet per acre of silty water might produce ground-surface coatings from 0.20 to 1.93 inches thick.[10]

The fertilizing value of river silt is well known. The Nile Valley in Egypt is a notable example. Farmers are familiar with the fertility of alluvial deposits along natural streams. Such deposits usually contain enough sand and relatively large silt particles to provide adequate permeability. In irrigation canal flows, suspended sand and the heavier silt particles often are removed by desilting works at points

of diversion, or by deposition along the canals, so that only the very fine and more undesirable particles reach the irrigated fields. This means increased costs of keeping farm ditches open, maintaining proper field surfaces, and conducting cultural operations.

On most irrigation projects, particularly those located in the downstream portions of large river valleys, increased costs involved in using silty water overbalance such benefits as may be derived from the fertilizing value of the silt deposits. Thus, effects of suspended silt on the quality of irrigation water are more likely to be detrimental than beneficial.

Special silt problems may be experienced in mining regions. In such regions, runoff may pick up suspended loads of pulverized rock materials from mine tailings. Flows carrying rock flour are not desirable for irrigation, since they cover the soil and seedlings with films of impermeable matter, similar to the laitance that often forms on freshly deposited concrete.

REFERENCES

1. Collins, W. D., "Notes on Practical Water Analysis," *U.S. Geol. Sur. Water-Supply Paper* 596–H, 1928, reprinted in 1945.
2. Collins, W. D., and C. S. Howard, "Index of Analyses of Natural Waters in the United States," *U.S. Geol. Sur. Water-Supply Paper* 560–C, 1925.
3. ——— "Index of Analyses of Natural Waters in the United States, 1926 to 1931," *U.S. Geol. Sur. Water-Supply Paper* 659–C, 1932.
4. Dunnewald, T. J., "Salinity Conditions in the Big Horn River during the Years 1938 and 1939," *Wyo. Agr. Exp. Sta. Bull.* 240, 1940.
5. Eaton, Frank M., "Boron in Soils and Irrigation Waters and Its Effect on Plants, with Particular Reference to the San Joaquin Valley of California," *U.S. Dept. Agr. Tech. Bull.* 448, 1935.
6. ——— "Deficiency, Toxicity, and Accumulation of Boron in Plants," *Jour. Agr. Res.*, Sept. 15, 1944, pp. 237–277.
7. Eaton, Frank M., Roy D. McCallum, and Miles S. Mayhugh, "Quality of Irrigation Waters of the Hollister Area of California with Special Reference to Boron Content and Its Effect on Apricots and Prunes," *U.S. Dept. Agr. Tech. Bull.* 746, 1941.
8. Eaton, Frank M., and L. V. Wilcox, "The Behavior of Boron in Soils," *U.S. Dept. Agr. Tech. Bull.* 696, 1939.
9. Fireman, Milton, and O. C. Magistad, "Permeability of Five Western Soils as Affected by the Percentage of Sodium of the Irrigation-Water," *Trans. Am. Geop. Union*, August 1945, pp. 91–94.
10. Fortier, Samuel, and Harry F. Blaney, "Silt in the Colorado River and Its Relation to Irrigation," *U.S. Dept. Agr. Tech. Bull.* 67, 1928.
11. Hardman, George, and Meridith R. Miller, "The Quality of the Waters of Southeastern Nevada, Drainage Basins and Water Resources," *Nev. Agr. Exp. Sta. Bull.* 136, 1934.

12. Harmon, Burt, "Contamination of Ground-Water Resources," *Civ. Eng.,* June 1941, pp. 345–347.
13. Hill, Raymond A., "Salts in Irrigation Water," *Trans. Am. Soc. C. E.,* No. 107, 1942, pp. 1478–1518.
14. Howard, C. S., "Suspended Sediment in the Colorado River, 1925–41," *U.S. Geol. Sur. Water-Supply Paper* 998, 1947.
15. ——— "Quality of Water in the Upper Colorado River Basin," *Trans. Am. Geop. Union,* June 1948, pp. 375–378.
16. ——— "Quality of Water in the Northwest," *Trans. Am. Geop. Union,* June 1948, pp. 379–383.
17. Howard, C. S., and S. K. Love, "Quality of Surface Waters of the United States, 1943, with a Summary of Analyses of Streams in Colorado River, Pecos River, and Rio Grande Basins, 1925 to 1943," *U.S. Geol. Sur. Water-Supply Paper* 970, 1945.
18. International Boundary and Water Commission, United States and Mexico, "Flow of the Rio Grande and Tributary Contributions from San Marcial, New Mexico, to the Gulf of Mexico," *Water Bull.* 16, 1946, El Paso, Texas.
19. Kelley, W. P., "Permissible Composition and Concentration of Irrigation Water," *Trans. Am. Soc. C. E.,* No. 106, 1941, pp. 849–861.
20. Kelley, W. P., and S. M. Brown, "Boron in the Soils and Irrigation Waters of Southern California and Its Relation to Citrus and Walnut Culture," *Hilgardia,* November 1928, pp. 445–458.
21. Littleton, Robert T., and Herbert A. Swenson, "Geology and Ground-Water Hydrology of the Angostura Irrigation Project, South Dakota, with a Section on the Mineral Quality of Waters," *U.S. Geol. Sur. Cir.* 54, 1949.
22. Love, S. K., and P. C. Benedict, "Discharge and Sediment Loads in the Boise River Drainage Basin, Idaho, 1939–40," *U.S. Geol. Sur. Water-Supply Paper* 1048, 1948.
23. National Resources Committee, *Regional Planning, Part VI, The Rio Grande Joint Investigation in the Upper Rio Grande Basin in Colorado, New Mexico, and Texas, 1936–1937,* Vol. I, Washington, 1938.
24. National Resources Planning Board, *Regional Planning, Part X, The Pecos River Joint Investigation in the Pecos River Basin in New Mexico and Texas,* Washington, 1942.
25. ——— *The Pecos River Joint Investigation, Reports of the Participating Agencies,* Washington, 1942.
26. Palmer, Chase, "The Geochemical Interpretation of Water Analyses," *U.S. Geol. Sur. Bull.* 479, 1911.
27. Paulsen, C. G., "Quality of Surface Waters of the United States, 1945," *U.S. Geol. Sur. Water-Supply Paper* 1030, 1949.
28. Piper, Arthur M., "A Graphic Procedure in the Geochemical Interpretation of Water-Analyses," *Trans. Am. Geop. Union,* 1944, Part VI, pp. 914–928.
29. Scofield, Carl S., "South Coastal Plain Investigation, Quality of Irrigation Waters," *Calif. Dept. Pub. Works Bull.* 40, 1933.
30. ——— "The Salinity of Irrigation Water," *Smith. Inst. Rep.* 1935, pp. 275–287.
31. ——— "Quality of Water of the Rio Grande Basin above Fort Quitman, Texas, Analytical Data," *U.S. Geol. Sur. Water-Supply Paper* 839, 1938.
32. ——— "Recent Studies on Quality of Water for Irrigation," *Trans. Am. Geop. Union,* 1938, Part II, pp. 662–667.

33. Scofield, Carl S., "Salt Balance in Irrigated Areas," *Jour. Agr. Res.*, July 1, 1940, pp. 17–39.

34. Scofield, Carl S., C. Lloyd Moon, and Elmer W. Knight, "Subsoil Waters of Newlands (Nev.) Field Station," *U.S. Dept. Agr. Tech. Bull.* 533, 1936.

35. Scofield, Carl S., and L. V. Wilcox, "Boron in Irrigation Waters," *U.S. Dept. Agr. Tech. Bull.* 264, 1931.

36. Stabler, Herman, "Some Stream Waters of the Western United States with Chapters on Sediment Carried by the Rio Grande and the Industrial Application of Water Analyses," *U.S. Geol. Water-Supply Paper* 274, 1911.

37. Wilcox, L. V., "The Quality of Water for Irrigation Use," *U.S. Dept. Agr. Tech. Bull.* 962, 1948.

38. Woodbridge, C. G., "The Role of Boron in the Agricultural Regions of the Pacific Northwest," *Sci. Monthly,* February 1950, pp. 97–104.

Chapter 15

IRRIGATION OF SALINE AND
ALKALI SOILS

During recent years, problems in the irrigation of saline and alkali soils, or areas that may become excessively saline or alkaline when irrigated, have been receiving more and more attention. Since irrigation began in the West, many large areas of initially productive lands have been abandoned because of the gradual accumulation of excess salts in the root zones. Many additional areas have required the installation of costly drainage improvements. In some irrigated valleys, large proportions of the agricultural lands contain salts in such amounts as to reduce crop yields.

The presence of excess quantities of salts in root-zone soils is injurious to the growth of food plants. Relatively small quantities of certain salts may cause reductions in yields of sensitive crops, and only slightly greater quantities may prevent crop growth. Furthermore, certain types of alkali salts cause undesirable changes in the physical condition of the soil, which reduce permeability and increase difficulties of cultivation.

Salt problems in agriculture are peculiar to arid sections of the country. In humid climates, annual depths of rainfall are sufficient to leach excess quantities of soluble salts to drainage outlets or to depths below the root zones. In irrigated regions, ample supplies of irrigation water, properly applied, may accomplish the same results, provided satisfactory soil structures can be maintained and adequate subsoil drainage is available. When these provisions are not fulfilled, continued irrigation causes rising groundwater levels and increasing accumulations of soluble salts in the root zones.

The following pages present some discussions of saline and alkali soils, types of salts that are objectionable, and tolerances of different crops to salt conditions. Methods of reclaiming lands that have become excessively saline or alkaline are taken up briefly. Sources of more detailed information are listed at the end of the chapter. Con-

centrations of undesirable salts in the soil solution and permissible concentrations of such salts in the irrigation water are discussed in the preceding chapter.

Saline and Alkali Areas. Areas where excess quantities of soluble salts exist in the root zones may occur naturally, or may develop during the progress of irrigation. Most soils in arid regions contain soluble salts, and most water supplies used for irrigation contain some dissolved solids. Whether areas included in contemplated irrigation projects already contain excessive quantities of undesirable salts, or may accumulate excessive quantities during irrigation, are problems that should be solved before proceeding with any new development.

Some salt lands have been formed by deposition of materials during the drying up of salt lakes. Areas surrounding the Great Salt Lake in Utah may be cited as examples. However, such areas seldom, if ever, are suitable for reclamation. In general, most saline and alkali lands that can be reclaimed for agricultural purposes have received their excess salts from water transportation.

Accumulations of excess salts in saline and alkali soils are usually caused by upward capillary movements of soil moisture and evaporation at the ground surface. Absorption of moisture by plant roots also tends to concentrate the soil solution. When water tables are high and groundwaters carry heavy loads of dissolved solids, soil solutions soon become so highly concentrated that salts are precipitated in the root zones and at the soil surfaces. When irrigated lands are not provided with adequate subsoil drainage, continued deliveries of water carrying high concentrations of salts soon produce similar results.

Where groundwaters are heavily loaded with dissolved solids, any condition that raises the water table high enough to permit capillary movements of moisture to the soil surface tends to produce salt troubles. Inundations of certain low lands in southern California during the floods of January 1916 raised water tables high enough to permit movements of salts into the upper soil horizons.[8] In the Pecos Valley, some saline alluvial soils are believed to have derived their salts from evaporation of the waters in which they were deposited.[15]

The danger of saline or alkali areas developing under continued irrigation depends on drainage conditions, physical properties of the root zones, depths of water applied, salinity of the irrigation water, rainfall, and chemical constituents of the soils. Adequate drainage is most important. When adequate subsoil drainage is available and ample supplies of water can be secured for leaching purposes, the

development of serious salt troubles usually can be avoided. When adequate subsoil drainage is not available, the installation of an efficient system of drainage works constitutes an essential element of project construction.

Saline and alkali areas that develop during the progress of irrigation usually begin in poorly drained depressions, then spread laterally as salt depositions continue and as physical properties of the soils become impaired. The areas may grow in size until they require the abandonment of entire fields, or even entire projects. Small alkali areas are sometimes called buffalo wallows, scab spots, or slick spots. Saline or alkali areas sometimes develop along irrigation canals, as the result of rising water tables caused by canal seepage.

Types of Salts. The most common salts that affect the productivity of irrigation soils are the sodium carbonates, the chlorides, and the sulphates. Other salts that may be troublesome are the magnesium and potassium carbonates, the chlorides and sulphates, and the calcium chlorides and nitrates. Magnesium, potassium, and calcium are utilized in plant growth but cause salt troubles when present in the soils in excessive amounts.

In irrigation work, the term alkali soil was formerly used to designate any soil that contained excessive proportions of soluble salts. Soils that contained excessive quantities of caustic salts such as sodium carbonate, which dissolve organic matter and cause the formation of a dark-colored crust at the soil surface, were called black alkali. Soils that contained excessive quantities of neutral salts, which cause the formation of a white crust at the soil surface, were called white alkali.

During recent years, some authorities have been using the terms alkali soils and saline soils instead of black alkali and white alkali. An alkali soil is defined as one that contains alkali salts, usually sodium carbonate, and has a pH value of 8.5 or higher. A saline soil is defined as one that contains an excess amount of soluble salts, more than about 0.2 per cent, is not excessively alkaline, and has a pH value less than 8.5. Any soil that has a pH value higher than 7.0 has an alkaline reaction and may be termed an alkaline soil.

Black alkali is more injurious to plant growth than white alkali. However, both types of salts are injurious when present in relatively small proportions and may prevent plant growth when present in only slightly greater proportions. Only black alkali salts cause harmful effects on the physical properties of soils. Fortunately, black alkali soils are less common than white alkali soils. Both types can be reclaimed by proper corrective measures and appropriate cultural procedures, provided ample supplies of water are available.

The gradual accumulation of black alkali salts in the soil is called alkalization. The gradual accumulation of white alkali salts is called salinization. Similarly the gradual removals of black and white alkali salts are called dealkalization and desalinization. Black and white alkali soils are approximately the same as the Solonetz and Solonchak soils of the Russian classifications.

Black Alkali. Black alkali soils contain sodium carbonate (sal soda) as a predominating constituent, also abnormal amounts of absorbed sodium, together with some proportions of neutral salts. In certain soils, black alkali constituents may include some potassium carbonate (potash). Sodium is not an element considered essential for plant growth, although appreciable amounts are found in spinach, asparagus, sugar beet leaves, and certain other products.

Black alkali salts are both caustic and corrosive. They are highly alkaline. Soil reactions, where proportions of sodium carbonate are pronounced, may show pH values as high as 10 or even higher. Black alkali salts damage plant roots, dissolve the organic matter in the soil, and precipitate dark crusts at the ground surface as soil moisture evaporates. They may change the chemical composition of the soil solution, so that available amounts of certain plant nutrients are not sufficient to satisfy normal plant requirements. In general, soils containing black alkali salts in proportions greater than about 0.10 per cent by weight are not satisfactory for crop production.

Besides being directly harmful to plant growth, black alkali constituents cause changes in the physical condition of the soil that are indirectly injurious to plants and also detrimental to tillage. This is especially true in fine-textured soils containing considerable proportions of clay. Soils in which sodium salts accumulate tend to become deflocculated, that is, to puddle, lose permeability, and become waterlogged. Desirable crumby structures break down into massive single-grained structures, with impaired aeration throughout the root zones as well as reduced percolation characteristics.

White Alkali. White alkali soils contain neutral salts of sodium, magnesium, calcium, and potassium, usually the chlorides and sulphates. Sodium chloride (table salt) and sodium sulphate (Glauber's salt) are common in such soils. Sodium nitrate (Chili saltpeter), magnesium sulphate (Epsom salt), calcium sulphate (gypsum), and certain other neutral salts may be present. Small amounts of absorbed sodium may be present in some white alkali soils.

White alkali salts consisting largely of sodium chloride are more injurious to plant growth than salts made up principally of sulphate compounds. In general, white alkali soils containing soluble salts in proportions greater than about 0.20 per cent are not satisfactory for crop production.

White alkali salts precipitate white crusts at the ground surface as soil moisture evaporates, thus producing the soil appearances from which they received their name. They are noncaustic, do not dissolve organic matter, and do not injure the physical condition of the soil. When present in excessive amounts, they may cause some swelling of the soil, accompanied by the development of light and fluffy structures.

Degrees of Salinity. Degrees of salinity of soils where salt troubles have developed may be expressed as percentages of soluble salts in the root zones. Some authorities consider soils as nonsaline when they contain less than 0.2 per cent of soluble salts. Inasmuch as 1 acre-foot of soil weighs about 4 million pounds, a 0.2 per cent salt content would mean the presence of about 4 tons of soluble salts in each acre-foot of soil.

Kearney and Scofield used the following terms and percentages to designate different degrees of salinity in the root zones of areas where the predominating salts are of white alkali types: [7]

Salinity designation	Salt content, per cent
Excessive	More than 1.5
Very strong	1.0–1.5
Strong	0.8–1.0
Medium strong	0.6–0.8
Medium	0.4–0.6
Weak	0.1–0.4
Negligible	Less than 0.1

The above designations were given as applicable to lands where the predominating salts are sulphates. Where the salts consist largely of sodium chloride, the lower percentages are to be used. The classification does not apply to lands where soluble salts include large proportions of black alkali.

Crops on Saline Soils. Crops can be produced on saline soils when salt contents are not too excessive and do not include large proportions of sodium chloride. Proportions of soluble salts that soils can contain and still be farmed with some success vary with types of salts, physical conditions of the root zone, fertility, climate, quantity and quality of irrigation water, methods of irrigating, subsoil drainage, depths to groundwater, and kind of crops produced. Inasmuch as these conditions vary widely in different regions, saline soils in different irrigation projects require different treatments.

In general, particular degrees of salinity are more harmful to plant growth on coarse-textured sandy soils than on medium or fine-textured soils, because of the lower soil-moisture contents and resulting higher salinity of the soil solution. They are more harmful to growth in hot climates than in cool climates, because of the higher rates of transpiration. They are more harmful to growth on soils of low fertility than on soils of high fertility.

Plants are more likely to be injured by salts when in the seedling stage than when in advanced stages of growth. However, some sorghums germinate and begin to grow about as well in soils of medium salinity as in soils of negligible salinity.[7]

On areas where salt conditions are gradually developing under continued irrigation, crops may begin to suffer before the presence of excess salts becomes apparent. Relatively small accumulations of salts in the root zones may cause reductions in plant growth, particularly if salt-sensitive crops are grown. If salt-tolerant crops are grown, salt accumulations in the root zones may reach percentages that are toxic for salt-sensitive crops before the presence of excessive salt contents is suspected. Harmful effects on crop growth seldom become evident until salt accumulations reach excessive amounts. On most irrigation projects, the danger of imminent salt troubles is more likely to be indicated by rising groundwater levels than by conditions of crop growth.

Symptoms of Salt Injury. The first symptoms of salt injury in crop production are small reductions in plant size and crop yield. Such symptoms may not be noticed during early stages of salt accumulation. As salt contents of the soils gradually increase, plant growth becomes more plainly stunted and crop yields more definitely decreased. Plant leaves dry out, turn brown, curl at the edges, and become yellow, mottled, or otherwise discolored. When salt accumulations become excessive, leaves drop off, small twigs die, plants gradually lose their foliage, and finally all growth ceases.

The above-noted symptoms of salt injury may develop in crops grown on both black alkali and white alkali soils. The symptoms probably are due largely to osmotic effects which make it more difficult for plants to absorb water from the soil solution. Similar injuries to plant growth may be caused by deficiencies in water supply when excessive salt contents have not accumulated in the soils.

Some discolorations observed in plants grown on saline soils may be of a chlorotic nature and may be due to nutritional deficiencies. Such deficiencies may be due to the gradual depletion of certain elements by plant growth or to chemical changes that take place during the accumulation of salts. Thus, true causes of plant injury often are difficult to determine from appearances alone.

Effects on Crop Quality. Accumulations of salts in soils may have detrimental effects on crop quality as well as on crop yield. Some forage crops may absorb so much salt that they become unpalatable. Rhodes grass, which is highly salt tolerant, may absorb enough salt to become injurious to livestock. It is less sensitive to black alkali than most forage plants.

Cereals grown on saline soils may yield small and shriveled kernels. Root crops may yield small products of poor quality. Potatoes may be watery, less numerous, and too small to be marketable. Sugar beets may be small, have a low sugar content, and show too high an ash content of the juice. Sugar cane may have an abnormal salt content in the milling juice. Cotton crops grown on saline soils may produce fewer and smaller bolls. Ripening may be retarded, and the length and fineness of the fibers may be impaired.

Orchard fruits grown on saline soils may have inferior texture, flavor, and keeping qualities. Some investigations indicate that effects of salt conditions on the growth of peach trees may be cumulative from year to year. Other investigations indicate that small amounts of chloride in soil solutions may improve the flavor of tomatoes.

Effects of salt accumulations in soils on crop growth and quality of crop products were discussed in detail by Kearney and Scofield in 1936,[7] also by Magistad and Christiansen in 1944.[12]

Salt Tolerance of Crops. Different crops have different tolerances to salt constituents of soils. Some crops are unusually sensitive to salts. Others are more tolerant. Certain types of native grasses that are valuable for grazing are highly salt tolerant (see Chapter 2). Some deep-rooted plants, well established before salts begin to accumulate, extend their roots to lower levels and continue to grow until salinities near field surfaces increase to excessive percentages.

Date palms probably are the only cultivated plants that can be grown successfully on soils of very strong or excessive salinity. Of the more common field crops, sugar beets, milo, and certain grasses are among the more salt resistant. Beans, peas, and corn are some of the more salt sensitive. Corn is highly sensitive to salts and should not be planted on soils of more than negligible salinity. Some cereals can be grown for hay on soils where salt contents are too high for grain production.

Alfalfa is sensitive to salts while in the seedling stage but can be produced on soils of medium salinity after the plants become well established and the roots deeply entrenched. Some sorghums can be grown on soils of medium salinity. Sorghum is less sensitive to sodium carbonate than most crops. Cotton can be grown on soils of medium salinity.

Many field and laboratory investigations of crop growth under different conditions of salinity have been made in efforts to establish salt tolerances for different crops. Such tests have supplied much valuable information. However, available data still are too limited to justify definite conclusions regarding permissible salt percentages for particular crops. Table 1 shows relative salt tolerances for some crop plants arranged according to grades of tolerance rather than by

TABLE 1

RELATIVE SALT TOLERANCES OF SOME CROP PLANTS [5]

Weak tolerance	Medium tolerance *	Good tolerance *	Strong tolerance
Beans, wax	Onions	Barley (hay crop)	Sugar beets
Beans, navy	Squash	Tomatoes	Garden beets
Field peas	Carrots	Alfalfa	Milo
Horsebean	Asparagus	Cotton	Bermuda grass
Red clover	Cowpeas	Sorgo	Rhodes grass
Vetch	Rice	Kale	Alkali sacaton
Proso	Rye (grain crop)	Rape	grass
Oats (grain crop)	Barley (grain crop)	Perennial ryegrass	Rescue grass
Emmer (grain crop)	Wheat	Wild ryegrass	
Peaches, Elberta on	Oats (hay crop)	Italian ryegrass	
Lovell rootstock	Grain sorghums	Crested wheatgrass	
	Foxtail millet	Slender wheatgrass	
	Flax	Mountain bromegrass	
	Guayule	Tall fescue	
	Sunflower	Reed canary grass	
	Ladino clover	Sudan grass	
	Strawberry clover	Blue grama grass	
	Sweetclover		
	Smooth bromegrass		
	Meadow fescue		
	Orchard grass		
	Dallis grass		
	Tall oatgrass		

* A few plants listed live in strong salt concentrations but do not grow appreciably.

percentages of soil salinity, as presented by Hayward and Magistad in 1946.[5]

Peaches are the only orchard fruits listed in Table 1. They have a weak tolerance. Dates and pomegranates are highly tolerant of salt conditions. Olives, grapes, and almonds are somewhat salt resistant. Apples, pears, prunes, apricots, and most other orchard crops, including citrus fruits, are sensitive to salts. Among the citrus fruits, lemons probably are the most sensitive.

Beets and tomatoes are the more salt-resistant garden products. Beans probably are the most sensitive. In general, garden products may suffer salt injuries when planted on soils containing more than about 0.20 per cent of soluble salts.

Choice of Crops. Proper choice of crops is an important factor in maintaining profitable agriculture on areas where salt conditions are not too objectionable. When suitable crops are grown, further accumulations of salts often can be prevented. On some projects, continued growth of suitable crops, together with heavy applications of irrigation water, may accomplish the reclamation of soils containing excessive accumulations of white alkali salts.

Rice constitutes an efficient reclamation crop in regions where climatic conditions are favorable and ample supplies of water can be secured. Rice requires continuous flooding during the growing season. Consequently, salts can be gradually leached out of the soil while crops are grown. This is especially true where soils or irrigation waters contain appreciable proportions of calcium compounds.

Shallow-rooted crops should be grown on saline soils where water tables are relatively close to the ground surface. Suitable crops include various grasses, sweetclover, Ladino clover, strawberry clover, and some cereals that can be grown for hay. Sometimes lands with shallow depths to groundwater can be utilized as permanent pastures.

Where the root-zone soil is permeable, the subsoil well drained, and the water table 5 feet or more below the ground surface, most crops tolerant of the particular salt conditions can be produced profitably, provided sufficient irrigation water of proper quality is available. However, close-growing crops that can be irrigated by flooding are more desirable than row crops, since flooding accomplishes a more uniform leaching of the soil than furrow irrigation. Where furrow irrigation is practiced, excessive salt contents tend to accumulate in ridges between the furrows.

Close-growing crops, besides being suitable for flooding, shade the ground surfaces better than row crops and thus reduce soil-moisture evaporation and upward movements of moisture. Alfalfa is especially efficient in reducing evaporation from the soil. Other crops that can be flooded to depths sufficient to produce some deep percolation include Bermuda grass, sweetclover, western wheatgrass, and strawberry clover.

Cultural Procedures. In producing crops on saline areas, adequate cultural procedures are fully as important as proper choice of crops. The land should be carefully leveled, seed beds carefully prepared for planting, and irrigation water applied in such depths as may be required for normal growth and leaching purposes. When intertilled crops are grown, fields should be cultivated as soon as possible after each irrigation.

Special precautions should be exercised in leveling saline areas prior to the beginning of crop production. This insures uniform irrigation and eliminates low spots where water might be retained when deliveries are discontinued. Low spots often constitute starting points in the development of serious salt troubles.

Seed beds should be thoroughly irrigated before planting, more than once if necessary, so that some excess salts in the topsoils can be washed downward by percolation and so that sufficient moisture will be available for germination. After planting, soil surfaces should be kept moist by frequent light irrigations, until plants become well established. Later, as plants become more fully developed, water should be applied as frequently and copiously as possible without injuring crop growth, so that further leaching can be accomplished. During hot weather, water should not be held on the fields long enough to cause scalding of the plants.

On newly developed lands, green manures may be needed in order to supply organic matter. All available barnyard manures should be spread over the fields. Commercial fertilizers can be applied where needs for certain elements are demonstrated. Carefully selected crop rotations should be begun as soon as feasible.

In raising intertilled crops and irrigating through furrows, some crops such as sorghum or cotton can be planted along the bottoms of the furrows, just after a thorough irrigation. Lettuce and melon crops are sometimes planted along water lines at the edges of the furrows. Since salts tend to accumulate between furrows, the production of row crops should be followed by leveling and leaching during the winter months and by the planting of close-growing crops that can be irrigated by flooding during subsequent seasons.

Reclaiming Salt Areas. Areas where root zones contain excessive proportions of soluble salts usually can be reclaimed when sufficient supplies of good water are available. The reclamation of white alkali soils seldom is difficult, but the reclamation of black alkali soils may be troublesome.

White alkali soils are reclaimed by draining the subsoils, flooding the ground surfaces, and keeping water on the fields until considerable proportions of the soluble salts are leached to depths below the root zones. In general, salt-tolerant crops can be planted on white alkali soils as soon as drainage improvements and initial leaching operations are completed. Crop production then can be continued during the remaining steps of reclamation, using selected crops and proper cultural procedures as previously discussed.

Black alkali soils are reclaimed by draining the subsoils, applying certain chemicals to the ground surfaces as soil amendments, and flooding the fields repeatedly until the resulting compounds are leached from the root zones and the physical properties of the upper soil layers become suitable for tillage. Black alkali soils are more difficult and costly to reclaim than white alkali soils, owing to the poor initial condition of the soil, low permeability, cost of chemicals, and relatively long time required for soil amendments to become effective. Planting of crops may have to be deferred until the physical properties of the soils become adapted to plant growth and crop tillage.

During preliminary stages of reclamation on black alkali soils, the growth of any type of vegetation, including weeds, should be permitted. The development of root systems tends to loosen the topsoil, facilitate infiltration, and add valuable organic material. The physical properties of the topsoil can be improved and the growth of vegetation encouraged by spreading barnyard manures and disking. The growth of salt-resistant cover crops that can be turned under as green manures should be started as soon as possible. This tends to increase available supplies of nitrogen as well as to improve soil structures.

Methods of reclaiming both black and white alkali soils in California were described by Kelley in 1937.[8]

Soil Amendments. Soil amendments used in reclaiming black alkali soils replace excessive sodium contents with calcium. The resultant sodium compounds are then removed by leaching. Thus the soils are changed from sodium soils to calcium soils. This results in improved permeability and more favorable conditions for aeration, root development, plant growth, and culture.

Although several chemicals may be used as soil amendments, a comparatively cheap and often used compound is calcium sulphate (gypsum). Pulverized gypsum is broadcast over the field surfaces and worked into the soil by plowing, disking, or harrowing, before flooding the ground with leaching water. Applications are usually made at rates of from 5 to 10 tons per acre, depending on amounts of excess sodium in the soil.

Other chemicals that may be used as soil amendments include sulphur, aluminum sulphate, and ferrous sulphate. These compounds react with the calcium carbonate content of the soil, forming the calcium sulphate needed to improve physical conditions. Sulphur has produced good results when applied in amounts as small as 1,000 pounds per acre. It is relatively cheap but requires some time for oxidation. When sulphur is applied, leaching must be deferred for several months. Reclamation operations can be hastened to some degree by applying the sulphur in ground or pulverized forms.

In California, applications of iron sulphate were found to produce rapid results in reclaiming black alkali soils. The applications were made at rates of 5 and 9 tons per acre. They were somewhat more expensive than other soil amendments.[8]

Investigations on the Newlands Project, Nevada, reported by Knight, showed that beneficial results could be obtained by adding ground gypsum to the irrigation water, adding sulphuric acid to the irrigation water, or applying alum to the field surfaces. However, the last two treatments were expensive.[11]

Leaching Operations. Leaching operations are usually conducted during the fall or winter months, when water supplies are not needed for irrigation. Fields of suitable size are enclosed by dikes, built high enough to permit flooding to depths of several inches or a foot. Some leveling may be needed to insure adequate depths of flooding at all locations. On sloping lands, dikes can be built along contour lines and the flooding conducted in narrow strips.

Flooding is usually maintained for several days. The water supply is then shut off and flood waters allowed to percolate through the soil. After ground surfaces dry, flooding operations are repeated until most excess salts have been washed to depths below the root zones. Drying between leaching periods stimulates root growth, aids aggregation, and permits the formation of surface cracks that facilitate infiltration during subsequent flooding. Soil samples should be taken and salt contents analyzed, after each flooding, in order to determine the efficiency of the leaching operations.

Where lands are covered with encrusted salts, alternate flooding and draining, prior to leaching, may remove appreciable quantities of soluble salts and thus facilitate subsequent leaching. This method of reclamation, without subsequent leaching, has been used on alkali soils in Iran and has permitted the production of good wheat crops for many years.[16]

Leaching operations usually produce quick results on white alkali soils. When conducted during the fall months, small grains often can be grown the following season. On black alkali soils where applications of soil amendments are necessary, reclamation operations may have to be continued two or three years before crop yields approaching normal values can be produced.

REFERENCES

1. Botkin, C. W., "The Effects of Acidifying Amendments on Impermeable Soils," *N. Mex. Agr. Exp. Sta. Tech. Bull.* 210, 1933.
2. Curry, Albert S., "Saline Soils and Their Management," *N. Mex. Agr. Col. Ext. Service Cir.* 105, revised, 1939.
3. Gardner, Robert, "Some Soil Properties Related to the Sodium Salt Problem in Irrigated Soils," *U.S. Dept. Agr. Tech. Bull.* 902, 1945.
4. Gardner, Robert, R. S. Whitney, and Alvin Kezer, "Slick Spots in Western Colorado Soils," *Colo. Agr. Exp. Sta. Tech. Bull.* 20, 1937.
5. Hayward, H. E., and O. C. Magistad, "The Salt Problem in Irrigation Agriculture," *U.S. Dept. Agr. Misc. Pub.* 607, 1946.
6. Hibbard, P. L., "Alkali Soils; Origin, Examination, and Management," *Calif. Agr. Exp. Sta. Cir.* 292, reprinted 1931.
7. Kearney, T. H., and C. S. Scofield, "The Choice of Crops for Saline Land," *U.S. Dept. Agr. Cir.* 404, 1936.
8. Kelley, W. P., "The Reclamation of Alkali Soils," *Calif. Agr. Exp. Sta. Bull.* 617, 1937.
9. Kelley, W. P., and Alexander Arany, "The Chemical Effect of Gypsum, Sulfur, Iron Sulfate, and Alum on Alkali Soil," *Hilgardia,* September 1928, pp. 393–420.
10. Kelley, W. P., and S. M. Brown, "Principles Governing the Reclamation of Alkali Soils," *Hilgardia,* January 1934, pp. 149–177.
11. Knight, E. W., "Agricultural Investigations on the Newlands (Nev.) Reclamation Project," *U.S. Dept. Agr. Tech. Bull.* 464, 1935.
12. Magistad, O. C., and J. E. Christiansen, "Saline Soils, Their Nature and Management," *U.S. Dept. Agr. Cir.* 707, 1944.
13. McGeorge, W. T., "Factors Contributing to the Reaction of Soils and Their pH Measurement," *Ariz. Agr. Exp. Sta. Tech. Bull.* 78, 1938.
14. McGeorge, W. T., and R. A. Greene, "Oxidation of Sulphur in Arizona Soils and Its Effect on Soil Properties," *Ariz. Agr. Exp. Sta. Tech. Bull.* 59, 1935.
15. National Resources Planning Board, *The Pecos River Joint Investigation, Reports of the Participating Agencies,* Washington, 1942.

16. Pittman, D. W., "Observations on Alkali Soils in Iran," *Procs. Utah Acad. Sci., Arts, and Letters,* Vol. 21, 1943–1944, pp. 97–99.

17. Scofield, C. S., "Soil, Water Supply, and Soil Solution in Irrigation Agriculture," *U.S. Dept. Agr. Yearbook,* 1938, pp. 704–716.

18. Snyder, Robert S., and others, "Alkali Reclamation Investigations," *Idaho Agr. Exp. Sta. Bull.* 233, 1940.

19. Thomas, Edward E., "Reclamation of White-Alkali Soils in the Imperial Valley," *Calif. Agr. Exp. Sta. Bull.* 601, 1936.

20. ——— "Reclamation of Black-Alkali Soils with Various Kinds of Sulfur," *Hilgardia,* July 1936, pp. 127–142.

21. Wursten, J. L., and W. L. Powers, "Reclamation of Virgin Black Alkali Soils," *Jour. Am. Soc. Agron.,* Vol. 26, 1934, pp. 752–762.

Chapter 16

IRRIGATION PREPARATIONS AND PROCEDURES

Irrigation preparations and procedures are important factors in developing successful agriculture on farm lands in irrigated regions. Inadequate preparations for irrigation, improper procedures during irrigation, or both, may result in poor crop yields, even when soil conditions are favorable and ample supplies of good water are obtainable.

Preparations for irrigation on a particular farm include (1) the selection of a general layout for subdividing and irrigating the area in units of suitable dimensions; (2) the installation of a distribution system that will permit deliveries of water to the different units; and (3) the grading of field surfaces and construction of such features as may be needed during applications of water. All three items are more or less interrelated and should be thoroughly considered before adopting a definite plan and beginning construction.

Irrigation procedures include (1) methods of delivering water to field units; (2) frequencies of irrigation; and (3) depths of water applied per irrigation. They depend principally on soil conditions, types of crops produced, and amounts of soil moisture that may become available for plant growth as a result of rainfall.

Some comparatively flat lands, suitable for the growth of native grasses or other forage crops, can be utilized without the installation of complicated distribution systems or much preliminary preparations. Several mountain meadows in Colorado, Wyoming, and other states, irrigated by wild flooding, are examples. However, in the development of large irrigation projects, for diversified crop production, farmers usually must spend considerable sums of money for distribution systems, land grading, and other preparations before water can be properly applied to the fields.

The following pages discuss the more usual types of irrigation preparations and procedures practiced in western United States. Sprinkling methods of irrigation, sometimes used in the West and often used in supplying water to supplement rainfall in humid regions, are taken up briefly. Subirrigation methods which are feasible in certain localities are also treated briefly. References to reports that contain more detailed information on irrigation practices are listed at the end of the chapter.

Preparations for Irrigation. Most arable lands for which water is available can be prepared for irrigation. Whether costs of preparation justify their development depends on topographic conditions, depths of suitable soils, crops that can be grown, costs of crop production, and probable market values of crop products. Lands for which costs of development are not justified by estimated financial returns are omitted from the irrigable acreages.

In considering the feasibility of preparing a particular area for irrigation, the first requisite usually is an accurate topographic map, preferably one that shows contour lines for each 6 inches or 1 foot of elevation. Studies of such a map will show the possible methods of dividing the area into separate irrigation units, installing an adequate distribution system, and grading field surfaces to conform with contemplated irrigation procedures. The most practicable and economic plan can then be adopted for development. Small farms with uniform gradual slopes sometimes can be prepared for irrigation without a topographic map.

Lands that ordinarily involve minimum costs of preparation are the comparatively smooth areas with rather flat slopes, down which water can move at adequate but not excessive velocities. Such lands permit the location of supply ditches on desirable grades, do not require large amounts of grading, and facilitate efficient applications of water to different parts of the areas.

In general, difficulties and costs of preparing land for irrigation increase with increasing ground slopes and increasing irregularities in topography. When ground surfaces are too steep and irregular, special methods of irrigation may be required, or the growth of special crops may be necessary. Sometimes such areas can be irrigated from sprinkling installations and utilized in producing valuable fruit crops. Areas where ground surfaces are irregular and soils too shallow to permit proper grading can also be irrigated by sprinkling. Some comparatively steep fields that can be flooded from high-line ditches may be utilized as permanent pastures.

Lands that are unusually flat often require very careful grading and leveling. Such operations must be conducted with extreme precision in order to insure uniform depths of water during irrigation and permit complete surface draining when deliveries are discontinued. Otherwise excess evaporation at undrained depressions may soon bring salts to the topsoils and begin the development of saline or alkali troubles.

Methods of preparing farm lands for irrigation were described in detail in a government bulletin by Lewis issued in 1943.[23]

Farm Irrigation Layouts. Farm irrigation layouts should be planned so that all subdivisions can be supplied with water, as needed, with the minimum of water loss, trouble, and expense. The layouts should be suitable for the crops to be grown, also for the contemplated methods of irrigation. Inasmuch as crop rotations will be desirable in most subdivisions, the necessity for using different irrigation methods during different growing seasons should be considered. Quantities of water available for use and times of delivery, as provided in the water-right contract, also should be considered.

In general, the main supply ditch should be relatively large, as short as possible, and should be located so as to bring water from the project canal to the highest part of the farm. Head ditches and laterals should be located so as to permit distribution of water to all irrigation units. Waste ditches usually are needed at the lower edges of the farm, to remove excess water during irrigation and drain the fields when deliveries are discontinued.

Head ditches often are located along the highest boundary of the farm, and lateral ditches along the tops of ridges running approximately normal to the head ditches. Sublaterals are located as needed. In contour irrigation, head ditches are run down the slopes and water released to contour basins or strips on both sides. In locating permanent ditches, the crossing of deep drainage courses or other depressions should be avoided as far as possible.

In planning an irrigation layout, different arrangements of irrigation units and supply ditches should be considered. Some layouts will be more expensive than others. Some will be more suitable than others. Some costly layouts that are desirable may not be justified because of the farmer's financial resources or because of low values of crops that can be produced. However, tentative plans for all feasible layouts should be drawn on the topographic map and costs estimated before adopting a layout and proceeding with its development.

A rectangular layout of irrigation units is preferable whenever feasible. Rectangular layouts do not include small irregular areas that are troublesome to water and cultivate. Most farmers prefer rectangular layouts, even when more costly preparations of land surfaces are necessary. In rolling country, where costs of preparing land are excessive, layouts may be made in conformance with natural topography. Studies of alternative plans for irrigating 1 square mile in southern Texas, reported by Welty, showed that a natural layout, made to fit the topography, was only about 68 per cent as costly as a layout made with rectangular subdivisions.[38]

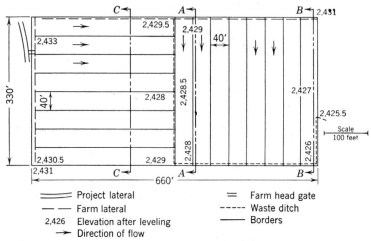

FIGURE 1. Typical layout for border-strip irrigation. (After Lewis.)

Figure 1 shows a layout for border-strip irrigation abstracted from a Department of Agriculture bulletin by Lewis.[23] Farm laterals carry water from the project ditch along the upper ends of the strips and waste ditches collect unused water at the lower ends. Strips are 40 feet wide and about 300 feet long.

Water Distribution Systems. Water distribution systems usually consist of permanent and temporary earth ditches, together with such features as may be required to control ditch flows. Main supply and large distribution ditches are planned for continued use during successive seasons. Some laterals and sublaterals may be temporary and may be reconstructed each season.

In so far as possible all ditches, whether permanent or temporary, should be excavated on grades that will permit adequate but not erosive velocities. Excavated materials should be deposited in banks along the ditches, and flow lines should be carried close to or above natural ground surfaces, to facilitate diversions to adjoining fields. Temporary dams can be placed as needed to raise ditch water surfaces high enough for diversion.

Appropriate grades on particular farms depend principally on quantities of water to be conveyed and characteristics of soils through which the ditches must be excavated. Permissible canal velocities through different soils, as reported by Fortier and Scobey, are shown in Table 1.[13]

TABLE 1

PERMISSIBLE VELOCITIES IN CANALS EXCAVATED THROUGH DIFFERENT SOILS [13]

Materials excavated for canal	Clear water, no detritus	Water containing collodial silts	Water containing noncolloidal silts, sand, or gravel
Fine sand, noncolloidal	1.50	2.50	1.50
Sandy loam, noncolloidal	1.75	2.50	2.00
Silt loam, noncolloidal	2.00	3.00	2.00
Alluvial silts, noncolloidal	2.00	3.50	2.00
Ordinary firm loam	2.50	3.50	2.25
Volcanic ash	2.50	3.50	2.00
Fine gravel	2.50	5.00	3.75
Stiff clay, very colloidal	3.75	5.00	3.00
Graded, loam to cobbles, noncolloidal	3.75	5.00	5.00
Alluvial silts, colloidal	3.75	5.00	3.00
Graded, silt to cobbles, colloidal	4.00	5.50	5.00
Coarse gravel, noncolloidal	4.00	6.00	6.50
Cobbles and shingles	5.00	5.50	6.50
Shales and hardpans	6.00	6.00	5.00

Velocity, f.p.s., after aging, in canals carrying:

Suitable methods of excavating ditches depend on the size of the ditch. Temporary farm ditches used in delivering water to small irrigation units often can be made with a plow. Permanent ditches of medium size, such as those needed on small farms, can be excavated with manufactured V-shaped ditchers of steel construction, or with similar wooden ditchers assembled on the farm. Main supply ditches for large areas may require the use of scrapers or even larger and more complicated excavation machinery.

When water supplies must be conveyed down relatively steep slopes, where earth materials might be eroded, the use of flumes instead of ditches may be desirable. Flumes also may be needed to carry ditch flows across deep gullies or other depressions. When depths of depressions exceed about 25 or 30 feet, the use of inverted pipe siphons instead of flumes may be warranted. Siphons also may be used to carry ditch flows under roadways. Shallow depressions of only 2 or 3 feet can be filled with earth and flows carried across in ditches along the tops of the embankments.

Flumes may be constructed of timber or galvanized steel. Galvanized metal flumes are more watertight and durable. When properly installed on well-built trestles, with concrete footings, they are more satisfactory and permanent than timber flumes.

Where pipe installations are required, wood, concrete, or steel pipes may be used. Concrete or steel pipes usually are more desirable. When wood pipes are installed, they should be constructed with treated materials, in order to avoid the rapid deterioration that may take place during alternate wetting and drying.

Ditches excavated through loose permeable soils may need to be provided with some type of lining that will reduce seepage losses. In some ditches, clay added to the ditch flow will settle out and seal the pore spaces along the bed and banks. Various lining materials that have been tried with some success include puddled clay, oil, asphalt, bentonite, wood, metal, gunite, and concrete. Concrete, although more costly than some materials, usually is most effective, especially in frost-free climates. In cold climates, concrete linings often are reinforced to prevent cracking and deterioration under frost action.

Adequate ditch linings, particularly concrete, are also valuable in that they permit the conveyance of water at velocities higher than would be permissible in unlined channels.

In regions where water supplies are limited and are used in the growth of valuable crops, seepage losses and evaporation during transit can be practically eliminated by installing underground pipe distribution systems. Where such systems are used, water is released to the irrigation units through vertical distribution stands, somewhat similar to hydrants. With underground pipe systems, no ditches are needed, traffic is unobstructed, and practically all areas can be utilized for crop growth. Such systems are often used in fruit-growing regions of the Southwest.

Distribution Capacities. Distribution capacities of ditch systems depend on size of the farm, amount of water obtainable under the water right, method of delivery at the project canal, ditch losses during conveyance, and maximum rates at which water can be applied to the irrigation units.

When project water is supplied by the rotation system, ditch capacities must be larger than when continuous flows can be diverted. The main supply ditch for the farm must be large enough to carry the maximum flow obtainable and usable. On small farms, capacities of supply ditches seldom should be less than two irrigating heads.

The size of the proper irrigating head depends on ground slopes, soil conditions, types of crops, size of irrigation units, methods of irrigating, and labor available to conduct the irrigation operations. Most of these controlling factors are more or less interrelated. The maximum flow that one irrigator can handle effectively seldom is as much as 5 second-feet during flooding operations, or as much as 2 second-feet during furrow irrigation. Heads actually used on most farms probably are somewhat lower.

On farms where water can be applied in large border, rectangular, or contour checks, heads as great as 20 or even 30 second-feet may be utilized. Heads of such size are ordinarily handled by more than one irrigator.

On farms where small flows are used in flooding and furrow irrigation, farmers can locate their ditches on suitable grades and excavate them to ample capacities with a limited amount of technical assistance. Table 2 shows approximate capacities in second-feet for some small farm ditches carrying water at different depths on different grades. Capacities of other ditches can be computed by the use of data in the Bureau of Reclamation Hydraulic and Excavation Tables or other similar tabulations.

On large farms, where greater distribution capacities are needed, main supply ditches and permanent structures should be carefully planned by engineering methods similar to those used in designing project distribution systems. Such methods are taken up in subsequent chapters on project canals and canal structures (see Volume 2).

Control Facilities. Permanent control facilities in farm distribution systems include a turnout or head-gate structure where water is diverted from the project system, and a suitable measuring device at or near the point of diversion. Other permanent control facilities may include division structures, drops, checks, or combined drops and checks.

Permanent division structures may be needed where the farmer's main ditch feeds two or more large supply ditches. Permanent drops may be needed to lower water surfaces and prevent erosion where ditch

TABLE 2

APPROXIMATE CAPACITIES OF SMALL FARM DITCHES *

(Second-feet)

Flow depth, ft.	Grade, ft. per 100 ft.				Grade, ft. per 100 ft.			
	0.20	0.30	0.40	0.50	0.20	0.30	0.40	0.50
	1-ft. bottom, 1½:1 side slopes				2-ft. bottom, 1½:1 side slopes			
0.4	0.4	0.5	0.6	0.7	0.8	0.9	1.1	1.2
0.6	1.0	1.2	1.4	1.6	1.7	2.1	2.5	2.8
0.8	1.9	2.3	2.6	3.0	3.0	3.7	4.3	4.8
1.0	3.1	3.8	4.4	4.9	4.8	5.9	6.9	7.7
	3-ft. bottom, 1:1 side slopes				4-ft. bottom, 1:1 side slopes			
0.8	4.0	4.9	5.7	6.3	5.2	6.4	7.4	8.3
1.0	6.0	7.3	8.5	9.5	7.9	9.7	11.1	12.4
1.2	8.4	10.4	12.1	13.4	11.0	13.5	15.5	17.4
1.4	11.3	13.9	16.1	18.0	14.7	18.0	20.7	23.2
1.6	14.6	18.0	20.7	23.2	18.8	23.0	26.6	29.9

* Kutter's n = 0.030; see Bureau of Reclamation Hydraulic and Excavation Tables.

flows are carried down relatively steep slopes. Permanent checks may be needed to raise ditch water surfaces high enough for diversion to adjacent fields. Sometimes drops and checks can be combined in single structures. Division structures, drops, and checks can be built with lumber or concrete.

Figure 2, published by the Farmers Home Administration, U.S. Department of Agriculture, shows a concrete check and drop that can be used in small farm ditches.[37] The water surface upstream from the structure can be adjusted by inserting flash boards in the rectangular notch.

In addition to permanent structures, several temporary and portable items are useful in controlling irrigation deliveries. Such items may include small division boxes, take-out boxes, spiles, metal or canvas checks, sand bags, pipes, hose, and other accessories.

Division boxes are used where small ditch flows are delivered to two or more branch ditches. Take-out boxes are used in carrying water through ditch banks to the fields. Sometimes water can be siphoned over ditch banks to furrows through short lengths of rubber or plastic hose. Small lath chutes, called spiles, may be used in taking water from small ditches or equalizing basins to corrugations. Gated surface

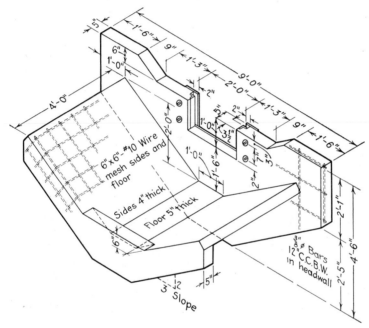

FIGURE 2. Concrete check drop for use in small farm ditches. (Farmers Home Administration.)

pipes may also be used in feeding corrugations. They can be adapted to irregular field surfaces.

Large portable pipe sections are sometimes used in flooding irrigation units. Porous canvas hose has been used to some extent in irrigating row crops in certain eastern states. Portable metal dams, canvas bags, or sand bags can be used as temporary checks where small flows are handled. Many different types of temporary control facilities have been illustrated and described in various publications.[23]

Measuring Devices. Sometimes the head gate at the point of diversion from the project system can be used in measuring the farmer's water. Calibrated head gates, often called meter gates, can be obtained from various commercial concerns.[17] When the head gate cannot be used in measuring diversions, the installation of a special measuring device such as a submerged orifice, weir, or measuring flume is needed.

Several types of submerged orifices are used in measuring water in farm ditches. Some are installed with fixed dimensions. Others are

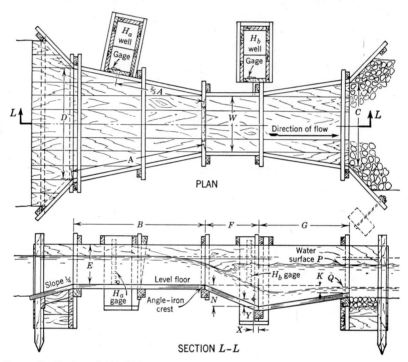

FIGURE 3.   Design of Parshall Flume for measuring irrigation flows in farm ditches.
(After Parshall.)

designed and installed in such a manner that the size of the opening can be adjusted. Some are designed and calibrated to measure flows in miner's inches and are called miner's inch boxes.[7] Submerged orifices can be used where available heads are limited, but the accuracy of the measurements may be impaired when ditch flows carry silt, sand, or floating materials that collect above the installations.

Weirs used in measuring water in farm ditches may be of rectangular, Cipolletti, or triangular-notch types. Where the available head is small, the use of a weir may not be feasible. Weirs, like submerged orifices, may not supply accurate data when deposits of foreign materials accumulate above the structures. In many irrigated regions, the use of weirs and submerged orifices is gradually being replaced by installations of the Parshall measuring flume. The Parshall measuring flume, developed at Fort Collins, Colorado, is especially designed for use in ditches and canals. It is more expensive than some measuring structures but has a high degree of accuracy and is not appreciably affected by considerable submergence. It permits the unobstructed passage of silt, sand, or other materials carried by ditch flows. Most reliable records are obtained when the flume is installed in a straight section of the ditch. Descriptions of the development, installation, and use of the flume have been published in several state and federal bulletins.[29]

Figure 3, taken from a Department of Agriculture bulletin, shows the design of a Parshall measuring flume that can be used in measuring ditch flows.[28] Dimensions needed for different ditch capacities up to 140 second-feet are given in Table 3. In most farm ditches, throat

TABLE 3

DIMENSIONS OF PARSHALL FLUME DESIGNS
FOR DIFFERENT CAPACITIES [28]

Capacity range,* sec.-ft.	See Figure 3 for location of dimensions																	
	W		*A*		*B*		*C*		*D*		*E*		*F*	*G*	*K*	*N*	*X*	*Y*
	ft.	in.	ft.	in.	ft.	in.	ft.	in.	ft.	in.	ft.	in.	ft.	ft.	in.	in.	in.	in.
0.03– 1.1	0	3	1	6⅜	1	6	0	7	0	10³⁄₁₆	1	4	½	1	1	2¼	1	1½
0.05– 3.9	0	6	2	0⁷⁄₁₆	2	0	1	3⅝	1	3⅝	2	0	1	2	3	4½	2	3
0.09– 8.8	0	9	2	10⅝	2	10	1	3	1	10⅝	2	6	1	1½	3	4½	2	3
0.35– 16.1	1	0	4	6	4	4⅞	2	0	2	9¼	3	0	2	3	3	9	2	3
0.51– 24.6	1½	0	4	9	4	7⅞	2	6	3	4⅜	3	0	2	3	3	9	2	3
0.66– 33.1	2	0	5	0	4	10⅞	3	0	3	11½	3	0	2	3	3	9	2	3
0.97– 50.4	3	0	5	6	5	4¾	4	0	5	1⅞	3	0	2	3	3	9	2	3
1.26– 67.9	4	0	6	0	5	10⅝	5	0	6	4¼	3	0	2	3	3	9	2	3
2.63–103.5	6	0	7	0	6	10⅜	7	0	8	9	3	0	2	3	3	9	2	3
4.62–139.5	8	0	8	0	7	10⅛	9	0	11	1¾	3	0	2	3	3	9	2	3

* Free flow.

widths *W* will be less than about 2 feet. Greater widths are needed in large main supply ditches. Unusually large flumes of the Parshall type have been used successfully in measuring canal flows of 2,000 second-feet or more.

Preparing Field Surfaces. Preliminary preparations of field surfaces include clearing of trees and brush, removal of all stumps, large roots, stones, or boulders that may interfere with tillage, and grading of ground surfaces to uniform slopes in the directions water is to flow during irrigation. These preparations should be followed by careful smoothing operations to remove all knolls and fill all low spots. Where rich topsoils are removed during grading, fertile conditions should be restored by heavy applications of barnyard manures or commercial fertilizers.

Special precautions in grading are required where shallow surface soils are underlaid by hardpans, impermeable clay beds, or porous sand and gravel deposits. Sloping areas with thin soil coverings may be graded and terraced in relatively narrow strips that can be utilized as separate irrigating units.

Rough grading of field surfaces usually can be done with scrapers drawn by teams or tractors. Bulldozers or other heavy equipment may be used where large quantities of earth must be moved. Smoothing and leveling operations can be conducted with large steel or timber floats. Such floats can be built on the farm. A drawing showing methods of assembling a satisfactory float can be secured from Bureau of Reclamation offices.[5]

After field surfaces are graded and leveled, levees, dikes, borders, ridges, furrows, corrugations, equalizing basins, waste ditches, or other necessary incidental features can be constructed or excavated as required for subsequent irrigation procedures.

Borders used in strip or basin irrigation are commonly built with flat side slopes, so that farm implements can be easily moved over them when necessary. Ordinarily, they need not be higher than 8 to 10 inches after settlement has taken place. Most crops, especially alfalfa, can be grown on the borders as well as in the enclosed strips or basins, thus increasing crop yields.

If desirable, special equipment for use in land preparations can be purchased from local dealers in agricultural machinery. Two-way plows, buck scrapers, ditchers, adjustable crowders, floats, border drags, corrugators, and other items are useful. Different types of irrigation implements, together with detail drawings showing how several types can be built on the farm, have been described by the Farmers Home Administration.[37]

Irrigation Methods. Methods of applying irrigation water to arable lands vary with topography, soil conditions, feasible amounts of land preparation, crops grown, value of crop products, available water supplies, and other factors. Certain methods of general applicability are used to some extent in all irrigated regions. Methods of limited applicability, such as subirrigation, can be used only where special conditions prevail. In some regions, farmers have become accustomed to particular methods of applying water and continue to use such methods when others might be more desirable and economical.

Irrigation methods are commonly designated according to the manner in which water is applied to the soil or the nature of the irrigation unit to which the water is applied. Many designations are used in referring to different procedures, but all methods of irrigation can be considered under the following classifications:

1. Irrigation by surface flooding.
2. Irrigation through furrows.
3. Irrigation by sprinkling.
4. Subirrigation.

Irrigation by surface flooding may be controlled or uncontrolled. When uncontrolled, it is usually called wild flooding. When controlled, it is designated according to the shape or contour of the irrigating unit, or according to the method of delivering water to the area within the unit as, for example, flooding from field ditches or flooding from portable pipes.

In furrow irrigation, water may be delivered to the soil through large, widely spaced furrows (the original furrow method) or through small closely spaced furrows (now commonly called the corrugation method). Corrugations are simply small furrows. Sprinkling irrigation may be designated according to the type of water-supply installation. Subirrigation may be artificial or natural, according to whether the water is supplied to the roots from underground pipes or by capillary movements from a high water table. The latter is the common method. Artificial subirrigation is too expensive to install and too troublesome to maintain.

Applications of water by controlled flooding and through furrows are the two general methods commonly used on large irrigation projects in western United States. Wild flooding is used to a limited extent in some regions where growing seasons are relatively short. Natural subirrigation is used on some delta lands in California, in parts of the San Luis Valley, Colorado, and on certain areas in other western states where topography, soils, and water supplies are favorable.

In general, furrow irrigation is used for row crops and flooding methods for close-growing crops. In some regions, small furrows or corrugations are used for small grains and forage crops. When new fields of alfalfa are initially supplied through corrugations, the small furrows gradually fill up and irrigations during subsequent seasons may resemble flooding more than furrow irrigation.

Orchard fruits are commonly irrigated through large furrows or by flooding in contour checks or relatively small level basins. Sprinkling irrigation, often used on truck and fruit lands in humid regions, is used in some western orchards where unusually valuable crops are produced; also in some fields where conditions are unfavorable for surface methods of irrigation.

Wild Flooding. In wild flooding, water is turned on to unprepared land surfaces and allowed to follow natural slopes without much guidance or obstruction. It is sometimes used on rough lands but cannot produce uniform irrigation on such areas. It is most applicable on relatively smooth areas, sloping gradually and uniformly toward natural drainage courses. Inasmuch as the flooding is uncontrolled, only small depths of infiltration can be obtained without excessive waste.

Wild flooding is used in producing native grasses for hay and in maintaining pastures on some large ranches in the mountain states. It is sometimes used as temporary measures on newly developed farms, then replaced by more efficient methods as soon as land surfaces can be properly prepared and distribution systems installed.

Irrigation by flooding from field laterals has sometimes been discussed as wild flooding. However, it seems better to consider this as a method of controlled flooding.

Flooding from Field Ditches. Flooding from field ditches is a method of controlled flooding. It is the common method of irrigating forage and cereal crops in the Rocky Mountain states, where it is said to have originated. It requires careful location and proper spacing of field laterals, but it does not require expensive land preparations. Small knolls should be cut off and depressions filled, but precise grading and smoothing operations are not essential. The method can be used on relatively steep slopes as well as on flat areas. Furthermore, it can be used with relatively small flows as well as with larger discharges.

Supply ditches may be run down the slopes and laterals on flat grades approximately along contour lines; or supply ditches may be run along the higher edges of the fields and laterals diagonally or normally down the slopes. When laterals are run down the slopes, normal to contours, they should be located so that water can be diverted to areas on both sides of the ditches.

The proper arrangement and spacing of ditches on a particular farm depends largely on topography and soil texture. Steep slopes require closer spacing of laterals than flat slopes. Porous soils require closer spacing than tight soils. On porous soils, complete flooding of the irrigation unit is difficult to obtain without excessive percolation. On clay soils, adequate infiltration is difficult to attain without excessive waste. On different farms, with different soils and slopes, proper spacings of field laterals may vary from less than 50 to more

FIGURE 4. Diverting water from field ditch on Lower Yellowstone Project, Montana. (Courtesy Bureau of Reclamation.)

than 200 feet. Lands best adapted to irrigation by flooding from field ditches are those with soils of medium texture and intermediate ground slopes.

In flooding lands from field ditches, irrigation operations are usually begun at the higher areas, then continued progressively toward the lower elevations. This may require the irrigator to work on wet ground, but it has the advantage of permitting use of waste waters on the lower areas. When irrigation is begun at the lower areas, subsequent applications of water on the higher lands may result in overirrigation at the lower elevations.

Diversions of water from field laterals must be carefully controlled in order to obtain uniform irrigation. With the small heads of 1½ to 3 second-feet ordinarily used, one man seldom can irrigate more than 3 or 4 acres a day. Irrigation by flooding from field ditches is difficult to conduct satisfactorily during the night.

Figure 4 shows water being diverted through cuts in the banks of a field ditch on the Lower Yellowstone Project, Montana. The temporary check dam in the left background holds the ditch water high enough to flood the field surfaces.

Flooding in Border Strips. Flooding in border strips is a method of controlled flooding widely used for forage and grain crops in Arizona and California and, to some extent, in other western states. It can be used on all types of soil and can be adapted to considerable variations in topography. It requires more precise and expensive land preparations than flooding from field ditches, but it usually does not require as much labor in conducting irrigation operations, especially when large heads are available. Heads of 20 second-feet, or even more, are sometimes used in supplying border strips. With large heads, two or more strips are irrigated at the same time.

Border strips are long, narrow, parallel irrigation units, laid out in the direction of the ground slope and separated by low levees or borders. Water is supplied to the strips from a permanent ditch along the upper end of the field and allowed to flow down the strips between the borders. The method may be used on both steep and flat slopes, but intermediate slopes usually are more desirable. Where crop rotations are practiced, strips that are not too steep or flat may be used for subsequent furrow irrigation of row crops, without releveling or other material changes in irrigation arrangements, except excavation of furrows. A typical layout is shown in Figure 1.

Border strips should be carefully graded and leveled. Short sections at the upper ends should be level longitudinally as well as transversely, so that water can spread to the borders before starting down the slopes. Below these sections, ground surfaces should be level transversely between borders.

Slopes down the strips should be continuous and uniform whenever feasible. They may contain minor changes in slope where excessive grading otherwise would be necessary. In such fields, the steeper grades should preferably be at the downstream ends of the strips, in order to avoid overirrigation. On clay soils, small cross dikes may be needed at intervals along the strips, to retard the flow of irrigation water and produce ponding that will aid infiltration.

Small drainage ditches, to remove excess irrigation water, usually are excavated along the lower ends of the strips. Sometimes short lengths of borders are omitted at the lower ends, so that excess water can flow through adjacent strips before reaching drainage ditches.

Proper sizes of border strips on particular farms vary with soil conditions, ground slopes, and amounts of water available. In general, widths of strips should be smaller on steep slopes than on flat slopes. Strips generally can be longer on medium slopes than on either flat or steep slopes. Table 4 shows widths and lengths of strips that are

TABLE 4

SUITABLE DIMENSIONS FOR BORDER STRIPS ON DIFFERENT SOILS [12]

Irrigating head, sec.-ft.	Sand		Loam		Clay	
	Width *	Length *	Width	Length	Width	Length
1	20–30	200–300	30	300–400	30	440–660
1–2	30–40	300–400	30–40	440–660	30–40	660
2–4	30–40	440	40	440–660	50	660–800
4–8	40	440–600	50	660–880	50	880–1,320
Desirable grades †	..	3½–12	..	2¼–7	..	1¼–3½

* Dimensions in feet.
† Inches per 100 feet.

suitable on different soils, irrigated with different heads, as recommended by Beckett and Brown.[12] Desirable grades for the different soils are shown at the bottom of the tabulation.

Flooding in Level Checks. Flooding in level checks, surrounded by small levees, can be used in producing forage and cereal crops on comparatively flat lands. Where topographic conditions are favorable, checks may be laid out as rectangular areas, approximately parallel to the contours and normal to the sides of the field. Such checks are called rectangular checks. Where the topography is more irregular, checks may be laid out along the contours. Such checks are called contour checks.

In general, field ditches are run down the slopes and water diverted to checks on both sides. Checks are filled to desirable depths, and flooding is maintained until sufficient infiltration takes place. Water usually is admitted to each check separately, but, where soils are tight, ponded water may be drained into adjacent lower checks. To facilitate initial coverage, a slight fall of 1 or 2 inches is commonly provided along the length of the check.

Check sizes vary with ground slopes and soil conditions. They ordinarily vary from about 0.5 to 2 acres but may be a little larger

FIGURE 5.   Rice fields under irrigation in Brazos River basin, Texas.   (Courtesy
Bureau of Reclamation.)

or smaller. They can be longer on tight soils than on porous soils, but lengths seldom exceed about 400 feet. Widths are determined primarily by surface slopes. The drop from one basin to the next is usually about 4 to 6 inches.

Relatively large heads can be used in irrigating checks when ample water supplies are obtainable. With large heads, two or more checks can be supplied simultaneously. With small heads, the entire flow must be diverted to one basin. A flow of 5 second-feet will cover a 1-acre check to a depth of about 5 inches in 1 hour. Irrigation usually is begun at the higher checks and continued progressively to lower elevations.

Amounts of land preparation needed for flooding in level checks are about the same as for flooding in border strips. Labor requirements during irrigation also are similar. Check irrigation is better adapted to leaching operations than flooding on sloping lands but is not so satisfactory for crop rotations. When row crops requiring furrow irrigation are to be planted, levees must be removed and field ditches relocated, so that furrows can be excavated on adequate grades.

The irrigation of orchards in small square or rectangular units, commonly called basin irrigation, is a special type of flooding in checks. The basins are usually smaller than for field crops and require less grading. Sometimes they include only one tree per basin. When soils and ground slopes are favorable, they may include several. In some parts of the Southwest, contour checks are used in orchard irrigation. When ample water supplies are available, contour checks on clay soils may contain more than a hundred trees. The use of contour checks in orchard irrigation has been described in a University of California publication.[4]

Rice crops, which require continuous flooding during the growing season, are commonly produced in level checks enclosed by small levees. Figure 5 shows typical rice fields under irrigation in the Brazos River basin, Texas. Water draining through the cut in the levee in the foreground is pumped back to the storage canal.

Flooding with Portable Pipes. Flooding with portable slip-joint pipes is a method sometimes used in irrigating crops in regions where water supplies are scarce and costly and are obtained by pumping. When distribution systems are properly installed and irrigation operations carefully conducted, the use of this method practically eliminates losses by percolation and surface waste.

The portable-pipe method can be used in irrigating orchards and alfalfa fields. Alfalfa fields are irrigated after each cutting and are supplied with depths sufficient to maintain growth until the next cutting. The method is not suitable for field crops after plants attain some size, because of difficulties involved in moving the pipes without damaging the crops.

In the portable-pipe method of irrigation, permanent pipe distribution systems, usually concrete, are run from the pumping plants to the fields, and supply lines are provided along the upper ends of the irrigation units. Pumping pressures are kept high enough to force water to points of delivery. Distribution systems may be installed above or below ground, preferably the latter. When installed underground, vertical risers are located at the irrigation units. Valve sections, designed to permit attachments of slip-joint pipe, are located so that water can be delivered to all units.

Slip-joint pipe sections are generally 10 feet long. They may be made of aluminum but are commonly made of 20 or 22 gage galvanized iron. They may be from 6 to 10 inches in diameter, depending on the size of the head. Usual irrigating heads are less than 2 second-feet. Irrigation is begun at the upper end of the field, and the delivery line is lengthened by adding pipe sections until all areas are supplied with water. The sections can be handled by one man and can be added or removed without shutting off the water.

Installations required for irrigation with portable pipes are expensive. However, the costs are offset to some extent by savings in land preparation. Extensive and precise grading is not necessary. Only nominal amounts of surface smoothing are needed, inasmuch as pipes can deliver water to knolls as well as to depressions. Irrigation operations are burdensome and must be conducted skillfully. The method is used to some extent for supplemental irrigation in humid regions as well as in certain parts of the West.

Furrow Irrigation. Furrow irrigation is commonly used for cultivated row crops such as corn, cotton, potatoes, and sugar beets. Furrow irrigation may also be used for orchard fruits, small fruits, and vegetables. Small furrows or corrugations may be used in irrigating small grains and starting semipermanent crops such as pastures, alfalfa, clover, and grasses.

In general, the proper size, spacing, and length of furrows depends principally on soil conditions and type of crop. Large furrows are used for widely spaced crops such as corn, and small furrows for closely spaced crops such as sugar beets. Spacing of large furrows depends largely on the particular crop and desirable spacing of the crop rows. Furrows 8 to 10 inches deep are suitable for some crops.

Corrugations may be spaced from 1½ to 3 feet apart, depending on soil texture and subsoil conditions. They are usually made about 4 inches deep and only slightly wider. Some crops, such as lettuce or sugar beets may be planted on ridges with furrows between alternate rows. Such methods, sometimes called the ridge system of irrigation, may be used on slopes too flat for ordinary furrow methods. Figure 6 shows typical 2-row ridges irrigated through furrows.

Furrows should never be of excessive lengths. When too long, depths of infiltration may be too great at the upper ends and insufficient at the lower ends. In producing field crops, maximum lengths are permissible on tight clay soils where slopes are flat.

Furrows as long as ¼ mile have been used on such fields. However, shorter lengths probably are more desirable. On soils of medium texture, furrows may be from about 300 to 600 feet long, depending on grades and irrigating heads. The steeper grades require the smaller heads and shorter lengths. Heads large enough to supply long furrows with ample water may cause erosion when slopes are relatively steep.

FIGURE 6. Typical 2-row ridges irrigated through furrows. (Courtesy Bureau of Reclamation.)

On steep sandy soils, lengths may be limited to 200 or even 100 feet.

Corrugations may be used on grades too steep for irrigation through large furrows. When crops requiring large furrows are produced on steep lands, the rows should be planted approximately along contours, or diagonally with the contours, so that furrows can be excavated on suitable grades.

In orchard irrigation, several furrows are commonly used between rows of trees. Such furrows are often connected by cross furrows, in order to obtain greater infiltration. In some orchards, wide, shallow furrows that permit increased penetration of water and the use of larger heads without erosion may be suitable. Such furrows are usually made about 2 feet wide. In sloping orchards, furrows may be located approximately along contour lines. On relatively tight soils, they may be zigzagged back and forth down the slopes, in order to reduce velocities and permit increased infiltration.

In furrow irrigation, head ditches are usually run along the high sides of the fields, and furrows down the slopes. Water to supply furrows may be taken through spiles installed in the ditch banks, or over the banks by means of siphons (see Figures 7 and 8). The rubber

FIGURE 7.   Installing spiles in ditch banks to admit water to furrows.   (Courtesy Bureau of Reclamation.)

ball shown in Figure 8 is placed in the end of the siphon at the time of filling, then removed when the siphon is placed in position. Flows taken through cuts in ditch banks may be distributed between two or more adjacent furrows, depending on available heads and furrow needs.

In supplying corrugations, an equalizing basin, parallel to the head ditch, often is desirable. With an equalizing basin, where the water level is the same from end to end, spiles can be set at equal elevations at the entrances to the corrugations, so that uniform flows can be admitted to all furrows. Gated surface pipes or flumes are also used in supplying corrugations. Pipes or flumes may be desirable where field surfaces are irregular. Underground pipes with risers to supply the furrows are often used in orchard irrigation.

Fields with widely varying soil conditions and surface slopes usually can be supplied with water by some type of furrow irrigation. As stated in the preceding chapter, furrow irrigation on saline or alkali lands may result in gradual accumulations of salts between the furrows. In orchards, such effects may be reduced to some extent by wide shallow furrows.

FIGURE 8.   Siphoning water from ditch to furrows during irrigation of cotton.
(Courtesy Bureau of Reclamation.)

Use of Porous Hose.   Porous canvas hose is used to some extent in delivering supplemental water to potatoes, strawberries, and other low-growing row crops in eastern United States. This method was developed in Michigan during 1929 and 1930.[30] It is understood that the method was patented and that the patent has been assigned to the Michigan State Board of Agriculture.[35]

In irrigating with porous hose, water is pumped from convenient sources and piped to the high sides of the fields. Lines of hose, closed at the lower ends, are run from the supply pipes along the crop rows and moved from row to row until all areas are irrigated. Hose lines may be as long as 500 or 600 feet. They may be laid across low knolls as well as through shallow depressions. Water seeps through the pores in the canvas and moistens the soil in strips 2 to 3 feet wide along the hose locations. Relatively low pressures of 5 to 10 pounds per square inch are sufficient to force water through the hose.

Porous hose for irrigation is usually made with 8- to 12-ounce canvas and in 50- or 100-foot lengths. Diameters may vary from $2\frac{1}{2}$ to 3 inches. Different lengths and different diameters may be used in assembling lines for particular locations, depending on grades, total lengths, and surface irregularities. Assemblies should be made so that water will seep through the hose at equal rates at all locations.

The use of porous hose in irrigation does not involve high costs of equipment but does require considerable labor during operation. The method is not suitable for irrigating close-growing crops such as forage crops and small grains, or for high row crops such as corn. For irrigating low row crops, it has the advantages of requiring but little if any land preparation and practically eliminating waste of water.

Irrigation by Sprinkling. In irrigation by sprinkling, water is applied to plants and soils in a manner similar to natural rainfall. The method is sometimes referred to as overhead irrigation. In orchard districts, sprinkling systems are referred to as overhead when they distribute water over the trees, and as undertree when they distribute water under the trees.

Sprinkling systems may also be referred to as permanent or portable systems, depending on conditions of installation. Portable systems attached to permanent supply pipes may be called semipermanent systems.

Irrigation by sprinkling from permanent installations has long been practiced in humid regions as well as in arid and semiarid regions. Inasmuch as installation costs are relatively high, permanent systems have been used principally in irrigating gardens, truck crops, nurseries, orchards, and other valuable crops. Permanent sprinkling systems, although expensive, require but little labor during operation.

Since about 1930, several types of portable sprinkling systems have been developed and adapted for use in irrigation. They can be used in irrigating pastures and some field crops as well as in supplying water to gardens and orchards. Portable systems are less costly than permanent systems but require more labor during operation. Both permanent and portable systems require expenditures for power to maintain adequate pressures during operation.

Some type of sprinkling installation usually can be adapted to any arable area, regardless of ground slopes, surface configurations, or soil conditions. Sprinkling methods of irrigation do not require leveling or other costly land preparations. They can be used on lands too steep for surface methods. They can also be used on lands where soils are too shallow to permit the leveling needed for surface methods. They permit more timely and satisfactory applications of water and may be desirable on unusually pervious soils, even when surface methods are feasible. Probably the most important advantage of sprinkling is the prevention of soil erosion, and the most important disadvantage the cost of installing the system.

Sprinkling installations are adaptable to limited water supplies, but all water must be clean. Sand, silt, or floating materials that might clog the nozzles should be screened out before the water enters the sprinkling system.

Portable sprinkling methods are not suitable for close-growing field crops where movements of sprinkling lines would damage crop growth. Sprinkling methods should not be used for crops that are susceptible to the development of plant diseases under sprinkling. For instance, sprinkling methods are not suitable for vineyards because they tend to cause mildew.[9]

When sprinkling operations are carefully controlled, losses of water by percolation and surface runoff can be practically eliminated. Losses by evaporation probably are higher than during surface irrigation. Some tests have indicated negligible amounts of evaporation from sprayed water while in the air. However, after plants become well developed, evaporation of moisture intercepted by the foliage during sprinkling must be appreciable.

Measurements during irrigation of avocados on sandy loam soils in southern California showed that average seasonal deliveries during 7 years were about 6 inches higher for sprinkling than for furrow irrigation. Other measurements, also in southern California, showed about the same irrigation efficiencies for both methods. Some advocates of sprinkling claim that depths of water used in irrigation can be reduced by adopting sprinkling methods. This probably is true where surface irrigations are difficult to control, as in areas of rough topography or areas utilized in producing shallow-rooted crops that require frequent light irrigations. However, it is doubtful if such claims can be generally substantiated.

Sprinkling installations can be used to spread liquid fertilizers as well as water needed for irrigation. Overhead installations in orchards can be used to spray the foliage with insecticides, but subsequent sprinkling may wash the chemicals off the leaves. Effects of sprinkling methods on insect control and plant diseases in orchards were investigated in Washington and reported in 1932. From the viewpoint of plant diseases, undertree sprinklers were found to be more desirable than overhead sprinklers.[27]

Sprinkling Installations. Permanent sprinkling installations include pumping plants, main supply pipes, and such lateral pipes as may be needed to distribute water to all areas. Water may be pumped from surface or subsurface sources. Main supply pipes may be installed along the ground surface or underground, preferably the latter.

Lateral distribution lines in permanent systems may be laid at or below ground levels, with revolving sprinklers mounted on risers that extend above the trees or crops. The proper spacing of sprinklers depends on the type of sprinkler and the operating pressure. Sprinklers that turn slowly are usually more desirable than whirling types, inasmuch as they distribute water over larger areas and thus permit wider spacings of lateral pipes. In lawn systems, sprinklers are installed at ground levels.

Lateral distribution lines may also be parallel perforated pipes called nozzle lines. Such lines are mounted a few feet above the ground and are supported by posts several feet apart. Perforations in the pipe are about 3 or 4 feet apart, in a continuous line, and are equipped with nonrusting nozzles. The pipes are arranged so that they can be turned to discharge jets at any angle, on either side of the pipe.

Portable sprinkling systems usually include a movable pumping plant that can pump water from a supply ditch, short sections of light-weight pipe that can be easily moved, and quick-acting couplings that can be used in assembling lines of required length. Pipe sections usually are 20 feet long, but other lengths can be obtained if needed. Sprinklers may be attached to couplings or pipe sections, by short risers that raise the sprinklers above crop levels.

In low-pressure portable systems, light-weight perforated slip-joint pipe or eyelet canvas hose are sometimes used as sprinkling lines. Such lines distribute water over narrow strips and must be moved more frequently than portable pipes equipped with sprinklers. Pressures of 5 to 15 pounds per square inch may be used in perforated pipes, and pressures of 5 to 10 pounds in eyelet hose. The more usual types of permanent and portable sprinkling systems are designed for operation under pressures of 20 to 50 pounds per square inch.

Any type of sprinkling system to be installed for irrigating fruit or field crops should be carefully chosen and accurately designed to satisfy particular conditions. Details of different systems are described in manufacturers' publications, also in several state and federal bulletins.[35] Hydraulic problems involved in planning sprinkling installations were discussed by Christiansen in 1942.[9] Sprinkling installations and methods used in irrigating orchards in British Columbia were described by Wilcox in 1947.[39]

Comparative cost data for sprinkling and surface methods of irrigation on five farms in western United States were presented in a recent Bureau of Reclamation publication. Although the farms represented soil and topographic conditions unfavorable for surface irrigation, annual costs of applying water were generally higher for sprinkling than for surface irrigation. Average annual costs per acre, including water and interest, were approximately 40 dollars for surface irrigation and 49 dollars for sprinkling.[6]

Subirrigation. Natural subirrigation can be used on smooth, gently sloping lands where permeable sand, sandy loam, or peat soils are underlain at shallow depths by impermeable strata or naturally high water tables. The method is inexpensive, easy to conduct, and adaptable to many field and truck crops. Inasmuch as it brings salts to the ground surface, it should not be used where soils or water supplies contain excess salts that cannot be removed by leaching during nongrowing seasons.

Field surfaces are prepared and planted in the usual manner. Small parallel ditches are then excavated on relatively flat grades, filled with water, and kept full until seepage raises the water table high enough to produce moist conditions in the topsoils. This may require from several days to a month or longer. Ditch flows are then regulated so as to maintain adequate supplies of moisture in the root zones. Flows are reduced or discontinued, and topsoils allowed to dry just before harvesting.

Proper spacings of field ditches are commonly determined by trial. They vary with soil conditions and depths to impermeable strata or normal water tables. In the San Luis Valley, Colorado, spacings vary from about 50 to 250 feet. Where soils are less permeable, desirable spacings may be less. Wide, shallow ditch sections usually are preferable.

Subirrigation requires adequate water supplies. The method is not highly efficient, but appreciable portions of the losses ordinarily are recovered for use on downstream projects. In general, land slopes of about 5 to 10 feet per mile are most satisfactory for this method.

Applications of water by subirrigation methods require but little labor. One man can take care of large fields. However, the applications should be carefully supervised. Periodic measurements of water-table elevations are desirable. Unless properly controlled, ground-water may rise high enough to cause flooding of adjacent fields at lower levels. For this reason, subirrigation often is regulated by community associations instead of by individual farmers.

Sometimes drains, sloughs, or old river channels are dammed to raise water levels and produce seepage needed for subirrigation on adjoining lands. Pastures on bottom lands along river channels often are maintained by natural subirrigation, without requiring any attention by the owners.

Artificial subirrigation through closely spaced tile lines is sometimes practiced in producing shallow-rooted truck crops of high value. The installations are expensive and often troublesome. They are difficult to maintain in proper condition, inasmuch as the plant roots tend to clog the tiles.

Time and Depth of Irrigation. The proper time to irrigate and the proper depth of water to apply during an irrigation vary with local conditions of soils, crops, and weather. The variations are too wide to permit definite recommendations as to actual times and depths of irrigation.

Proper frequencies of irrigation vary with rates at which crops use water and amounts of soil moisture that become available for plant use as a result of rainfall. Rates at which crops use water vary with crop types, stages of growth, density of stands, and weather conditions, particularly temperature, wind, and humidity. Proper depths of irrigation vary with depths of root zones, field capacities of root-zone soils, and moisture contents at the time of irrigation.

In general, applications of water should be delayed until moisture contents of the root zones are reduced almost to the wilting point. Water should then be applied in depths just sufficient to raise moisture contents to field capacity. Greater depths cause losses by percolation and should not be applied, except when leaching of excess salts from the root zone is desirable. Lengthy periods of saturation are objectionable, since plant growth requires soil air as well as soil moisture.

Soil characteristics, depths of root zones, soil-moisture properties, rates of transpiration, and water requirements of crops are discussed in preceding chapters.

In hot arid climates, large amounts of water are needed during months of maximum growth. In such regions, depths of application per irrigation may be as great as 6 or 8 inches. In the Coachella Valley, southeastern California, depths applied during months of greatest use varied from 8.3 inches for grapes to 15.4 inches for citrus trees (see Table 13 of Chapter 11). Maximum monthly applications for other crops were 9.4 inches for truck products, 13.6 inches for alfalfa, 13.9 inches for cotton, and 14.6 inches for mature date trees.

The Coachella Valley is one of the warmest and driest irrigated regions in western United States. In cooler, more humid regions, monthly uses and depths of application per irrigation are lower. On most western irrigation projects, depths per irrigation probably vary from about 2 to 6 inches. Investigations in Utah showed that depths greater than 5 inches usually resulted in irrigation efficiencies lower than 50 per cent (see Chapter 12).

Heavy irrigations before planting often are needed in regions where winter and spring precipitations do not supply root zones with sufficient moisture. After planting, light, frequent irrigations are needed until plants become well established. Subsequent irrigations of deep-rooting crops can then be gradually increased and made at longer intervals, in order to encourage downward extensions of root systems. When plants can secure moisture from increased depths, greater supplies of plant nutrients become available. Greatest depths of irrigation are needed when crops are making greatest growth. For many crops, depths can be decreased somewhat as the plants approach maturity.

Forage crops that use large quantities of water, such as alfalfa, sometimes are supplied with heavy irrigations early in the growing season, when ample supplies are obtainable; then with lighter irrigations later, when more water is needed for other crops. Farmers who can raise diversified crops ordinarily can make the best use of their water supplies.

Sometimes desirable depths of irrigation may not be feasible, owing to limited water rights, scarcity of labor, or other local conditions. Deliveries of small heads must be continued through lengthy intervals in order to supply appreciable depths to large acreages. Table 5 shows the hours and minutes different flows must be continued in order to supply 1 acre with depths of 2 to 8 inches.

Determining Moisture Conditions. Irrigation farmers should determine moisture conditions in their soils at intervals throughout the growing season. They should determine depths of penetration during irrigations, in order to insure that root zones are receiving sufficient moisture. They should determine moisture contents as soil water is

TABLE 5

TIME REQUIRED TO SUPPLY 1 ACRE WITH DIFFERENT DEPTHS
OF IRRIGATION WATER *

Flow delivered		Time to irrigate 1 acre with depths, in in.												
G.p.m.	Sec.-ft.	2		3		4		5		6		7		8	
		hr.	min.	hr.	min.	hr.	min.	hr.	min.	hr.	min.	hr.	min.	hr.	min.
100	0.22	9	03	13	35	18	06	22	38	27	09	31	41	36	12
150	0.33	6	02	9	03	12	04	15	05	18	06	21	07	24	08
200	0.45	4	32	6	47	9	03	11	19	13	35	15	50	18	06
250	0.56	3	37	5	26	7	14	9	03	10	52	12	40	14	29
300	0.67	3	01	4	32	6	02	7	33	9	03	10	34	12	04
350	0.78	2	35	3	53	5	10	6	28	7	45	9	03	10	21
400	0.89	2	16	3	24	4	32	5	39	6	47	7	55	9	03
450	1.00	2	01	3	01	4	01	5	02	6	02	7	02	8	03
500	1.11	1	49	2	43	3	37	4	32	5	26	6	20	7	14
600	1.34	1	31	2	16	3	01	3	46	4	32	5	17	6	02
700	1.56	1	18	1	56	2	35	3	14	3	53	4	32	5	10
800	1.78	1	08	1	42	2	16	2	50	3	24	3	58	4	32
900	2.01	1	00	1	31	2	01	2	31	3	01	3	31	4	01
1,000	2.23	0	54	1	21	1	49	2	16	2	43	3	10	3	37
1,100	2.45	0	49	1	14	1	39	2	03	2	28	2	53	3	17
1,200	2.67	0	45	1	08	1	31	1	53	2	16	2	38	3	01
1,300	2.90	0	42	1	03	1	24	1	44	2	05	2	26	2	47
1,400	3.12	0	39	0	58	1	18	1	37	1	56	2	16	2	35
1,500	3.34	0	36	0	54	1	12	1	31	1	49	2	07	2	25

* After R. T. Burdick, Colorado State College Farm Bulletin, July–September 1940.

gradually depleted, so that they can make further irrigations before crops begin to suffer for lack of moisture.

Depths of penetration during irrigation can be determined by digging or by pushing a probe downward until increased resistance to further movement shows that dry soil has been reached. A suitable probe can be made by welding a cross bar at the top of a ½-inch steel rod, about 4 feet long. Resistance to penetration through different soils varies with soil texture and structure, but the farmer can easily calibrate his probe by a few comparisons with depths of penetration shown by digging.

Experienced farmers can tell from crop appearances when additional moisture supplies are definitely needed. Inasmuch as irrigations generally should be made before plants show needs for moisture, reliance on crop appearances may result in delayed growth and reductions in crop yield.

Probably the best way to determine needs for irrigation is to take soil samples at different depths in the root zone. When the samples can be kneaded into forms that retain their shape on release of pressure, the soils usually contain enough moisture for crop growth. Many irrigation farmers use such methods, especially for soils of medium texture. Such methods may not be reliable when soils contain high percentages of clay particles.

More accurate information regarding needs for irrigation can be obtained by determining moisture contents of the samples, as discussed in Chapter 4. However, owing to lack of time, experience, and equipment, such methods are seldom used except by the more scientific managers of large farms.

Improper Applications of Water. Improper applications of irrigation water may result in harmful effects on both soils and crops. Harmful effects on soils pertain principally to salt conditions and available supplies of plant nutrients. Harmful effects on crops pertain principally to yields and qualities of crop products.

Insufficient depths of irrigation may result in gradual accumulations of salts in the topsoils, as discussed in the preceding chapter. Excessive depths of irrigation may result in leaching valuable plant nutrients from the root zones, so that fertilizing practices become necessary. Overirrigations on steep lands may cause serious erosion of topsoils. When lands are not adequately drained, continued overirrigations cause rising groundwater levels and may cause the development of seeped areas that can no longer be utilized. When lands become seeped, the only remedy is the construction of drainage systems that may or may not be feasible at reasonable costs.

Applications of too little water during the growing season commonly result in decreased yields. For some crops, applications of too much water have similar but less pronounced effects. Some forage crops, such as alfalfa, show no reductions in yield with increased depths of irrigation. Pronounced seasonal undersupplies or oversupplies, applications of water at certain critical periods in crop growth, or failure to supply water at critical times may damage qualities of crop products as well as yields.

For cereal crops, oversupplies of water may cause increases in straw and fodder, but decreases in quantities of grain. Pronounced undersupplies may result in shrunken, poorly filled kernels, or even complete crop failures. Ample but not excessive supplies of soil moisture should be available for cereals during the heading and filling stages. In Utah, Greaves and Carter found that increases in irrigation water up to a seasonal total of about 3 feet produced increases in mineral contents of barley, oats, and wheat, probably owing to greater bacterial activity in the soil and greater plant transpiration.[15]

Improper amounts of irrigation water and improper times of application may facilitate the development of certain plant diseases. They may also facilitate the growth of certain insect pests. Such considerations are especially important in the production of fruit and vegetable crops.

REFERENCES

1. Bliesner, Gustav H., "Sprinkler Irrigation," *Wash. State Col., Agr. Ext. Service Bull.* 336, 1946.
2. Bloodgood, Dean W., and Albert S. Curry, "The Influence of Irrigation Head and Length of Run on the Use of Water for Alfalfa," *N. Mex. Agr. Exp. Sta. Bull.* 197, 1931.
3. Boyd, George R., "Clearing Land of Brush and Stumps," *U.S. Dept. Agr. Farmers' Bull.* 1526, revised, 1933.
4. Brown, J. B., "The Contour-Check Method of Orchard Irrigation," *Calif. Agr. Ext. Service Cir.* 73, 1933, revised by Marr, 1949.
5. Bureau of Reclamation, "Farmer's Irrigation Guide," *Cons. Bull.* 2, U.S. Dept. Int., 1939.
6. ——— *Sprinkler Irrigation*, U.S. Dept. Int., 1949.
7. Christiansen, J. E., "Measuring Water for Irrigation," *Calif. Agr. Exp. Sta. Bull.* 588, 1935.
8. ——— "Irrigation by Sprinkling," *Calif. Agr. Exp. Sta. Bull.* 670, 1942.
9. ——— "Hydraulics of Sprinkling Systems for Irrigation," *Trans. Am. Soc. C. E.,* No. 107, 1942, pp. 221–250.
10. Fortier, Samuel, "The Border Method of Irrigation," *U.S. Dept. Agr. Farmers' Bull.* 1243, revised, 1937.
11. ——— "Orchard Irrigation," *U.S. Dept. Agr. Farmers' Bull.* 1518, revised, 1940.
12. Fortier, Samuel, and others, "Irrigation Practices in Growing Alfalfa," *U.S. Dept. Agr. Farmers' Bull.* 1630, revised, 1940.
13. Fortier, Samuel, and Fred C. Scobey, "Permissible Canal Velocities," *Trans. Am. Soc. C. E.,* Vol. 89, 1926, pp. 940–984.
14. Goodrich, R. D., "A Formula for Border Strip Irrigation," *Civ. Eng.,* April 1934, pp. 210–212.
15. Greaves, J. E., and E. G. Carter, "The Influence of Irrigation Water on the Composition of Grains and the Relationship to Nutrition," *Jour. Biol. Chem.,* December 1923, pp. 531–541.
16. Hamilton, J. G., and others, "Irrigated Pastures for Forage Production and Soil Conservation," *U.S. Dept. Agr. Farmers' Bull.* 1973, 1945.
17. Hardesty Division, Armco Drainage and Metal Products, Inc., *Handbook of Water Control,* Denver, Colo., 1946.
18. Huberty, M. R., and J. B. Brown, "Irrigation of Orchards by Contour Furrows," *Calif. Agr. Ext. Service Cir.* 16, revised, 1932.
19. Israelsen, Orson W., and others, "Soil Erosion in Small Irrigation Furrows," *Utah Agr. Exp. Sta. Bull.* 320, 1946.

20. Israelsen, Orson W., and others, "Water-Application Efficiencies in Irrigation," *Utah Agr. Exp. Sta. Bull.* 311, 1944.

21. Jones, Jenkin W., and others, "Rice Culture in the Southern States," *U.S. Dept. Agr. Farmers' Bull.* 1808, 1938.

22. Lewis, M. R., "Design of Small Irrigation Pipe Lines," *Ore. Agr. Exp. Sta. Cir.* 142, 1941.

23. —— "Practical Irrigation," *U.S. Dept. Agr. Farmers' Bull.* 1922, 1943.

24. Marr, James C., "The Corrugation Method of Irrigation," *U.S. Dept. Agr. Farmers' Bull.* 1348, revised, 1931.

25. McLaughlin, W. W., "Irrigation of Small Grain," *U.S. Dept. Agr. Farmers' Bull.* 1556, revised, 1940.

26. Nuckols, S. B., "Sugar-Beet Culture under Irrigation in the Northern Great Plains," *U.S. Dept. Agr. Farmers' Bull.* 1867, 1941.

27. Overley, F. L., C. P. Harley, and others, "Irrigation of Orchards by Sprinkling," *Wash. Agr. Exp. Sta. Bull.* 268, 1932.

28. Parshall, R. L., "Measuring Water in Irrigation Channels," *U.S. Dept. Agr. Farmers' Bull.* 1683, revised, 1941.

29. —— "Improving the Distribution of Water to Farmers by Use of the Parshall Measuring Flume," *Colo. Agr. Exp. Sta. Bull.* 468, 1945.

30. Robey, O. E., "Porous Hose Irrigation," *Mich. State Coll. Ext. Div. Bull.* 133, 1933.

31. —— "Development of the Porous Hose Method of Irrigation in Michigan," *Agr. Eng.,* August 1934, pp. 282–283.

32. Rubey, Harry, "Supplemental Irrigation for Missouri and Regions of Similar Rainfall," *Mo. Eng. Exp. Sta. Bull.* 33, revised, 1947.

33. Ryall, A. Lloyd, and W. W. Aldrich, "The Effect of Water Deficits in the Tree upon Maturity, Composition, and Storage Quality of Bosc Pears," *Jour. Agr. Res.,* Feb. 1, 1944, pp. 121–133.

34. Staebner, F. E., "Tests of Spray Irrigation Equipment," *U.S. Dept. Agr. Cir.* 195, 1931.

35. —— "Supplemental Irrigation," *U.S. Dept. Agr. Farmers' Bull.* 1846, 1940.

36. Taylor, C. A., "Irrigation Problems in Citrus Orchards," *U.S. Dept. Agr. Farmers' Bull.* 1876, 1941.

37. United States Department of Agriculture, "First Aid for the Irrigator," *Misc. Pub.* 624, Farmers Home Administration, 1947.

38. Welty, P. A., "The Subdivision of Irrigated Land," *Civ. Eng.,* May 1932, pp. 295–298.

39. Wilcox, J. C., "Sprinkler Irrigation of Orchards in British Columbia," *Can. Dept. Agr. Farmers' Bull.* 144, 1947.

NAME INDEX

SUBJECT INDEX

531